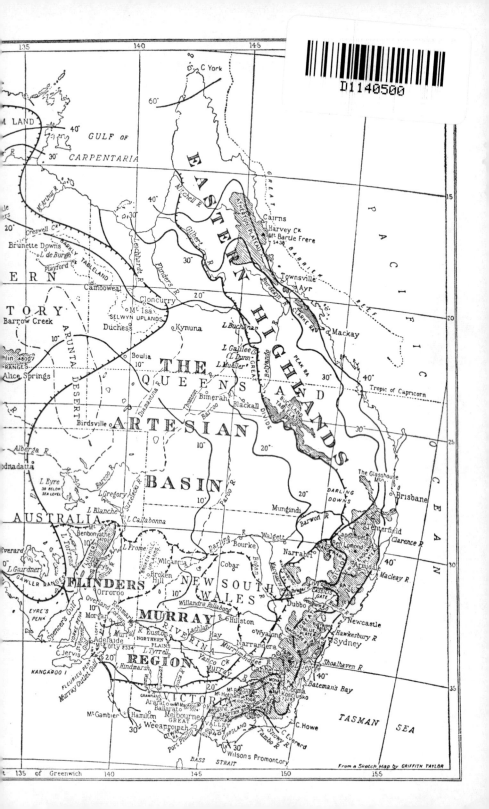

AUSTRALIA

OTHER BOOKS BY GRIFFITH TAYLOR

A. GEOGRAPHY

AUSTRALIA, PHYSIOGRAPHIC AND ECONOMIC (*4th edition*)	*Oxford, 1928*
A GEOGRAPHY OF AUSTRALASIA (*Elementary*)	*Oxford, 1914*
*NEW SOUTH WALES	*Melbourne, 1912*
*GEOGRAPHIC LABORATORY (AUSTRALIA)	*Sydney, 1925*
*WALL ATLAS OF AUSTRALIAN MAPS	*Oxford, 1929*
AUSTRALIA, A DESCRIPTIVE TEXT (*Junior*)	*Chicago, 1931*
GEOGRAPHIC LABORATORY (NORTH AMERICA)	*Toronto, 1938*
*EDUCATION FOR CITIZEN RESPONSIBILITIES	*Princeton, 1942*
NEWFOUNDLAND	*Toronto, 1946*
*JUGOSLAVIA	*Berkeley, 1947*
CANADA (ADVANCED)	*London, 1947*
*GEOGRAPHY IN THE TWENTIETH CENTURY†	*New York, 1951*
SYDNEYSIDE SCENERY	*Sydney, 1958*
JOURNEYMAN TAYLOR (*Biography*)	*London, 1958*

B. METEOROLOGY

*CLIMATE AND WEATHER OF AUSTRALIA	*Melbourne, 1913*
AUSTRALIAN ENVIRONMENT (*Government Printer*)	*Melbourne, 1918*
AUSTRALIAN METEOROLOGY	*Oxford, 1920*
*KÖPPEN'S WORLD CLIMATOLOGY, VOL. IV	*Berlin, 1932*

C. ANTARCTICA, ETC.

WITH SCOTT—THE SILVER LINING	*London, 1916*
PHYSIOGRAPHY OF MACMURDO SOUND (HARRISON)	*London, 1922*
*HINTS TO SCIENTIFIC TRAVELLERS, VOL. IV	*The Hague, 1926*
ANTARCTIC ADVENTURE AND RESEARCH	*New York, 1930*
*PROBLEMS OF POLAR RESEARCH	*New York, 1928*
*ARCTIC SURVEY (NEW NORTH WEST)	*Toronto, 1947*

D. GEOLOGY

THE ARCHEO-CYATHINAE (CAMBRIAN CORALS)	*Adelaide, 1910*
*HANDBUCH DER REGIONALEM GEOLOGIE, VOL. I	*Leipzig, 1939*

E. ETHNOLOGY AND ENVIRONMENTAL CONTROL

ENVIRONMENT AND RACE		*Oxford, 1927*
ditto	*Japanese Edition*	*Tokyo, 1930*
ditto	*Chinese Edition*	*Shanghai, 1938*
ATLAS OF ENVIRONMENT AND RACE		*Chicago, 1933*
ENVIRONMENT AND NATION (*2nd edition*)		*Toronto, 1947*
ENVIRONMENT, RACE AND MIGRATION (*3rd edition*)		*Toronto, 1946*
*HUMAN ORIGINS, AN INTRODUCTION TO ANTHROPOLOGY		*Chicago, 1945*
OUR EVOLVING CIVILIZATION		*Toronto, 1947*
URBAN GEOGRAPHY (*2nd edition*) (*also in Spanish*)		*London, 1951*

F. TAYLOR—SEIVEWRIGHT—LLOYD SCHOOL TEXTS

CANADA AND HER NEIGHBOURS (*also in French*)	*Toronto, 1952*
SOUTHERN LANDS	*Toronto, 1953*
LANDS OF EUROPE AND ASIA	*Toronto, 1954*

* Joint Author.   † Editor.

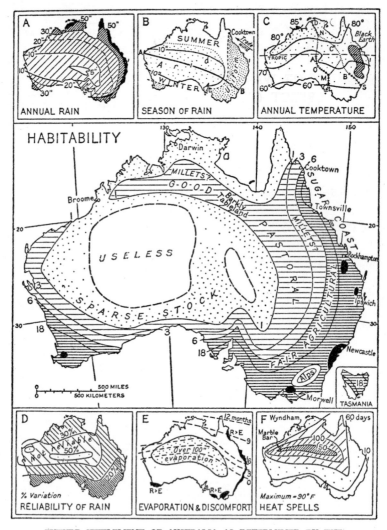

FUTURE SETTLEMENT OF AUSTRALIA AS DETERMINED BY THE
ENVIRONMENT

showing approximate lines of equal population (to the square mile). Black areas are the chief
coal-fields. *Small maps:* A, annual rainfall; B, seasonal rains (the line AB separates summer
from winter rains); C, temperature (the suggested railway routes are indicated from Alice
Springs [A] or Bourke [B] to Newcastle Waters [N], Marree [M]); D, rain reliability; E,
evaporation and discomfort; F, regions experiencing long periods of heat (days over 90° F.).
For discussion, see p. 475

(*From 'Limits of Land Settlement'*)

AUSTRALIA

A STUDY OF WARM ENVIRONMENTS AND THEIR EFFECT ON BRITISH SETTLEMENT

by

GRIFFITH TAYLOR

D.Sc., B.E. (Mining), B.A. (Cantab.), Hon.D.Litt., F.Aus. Acad.

*Emeritus Professor of Geography in the University of Toronto
Formerly Physiographer in the Commonwealth Weather Service
and Professor of Geography in the University of Sydney
President of British Geographers (B.A.A.S.) 1938
and of American Geographers (A.A.G.) 1941*

*With 4 half-tone plates, 158 text illustrations,
and endpaper map*

LONDON : METHUEN & CO LTD

First Published June 27th 1940
Second Edition, revised March 1943
Reprinted three times
Sixth Edition, enlarged December 1951
Reprinted with minor corrections 1955
Seventh Edition 1959
Reprinted with minor corrections 1961
Reprinted 1966

7.3
CATALOGUE NO. 02/3047/34

Printed and bound in Great Britain by Butler & Tanner Ltd., Frome and London

PREFACE

IN an address given in London in 1931 I discussed the evolution of geographical research in Australia (*Scot. Geog. Mag.*, 1932). I pointed out the debt which Australia owed, primarily to two men, as regards early progress in geography. These leaders in science were Professor Sir Edgeworth David and Professor J. W. Gregory. The latter was only in Australia for a few years, but he produced the first modern text on Geography in his *Victoria*, published in 1903. This was followed by a valuable book entitled *Australasia* (in *Stanford's Compendium*) in 1906. This has remained up to the present almost the sole general account of the continent on a large scale, but it was necessarily somewhat like a gazetteer in its treatment. The present book is an attempt to produce a text for use in High Schools and Universities along modern lines. My chief aims have been to express the data graphically, preferably by isopleths, and as much as possible to suggest causes.

On reading the completed manuscript I feel that I should perhaps apologize for the rather personal approach, which is more apparent than is usual in a text of this kind. My excuse is that for some twenty years I was almost the sole professional geographer in the Commonwealth, either as a member of the Commonwealth Weather Service or of the Department of Geography in the University of Sydney. Hence I have been in a very favourable position to see geography develop in a pioneer continent; and although it is some years since I left Australia I have been giving courses of lectures on that continent each year, and have kept in touch with recent developments.

I have to thank the various Australian Government officials to whom I have applied for information for their uniform courtesy. The *Commonwealth Year Book* is of course indispensable for the student of Australian Geography. It is not as well known as it should be that an up-to-date bibliography is to be found in each of these Year Books. Rand, McNally & Company of Chicago have kindly allowed me to use several maps from a book of mine which they published. It may not be out of place to state that this elementary book (*Australia*, 1931) contains about 200 photographs, of a sort which cannot, I think, be so conveniently consulted elsewhere.

vii

SIXTH ENLARGED EDITION

WITH the return of peace and the publication of postwar statistics it is possible to make a fresh survey of Australian conditions. In the present much-enlarged edition this has been done, and lengthy descriptions of new developments in the Commonwealth have been added. These are largely based on my extensive journeys in 1948, due to an invitation from the Commonwealth University at Canberra. I traversed Australia four times, including a journey from Hobart to Darwin, thus linking earlier traverses in central and northern Australia. A dozen new maps will be found in the present volume, and many of the tables have been revised. Among subjects much more fully treated are exploration, evaporation, topographic control, Heavy Industry, Northern Territory, Murray irrigation, the Mallee, and hydro-electric power. This book (like the companion volume on Canada) contains over 150 maps and diagrams largely stressing structure, and correlations of one sort or another. I believe that more and more geographic texts of this kind will appear when it is realized that 'Geography'—as its etymology implies—is fundamentally concerned with *graphic representation linked with earth sciences.*

GRIFFITH TAYLOR
University of Toronto

TORONTO
July 1950

SEVENTH ENLARGED EDITION

MANY of the tables have been revised, and new sections dealing with Droughts, Sparseland Populations, Central Australian topography, Tourist Trade, Australian-Antarctica, and several pages on recent Industrial Growth have been added. Three new maps show Darwin Soils, Industrial Expansion, and Isoterps of Comfort.

Sydney 1958

CONTENTS

ix

TEXT ILLUSTRATIONS

PLATES

PART I

POSITION, DISCOVERY AND GENERAL PHYSICAL FEATURES

CHAPTER I

INTRODUCTION

AS a field for the study of the white man's utilization of the earth no continent surpasses Australia. In the first place the settlement is so recent—dating, indeed, only from 1788—that all the events of the experiment belong to modern times and their records are relatively easily accessible. In the second place Nature has, as it were, garbed herself in the robes of a teacher and displayed a continent with the least complexity of outline, build and structure, so that it may be said to resemble a 'blackboard' on which our geographical problems may be elucidated. Yet our 'blackboard', while free from the structural or climatic complexities of other continental fields, offers sufficient variety for the exercise of the powers of a geographer in explaining the relation of man to his environment, even though Man is 97·8 per cent 'British' and the Environment perhaps 87 per cent 'warm and dry'.[1] This, then, is the outstanding problem of Australia. How has a people of British nationality fared when it emigrated across the world to an empty land of nearly 3 million square miles? Had the new land been actually at the antipodes of Britain the problem would have been simpler—for the two environments would necessarily have been somewhat the same. But there is nothing in Australia resembling the cool wet lands of Britain. There is only a negligible part of Australia in the same latitude as *any part* of Europe. Our emigrants blindly occupied lands in a continent whose hottest northern regions correspond to Nigeria and whose most southern lands are like those of Spain. Here, indeed, is an interesting experiment in anthropo-geography.

Let us contrast for a moment the complexity of Europe with the state of affairs in Australia. In structure Europe consists of a northern belt of Caledonian Highlands, a Carboniferous syncline, a chain of Armorican 'Blocks', and in the south the young mountains of the 'Alpine Storm'. These varying topographies are crossed obliquely by rainfall belts ranging from the very wet to the semi-desert. The human factor is also most complex, consisting of three major races (Alpine, Nordic and Mediterranean) speaking three major languages (Teutonic, Romance, Slav) and subscribing to

[1] About 87 per cent of Australia has a rainfall below 30 inches.

3

three major religions. Superimposed on this foundation mosaic are thirty separate nationalities each prone to erect barriers against its neighbours!

In Australia we find a remarkable unity in most of these features. The dominant structure is the *Ancient Shield* of western and central Australia. Only low crustal ripples affect the remaining third of Australia. The climate is warm and dry throughout except for the narrow 'Eastern Crescent' with its 'wings' reaching to Cairns and Perth. There has never been a racial problem; for the few aborigines have almost been ignored in the march of settlement. The white settler is a Britisher, and is in happy ignorance as to which of the three European races his forefathers represented. Religion has had only a small place in politics, and the English language (with a touch of cockney) is spoken so uniformly throughout that no man can distinguish the Queenslander from the Tasmanian.

If we turn to Africa we find a continent with many more similarities to Australia. Considering its large size, it is less complex than Europe, and indeed Schwarz has declared that one dominant *motif* runs throughout, summarized by the phrase 'the black man and the thorn tree'. In some such fashion we may perhaps venture to assert that the '*mulga-dotted* [1] *peneplain*' epitomizes the major portion of Australia. We cannot introduce the human factor into our summary, for the Australian is a town-dweller. The northwestern *half* of the continent contains not (as one might expect) 50 per cent of the population, but less than one-half of 1 per cent! This book will try to explain why in a *new* land 62 per cent of the population should be urban, while in some ancient industrial countries of Europe the proportion of rural dwellers is much greater.

Economic Australia and Empty Australia

Indeed, the most striking fact in the geography of Australia is its division into two parts, which I have been accustomed to name *Economic Australia* and *Empty Australia* (Fig. 1). The former contains large areas of valuable lands which still await adequate occupation. Probably they are the best second-class lands still open to white settlement anywhere. Few people realize, however, how quickly this exploitable land merges into the type which I have termed *Empty Australia*. To Americans this may be made clear if one compares the early advance from Sydney to the empty west with the similar movement in the United States. The Australian reached an arid environment rather like that of Arizona at 450 miles from the coast, while the American in a similar journey was

[1] The mulga is a xerophytic acacia about 15 feet high (see Fig. 35).

just reaching the *beginning* of the best section of the United States in eastern Ohio.

It may surprise some readers that no reference is made to the gum-tree or to sheep in our 'motif'. It is true that the average Australian sees the eucalypt everywhere, and that he has only to go inland a relatively short distance to see the ubiquitous flocks of sheep. But before he reaches the more dominant dry regions of the continent he has left behind him the eucalypt as the universal tree, and has in general reached the cattle areas or those entirely empty lands still found unsuitable for any stock. Indeed, few folk realize that the cattle-lands of Australia are more extensive than those used for sheep—though the latter is the better-paying industry.

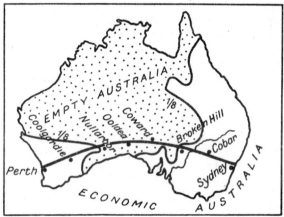

FIG. I.—A DIAGRAM SHOWING AUSTRALIA DIVIDED INTO TWO SECTIONS
BY THE LINE OF '⅛ OF A PERSON PER SQUARE MILE'
The eight stages on the traverse of Australia are shown on Photos 1–8

In these dry inland areas there are still scattered eucalypts, but the dominant genus is the *Acacia*. This name, however, is unknown in the 'Bush', and so I have adopted the mulga, the most abundant of the acacias, as the characteristic tree of the vast rolling plains of Australia.

A necessary corollary of the fact that nearly all Australians live in the fertile 'crescent' of Economic Australia is that until lately there was a general ignorance of conditions in three-quarters of the continent. Indeed, until 1917 no railway completely crossed the arid lands. Since that date many Australians have seen something of 'Empty Australia', for the Trans-Australian Railway (linking Perth to Adelaide) crosses not only 1,200 miles of semi-desert steppes, but also some 50 miles of the desert of 'fixed dunes'. These latter extend almost uninterruptedly from Ooldea (on the railway) to the Indian Ocean 1,100 miles to the north-west. Such large areas cannot now be ignored by the public as they were in earlier years. There was naturally little passenger traffic on the few earlier railways (like that running north from Adelaide to Oodnadatta) which merely tapped the borderlands of the great central desert.

Resulting from the unfamiliar character of the Australian Environment there developed a rather peculiar attitude toward future settlement. This was justified by a somewhat too free use of what we may call 'geographic shibboleths'. For instance, it was stated that 'lands in the southern hemisphere are in general colder than similarly situated lands in the north'. Hence, said the pundits, our tropical lands would be found better suited for white settlers than were tropics elsewhere. Again, 'tropical lands are generally covered with dense forests'. Hence such forests were shown on our maps throughout the northern littoral; whereas at best only narrow 'corridor' jungles occur along some of the rivers. The writer well remembers the surprise expressed by the head of a Commonwealth Department when he found that the region just south of Darwin was clothed in a straggly eucalyptus 'scrub', which in no way resembled a tropical jungle. 'The interior of Australia is necessarily cool because it is a high plateau.' In truth, the very moderate elevation of 1,200 feet or so makes little difference to the intensely hot days—though the absence of water and cloud certainly leads to considerable radiation at night.

Perhaps earlier than in the United States the Government was concerned with the problem of an adequate population. The nearest lands are those of Java with its 35 millions; India with 315 millions; China and Japan with 500 millions. It was natural for Australians to dread the swamping of their nation by Asiatics of a low standard of living, and this feeling has led to the general adoption of a strict 'White Australia' policy. Obviously the best practical method to counteract a possible Asiatic immigration was to fill up the continent with British—or at any rate European—settlers. Unfortunately, the Government adopted the plan of proclaiming the remarkable attractions of the empty lands of Australia, including the huge tropical areas, without an adequate knowledge of the lands involved. This propaganda is often justified as an antidote to the 'crying of stinking fish' (by the impartial student) which so annoys the 'patriotic' politician. Unfortunately, the local Australian is more likely to be affected by such unwarranted propaganda than is the distant European. Much economic loss through unwise settlement in the arid and tropical parts of the country has already resulted. Especially is this true as regards the attempts to develop a farming population in Northern Territory. However, in recent years the very *slow* growth of settlement in the centre, north and north-west of the continent is now understood to be inevitable; and to be due to the inherent unsuitability of such lands for notable populations, at any rate under present economic conditions.

The Australian is not a 'dog in the manger' as regards his empty lands—keeping other folk out of an unused paradise. There are no really attractive unused lands left in Australia except in the *alienated* portions of the East and South (Fig. 138).

Yet it is not too early to say that the 7 millions of Australia could grow to 27 millions—but not by settlement in the *Empty* half of Australia. Some years ago the writer travelled along the coast of New South Wales from Eden in the far south to Ballina in the far north. In the opinion of a climatologist who has given much attention to this specific problem, this coastal strip is blessed with a climate more attractive even than that of California. Temperature and rainfall conditions are nearly ideal; soils and topography, while rarely first-class, are not often of a type to obstruct some settlement. Yet in this traverse of 600 miles there is only one section in the centre (about 150 miles long from New-castle to the Shoalhaven) with anything approaching close settle-ment. In the remaining 450 miles there are only two towns, both in the far north, which have over 5,000 inhabitants. Moreover, in the whole littoral belt of New South Wales (an area 200 miles wide), the climatic controls are perfectly satisfactory (though the soils are poor in considerable areas). Yet half this area of over 100,000 square miles has a density of less than 3 persons per square mile. It is to such lands in the 'Economic Half' of Australia that those in authority who desire to strengthen Australia should direct their main attention.

A Traverse across Australia

In the course of many discussions I found that the best way to drive home to Australians a rough quantitative picture of their inheritance of 3 million square miles was to borrow the method of the mining engineer. If he wishes to obtain quickly a reasonable estimate of the value of a large mining property (say an iron deposit) he makes a 'grab sample'. He rules a line across the area, and takes samples along it at a number of places at equal distances apart. We can imitate this procedure by ruling a line across Australia, and considering the salient *typical* features at a number of stations at equal distances apart—along this line (Fig. 1). The writer proposes to use a line from Sydney to Perth—for he has traversed this region, most of it more than once. For our samples we will use photographs. It should be noted that the traverse is the most favourable one across Australia from east to west, and indeed the most favourable of all, except one down the east coast, which would clearly not give any clue to the *general* character of Australia's environment.

Let us then mark out seven stages, and since the continent is 2,100 miles wide, these 'grab samples' will be approximately 300 miles apart. Photographs are given illustrating the regions near Sydney, Cobar, Broken Hill, Coward Springs, Ooldea, Nullabor Plains, Coolgardie and Perth.

First Stage.—On the journey from Sydney to Cobar we soon leave the narrow fringe of tropical jungle (see No. 1) which occurs sporadically along the coast with its 50 inches of rain. It is described in Chapter V. We cross the rugged, well-watered Blue Plateau and reach perhaps the best belt in Australia, the western slopes with their 20 inches of rain. Here we traverse the whole of the wheat belt and the main sheep belt of Australia before we reach Cobar with its 15 inches of rain. In this part of the continent this rainfall marks about the limit of wheat farming and therefore of close settlement. To the west there is not enough 'permanent water' even for stock, for the rivers only flow in rainy seasons. Hence close to Cobar we find that the provision of dams and wells is necessary to supply water for the sheep, though the natural herbage gives them plenty of food. The second of our photographs (see No. 2) illustrates this characteristic feature of the pastoral district near Cobar. Harrington 'tank' collects rain-water (by means of shallow channels) from the immediate vicinity, and the water is deep enough to persist from one rain-storm to another. This district is on the border of winter and summer rain regions and the precipitation is about an inch in each month of the year.

Second Stage.—We now cross plains sparsely covered with small trees and shrubs which grow smaller and more scattered as we approach the Darling River (at 300 feet elevation). Here at Wilcannia we cross the 10-inch rain-line, which is often used as the limit of desert lands. The Darling River, though a huge stream in flood times, at times has ceased to run for eighteen months. From this point in our traverse until we reach Perth we shall not see a river of the usual type, though after the infrequent rains of course small creeks may flow for a few days. Sandy plains lie west of the Darling, which, however, readily become covered with spear grass or wild oats after rain. Saltbush is common, and there are scattered acacias and Leopard-Wood (*Flindersia*). Thirty miles from Broken Hill we reach the gentle slopes of the uplifted 'Horst'.[1] This rises

---

[1] *Horst* is an uplifted block of the earth's crust. *Graben* is a depressed block.

I

PHOTO I.—THE MALAYAN FLORA ON THE EAST COAST

(N.B.—THE EIGHT PLACES PHOTOGRAPHED ARE SHOWN ON THE TRAVERSE CHARTED IN FIG. I)

PHOTO 2.—HARRINGTON'S TANK NEAR COBAR

PHOTO 3.—WESTERN SLOPES OF THE BROKEN HILL UPLANDS, SHOWING FANS

PHOTO 4.—THE ARTESIAN BORE AT COWARD SPRINGS; NOTE DATE PALMS

to 1,000 feet and contains the richest mine in Australia. But its surface is usually almost bare of vegetation, except for occasional small trees of the type described already. In the photograph (No. 3) the rocky western slopes with their scattered mulga trees appear at A. There are very interesting fans (B and C) whose length indicates marked variations in past rainfall. The Lake Frome Plain appears at D. Before metals worth £130 millions were obtained at Broken Hill it had been divided into cattle stations. After the famous lode is exhausted in a decade or two it will return to its sparse pastoral occupation.

Third Stage.—We are now approaching the driest part of the continent. In rapid succession we cross the 7-inch isohyet near the border of the state, then the 6-inch north of Lake Frome, and the 5-inch near Lake Gregory. Here we meet with large sandhills which isolate the lakes and through which the Barcoo River winds to Lake Eyre. But these lakes are only shallow *playas*—occasionally containing a few inches of salty water, but mostly appearing as a layer of glistening salty mud. Our next photograph (No. 4) is taken at Coward Springs on the North–South Railway, nearly the driest place in Australia. The country exhibits loamy soils containing much gypsum, or else sheets of desert pebbles (gibbers). The chief feature, however, is that there are countless 'mound springs' where the water of the Great Artesian Basin overflows at the surface. A number of artesian bores have been put down of which one is illustrated in the photograph. A group of date palms is watered by the bore. Lake Eyre is, I believe, visible from the roof of the goods shed.

Most significant, however, is the presence of the North–South Railway. When the writer visited Coward Springs the railway had been in operation for thirty years, though one train a fortnight was found to be sufficient. There was no other station of importance for 50 miles each way. During this period Chicago had added 1 million inhabitants—but Coward Springs only contained four houses, two of which were empty. It should be clear that regular communications and large supplies of artesian water are not enough to bring population to these arid lands. The vegetation is mainly scattered saltbush—and the stock graze chiefly on rare depressions where the soil is marshy after the rare rains. Similar areas of desert-pebbles cover huge areas of the Sahara, and the latitudes and climates of the two regions are similar.

Fourth Stage.—Our next traverse brings us to Ooldea on the Transcontinental Railway, some 300 miles to the west. We pass from regions with 5 inches of rain to those with 8 inches, but there is little change in the undulating plains. Gibber country and gypsum country alternate, all sparsely covered with saltbush. Cattle in small numbers do well here. Crown Hill Station covers nearly 3,000 square miles, and limited amounts of ground water can be obtained in many places by wells about 100 feet deep. Sheep have of late years been replaced by cattle, owing to the dingo pest. Crown Hill and Mount Eba, the next station, are the outermost ranches in this part of Australia. Beyond them to the northwest is the uninhabited desert. East of Ooldea we cross the low granite hills which help to separate the Great Artesian Basin from the Tertiary limestones of the Nullarbor Plains. Just on the junction we cross a tongue of desert sandhills some 50 miles wide. These are built up of red sand, and are dotted with mulgas and other desert trees and shrubs. In the photograph (No. 5) is shown the pumping station, which sends water from many shallow wells to the railway 5 miles to the south. Our camels can be seen in the hollow.

Fifth Stage.—The limestones beyond Ooldea show a *karst* [1] topography. The rains are fairly reliable, falling mainly in winter, but they percolate deep into the limestone and there is great difficulty in conserving surface water. From Ooldea the railway runs westward for 300 miles as straight as an arrow, over saltbush plains almost devoid of trees (hence the name Nullarbor). One of the numerous sink-holes is shown in Photograph No. 6. There is no settlement except that due to the maintenance of the railway. Our traverse runs practically along the 9-inch isohyet from Ooldea to Loongana. The region is one of the most monotonous in the world. Cook is perhaps the only 'town', and contains about 100 people engaged in railway repairs, &c. Some day there will be a sparse pastoral occupation on these plains, for they cover a small artesian basin. Unfortunately, much of the water is too salty even for stock, though there is vegetation enough to support numerous flocks and herds, and small trees become abundant. There is a fair amount of feed for stock west of Zanthus, and it is possible to make dams to hold surface water. Hence sheep are spreading to the south-east of Kalgoorlie.

Sixth Stage.—From Loongana to Coolgardie the rainfall and elevation (900 feet) keep much the same, but there is a marked change in the geology near Zanthus. To the west we reach the great granite shield of West Australia, which leads to a better supply of surface water and to the development of a scrubby forest. We pass through the flourishing gold-mines of Kalgoorlie where the population numbered 17,300 in 1933, and reach Coolgardie, the scene of our photograph (No. 7) about 20 miles further. Since

---

[1] *Karst* is a rather barren region of surface limestone.

PHOTO 5.—FIXED DUNES, NEAR OOLDEA (S.A.)

PHOTO 6.—CAVE IN THE LIMESTONE ON THE NULLARBOR PLAIN
(L. K. WARD)

PHOTO 7.—THE OLD GOLD-MINING TOWN OF COOLGARDIE

PHOTO 8.—FINE EUCALYPTUS FOREST ON COAST OF SWANLAND
(AGENT-GENERAL, W.A.)

we are more concerned with the permanent resources of the region than with relatively short-lived gold-fields, it is more logical to choose the environs of Coolgardie than those of Kalgoorlie. It is about 1,300 feet above the sea, a vast undulating plain sparsely covered with salmon-gum, gimlet-wood and other stunted trees. After rains the usual rapidly growing desert plants cover much of the scanty soil for a time.

Seventh Stage.—Exactly the same kind of country extends westward to Southern Cross, about 200 miles from the coast. Here we leave the semi-desert country which we have traversed continuously since we left Cobar 1,800 miles to the east, and again enter agricultural lands. In this south-west triangle of Australia (to which the name Swanland has been given) is an area as large as Victoria, which differs entirely from the rest of the huge state of Western Australia. Wheat is grown as far east as Southern Cross and extends west nearly to Perth. The rainfall increases rapidly from 10 inches to 30 inches, each rainbelt having its appropriate type of eucalypt. Although trees up to 2 feet in diameter will grow in this section even where the rainfall is only 10 inches, it is not till we reach the coast that a veritable *forest* of large eucalyptus trees is met with, such as is illustrated in our last photograph. (Note two men amid ferns in No. 8.)

Summary.—In our traverse of seven stages across perhaps the best section of Australia we have learnt that the first stage and half the seventh are agricultural lands and that all the remainder are either sparse pastoral lands or unused semi-desert. The geographer is as much interested in empty lands as in those capable of close settlement. He cannot ignore the great problem of Australia, however much vilification he may meet from short-sighted critics. To answer the question, 'How shall the hot arid lands be developed?' the scientific method is surely to compare and grade the various regions in Australia, and to see how man in older settlements elsewhere has fared in analogous regions. To such analogous regions I have given the name 'homoclimes'. A scientific study of land utilization in Australia is largely a study of homoclimes.

Method of Investigation

Generalizing somewhat, we find that there are two rather different schools among professional geographers which can be illustrated by the methods of studying the geography of any large area. I may quote two recent volumes of the 'Geographie Universelle', i.e. those dealing with Central Europe by De Martonne and with the Russian Republics by D'Almeida. In the former study the first part consists of preliminary chapters on Climate, Relief, Life and Nationality. The bulk of the book, however, is devoted to *regional studies* each based on the *build* of the district considered. I think no geographer objects to the use of 'natural regions', but there is much discussion as to the emphasis which is to be laid on build, and especially on the underlying geology. De Martonne gives the geological background in almost every case, often illustrated by block diagrams which show at a glance how the environment depends on the geology and topography. The present writer entirely agrees with this treatment and will endeavour to follow this plan (in so far as incomplete data permit) in the chapters which follow.

In the Russian volume almost no attempt is made to study the geological basis of the build of the area. Indeed, topography itself is not much noticed, and the economic and human aspects of the vast region occupy almost the whole book. No one doubts the value of the two latter sections of geographical technique; but to the writer an entirely incomplete picture of the country is given where the 'terrain' (as distinct from 'man') is given so little place in the discussion. It is a pity that the most interesting field in the geographer's territory—that relating environment to man—is often untilled. This condition arises especially in those schools where topography is left to the geologist (who has little or no interest in the way in which man spreads over the topography); and where, as often occurs, the geographer has little interest in geology and so devotes all his attention to the 'human' aspects of geography. The writer may be prejudiced; but he feels that two of the greatest advances in geography in recent years have been the concept of the 'topographic cycle' and the extended use of the block diagram. Both of these we owe in great measure to the veteran American geographer, William Morris Davis.

Application to Australia.—While there are almost as many methods of approach to the study of a continent as there are authors concerned, the writer has always felt that there are two 'keys' to this particular problem. One of these is the 'heuristic' key and the other the 'evolution' key. The former implies that the student shall approach the study along the path of *discovery* followed by the pioneers. We shall use this method in part in deciding the order in which the Australian regions are considered. The latter concept implies that the student shall follow Nature in her treatment of the subject. In other words, the geological processes determine the topography, and these in large part control the climate. The native flora and fauna depend in turn chiefly on soil and climate. Man himself can do nothing with a land until nature has spread her green mantle thereon. Before these preliminary descriptive chapters it is, however, convenient to insert discussions on 'World Position' and on 'Discovery'; especially as geographers have naturally given less attention to the Australian continent (tucked away in the south-west corner of the Pacific Ocean) than to most other large areas.

The second part of the book is devoted to the Natural Regions, considered primarily as regards their topographic features, rainfall and vegetation. The oldest settlements (in New South Wales) are described first, and then the other regions included in the 'warped' highlands of the east and south-east. The regions making up the lowlands (geosyncline) and the Western Shield are next considered in some detail.

The third part of the book deals with the economic aspects of the Commonwealth as a whole. The founding of the states and the gradual process of exploration and settlement are discussed. Then follow eight chapters dealing with the agricultural, pastoral and mining industries. A brief discussion of the islands in the south-west Pacific follows. Problems of population and policy are discussed in the last chapter of the book.[1]

CENSUS OF JUNE 1954

State	Area	Proportion	Population	Proportion	Density*
New South Wales	309,433	10·4	3,462,313	38·1	11
Victoria	87,884	2·9	2,480,877	27·3	28
Queensland	670,500	22·5	1,322,752	14·7	2
South Australia	380,070	12·8	808,243	8·9	2
Western Australia	975,920	32.8	649,415	7·1	1
Northern Territory	523,620	17·6	16,140	0·1	—
Aust. Cap. Territory	939	—	31,144	0·3	32
Tasmania	26,215	0·9	319,511	3·4	12
Total	2,974,581	100	9,090,359	100	3

* Persons per square mile

In March 1959 the population was 10 millions.

[1] A bibliography of recent geographical literature appears at intervals in the journal, *The Australian Geographer*, which is published in Sydney. Here also a number of valuable papers, chiefly dealing with details of the regional geography of New South Wales, may be consulted.

In the last few years Federal economic surveys in the tropics, and local survey-volumes for the most of New South Wales, are being made available to the public. They contain invaluable maps.

Two very readable books by C. F. Laseron deal with the Scenery and Geology of Australia. They are *The Face of Australia* and *Ancient Australia* (Sydney, 1954).

CHAPTER II

WORLD POSITION AND DISCOVERY

SECTION I

THE WORLD-PLAN AND AUSTRALIA'S POSITION IN IT

AUSTRALIA was the last of all the continents (excluding Ant-arctica) to be discovered, and this was due to its remoteness. The direct antipodes of Spain, the great exploring nation of late medieval times, is New Zealand, while the antipodes of Australia is approximately the Sargasso Sea in the North Atlantic. Indeed, according to the Tetrahedral Theory,[1] Australia constitutes (with East Asia) the projecting land-area which 'opposes' the Atlantic Ocean; and, as that theory demands, 'Austral-Asia' is mainly built up of an ancient shield linked by the south-east lands of Asia to the ancient Angara Shield of the north. Apart from illustrating the remoteness of Australia from the most progressive European lands, this Tetrahedral Theory would seem at first glance to have little bearing on our study. If, however, we realize that the three main continental masses, America, Eur-Africa and Asia-Australia, consist essentially of broad northern lands tapering off to smaller southern lands, then this Tetrahedral Theory is an important factor in the distribution of *homoclimes* (p. 74), as we shall see in later sections.

Whether we adopt the Tetrahedral Theory or not, it is obvious that in its simplest form the World Plan consists of an alternation of lands and seas which may be compared to a pair of interlocking 'gear' wheels, as illustrated in Fig. 2. In the northern hemisphere is a 'land ring' with three cogs projecting southward. In the southern hemisphere is an 'ocean ring' with three cogs projecting northward. This plan was described by Lowthian Green in 1876, long before the deep Arctic Ocean and high Antarctic Continent were made known between 1897 and 1904. Their subsequent discovery was a strong corroboration of the validity of the theory he put forward.

[1] A simple discussion of the Tetrahedral Theory in its application to World Geography will be found in the present writer's *Environment, Race and Migration*, 1937 (Chapter III, especially Fig. 14). Briefly the theory suggests that the earth approximates an inverted pyramid in shape, standing on the apex (or South Pole). The three main oceans occupy the centre of the three sloping faces, and the Arctic Ocean occupies the centre of the flat upper face. It is due to Lowthian Green.

o geographer
lation of one

of the World
by the geo-

PACIFIC OCEAN

s' IN THE

with the Pacific

est, if one
sibilities of
place, the
trols which
tion, soils,
rium is ex-
the prob-
way of the

vegetation. For instance
same way. All savannas
forests give rise to the
similar occupations; and
early stage to see where
World Vegetation. We
bilities and of its homo
   In Fig. 3 the outline i
continental land-mass, b

90°
80°
70°
60°
50°
40°
30°
20°
10°
EQ
10
20
30
4
5

LATITUDE

FIG. 3.—STANDA
O

The major climatic
equator. The domina
has been called the
between the natural
those adopted by many
ing table. The emphas
that most plants begi
   Since Australia is s
expect to find that th
agree rather well with
shown if we superi
diagram. The discuss

CLIMATE AND VEGETATION REGIONS

Vegetation	Temperature	Rainfall
Ice-Cap	Under 32°	Light summer
Tundra	Warmest month = 50°	Light summer
Conifers	Under six months = 43°	Light summer
Broad-Leaf Trees	Over six months above 43°	Uniform
Mediterranean Flora	All over 43°	Winter
Cool Desert and Steppe	Some below 43°	About 10 inches (winter)
Hot Desert	None below 43°	Under 15 inches (summer)
Savanna	„ „ „	Summer
East Coast Tropical Forest	Over 70°	Uniform
Selva	„ „	Uniform

and of its climatic controls is deferred until a later chapter of the book.

World Position

It will be clear from the preceding paragraphs that the latitude of Australia, as in all other lands, is responsible for some good and for some evil factors as regards settlement. It is well to dwell for a moment on a fundamental principle of Climatic Control. Many students do not realize that the responses of man and of plants to a climate are often different. The most luxuriant riot of plant life occurs where the climate is at its hottest and wettest—say in the jungles of the Amazons or the Guinea Coast. But this is one of the least attractive environments for a vigorous *human* community, though it may produce certain valuable crops better than any other region. We must therefore differentiate between a good climate for *crops*, and a good climate for man. Moreover, in Australia we are primarily concerned with man of *British* ancestry. Indeed, in Australia these two types of climate—suitable for crops, or suitable for men—are involved in most of the problems of settlement. There are, for instance, essentially two types of tropical climate. The hot *wet* type suitable for crops, and the hot *dry* type of little value for crops, but not particularly harmful to man. Most of the Australian tropics belong to the latter type, for which reason their freedom from tropical disease is to some extent balanced by the lack of any agriculture.

It is convenient to classify the various belts of latitude into five divisions according as to their suitability for close white settlement. Probably few geographers would object to the following generalized

2

classes, which are arranged from the best to the worst:

LATITUDE AND CLIMATES

Name	Latitude	Character	Typical country
I. Best Temperate	35–50°	Excellent for man and crops	Italy and France
II. Cool Temperate	50–65	Excellent for man, crops fair	Canada
III. Wet Tropical	0–15	Excellent for crops, poor for man	Equatorial lands
IV. Dry Semi-Tropical	15–35	Desert in west and centre; very good in east	Australia
V. Polar	65–90	Very poor for man or crops	Tundra and ice-cap

In the above table, naturally general rather than particular conditions are considered, and such factors as soil and topography are

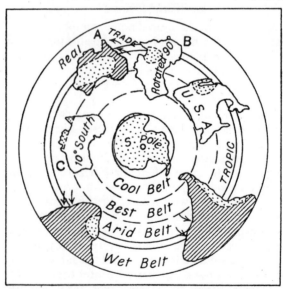

FIG. 4.—THE CONTINENTS IN RELATION TO THE VARIOUS LATITUDE BELTS

Two hypothetical positions of Australia and U.S.A. (inverted) are also shown. Deserts shown dotted

ignored. One cannot, however, altogether ignore what may be termed the 'aspect' of a country, i.e. whether in the western, central or eastern part of a continent. This is of most importance in the semi-tropical lands, and of little consequence near the equator or poles. It is of especial significance in regard to the general *shape* of a continent, as may best be understood from a discussion of the illustration (Fig. 4).

In Fig. 4 the four southern continents are shown in relation to the five belts of latitude mentioned above. Antarctica is entirely included within the *Polar* Belt. There is no land except the tip of South America within the *Cool Temperate* Belt. So also the *Best Temperate* Belt in the southern hemisphere only includes a small part of South America, New Zealand, Victoria and Tasmania. It is the next belt, the *Arid Semi-Tropical* Belt, which most concerns us in this study. This is the region of the Trade Winds (and of the Anticyclone Belt) and is dominated by easterly winds. These are wet *onshore* winds in the lands with an easterly aspect, and dry offshore winds in the centre or westerly aspects of a continent. Hence it should be clear that the broader a continent in this belt, the larger will be the area of dry land. The following table shows the width of the Arid Semi-Tropical lands both in the northern and southern hemispheres:

RELATION OF DESERTS TO WIDTH OF LAND ALONG THE TROPICS

Hemi-sphere	Land	Width in miles	Humid east	Desert part
North	African-Asian Land Mass (Cape Blanco to Shanghai) (Mexico is too narrow)	7,700	700	7,000
South	Australia	2,400	600	1,800
	South Africa	1,300	600	700
	South America (complicated by Andes)	1,600	1,300	300

The interesting column in this table is that labelled 'Humid east', for it shows that the relatively wet eastern littoral is of about the same width (600 or 700 miles) whatever the width of the land in this belt. Two of the areas (Mexico and South America) are too irregular to be of much value in our comparison. The width of the desert in the case of North Africa, South Africa and Australia is clearly proportionate to the *width* of the land involved. It is because Australia extends so far along the Tropic of Capricorn that it contains so large a proportion of desert and semi-desert. If, however, Australia (A) were rotated through 90°, taking the position shown at B in Fig. 4, it seems likely that though the eastern wet littoral would be much the same width, the desert area would be much *narrower*.

In this figure, the United States is shown transferred to the southern hemisphere (by swinging over with the equator as a hinge). It is seen that U.S.A. lies almost wholly in the 'Best Belt' of the table given on page 18. It has often been stated that the aridity of central Australia is due to the absence of high mountains. This is not the main reason; it is the latitude and winds rather than elevation which are at fault. If one could 'push' Australia southward through 10° or 15° of latitude (as indicated at C in Fig. 4), then there would be some reason for the statement, made by some politicians, that 'Australia, being of the same size as U.S.A., is destined to hold as important a position in the future'.

The latitude of Australia is therefore a disability, and it is easy to show that its smooth outline (resembling a bean) is of no climatic advantage. The wonderful croplands of the 'Middle West' of U.S.A. are not paralleled elsewhere, because no other land in similar latitudes has a warm sea, like the Gulf of Mexico, just to the south. If this Gulf were land, the 'Middle West' would be as dry as southern central Australia. On the other hand, if the desert of central Australia could be replaced by a similar enormous gulf, it is probable that the southern lands of Australia would be much better watered than at present.

SECTION II

THE EVOLUTION OF THE MAP OF AUSTRALIA

There seems today little doubt that the first accurate report of any Australian coast resulted from the voyage of Captain Jansz in the *Duyfken* (Dovekin) early in 1606. But rumours of the large island to the south of the East Indies were heard by the first European travellers in south-eastern Asia. Some little attention may therefore be given to the maps published before Jansz's voyage.

In early medieval times nothing definite was known of any land south of the equator. The early maps were reasonably accurate in the Mediterranean region, but became mere guesswork toward the Indian Ocean (Fig. 5). The cartographer of the eighth century used a ring of sea (known as 'Oceanus') to bound his map. Below the crude outlines of Africa and India he filled in the southern segment with an unknown land. In his own words 'Here lies a fourth part beyond the interior (i.e. Indian) Ocean, which on account of the heat of the sun is unknown to us, where may live the fabulous antipodeans.' In Arabian maps of the ninth to twelfth century (such as that by Idrisi) we find southern Africa curved to the right so that the Indian Ocean becomes a gulf like the Mediterranean. In a map made in south-west France about 1050, three islands appear to the south-east of India named Scolere, Crise and Argire. These have been taken without much reason to represent Socotra, Malaya and Sumatra. About 1295 Marco Polo returned from China by way of the East Indies. He gained much information from the Arabs as to the islands to the south. He refers to Java Major and Java Minor, and it has been assumed by Collingridge [1] that the latter name refers to Sumatra, while Java Major (which Marco Polo called 'the largest island in the world') is Australia.

Owing to the enthusiasm of Prince Henry the Navigator, a beautiful map of the world was constructed in Venice by Fra

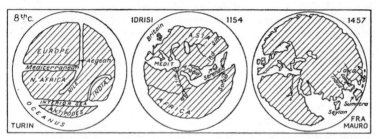

FIG. 5.—THREE EARLY MAPS OF THE OLD WORLD, SHOWING THE GRADUAL ADVANCE IN KNOWLEDGE OF THE SOUTH-EAST

Mauro about 1457 (Fig. 5). Here, long before the Portuguese reached the Cape of Good Hope, the shape of South Africa is clearly indicated. Indeed, we are told that an *Indian* ship in 1420 doubled the Cape and sailed far north up the west coast. It was not, however, till late in 1486 that Bartholomew Diaz reached the Great Fish River (east of Port Elizabeth) and rounded the first southern continent.

It is a curious fact that the Nuremburg globe made by Behaim in 1492 shows a projection from south-east Asia which reaches south of the Tropic of Capricorn. This projection is taken by Collingridge to indicate the west coast of Australia. It seems more likely to be borrowed from the ancient Ptolemaic maps, which showed the Indian Ocean limited by 'Terra Incognita' to the south and south-west. A town of 'St. Thomas' is marked on this coast, which may be an erroneous location of an old settlement really near

[1] George Collingridge, *The Discovery of Australia*, Sydney, 1895, with many maps.

Madras. The Hunt-Lenox Globe of 1511 shows the name *Loac* in this projection, and 'fragments' of the legendary Terra Incognita are scattered over the Indian Ocean. It is possible that *Locach*—an old name for Siam—is indicated.

Early Charts of the Sixteenth Century

In September 1509, the Portuguese Sequiera reached the spice emporium of Malacca, and Magellan was a member of his expedition. They soon penetrated to the Spice Islands of the Moluccas, which lay further to the east, for in 1511 three ships under de Abreu (Fig. 8) sailed along the coasts of Java and as far as Ternate and Amboyna. On this voyage the Portuguese had reached the area of Australian flora and fauna, for they crossed the Bali-Lombok line, which (as discovered by Wallace) bounds the Asiatic region. By 1530 fairly accurate charts by Rodriguez, dealing with the East Indies, were available to the Portuguese.

In 1521 Magellan circumnavigated the globe, though he was killed in the Philippines, just when he reached the scene of his previous voyages (around 1511). It is curious that in several maps published about this time the mysterious *Loac* peninsula with its attendant islands was omitted, so that the newly discovered Pacific extended from America clear westward to Africa! Magellan's ship on its return through the Indian Ocean actually sailed parallel to the north-west coast of Australia, though at a distance of several hundred miles (Fig. 8). A second expedition under Loyasa followed Magellan's route in 1526, but nearly all the ships and crews were lost on their hazardous voyage. It seems likely that they discovered the sub-Antarctic island of South Georgia on this occasion. A later expedition under Saavedra explored the north coast of New Guinea in 1528 and 1529.

About 1530 a new series of charts developed in which a large continent surrounded the South Pole and extended across the southern parts of the Pacific and Indian Oceans. Possibly this modification was due to the lands seen south of Magellan's Straits in 1521, which seemed to support Ptolemy's maps, in which the ocean south of Asia was bounded by continuous land to the south. Wytfliet showed such a huge southern land in 1597 (Fig. 6B).

On a very interesting world map of Orontius Finaeus of 1531 we find such a return to the great Antarctic Continent which fills most of the southern hemisphere south of Capricorn. In place of being named 'Terra Incognita' it is labelled 'Terra Australis', and a note in Latin adds that it has been recently discovered, but is not fully known. The name 'Australis' merely means 'southern' and has no real bearing on the discovery of Australia. Several

other names, such as 'Brasielie Regio' and 'Regio Patalis', have
been taken from earlier maps and placed apparently haphazard on
the Terra Australis. 'Patalis' may be an echo of 'Patagonia' or of
the River 'Plate'. Schoner (1533), Mercator (1569) and Wytfliet
(1597) seem to have copied this map.

Another interesting series of maps began about 1536 when the
famous Dauphin Chart was drawn for the Dauphin of France,
afterward Henry II. It appears on a sheet of vellum about 8 feet
by 4 feet, and displays a large continental area 'Java la Grande'
immediately south of Java. Upon the north coast of Java we can
read the name Curabaia, which refers to the modern port of Sura-
baya, and on a projection of Java la Grande appears Symbana,

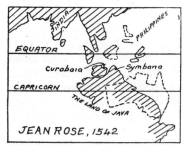

FIG. 6A. — A MEDIEVAL MAP SHOW-
ING A LARGE LAND CALLED JAVA,
NEAR THE POSITION OF AUSTRALIA
(SHOWN BY BROKEN LINES)

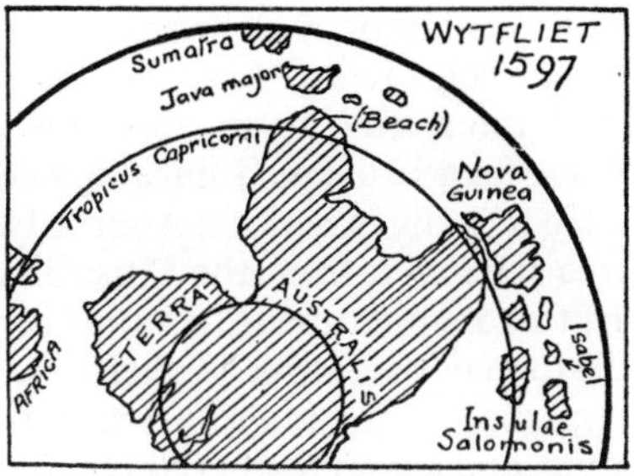

FIG. 6B. — WYTFLIET'S MAP SHOW-
ING A LARGE CONTINENT AROUND
THE SOUTH POLE

The position of 'Beach' on Mercator's
map of 1569 is indicated

(*Both maps after Collingridge*)

which is probably Sumbawa Island (Fig. 6A). The most logical
explanation of this map is that the Portuguese had no knowledge
of the south coasts of Java or Sumbawa, but were told by the
Arabs and Malays that a huge land lay just to the south of Java.
The Malays, no doubt, visited the Australian coasts to collect
trepang, just as they were seen doing during the later Dutch and
English voyages of exploration. One imagines that the Malays and
perhaps the Arabs knew that the coasts trended to the south-west
and south-east from the Arafuera Sea. On the Dauphin map there
are some thirty names given on the coasts of Java la Grande, but
it seems likely that they represent a voyage rather of imagination
than discovery.

Jean Rose of Dieppe seems to have copied these details on his
map published in 1542. The navigators' knowledge of longitude
was nebulous at this time, but I have attempted to add the approxi-

mate position of Australia to his map (Fig. 6A). I have used the distance from India to the East Indian islands as a rough scale of longitude. It illustrates the points already discussed in the Dauphin map. On the west is perhaps a hint of the deep gulfs which characterize north-west Australia. The eastern coast of Java la Grande has somewhat the general direction of the north-east of Australia. Most significant of all in this series of maps is the absence of land to the south-east and south-west of the 'Land of Java', thus showing fairly accurately the separation of the Pacific and Indian Oceans by a large continent. In 1544 Sebastian Cabot published a fine world map in which the East Indian islands are much more accurately shown. He wisely omits any attempt to draw the south coasts of Java, Sumbawa and Flores; but gives good representations of Timor, Gilolo and parts of Borneo and New Guinea.

In 1569 Gerard Mercator issued a map of the world which is very interesting in its Australian area. The East Indian festoon from Java to New Guinea is well shown. The latter island bears a label to the effect that Andrea Corsali (a Florentine) believes that it is separated from the 'Australian Continent' by a narrow strait. In this map Arnhem Land is labelled 'Beach', which is probably a draftsman's error for Locach. The large gulf to the east of 'Beach' is perhaps to be identified with the Gulf of Carpentaria. Drake in 1579 and Cavendish (1588) carried the English flag through the East Indies, but neither added anything to our knowledge of Australian coasts.

The Last Spanish Voyages

Some reference must, however, be made to Mendana's voyage in 1567 (Fig. 8). Many Spanish expeditions followed Magellan across the Pacific to develop their new territory of the Philippines, but naturally they sailed considerably north of Australian waters. However, Mendana, taking a more southern route, discovered the Solomon Islands and named Ysabel, Malaita and Guadalcanar. Nearly thirty years later another expedition under Mendana was sent from Spain to colonize the Solomon Islands. He was expressly commanded to try and discover the great continent, which appeared in this area on so many of the later maps. Mendana's ships carried a number of women, and this was probably the first attempt to settle any *Australian* lands. In September 1595, they reached a festoon of islands 300 miles south-east of the Solomons which they named Santa Cruz. Here Mendana died and the attempt at colonization failed. His ships proceeded to the Philippines and later returned to America.

De Quiros, who was second to Mendana in 1567, led another

expedition to these waters in 1606 with a view to exploring and 'evangelically subduing' such lands as they discovered. He in turn reached the Melanesian islands, south of his earlier voyage, and so discovered the New Hebrides on May 1st, the day sacred to St. Philip and St. James (Fig. 8). De Quiros held a solemn festival on the shores of the Bay of St. Philip and St. James, and took possession 'of the site on which is to be founded the city of New Jerusalem, and of all the lands which I sighted, and am going to sight, and of all this region of the south as far as the Pole, which from this time shall be called Austrialia del Espiritu Santo'.

Today this land is known to be merely an island 70 miles long and 40 broad, and it is usually known more briefly as 'Santo'. De Quiros seems to have modified the old name Terra Australis in honour of the Austrian dynasty of the King of Spain; but 'Austrialia' was soon changed to 'Australia' in early accounts of the discovery of the New Hebrides.[1] The most important portion of the expedition's work in Australian waters still lay before them. De Quiros was ill and disheartened, so that he decided to return northward and eastward to Mexico. However, one of his ships under Torres and Prado carried out the original plan of exploring to the west of the Solomons (and New Hebrides); but an account of this famous voyage must be deferred until the exploit of the *Duyfken* has been described.

The Dutch came to the Spice Islands purely and simply for business reasons. They had little of the zeal for exploration which animated many of the English captains, and none for evangelizing the heathen. In 1526 Saavedra named the north coast of New Guinea the 'Land of Gold', and the actual discovery of Australia was due to an attempt to collect more gold on the unknown coasts of New Guinea. In November 1605 a Dutch ship called the *Duyfken* was sent eastward from Java for this purpose. There seems some doubt as to the tonnage of this famous ship, whether 30 or 60 tons; and no accurate account of the discovery by Jansz has been preserved (Fig. 8). All that we know is included in the instructions given to Tasman in 1644 before his second voyage. Collingridge gives the following translation:

Captain William Jansz discovered the south and west coast of New Guinea for about 880 miles from 5° to 13¾° south latitude. They found this extensive country for the greater part desert, but in some places inhabited by wild cruel black savages, by whom some of the crew were murdered. For this reason they could not learn anything of the land or waters, as had been desired of them; and by want of provision and other

---

[1] H. N. Stevens, however, gives the Spanish text as '*australia del spiritu santo*' in *New Light* (1930), p. 124.

necessaries they were obliged to leave the discovery unfinished. The furthest point of the land was called in their map Cape Keer Weer, situated at 13¾° S. [Fig. 7A.]

This famous event occurred about March 1606. Apparently Jansz was unaware that he had crossed Torres Straits (though they are 100 miles wide) and had coasted for 200 miles along the shores of the unknown southern continent. This is easier to understand when one knows that the shallow straits are filled with coral reefs and small islands, so that Jansz no doubt thought he was merely crossing a gulf in the coasts of New Guinea. We have seen that such a strait had been suggested on the maps for nearly a century —but probably the Dutch sailors placed little reliance on the imaginative charts made by stay-at-home cartographers.

A few months later the Spanish ship *San Pedrico* was approaching the same waters. Until lately Torres has always been accepted as the leader, but a recent book by H. N. Stevens makes it probable that Diego de Prado y Tovar was the leader and Torres merely his second-in-command. However, this makes little difference to their discoveries, save that the passage north of Australia might have been named Prado Strait instead of Torres Strait if the full truth had been known. De Quiros left Santo on June 11th, and Torres made an unsuccessful attempt to get in touch with him. He thereupon sailed south-westward, finding that the New Hebrides were only small islands. He seems to have had in mind the discovery of the 'Terra Australis', but they were poorly equipped, for he writes: 'I had at this time nothing but bread and water. It was the height of winter, with contrary wind and ill wills [of his crew].'

Torres turned north-west and fell in with the beginning of New Guinea, and coasted to the westward along the south side. It has been stated that his maps delineate Milne Bay, Orangerie Bay and Triton Bay. He especially describes the extremely shallow waters, as 'a bank of from 3 to 9 fathoms, [and] there is all over it an archipelago of islands without number. At the end of the eleventh degree [south latitude] the bank became shoaler, and here were very large islands and there appeared more to southward.' It is clear that Torres did not suspect that these islands represented the drowned extremity of a large continent. The writer has visited this region, and can readily understand the difficulty of distinguishing the mainland at Cape York from the adjacent similarly shaped islands. However, there is no doubt that Captain Jansz preceded Torres hereabouts by some six months and is the actual discoverer of the mainland.

The First Accurate Maps of Australian Coasts

We have now rapidly surveyed the growth of knowledge of a great south land through the Middle Ages. At first such a land appeared on the primitive maps to satisfy the feeling of 'symmetry' of old map-makers. Marco Polo, about 1300, brought back rumours of large lands south of China, which the map-makers tried to incorporate in their charts. The Arabs and Malays certainly knew something of the land separating the two great oceans, and this began to be indicated on charts about 1530. Two outlying regions of the Australian Territory, New Guinea and the Solomons, were explored within a few decades. As we have seen, the actual coast was visited in March 1606, though no log of the

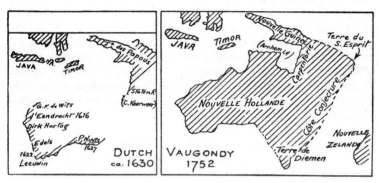

FIGS. 7A AND 7B.—TWO MAPS SHOWING THE DUTCH EXPLORATIONS OF AUSTRALIA ON CONTEMPORARY MAPS

(*After Collingridge*)

Little Dove's voyage has come down to us. Gerritsz's map of 1627 is therefore the first accurate representation of the actual coasts of Australia. A map of this date is shown in Fig. 7A.

In 1580 Philip of Spain became King of Portugal and did his best to prevent Indian goods reaching England or Holland. It is interesting to remember that Lancaster, the first English trader to the East Indies, sailed in 1591; and so preceded the first Dutch Fleet by several years. However, within the next few years 65 Dutch ships sailed to the East Indies by way of the Cape. In 1602 they founded their East India Company, and in 1609 won from Spain the right to trade freely in the East. At first they sailed north-east from the Cape, but gradually they learnt to use the Brave West Winds of the southern latitudes which carried them right across the Indian Ocean. Then a slight northing brought them into the region of the South-East Trades which drove the ships readily on to Java. Under these circumstances it was inevitable that the west coast of Australia should be discovered—for it opposes a barrier of 1,000 miles directly across the path of the voyager from the west (Fig. 7A).

There is in the museum of Amsterdam surely the most interesting plate in the world. It is a roughly flattened utensil made of pewter on which is a Dutch inscription, 'A.D. 1616 on the 25th October, there arrived here the ship *den Eendraght* [Union] of Amsterdam; skipper Dirck Hartog'. It was discovered in West Australia lying below its pole of rotten wood by a later Dutch ship in 1697, when Vlaming visited Dirk Hartog's Island off Shark Bay. In 1618 the *Zeewulf* discovered the coast near Port Hedland. Next year Houtman reached the vicinity of Perth, and the reefs off Geraldton still bear his name. On Gerritsz's map the land north of Perth is called Edel's Land, probably a misprint for Dedel, the supercargo of Houtman. The best-known Dutch name in Australia is Cape Leeuwin at the south-west corner of the continent; which was discovered in 1622 on the voyage of the ship *Leeuwin* (Lioness). In the same year the English ship *Trial* was wrecked on the reefs near Onslow and nearly 50 men were lost. The survivors reached Java in boats (Fig. 7A).

The Dutch did not realize any more clearly than many of the politicians of Australia that there are two types of tropical lands. Near the equator are the jungles of the wet tropics, farther from the equator are the dry savannas merging into the deserts near the Tropic of Capricorn. The only modification of this latter, less-attractive, type is found in lands with an *easterly* aspect. It was, of course, precisely these lands (in *east* Queensland) which the Dutch did not discover. Hence they inevitably developed a very unfavourable opinion of the great South Land; for in the whole of their discoveries they only saw two small areas (near Perth and Hobart) which have since been found suitable for close settlement.

In 1623 Carstenz sailed from Java to see if the northern coasts of Australia offered stores of spices such as were to be obtained in the neighbouring islands to the north. Even from his ship, Carstenz could see the snow-covered mountains of New Guinea—a remarkable sight so near the equator, and only to be paralleled in the Sierra Nevada of north-east Colombia. He was unable to penetrate the reefs of Torres Straits and so placed the words 'Shallow Bight' on his chart. The *Arnhem*, one of his ships, was blown westwards across the Gulf of Carpentaria, and so added Arnhem Land to the meagre names of the Australian map (Fig. 7B). A few years later the *Gulden Zeepaard* ran eastwards from Cape Leeuwin for a thousand miles and discovered the Great Australian

Bight. It is shut in by a monotonous line of cliffs (probably a fault scarp) some 500 feet high, and supports practically no settlement to this day. Captain Thyssen turned back at Nuyt's Archipelago —just where the farming lands of South Australia begin (Fig. 7A). Few tales of the sea are more terrible than the story of the wreck of the *Batavia* under Pelsart in 1629. The ship struck on the Houtman Reefs (150 miles north of Perth) and 220 people were landed on these barren rocks. While Pelsart sailed in a small boat to Batavia, the supercargo who remained on the reefs plotted to seize the rescuing ship and turn pirate. He killed some forty of the crew, but Pelsart was warned on his return and most of the mutineers were executed. Two, however, were marooned on the mainland and so perhaps may be styled the first white settlers in Australia. A very improbable suggestion is that the tawny-haired aborigines of West Australia have some trace of their blood (p. 459).

Tasman's Voyages

Although this great Dutch navigator was the first to circumnavigate Australia, he added little to the knowledge of the coastlands except in the north-west. He sailed in August 1642 on his first voyage, making first for Mauritius to revictual and then turning eastward to take advantage of the Brave West Winds (Fig 8). He sailed far south of Thyssen's route, and the first land he saw was the mountainous west coast of Tasmania on November 24th, near Macquarie Harbour. (Flinders, in 1798, named two prominent peaks in the vicinity Heemskerk and Zeehan after Tasman's two ships.) Tasman gave names to several places on the south coast, such as Maatsuyker Island, Storm Bay, Tasman Maria and Schouten Islands, which still appear on our maps. His men landed in Blackman's Bay near the isthmus of Tasman's Peninsula, and next day they placed a flag on the south coast of Marion Bay. On December 4th he left 'Anthony Van Diemen's Landt' (now Tasmania), and on the 16th he discovered New Zealand, seeing first of all Cape Farewell at the west end of Cook Strait.

After a cruise to the north-east, on which he discovered the Tonga and Fiji Islands, Tasman returned to Batavia via the north coast of New Guinea. The chief result of his voyage was that it showed that no huge southern continent linked the newly discovered Australian lands to the mysterious Antarctic continent, which was still placed in the south of the Pacific. We must remember that such a 'Terra Australis Incognita' was shown on Dutch maps as late as 1612. In his second voyage (1644) Tasman explored the south coast of the Gulf of Carpentaria, and showed that it extended no great distance into the 'South Land'. His journal has disappeared, though luckily the chart of 1644 has been preserved. Australia, as it was shown after Tasman's two voyages, is shown in the 1752 map by Vaugondy (Fig. 7B).

For well over a hundred years after Tasman no further explorations of importance were made in Australian waters. A complete gap in the coastline extended from the Great Australian Bight around the south-east and east coast up to Cape York. In other words, it was left to the English to explore almost the whole of the

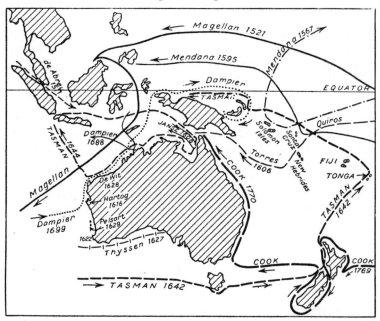

FIG. 8.—ROUTES OF THE EXPLORERS FROM 1511 TO 1770 IN THE SEAS NEAR AUSTRALIA

coastline of what I have called 'Economic Australia'. Yet we cannot dismiss this period of 126 years without a few words. In 1696 Vlamingh explored Rottnest Island off Perth—so named from the numerous small marsupials, which he called 'rats'. He then rowed many miles up the Swan River, where they saw plenty of Black Swans. He made more careful maps to the north—finding a forbidding coast, for the most part, where (as we now know) the trade winds blow fairly regularly offshore and the rainfall is below 10 inches a year.

The first and one of the most interesting of the British explorers was William Dampier. In the words of G. A. Wood, 'His joy would have been to travel like Banks in the Endeavour, or like Darwin in the Beagle. . . . Travel somehow he must, and the best people to travel with in his day were pirates. Therefore, Dampier became a pirate.' At 18 he went to Newfoundland, and then to Java. At 22 he was in Jamaica, and then left for the Spanish Main to cut logwood. He crossed to Panama and sailed down the coast to Juan Fernandez. At 30 he was in Virginia and then made another voyage to Juan Fernandez and the Peruvian coast. He now joined the semi-piratical *Cygnet*, in which he sailed from Mexico to the Philippines. From here they went south-west to the Spice Islands and so south to the rarely visited Southland, now becoming known as New Holland.

In January 1688 Dampier reached what are now called Cygnet Bay and Buccaneer Archipelago (near King Sound) in the Kimberleys (Fig. 8). Here they stayed for more than three months in the hottest part of the year in one of the hottest regions in the world. When they reached Indian waters Dampier fled from the pirates and wandered through Sumatra, Tonquin and India and finally reached England again in 1691. A journal of these voyages was published in 1697. In July 1699 he once more reached Australia near Houtman's Reefs in his own ship, the *Roebuck*. Thence he sailed north up the arid coastline almost as far as his old anchorage (Fig. 8). At Roebuck Bay (Broome) they landed in their constant search for water and were much disappointed in the 'Pindan country', i.e. sparsely forested scrubby savannas, of the hinterland. Dampier hoped to find better country, where the British trader might collect spices, further to the east. He therefore sailed around New Guinea and added greatly to the knowledge of the north-east coast. He explored New Britain and then returned to England.via the Cape of Good Hope.

Dalrymple and Bougainville

Toward the middle of the eighteenth century there was renewed interest in the unknown 'Terra Australis'. The cartographer Dalrymple, who had lived some time in India, was convinced that a great continent extended from Cape Horn across the South Pacific toward the Solomon Isles and Tasmania. He published a book in 1769 putting forward his conclusions based on observations by all the navigators in those waters. He thought it likely that this Southern Continent had a population of 50 millions. France was affected by the same hopes of colonizing a new land in temperate latitudes, and it is one of the chances of history that Bougainville did not anticipate Cook in the discovery of the east coast of Australia. The great French navigator reached Cape Horn in

December 1767 and then commenced his search for Terra Australis. He found no lands except a few small islands such as that southern paradise, Tahiti. In May 1768 he reached Samoa and the New Hebrides. As late as 1756 maps had been published showing that these islands were probably part of 'New Holland', in spite of Torres' voyage in 1606 (Fig. 7B). However, Bougainville sailed due westward until he saw breakers to the north-west that appeared to stretch without end. He was, in fact, facing that colossal rampart of coral reefs, which is known as the Great Barrier Reef, and indeed was not far from Cooktown, near which Cook was nearly wrecked two years later. But he turned away to the north-east, and after dangerous weeks amid the reefs of eastern New Guinea, he managed to reach the safer seas north-east of that great island. He had done little but show how keen was French interest in this quarter of the world.

Captain Cook's Discoveries in 1769–1770

The discoverer of 'Economic Australia' was born near Whitby, Yorkshire, in 1728. He gained early sailing experience in the coal-boats in the North Sea, but later joined the navy and in 1758 sailed in the British Fleet to help Wolfe in Canada. Here he was engaged in marine surveying along the St. Lawrence and around Newfoundland. He was also interested in astronomy and wrote a paper in 1766 on the eclipse of the sun. Few officers in the navy could be better equipped to lead an astronomical expedition to the South Seas. When, therefore, the British Government agreed to send a party to Tahiti to observe the Transit of Venus, it was to Cook that they entrusted the leadership. His ship, the *Endeavour*, was actually one of the bluff, roomy coal-boats built at Whitby with which Cook was so familiar.

In addition to the astronomical research at Tahiti, Cook was instructed to proceed south to latitude 40° and then west to New Zealand, which he was to explore. Thereafter he might return to England by any route he desired. During the early part of 1769 he sailed over much of the South Pacific, but found no trace of Dalrymple's continent. In April he reached Tahiti and was favoured with fine weather during the transit. He then sailed southward to what should have been the centre of Dalrymple's continent. He now turned westward to show that Tasman's Staten Land (New Zealand) had no connexion with the Staten Land found off Cape Horn in 1615.

Early in October 1769 Cook reached Poverty Bay in New Zealand (Fig. 8), and after six months spent in making an accurate survey of its coasts he sailed from Cape Farewell on April 1st,

1770. He had decided to sail westward until he met with the coast of New Holland—of which the whole eastern portion was uncharted. He hoped to reach Tasmania where Tasman left it—but a southerly gale drove him just north of Bass Straits, so that he first sighted Point Hicks on April 20th about 40 miles west of Cape Howe. He naturally decided to sail northward so as to map in the great unknown extent of coast which lay somewhere between Point Hicks and New Guinea.

During the next four months Cook was busy charting the most important coastlands in Australia. He desired to find a satisfactory harbour, but saw none very attractive as he sailed up the south coast. After a voyage of a little over a week he reached a suitable inlet, the famous Botany Bay. On the southern headland they dug a small well (which is still preserved). His scientific companion, Joseph Banks, was as delighted with the new plants which abounded on every side as Cook was with the meadows on the western shores. They stayed there a week, and their observations directly led to the foundation of the first British settlement in Australia some eighteen years later.

On May 7th he again sailed northward and at noon he noticed a break, one mile wide, in the frowning sandstone cliffs, and gave the inlet the name Port Jackson. Within this narrow bay was destined to develop one of the largest cities of the southern hemisphere, while much of Botany Bay is nearly as empty as when Cook visited it. His next landing was made in Queensland at Bustard Point, just south of Gladstone. A few days later he entered the reef-strewn lane within the Great Barrier, and on June 20th at 11 p.m. the ship struck the jagged coral rocks of the 'Endeavour Reef'. However, twenty-four hours later she was floated off and the hole temporarily plugged. A few days later she was beached where now Cooktown stands; and it was not till August 6th that Cook managed to sail onward. Perilous reefs drove him out beyond the giant wall of the outer rampart. Equally perilous seas drove him back somewhat further north, thus accounting for the gap in his wonderful coastal charts (between Cape Flattery and Cape Weymouth).

On August 21st Cook entered Torres Straits and so finished his great contribution to Australian cartography. However, owing to three months' delay in Batavia, where nearly all his crew fell sick, he did not reach England until July of the next year. A few lines must, however, be devoted to Cook's famous second and third voyages. In the second (1772–5) he cruised in the southern waters of the three great oceans and effectively removed the southern 'Terra Incognita' from the maps as far as concerns regions north of the Antarctic Circle. Furneaux, one of his captains, explored the east coast of Tasmania in March 1773. In Cook's third voyage he explored the North Pacific, and was killed in the isle of Hawaii in February 1779.

Cook's Successors

There still, however, remained a thousand miles in the southeast between the Bight and Point Hicks represented by a blank on the charts. Moreover, it was remarkable that no large river had been found anywhere on the coasts of Australia. This huge gap was not surveyed until after the settlement of Australia had commenced. We will leave for a later chapter the story of the First Fleet, which arrived in Botany Bay in January 1788, and continue the narrative of the charting of the coasts of Australia. Two young men from Lincolnshire (the county of Banks) had the honour of completing the survey. They were Lieutenant Flinders and Surgeon Bass.

Seven years after the arrival of the First Fleet, Governor Hunter gave Bass a whale-boat to solve the most obvious problem—whether Tasmania was joined to the mainland or not. Furneaux had doubted if there was a strait north of the small islands named after him. At the end of 1797 Bass rounded Cape Howe and then proceeded westward to Wilson's Promontory, where he found some convict castaways, and made the first survey on January 5th of an inlet which he called Western Port. He had traversed two-thirds of the straits—but had not completely solved the problem, when he had to return. In October 1798 Flinders and Bass were given a small sloop, built of the famous pines from Norfolk Island —a small 'colony' of the young colony which lay 900 miles to the east of Sydney. Flinders reached northern Tasmania early in November and surveyed the mouth of the Tamar. On December 9th he turned southward, having rounded the Hunter Islands and so proved that Tasmania was an island. A few days later he linked up with Tasman's charts. Next year he was in England preparing for his stupendous surveys in the *Investigator*. Meanwhile Lieutenant Grant was ordered to proceed to Sydney by the new route through Bass Straits, and to him fell the honour of discovering the west coast of Victoria in December 1800. He missed Port Phillip, however, and this was explored by Murray in February 1802.

In 1800 Baudin, a French navigator, had left France to explore the unknown south coasts of Australia. He thought it likely that a wide strait might extend north to the Gulf of Carpentaria and so divide New Holland in two. (Somewhat the same state of uncer-

tainty exists today with regard to the continent of Antarctica.
Does an icy lowland link the Ross and Weddell Seas?) Luckily for
Britain, Baudin was the reverse of energetic, and sailed up the
west coast instead of attempting to discover the southern coasts.
Not till March 1802 was he off the unknown coasts of South
Australia. Meanwhile Flinders reached Cape Leeuwin in Decem-
ber 1801. During January he verified the Dutch discoveries of
1627 in the Bight, and during March he made accurate maps of

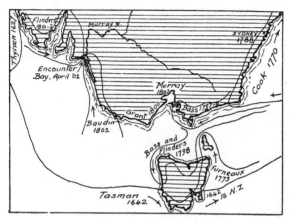

FIG. 8A.—THE LAST COASTAL EXPLORATIONS, 1770 TO 1802

the Gulfs of South Australia, which at first seemed likely to connect with Carpentaria. On April 8th he had finished the survey
of the gulfs, and was sailing eastward across a broad, sandy bay
when he saw the ships of his friendly rival, Baudin. So originated
the name 'Encounter Bay'. The Frenchman had just explored
some 150 miles of coast, which still bears his names Rivoli and
Lacepede, and the survey of Australia was completed. Where,
however, did the drainage of the huge continent enter the sea?
It is a curious coincidence that the only large river of Australia
enters Encounter Bay precisely at the last place to be charted by
cartographers! (See p. 242.)

CHAPTER III

EVOLUTION OF THE CONTINENT

THE seven continents may be divided into two groups according to their build or structure. Africa is typical of the less numerous class. They consist essentially of stable portions of the earth's crust, which seem to have resisted most of the folding forces of the globe throughout much of geological time. It seems likely that

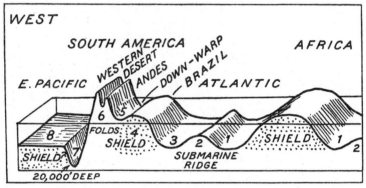

FIG. 9.—A MUCH-SIMPLIFIED SECTION ACROSS THE ATLANTIC AND INDIAN
MORPHS (MIRROR-IMAGES) SYMMETRICAL
N.B.—Note the structures of the 'Western

Antarctica and the subcontinent of Greenland belong to this type of land mass. All three have been subjected to *epeirogenic* movements, in which the continent was lifted *en masse*. The remaining continents are much more complex in build, but still conform to a well-defined pattern. This is best exhibited in South America and Australia. But North America, Europe and, to a lesser degree, Asia, all conform to this second 'American' type of build.

Both types are illustrated in the vertical section along the Tropic of Capricorn reproduced in Fig. 9. Here are given somewhat generalized sections of three southern continents. Africa is in the centre, and it will be noticed that it is flanked on each side by a very definite sequence of land forms—which characterize the crust to west and east of Africa. This sequence is as follows on each side of the African Shield—(1) Floor, (2) Submarine Ridge,

36

(3) Floor, (4) Shield, (5) Downwarp, (6) Young Folds, (7) Oceanic
Deep. Many years ago W. M. Davis showed that in Europe and
North America the main elements of the build are arranged as
are the left and right hands. One continent is the mirror-image
(*enantio-morph*) of the other. The two southern continents shown
in Fig. 9 offer a much better pair of such enantio-morphs. It is
of course necessary to ignore the position of sea level, which is of
little importance in this comparison of crustal folds, &c.

No doubt the common factor producing this close resemblance
between South America and Australia has been the 'Yielding of
the Crust' around the margins of the Pacific. The *floor* of the
Pacific itself seems to be a gigantic resistant shield. This yielding
has produced the two 'Deeps' where the mobility is greatest.

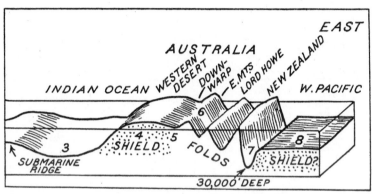

OCEANS TO SHOW THAT SOUTH AMERICA AND AUSTRALIA ARE ENANTIO-
ABOUT AN AXIS THROUGH AFRICA
Deserts' in the two enantio-morphs

Between the Deeps and the nearest continental shields, a series of
crustal buckles has developed, which are high and narrow in South
America, but broader and less elevated in Australasia. In reality
the Andes are analogous to the New Zealand and New Caledonia
ridges, rather than to the humble highlands of Australia which
culminate in Kosciusko (7,312 feet).

Some writers have claimed that the Australian continental mass
properly includes the adjacent 'festoons' which rise as Lord Howe
Island and Norfolk Island above the sea (Fig. 10). What seems
clear is that the major crustal folds near New Zealand die away
to the west against the West Australian Shield. But even the small
'waves' (with an 'amplitude' of only a few thousand feet), which
can be traced on the mainland itself, have a profound effect in
determining the environment in the south-east, as is shown in

TABLE OF ANALOGIES

		Australia	South America
Regions of greatest movement	Fore-deep	'Tonga Deep', 30,000 feet deep	'Atacama Deep', 25,000 feet deep
	Young Mts.	Festoon ridges of New Zealand and New Caledonia	Andean Ridges
Lesser movement	Geosyncline or downwarp	Valley of Cooper and Darling	Valley of Upper Amazon and La Plata
Stable regions	Shields on African side	West Australian Shield	Brazil-Guiana Shield

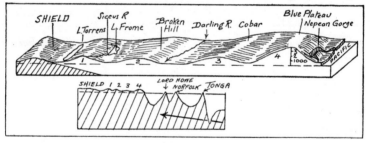

FIG. 10.—FOUR LATE BUCKLES OR WARPS IN SOUTH-EAST AUSTRALIA BETWEEN THE SHIELD AND SYDNEY

Their relation to the deeper eastern crustal folds and to the Tongan Deep is shown in the lower section. The Flinders Range is labelled 1

Fig. 10. In this illustration (lower figure) we see the profound 'deep' off Tonga descending to 30,000 feet below sea level. The ocean between the Norfolk Island and Lord Howe Island ridges is about half that depth.[1] The small 'waves' on the mainland constitute (*a*) the Blue Plateau (4,000); (*b*) the Cobar Peneplain, which is 500 feet above the general level, and about 1,000 perhaps above the floor of the Darling Geosyncline; (*c*) the Barrier Horst at Broken Hill, somewhat higher; (*d*) the Lake Frome Valley; (*e*) the

[1] A cluster of submarine peaks, rising 12,000 and 14,000 feet from the ocean floor, has been discovered in the Pacific Ocean. They occur about 100 miles east of Brisbane in latitude 28° S. They are probably of volcanic origin and connected with the folding.

Flinders Range rising about 2,000 feet; and finally (*f*) the Lake Torrens Rift which is close to the eastern margin of the great West Australian Shield.

The control exercised by these four small 'waves' on communication and settlement will be fully discussed later, but one or two salient features are indicated in this illustration. Two of the chief mineral fields in Australia are those of Broken Hill and Cobar. Had it not been for these warps, it seems unlikely that either of these portions of the crust would have been raised above the alluvials of the Tertiary Geosyncline (see p. 353), in which case the rich zinc-lead and copper-mines would not have been discovered. Secondly, the recency of this uplift is indicated by the remarkable character of the rivers. Notice the Nepean River (on the eastern slopes of the Blue Plateau) which flows north parallel to the coast, sometimes as a senile river on the coastal plain but at times in a *gorge* (600 feet deep) in the rising Plateau (Fig. 10). The Siccus River has an even more striking course. Its ancient gravels show that it flowed to the south-west from Lake Frome, right across the present position of the Flinders Range (1), which slowly rose as a broad warp. A bed of river gravel some 600 feet deep caps the Range at Orroroo, and this is now nearly 2,000 feet above the former headwaters of the Siccus near Lake Frome (see p. 169).

Palaeogeography of Australia

The last section has shown that the continental structure is dominated by a shallow downwarp (or geosyncline) extending from the Gulf of Carpentaria southward to the Murray mouth (Fig. 9). Indeed, the former gulf is part of the geosyncline still covered by the sea. A rapid survey of the varying *changes in build* indicated by the stratigraphy of Australia shows that this present trough is the final position of an 'earth wave', which has shifted both east and west from this position in geological time. We may use the term Palaeogeography to express the discussion of these phenomena. They are best illustrated by a series of generalized block diagrams (Fig. 11). Since the geological strata are usually *marine* deposits, it follows that the formations marked on a geological map usually show where the *seas* were at the times specified. Thus in Cambrian times (about 450 million years ago) we know from the great 'coral reefs' of *Archaeocyathinae* and allied fossils, that seas occupied much of South Australia and the Kimberley region (W.A.). Indeed, during part of the Cambrian a great sea crossed central Australia and isolated the Western Shield. This is indicated in the lower left diagram in Fig. 11. We have, of course, almost no knowledge of the strata beneath the present-day seas, but the stratigraphy of New Zealand and New Guinea gives us some clue as to the position of ancient land masses to the east and north of Australia. Our attempts at palaeogeography are also handicapped by the fact that all traces of many ancient marine deposits (and seas) have no doubt often been removed by subsequent periods of erosion.

In Silurian times the earth-trough seems to have moved eastward to central Victoria and the Queensland coast. In Devonian times, some 300 million years ago, the seas seem to have been situated much where the present east coast lies.[1] During the closing years of the Palaeozoic period (150 million years ago) there were

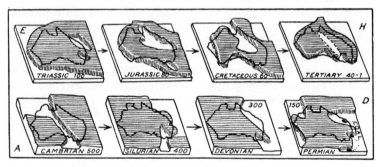

FIG. 11.—GENERALIZED BLOCK DIAGRAMS ILLUSTRATING THE EVOLUTION
OF AUSTRALIA

A geosyncline moves eastward (*A* to *D*) until Permian times, and then westward (*E* to *H*). The coal occurs in temporary lakes. Figures represent approximately millions of years ago

(*Mainly from data by Ward and Walkom*)

marked oscillations of these eastern seas, so that at times they became shallow marine-gulfs, and at times great fresh-water lakes. Tremendous mountains arose at the close of Carboniferous times in eastern Australia.

Permian times in Australia produced an environment well suited for the formation of coal (Fig. 11). Primitive trees now covered the land to a much greater extent than in earlier epochs; and ferns and mosses occupied swampy regions which probably resembled the present 'Everglades' of Florida. These plants slowly turned into peat. As the lakes very slowly subsided the peat layers

---

[1] Of course, during the many millions of years elapsing in the geological record, mountain ranges arose and were worn down to their 'stumps'. As we shall see, it is in these relics of the *ancient* folded and shattered crust that most of the metal mines of Australia occur.

became thicker and thicker. To produce a foot of coal, something like 30 feet of peaty material is necessary. If we find 33 feet of almost pure coal in a seam, we know that it represents about 1,000 feet of peat. Since the plants forming the peat grow only at the very surface of swamps, it can readily be deduced that a *very slow subsidence* of about 1,000 feet (so that the 'peat plants' can grow continuously on the older peaty soil below) is necessary to produce the thick seams of an immense coal-field like that of the Newcastle region.

In Mesozoic times the deposits are often of fresh-water origin, pointing to the presence of vast lakes in eastern Australia—as shown in the Triassic diagram (Fig. 11). These conditions of lakes and inland seas continued during Jurassic and Cretaceous times, but the axis of the downwarp now seems to be definitely moved to the west. These enclosed basins were filled with vast series of sands, capped often enough by shales and other impermeable deposits. Probably for a time south-west Australia was entirely isolated by the later Cretaceous seas. About this time we believe that Australia severed its connexion with Asia and with New Zealand; so that the animals in all three regions now developed along independent lines of evolution.

In early Tertiary times Australia seems to have been a more or less uniform peneplain, a region of lowlands probably with rivers wandering somewhat indefinitely to the south. Later the eastern coastlands subsided, followed by a depression of the southern coasts. But the continent by now has somewhat its present shape. In Miocene times or later the great 'Alpine Storm' has swept across the world from Europe, and buckled the crust into the Himalayan crests and hollows. These giant folds affected New Guinea and the crust to the east of Australia, producing the structures shown in Fig. 9. The mainland was depressed below sea level in the Murray Gulf and north of the Australian Bight. A great chain of volcanoes, pouring out alkaline lavas, extended from the Bass Straits to northern Queensland. These were later followed by vast flows of basic lava all round the coasts of Australia.

Somewhere about 1 million years ago (early Pleistocene) the topography of today emerged. Perhaps the best way to explain what happened is to consider that the present *lowlands* of Queensland and the Murray Basin remained *still*, while the Shield to the west was elevated about 1,000 feet, and the highlands to the east rose as a somewhat irregular wave to heights of from 2,000 to 7,000 feet. Thus our present-day geosyncline (*blank* in the top right block diagram in Fig. 11) is really somewhat of the type called a *Still-stand* by some geomorphologists. One cannot do better than quote Sir Edgeworth David's description of the last scenes in the evolution of the continent.[1]

During part of this Pleistocene Ice Age sea level is low, Bass Strait being nearly dry, and Torres Strait perhaps quite effaced, so that the rhododendron migrates from New Guinea to the Bellenden Ker Ranges of North Queensland. Now may we mark the Tasmanian aboriginal arriving towards the end of this Ice Age, while Bass Strait is still low; and perhaps a little later we may note the coming of the Australian aborigines in canoes with the tamed Asiatic wolf, the dingo. They land while the climate is still pluvial, and some at least of the large herbivores, now extinct, still survive. Sea level now rises, partly as result of melting of great ice sheets, and it has soon widened Bass Strait, restored Torres Strait, and drowned the lower ends of the river valleys around Australia.

In late Pleistocene time the Great Barrier Reef is steadily subsiding, while inland near Cairns the volcanoes of Lakes Eacham and Barrine are in eruption. In Victoria and south-east Australia small basaltic craters are still active, and near Mt. Gambier the activity is accompanied by an elevation of about 250 feet, the warp crossing the old valley of the Murray River, and forcing it westward and damming it, so as to form a lake below Renmark, the overflow of which cuts a new channel, a canyon of 200 feet deep, by which the waters escape to the sea. Near Ooldea a further elevation, of over 300 feet, shows that the land towards the Great Australian Bight is being tilted towards the north.

As we watch, another great change creeps over Australia. With the passing of the Ice Age comes desiccation. Lake Eyre ceases to overflow into Lake Torrens. Its waters shrink and become saline, or even entirely disappear. As we survey from our 'time machine' the garment of green which overspreads Australia, we realize that a great hole is forming at its centre, widening fast with time. That hole is a desert with a ragged edge of wilderness, a desert of wonderful red and purple colours, where the sun rises in glory and sets in splendour, where its heat so burns by day that it splits the rocks, but so great is the radiation at night that they are left cold, almost freezing. Truly a trying climate, but nevertheless healthy both for man and beast.

Aridity has come to more than a quarter of Australia, and even the coastal zones become drier than before. The giant marsupials, their supplies of food and water dwindling, perish in thousands, bogged around the dwindling mud springs and the shrinking waterholes. Once more, as in Cretaceous time, Eastern Australia is isolated from Western Australia, not, as then, by sea, but now by desert.

---

[1] *Explanatory Notes to the Geological Map*, Sydney, 1932. This small but authoritative book is the best general account of Australian Geology. The three-volume *Geology of the Commonwealth* by Sir Edgeworth David (edited by W. R. Browne) appeared in 1950. See also Bryan and Jones, *Geology of Queensland*, 1946; and the volume by E. de C. Clarke on Western Australia (*Geologie der Erde*, Leipzig, 1938).

Palaeogeographic Control of Resources

Some readers more familiar with geographies which almost ignore the geological aspects of the subject may wonder if the previous discussion is not somewhat out of place. Yet it can readily be shown that the distributions of the major economic resources of Australia are closely linked to the palaeogeography outlined above. Let us consider such important assets as metals, coal, water supply and soils. Each of these is associated with a particular phase in the evolution of the continent.

Metal-bearing ores in general are derived from deep-seated rocks of the crust, and have reached their present position usually as solutions in hot waters or as gases. In both cases cracking of the crust facilitates the upward movements of the ores. So also folding and other features of mountain-building bring dissimilar rocks together and help certain chemical changes which lead to ore deposition. These conditions are best met with in ancient rocks, where time and change have had the best chance to operate. As a result we find hardly any metal mines in Australia in rocks younger than Permian. The later rocks have not been folded or shattered in Australia, nor have they experienced so long a period in which to collect the mineral deposits as have the ancient rocks. Since Permian is the last period of the Palaeozoic Age, we can therefore divide Australia into two parts, Palaeozoic and Post-Palaeozoic, one of which contains all the metals and the other practically none. (It is perhaps unnecessary to state that fragmentary ores derived from *near-by Palaeozoic rocks* are often found in loose gravels of later origin.)

The second generalization is equally important. In Australia no land-floras seem to have developed before Permian times which were suitable for the production of coal. So that Pre-Permian deposits can be eliminated as a likely region for coal deposits. However, most of the succeeding epochs (notably in Triassic and Miocene times) saw the development of peat-bogs and forests which ultimately produced useful coal.

The third generalization concerns underground water-supply. It is clear that ideal conditions in this connexion are found where large basins of impermeable rock are filled with regular deposits of permeable sand, gravel, &c. Clearly, folding and faulting will be unfavourable to the production of large reservoirs. Moreover, rocks in general gradually become less and less permeable as they become older. We should therefore expect to find the chief water-bearing basins in the later rocks which have not been folded at all sharply, but whose deposits remain much as they were laid down

PALAEOGEOGRAPHY AND MAJOR RESOURCES

	Palaeozoic					Mesozoic			Tertiary			
	Cambrian	Silurian	Devonian	Carboniferous	Permian	Triassic	Jurassic	Cretaceous	Eocene	Miocene	Pliocene	Pleistocene
Million years ago:	500	400	300	200	150	100	80	60	40	30	10	1
Metals	Rich in Pre-Cambrian	Some	Rich	Some	Some	—	—	—	—	—	—	—
Coal	—	—	—	—	Rich	Rich	Rich	Some	—	Rich	—	—
Water supply	—	—	—	—	—	—	Rich	Rich	Some	Some	Some	Some
Soils	—	—	—	—	—	—	—	—	—	—	Some	Rich

Later estimates make Mesozoic and Palaeozoic times some 50 million years older.

originally. These conditions of permeability and quiescence have best been met in Australia in Jurassic times and later. It is therefore in these rocks that we find the artesian waters and groundwaters which are invaluable to the Australian settler.

Lastly the distribution of soils is closely connected with the build of the country. Soils naturally accumulate on low ground—especially in geosynclines (i.e. crustal troughs). They are rather rapidly removed in regions of recent uplift, for this elevation means a great increase in the erosive powers of the rivers, while deposition will chiefly occur only in relatively *small* areas in a region which has experienced uplift as a whole. Our study of the evolution of Australia has shown us that the continent as a whole has experienced uplift in the Pleistocene, the last phase of the geological record. Only in the great Tertiary Geosyncline (from Carpentaria to the Murray Mouth) is there an area where soil deposition on a large scale has taken place. It is one of the major misfortunes of Australia that this region of chief soil-deposition is in general too dry for dense agricultural settlement. We have only to contrast the climate of our geosyncline with the climates of the basins of the Mississippi, Ganges and Yangtze Kiang (all regions of great soil-deposition) to see how unfortunate it is that our rainy belt covers the Eastern Highlands rather than the Eastern Geosyncline. These generalized relations can be rather usefully summarized in a table (p. 44). Here the association of the four different resources with younger and younger formations is clearly indicated.

Salient Geological Features

The data given in the eight block diagrams in Fig. 11 can, of course, be readily correlated with the geological map of the continent. Throughout the series of eight maps we notice that most of West Australia has been above the sea throughout the geological record. This means that (so far as we know) practically no marine deposits since Pre-Cambrian times have covered West Australia. (It is possible, of course, that some marine deposits of *later date* have been wholly removed, leaving us no clue to their development.) Hence West Australia appears on the geological map (Fig. 12) as consisting mainly of Pre-Cambrian strata. The Cambrian seas shown on Fig. 11 as a gulf in South Australia are represented today as tilted and elevated slates, limestones, &c., forming the Flinders Range (3 and 1). The relations of the Shield to the later deposits are also illustrated in the generalized cross-section at the top of Fig. 12. Here we see the Cambrian strata (3) overlying the eastern edge of the Shield (1 and 2). Still further to the east (in this same section) the Palaeozoic strata (6) overlie (1), and these in turn form the floor of the Permian Basin containing strata (7). The permeable Jurassic rocks (9) cover these and are capped by the Cretaceous layers (10).

Turning once more to the main map (Fig. 12), we see that the elevated land along the east coast consists essentially of Palaeozoic

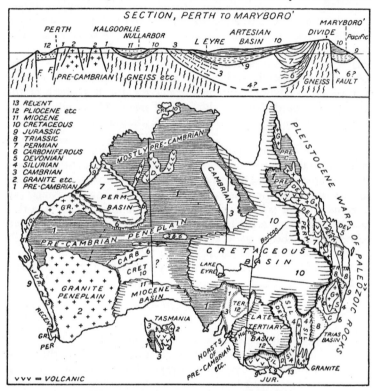

FIG. 12.—A MANTLE-MAP OF AUSTRALIA

In these maps the edges of the formations are emphasized, so that the later layers can be seen mantling the lower, older layers. Thus 12 lies over 10, which covers 3, which overlies 1. (Maryboro' is near Brisbane in Queensland)

(*The section across Australia is from T. W. E. David*)

strata (4, 5 and 6), containing several isolated basins of younger rocks which are mostly Permian (7) or Triassic (8). If younger sediments (such as 10 or 11) once covered these eastern rocks, they have been eroded away. This would be the natural result of the elevation of such a series of rocks, by a thrust from the east, as indicated by the heavy arrow in Fig. 10 (lower).

The Jurassic and Cretaceous marine gulfs of Fig. 11 appear on

Fig. 12 as the vast Artesian Basin at 10. The little patch of Miocene age (11), north of the Bight, shows where a Miocene gulf has since been elevated above sea level. The latest changes in topography have occurred in the Murray Basin. There was doubtless a long estuary extending far up the lower Murray until very late in the Tertiary. This has only lately been elevated to form dry land. The last deposit (not shown on the map in Fig. 12) consists of Fixed Dunes. There are two such areas marked in Fig. 29. They cover up all earlier rocks, and not only prevent satisfactory geological and mineral surveying, but also form an environment which so far has resisted even sparse pastoral occupation. The origin of these dunes is discussed in a later chapter.

Salient Topographic Features

The foregoing discussion makes it clear that Australia as a whole does not offer much variety in scenery. The great factor which has produced the world's finest landscapes has been the 'Alpine Storm', which passed the Commonwealth by. We must turn to New Guinea or New Zealand if we wish to examine the environments which result from great crustal disturbance in relatively recent times. There are in Australia no young folded mountains, active volcanoes, great icefields, fault-scarps, &c., which are so abundant in most of the vigorous 'young-mountain' areas of today. However, although sharp folding and faulting, which produce the most marked topographic features, are wanting, yet (as appears earlier) a considerable elevation *en masse* has occurred throughout much of Australia. Such an uplift is said to be *epèiro-gènic*, and almost all Australian scenery can be scientifically explained by such a movement. In the western half an arid peneplain of more than 1 million square miles has been raised (in the Pleistocene) to a height of 1,200 feet; while in the eastern third a peneplain has been differentially elevated (as a series of warps and horsts along the coast) to heights varying from 2,000 to 7,000 feet (see Fig. 13). Only in the broad geosyncline containing the Artesian Basin and the Murray system do the landforms remain much as they were in pre-uplift days.

The preceding statement, however, needs one qualification. An *uplifted* peneplain can only suffer extensive erosion on its margins, for here alone can the rapid marginal streams effectively dissect the peneplain by *headward* erosion. Thus for many a thousand years the central part of an uplifted peneplain (though it be in a state of siege) is protected from the attacks of the rivers— and remains as a monotonous, flat landscape, long after its edges are notched by deep juvenile gorges. No place in Australia shows this better than the Illawarra Scarp and its hinterland to the south-west of Sydney (Fig. 120). So also the immediate vicinity of Kosciusko itself exhibits late mature topography—though the Snowy River descends into a deep juvenile gorge within a few miles of the summit. For the same reason a traveller in *central* West Australia sees a landscape which has not materially altered since Pliocene times, though it is now probably 1,000 feet above its original level (Fig. 13).

Thus the character of the river valleys to a large degree depends

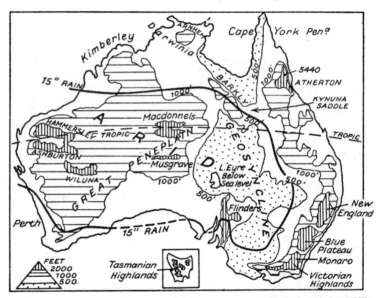

FIG. 13.—THE RELATION OF ELEVATION TO CLIMATE AND SETTLEMENT
N.B.—For more detailed correlations of rainfall and topography see the endpaper maps

on their location among the three major topographic divisions. The valleys of the Great Shield were dissected when the peneplain was at sea level. They are very broad, with ill-defined divides approaching the senile stage. There is so little rainfall through the area that one is likely to attribute the surprisingly small amount of change they have undergone in the last geological epoch to this absence of rain, but it is their position in the interior of a 'besieged peneplain' which has protected the surface, and explains their still possessing senile characters. Even with a heavy rainfall the valleys in a 'besieged peneplain' do not become juvenile until headward erosion cuts back to them.

All round the margins of the Shield, in the much wetter north and south-west, juvenile gorges are being notched in the edge of the Shield. Such small canyons are common behind Perth, as at the Mundaring Weir. In the Kimberleys also the coastal rivers have rapid streams flowing in well-marked gorges.

Throughout central and east-central Australia the rivers are late mature to senile in character. Those flowing in the geosyncline —for reasons already stated—probably exhibit much the same direction as they did in Pliocene times. They flow south or south-west. It is, however, in the eastern part of Australia that the changes in topography have been most striking. It has already been shown that the geosyncline has gradually moved westward. There is some evidence that the accompanying crustal wave form-ing the Eastern Highlands has also moved westward in the last geological epoch; but even if the highlands rose (from near sea level) in their *present* position, we can readily understand that all the drainage systems of eastern Australia would be very greatly disturbed.

In pre-uplift times it seems natural to suppose that the hardest rocks (probably the granites) acted as divides, since they would resist erosion more than would the associated Palaeozoic sediments. There is a rather complete line of granite bosses extending along the east coast, and they are charted in Fig. 14A. If Australia was a peneplain in Pliocene times—as seems likely—then the rivers would flow sluggishly but regularly toward the Tertiary geosyn-cline to the westward, as shown in Fig. 14A. A series of low warps and small crustal blocks, which together built up the rising high-lands of Pleistocene times, now developed along the present east coast. It was accompanied by lava flows in some areas (Fig. 14B). (There is some evidence for the belief that Australia in Pliocene times extended much further to the east.) All the rivers between the old divide (near the present coast) and the new divide (much further west) would be *reversed*, and now flow to the east.

If we examine the rivers reaching the east coast we find hardly an example of a regular symmetrical river system. Everywhere are elbows and reversed tributaries (e.g. Belyando, Clarence, Hunter), which seem to show that the drainage today is a temporary patch-work made up of fragments which once flowed to the west. It is true that the 'grain' of the country (alternation of hard and soft beds, &c.) runs in general north–south, which in part accounts for this confused pattern. But detailed studies of the topography of eastern Australia seem, to the writer, to support the view that we are dealing with an original *westward* drainage, which has been profoundly modified by the growth of a Pleistocene earth-wave right across the headwaters of many of the rivers. Further examples

3

will be given when the regions are described in detail, but it is
not too early to refer to the numerous small lakes—such as
Buchanan, Galilee and George—which are found precariously

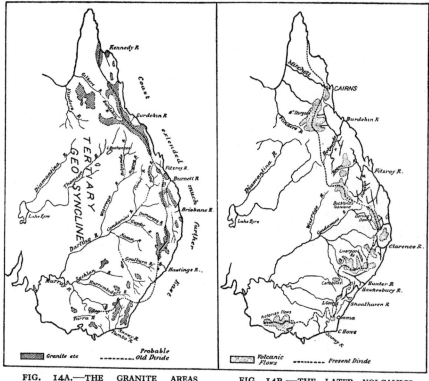

FIG. 14A.—THE GRANITE AREAS
OF EASTERN AUSTRALIA WHICH BE-
FORE THE GREAT UPLIFT PROBABLY
FORMED THE DIVIDE

The probable arrangement of early Tertiary
drainage is indicated

FIG. 14B.—THE LATER VOLCANICS
OF AUSTRALIA, CHIEFLY LATE TER-
TIARY BASALTS,

showing their association with the present
divide. Note the erratic elbows and reversals
on the coastal streams; and the absurdity of
the name 'Great Dividing Range'

perched right on the new divide (Fig. 14A). They probably
represent headwater streams (i.e. Thomson River) cut off by the
low Pleistocene warp. It is only fair to state that a number of
geologists stress structure (rather than warping) as the main factor
in this complicated drainage of eastern Australia.

The two chief depressions across the south-east Highlands are
the Cassilis Gate and the Lake George Gate which isolate the Blue
Plateau (Fig. 13 and Endpaper map).

CHAPTER IV

THE CLIMATES OF AUSTRALIA

SINCE Australia has so little land above 2,000 feet, and so simple a coastline, with only one notable gulf in the north, it is clear that the chief differences in climate must be due to latitude. Moreover, its shape is such as to minimize even this control, since its north–south extent is much less than its east–west extent. Roughly speaking, almost all of Australia extends between latitudes 12° S. and 38° S. (i.e. 26 degrees), which is much less of a latitude-range than is shown by any other continent. However, as we shall see, various portions of the continent are affected by the Belt of Tropical Cyclones, the Trade Wind Belt, the Anti-cyclone Belt and the Belt of Antarctic Cyclones. There is thus a considerable diversity of climate, even though there are no large areas as in other continents with specific characteristics due to elevation.

In a later section a detailed discussion of the chief topographic features will be given. We may assume in this preliminary account that areas of lower elevation than 2,000 feet will not very materially affect the climate of the region concerned. How much of Australia's 3 million square miles is above this elevation? I have made several estimates based on the rather sketchy orographic maps available, and the total is probably about 180,000 square miles, or less than 7 per cent.

Owing to the habit of many explorers of describing every moderate hill standing above the general level as a 'mountain', there would seem to be an enormous number in Australia. A long list of such 'mountains' is given in the *Commonwealth Year-Book for 1909* (Vol. 3, p. 59). A more modern treatment will be found in *Year-Book* 20 (1927). However, a reference to the orographic map (Fig. 13) will show that there are only three or four areas which deserve the name of mountains, exclusive of the region in the south-east of the continent.

Climate and Elevation

There are, of course, no striking 'Young Mountains' in Australia due to sharp folding, such as has produced the Alps of Europe. The major elevations of Australia are of the nature of gentle

51

warps or of horsts (raised fault-blocks). Details as to their evolution and general character will be given later. But the main features of the topography must be understood before the climates can be adequately described.

There are three main divisions of Australian topography: first, the great *Western Shield*, which is about 1,200 feet above the sea. Secondly, the great *Geosyncline*, which is below 1,000 feet and includes the Gulf of Carpentaria. It extends south to the mouth of the Murray. Thirdly, the *Eastern Highlands*, which extend south from Cape York, and include Tasmania. Only about seven or eight horsts or rounded bosses extend above the level of 2,000 feet, and these alone merit the name of 'mountains' (Fig. 13). From the point of view of climate it is advisable to divide them into *Tropical* and *Temperate* mountain areas, and from the point of view of economics, we may further classify them as *arid* or *humid* areas.

IMPORTANT ELEVATED AREAS

	Humid (over 15 in.)	Sq. miles	Arid (under 15 in.)	Sq. miles
Tropical	Atherton (Q.)	28,000	—	—
Temperate	New England (N.S.W.)	15,000	Hammersley	32,000
(or *on* Tropic)	Blue Plateau (N.S.W.)	15,000	Wiluna	12,000
	Monaro Plateau	21,000	Macdonnells	50,000
	Tasmanian Plateau	4,000	Musgraves	7,000
			Flinders	2,000
	Total	83,000		103,000

Thus there is an area of about 180,000 square miles above 2,000 feet, and it will be noted that only one of these regions, the Atherton Tableland, is well within the tropics. About half of the elevated area has a fair rainfall, the remainder being arid. The latter is clearly not of much value.

Among the humid areas the Atherton Tableland has a climate which is much improved by elevation, since it lies well north of the Tropic of Capricorn. Probably New England and the Blue Plateau have more attractive climates for the same reason. But the Monaro and Tasmanian Plateaux are definitely too cold during most of the year for important settlement, and would be more fully utilized if they were lower. However, both of these are of considerable value and interest as Tourist Resorts, and this is of course mainly owing to their elevation.

The Range of Climates in Australia

It is a matter of common knowledge that Australia as a whole is a hot, dry continent. The following table shows that there are three *hot* continents and four *cool* continents. These again can be classified in an interesting fashion according to the amount of rainfall they receive.

RAINFALL OF THE CONTINENTS

(approximate percentages)

Hot Continents (over 70° F.)				Cool Continents (under 45° F.)			
	Over 40 in.	40 to 20 in.	Under 20 in.		Over 40 in.	40 to 20 in.	Under 20. in.
	%	%	%		%	%	%
Australia	11	22	66	Europe	—	52	47*
Africa	28	18	54	North America	18	30	52
South America	76	8	16	Asia	15	18	67
				Antarctica	—	—	100?

* Only 5 per cent of Europe receives less than 10 inches of rain.

Thus South America is the *hot, wet* continent, and North America and Europe have the best claim to be called the *cool, wet* continents. Asia is the *cool, arid* continent, if we ignore Antarctica. Australia is the *hot, arid* continent, since Africa has a far less proportion of arid country.

Among the hot climates of the world Australia offers a number of varieties. Thirty-nine per cent is situated north of the Tropic of Capricorn, but very little of the continent is in the *hot, wet* latitudes, which extend about 18° north and south of the equator. Tropical Australia is in the Warm, Arid Belt (approximately from 18° S. to 38° S. of latitude), as is apparent in Fig. 4. Hence tropical Australia is more comfortable for man than the wet tropics (since it experiences a dry heat), but it sadly lacks the rich crops which characterize the wet tropics where soils are suitable. However, along the north coasts there are some very hot districts where the rainfall is heavy and the atmosphere muggy during a considerable part of the year. Wyndham (W.A.), for instance, is one of the few towns with an average temperature of 85° F. The writer some years ago was only able to find three other recording stations in the world as hot.

Turning to the other side of the picture, there is little doubt that south-east Australia has one of the most attractive climates known to man. As we shall see when we study homoclimes (similar climatic regions), it resembles in climate the French Mediterranean coasts and California. These are generally held to be the best all-round climates, at any rate from the tourist point of view. Indeed, lacking the fogs and cold seas of San Francisco, and having a better rainfall than Los Angeles, this Australian region will probably take its place as superior to much-advertised California in this respect! It is still a matter of surprise to Europeans that ski-ing and winter sports are characteristic of the

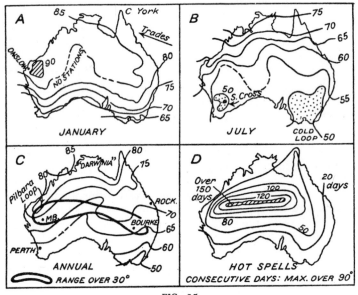

FIG. 15

At A, Average temperatures in January
B, Average temperatures in July
C, Average annual temperature (Note that 50 should be 55)
D, Average number of consecutive hot days

Monaro Plateau (N.S.W.) and the adjacent highlands. But it seems likely that in no part of Australia or Tasmania does snow persist right through the autumn. However, I have been told that snow lies all the year round in a small cirque valley on the southern side of Mount Anne in the south of Tasmania (Fig. 57). But the snow-line elsewhere is well above the mountain summits of the Australian Alps, though small glaciers were present in the Pleistocene Ice Age.

Temperature Control

Owing to the monotony of the surface of Australia the normal west–east arrangement of isotherms is better exhibited than in most continents. The isotherms march north and south with the sun, and only in a few regions is there a significant departure from the regular pattern. One might expect that in January (Fig. 15 at A) the hottest region in Australia would be at Cape York, but it lies in Western Australia just behind Onslow and right on the Tropic. Here the average temperature is over 90° F., whereas at Cape York it is only about 83° F. The same hot conditions in the west are apparent in February and March, while a 'hot loop' in the isotherm extends along this coast in April, May and June. This 'Pilbara loop' re-forms in September, and by December the hottest region in the continent is once more near Onslow. In the Annual Temperature map (Fig. 15 at C) this 'Pilbara loop' is quite evident. Indeed, only in mid-winter is this special concentration

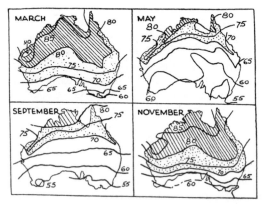

FIG. 15A.—AVERAGE TEMPERATURES FOR MARCH, MAY, SEPTEMBER, NOVEMBER

of heat near the west coast absent (Fig. 15 at B). Its explanation is bound up with the pressure and wind conditions which we shall examine later.

In the north-east of Australia the coasts are much cooler, and this is well shown in the January map, where the interior of New South Wales (far south of the Tropic) is over 85° F. and therefore hotter than Cape York. This special coolness in the north-east, due primarily to the on-shore Trade Winds, is exhibited throughout the summer; but in the cooler months (June to September) the isotherms run normally west–east. In the south-east, where the sole highland districts occur, there is naturally a 'cold loop' due to the topography, and this is most obvious from May to August (Fig. 15 at B). A rather cool area develops in July around Southern Cross (W.A.), but it is not a marked feature at other times of the year. Since a large part of the desert area in the west has no settlement or meteorological stations, it is obvious that all the isopleths [1] thereabouts are not very accurate. However, since this region is a plain about 1,200 feet above the sea, we may fairly assume that the isopleths cross the desert *evenly*.

In a relatively small continent crossed by the Tropic the range [2] of temperature is necessarily low. The isopleths are almost concentric with the coast, and the sole region with a range greater than 30° F. extends across the centre from Marble Bar to Bourke. The three northern projections (Kimberley, Darwinia and Cape York) have ranges less than 15 degrees, as have a few isolated points on the south coast and in western Tasmania (Fig. 15 at C).

As regards *frost*, so vital a factor in north temperate lands, it is of little importance in Australia. However, temperatures as low as 32° F. have been recorded everywhere except in the northern littoral. Indeed, frost may occur in the five cooler months anywhere south of a line joining Perth to Rockhampton. But since the temperature of the most southern town (Hobart in Tasmania) in the coldest month is 45·3° F., there is clearly not much danger to ordinary temperate crops from frost. As we shall see, however, frost risks have driven the sugar plantations northward out of some former sugar districts.

Of much more importance to the Australian settler are the periods of continued heat which adversely affect the continent during summer. These are known locally as 'Heat spells', and are charted in Fig. 15 at D. An arbitrary criterion of the *number of consecutive days with a maximum rising to* 90° *F.* has been adopted in the map. As might be expected, the inland regions are the worst in this respect. The isopleths in their distribution somewhat resemble those for 'Range of Temperature'. Marble Bar has experienced 150 days with the temperature rising day after day to 90° or more. In the more closely settled areas of the south and east the longest such period has never exceeded twenty days, though this figure has been reached throughout most of the wheat belt. It is interesting to note that Cape York has not been much benefited by its marine situation in this aspect of climate.

Pressure and Wind Conditions in Australia

The wind circulation in Australia is quite different from that of most other centres of white settlement. If we consider the con-

---

[1] *Isopleths* are 'lines of equal abundance', such as contours, isotherms, &c.

[2] This 'range' is the difference between the averages of the hottest and coldest months.

tinent as a whole the most characteristic feature perhaps is that it lies right in the belt of permanent Trade Winds. These do not, however, affect the southern coasts. In the southern hemisphere these winds blow from the south-east, and constitute the main *return* current to the equator in the lower atmosphere. But this belt swings north and south with the sun, so that other important controls affect much of Australia at various seasons.

The winds and average pressure conditions are, of course, closely related. The isobars in Australia are rather simply arranged in the various months. As we have seen in the temperature maps, there

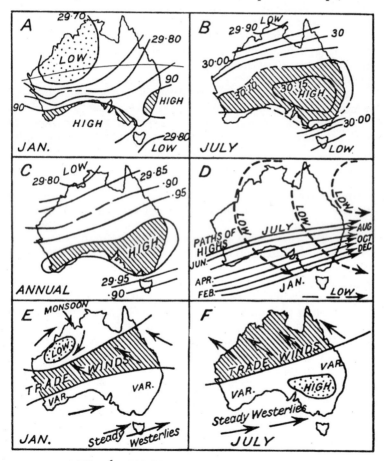

FIG. 16.—VARIATION IN PRESSURE AND WINDS

A, *B* and *C* are Pressures in January, July and Annual. *D* shows 4 paths of Lows and 7 average paths of centres of Highs. *E* and *F* show march of the Trade Wind Belt with the Sun

is a 'hot pole' in summer in the north-west, and a 'cold pole' in July in the south-east. The isobars are in accord in these characteristic months. In January (Fig. 16 at A) an almost permanent Low settles over the hot north-west with pressures below 29·70 inches. This Low appears to move away from the continent to the north-west during February and March. But as the hot weather returns in October we find the isobars tending to form a closed loop around the hot north-west again. In December a circular Low (with barometers under 29·70 inches) covers the hot Pilbara district so clearly defined in Fig. 15 at A. Throughout the year the isobars run from south-west to north-east in central Australia in the neutral ground between the hot north-west and cool south-east. In the cooler months from May to September there is fairly continuous high pressure over the south-east quadrant of the continent. This is illustrated in the map of the July isobars (Fig. 16 at B).

One characteristic feature of Australia is the regularity with which cyclones and anticylones cross the southern half of the continent as they move from west to east (Fig. 16 at D). So much is this the case that the 'static' average maps represented in Fig. 16 at A, B and C are likely to be misleading.

The Australian Cyclone

In a study which I made a number of years ago I showed that there were a number of characteristic types of Lows (or cyclones) associated with rain in the various regions of the continent. Of course, the chief value of pressure maps is to show us where changes in the distribution of *masses of warm moist air* are taking place. In the normal cyclone the eastern 'front' of the eddy, especially the northern tropical side, is usually the most favourable region for this invasion of warm moist air to take place. As Sir Napier Shaw pointed out some thirty years ago, the mass of cold air streaming into the eddy from the polar areas is heavier and tends to flow under the warm moist air. Hence the latter is lifted and chilled and rain is precipitated. The modern theory of the Polar Front (i.e. the advance of cold air masses), which is due mainly to Bjerknes, carries this suggestion much further. Hence today forecasting in many countries is mainly a matter of charting and interpreting the inter-relations of air masses. Very little work on these lines has been published for the Australasian area, so that we must still rely on the pressure distributions in our explanation of the incidence of rain.

In *Tropical* Australia the chief rains in the west and north accompany more or less circular Lows over the region concerned.

In the centre and Rockhampton areas 'Troughs' are the chief rain-bringers. On the north-east coast Highs are much the most favourable, but this is mainly because they strengthen the Trade Winds blowing from the sea on to the coastal ranges.

In *Temperate* Australia conditions are quite different. Only on the arid coast of Western Australia is the local Low the chief instrument. In the centre Troughs and Loops are the chief controls. But the *Antarctic Lows* are the dominant features in the southern half of Western Australia, in the Adelaide region, in Victoria and

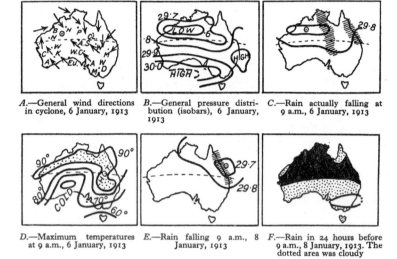

A.—General wind directions in cyclone, 6 January, 1913   B.—General pressure distribution (isobars), 6 January, 1913   C.—Rain actually falling at 9 a.m., 6 January, 1913

D.—Maximum temperatures at 9 a.m., 6 January, 1913   E.—Rain falling 9 a.m., 8 January, 1913   F.—Rain in 24 hours before 9 a.m., 8 January, 1913. The dotted area was cloudy

FIG. 17.—SIX MAPS SHOWING THE PHENOMENA ACCOMPANYING A SOUTHERN CYCLONE

(*From the writer's 'Australian Meteorology', Oxford, 1920*)

in Tasmania. In the south-east corner *East Coast Lows* and Troughs are of about the same importance.

Since the circulation of winds in an Australian cyclone is clockwise, and therefore the opposite of the wind direction in a European Low, it will be well to describe the general sequence of weather in Australia. We may consider the six maps dealing with a Low in the north part of the continent (in January 1913) given in Fig. 17. The wind direction is shown at A. We see that the area of low pressure produces a flow toward the centre. Each individual current of air is deflected somewhat to the left (owing to the Ferrel Effect), so that the final result gives us something like an eddy of winds with a clockwise motion about the centre as shown.

The pressure distribution is shown at B. The Low extends
across most of northern Australia, though usually the low-pressure
area is not so large. At C the rain falling around 9 a.m. is shown,
and is seen to be confined to the east. This is the front of the Low,
for the whole eddy is moving to the east, probably at about 40
miles an hour. The explanation of the rainfall is shown at D, where
the isotherms give the maximum temperature during the preceding twenty-four hours. We are dealing (as far as the low-level
air is concerned) with a warm mass of air moving south through
Queensland, and a cool mass moving to the north-west across
central Australia. This can be deduced from the surface winds.
There is no doubt that at higher levels the cold air is under-riding
the warm air, and lifting and chilling the latter. Hence the rain
occurs mainly in the front of the Low. In E we see the position
of the centre of the Low on January 8th. In F is given the sum-
total of all the scattered rains associated with this cyclone during
the twenty-four hours before 9 a.m. on January 8th. The rainfall
has been unusually widespread, especially in the *rear* of the last
position of the Low.

Typical Rain-bringing Cyclones

The writer has carried out a good deal of research on this
problem, which is summarized in two of his books (*Australian
Meteorology* and *Australian Environment*). In the year 1913, for
instance, the average velocity of the Anticyclones (Highs) was
522 miles in twenty-four hours, and there were about five distinct
anticyclones crossing the continent in each month. The average
paths traversed by these Highs are given in Fig. 16 at D, and the
relation to the sun's progress north and south can be readily
realized. Thus the centre of high pressure in the July map (Fig. 16
at B) represents the average position of these Highs, and lies on
the axis of movement shown for July in Fig. 16 at D.

Much the same conditions characterize the cyclones (Lows).
But usually a large part of their areas covers either the Tropical
or Antarctic *oceans*, so that it is not easy to chart the movement of
their centres. To the south of Australia the cyclones (which determine the rains in the southern littoral) also move steadily to the
east. But their centres are probably in the vicinity of latitude
55° S., which is far south of Australia's southern city of Hobart
(42° S.).

The Tropical Lows may appear off Darwin, and actually move
to the *west* for a few days. Then they curve south and south-east
(as shown by the broken lines) in Fig. 16 at D, and usually merge
into the Lows south of the continent. It is clear that they are eddies

in the general circulation of the lower troposphere,[1] for the latter follows much this direction. During the summer months these tropical cyclones seem to merge into the semi-permanent Low over the north-west. The latter in turn seems to 'bud off' numerous cyclones which continue in the normal direction to the south-east and east.

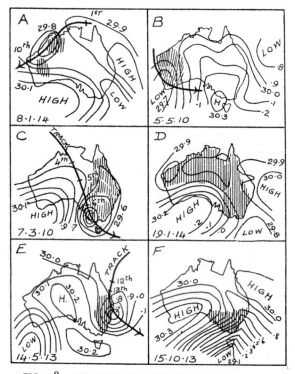

FIG. 18.—SIX TYPES OF RAIN-BRINGING CYCLONES

A gives rain in the north-west. *B* in the south-west. *C* is a Tropical Tongue affecting the south-east. *D* is a Tropical Trough. *E* is an East Coast Cyclone. *F* is the common Antarctic storm of winter. The heavy arrows show the paths of the cyclones

In Fig. 18 six important types of rainstorm are illustrated. At *A* we see a *Tropical Low* which had developed off Cape York on the 1st, and then slowly moved to the west. By the 8th it was centred near Broome, and on the 9th no less than 8·45 inches of rain fell at Onslow. This Low has many characteristics of the type

---

[1] The lower 5 or 6 miles of the atmosphere, below the stratosphere, is characterized by its somewhat *turbulent* structure, and is called the *troposphere*.

which develops into a 'Willy-Willy' (Hurricane) on the north-west coast.

At B is charted a *Winter Tropical Low* on the south-west coast. A loop appeared to develop around Pilbara, which formed a Low near North-West Cape on March 4th. Next day heavy rain fell from Roeburne to Albany. On the 6th a Trough formed along the coast, the west boundary being an oncoming High.

At C is shown a *Tropical Tongue*, at whose tip a well-marked cyclone developed later. The front of the Tongue on March 3rd was in Northern Territory, on the 4th it reached Alice Springs, and on the 7th a deep 'closed' Low developed near Adelaide. This Low gave widespread rains from Cooktown to Tasmania.

At D is given a *Tropical Trough*, which developed from an indefinite loop over Cloncurry on January 14th. This extended as a bulge to the south-east, and on the 19th formed a well-marked Trough between the two Highs, and so linked the northern low-pressure area to a Low off Tasmania. A large body of warm air was transferred to the south, and from its cooling gave rise to widespread rains throughout east Australia.

At E is an example of the characteristic *Autumn Storms* on the Sydney coast. On May 12th a High covered Australia, but a bulge in the isobar near Rockhampton developed into a loop near Bourke, and rain fell strongly around Brisbane. On May 14th a closed cyclone formed just south of Brisbane, and 166 points fell there. The cyclone then passed away to the east.

The most common rain-bringers in the south, the *Antarctic Lows*, are illustrated in F (Fig. 18). They are prevalent in winter; and, as explained before, the centres are usually far south of Australia. On October 12th a large low-pressure area around Pilbara (W.A.) surged southward a little, and a Trough opened to the south. Here a Low with moderate gradients developed. On the 15th an intense Low surged northward, with its centre somewhere near Macquarie Island. Here a pressure as low as 28 inches was recorded. Fairly heavy rains fell throughout Victoria on the 14th and 15th.

Rainfall in Australia

There is no more pregnant saying about Australia than that which characterizes so much of the continent, to the effect that 'the Australian Government is not leasing land but *rainfall* to the settlers'. Hence of all the varied climatic elements the decisive one is the rainfall; and it has now been fairly fully investigated in most parts of the continent. The control exercised by rainfall is indeed rather complex. In early studies it was deemed sufficient to consider only the *annual* rainfall of a district. But this figure only gives a very approximate idea of the possibilities of settlement based on climate. For instance, each of the four following stations has a *rainfall of 15 inches* a year, but the settler would make a grave mistake if he assumed that these rains were all of the same value (Fig. 19).

Roeburne (W.A.) [1] is marked by almost the most unreliable rainfall in Australia. In 1891 it received only 0·13 inch, while in 1900 no less than 42 inches fell. This district is only capable of sparse

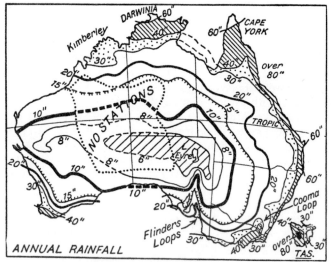

FIG. 19.—AVERAGE ANNUAL RAINFALL OF AUSTRALIA

Notice the 'wet loop' due to the Flinders Range and the 'dry loop' surrounding Cooma.
See also the endpaper map and Table on p. 76

pastoral occupation. *Tennant's Creek* (N.T.) is chiefly characterized by a totally dry period of seven months, and its possibilities for settlement are much the same as those for Roeburne. *Cobar* (N.S.W.) receives its 15 inches of rainfall spread out uniformly throughout the year, and it comes just within the dry-farming area. *Northam* (W.A.) obtains practically all of its rain during the wheat-growing period, and is consequently a very important farming district.

It is therefore obvious that the season of the rain and the certainty of its occurrence are matters as important as the total amount. There are still further refinements of value in estimating

[1] Roeburne is near Port Hedland, and Northam is near Perth. For Tennant's Creek, see Fig. 78 and Endpaper map.

the resources of the country. Cannon stresses the 'Effective Rain-fall', while Prescott points out the importance of the 'Saturation Deficiency'. These aspects will be discussed later.

The total rainfall map is given in Fig. 19. If the Government is 'leasing rain', one would, at first glance, think that the two northern peninsulas of 'Darwinia' and Cape York would be the most valuable parts of the continent, since they receive large totals. Both of these, however, are for the most part almost devoid of settlers. Kimberley, the next largest area with a rainfall over 30 inches, is also almost uninhabited except by aborigines. On the other hand, everyone knows that the south-east corner is the best part of the continent, yet only the merest fringe has a rainfall over 30 inches.

There are two areas of especially heavy rainfall, i.e. over 80 inches. Both of these are mountain scarps facing steady onshore winds. The wettest place in Australia is Harvey Creek in north-east Queensland, with a total rainfall of 166 inches a year. It lies on the scarp of the Atherton Tableland, and is swept all the year round by the Trade Winds from the south-east (Fig. 63). Second to this district is a highland area in the west of Tasmania, which lies in the path of the steady Westerlies. There are few settlers here, but Lake Margaret receives about 100 inches of rain in the year.

The greatest elevations are around Kosciusko and lie in the belt of *variable* winds. Partly for this reason the rainfall is not very heavy. However, a well-developed rain-shadow in the form of a *dry loop* in the 30-inch isohyet (reaching from Canberra to Cooma) marks the lee or east of the Kosciusko Plateau (Fig. 19). A very noteworthy response of rainfall to topography is exhibited by the Flinders Horst (S.A.). Here all the isohyets (especially the 10-inch) are bent sharply to the north, giving wet loops to the north-east of the two gulfs (*graben*) near Adelaide.

Apart from the areas already briefly discussed, the isohyets exhibit rather regular concentric ovals around Lake Eyre. But the ovals are somewhat eccentric, so that the precipitation gradient is steep to the east and slight to the west. Just around Lake Eyre are several places where gauges have shown on the average less than 5 inches of rain in a year. From here to the east coast (a distance of 900 miles) the rainfall increases to 60 inches. Thus the gradient is about 4 inches per degree (69 miles). But to the west of Lake Eyre the rainfall has only risen to 10 inches when the coast is reached some 1,600 miles away. Here the gradient per degree is 0·2 inch.

Since Australia is so regular in outline and so devoid of marked elevations, it is peculiarly well suited to illustrate Seasonal Rainfall in semi-tropical lands. Many years ago the writer devised a 'Solar Control Model' to show how the apparent movement of the sun north and south of the equator caused a somewhat similar movement of the main rain-belts.[1] This can readily be constructed by the reader from Fig. 20, while the general principles involved can be understood from the diagram itself. To make the model, take a piece of *tracing*-paper, and trace upon it the outline of Australia

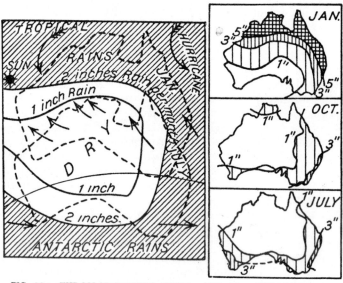

FIG. 20.—THE SOLAR CONTROL MODEL —TO SHOW SEASONAL CHANGES

Trace Australia from this map on a piece of transparent paper, and move over the chart

FIG. 21.—AVERAGE RAINFALL IN JANUARY, OCTOBER AND JULY

Contrast with stages in Fig. 20

(shown by broken lines in Fig. 20). Move the continent from the position shown for January to the position shown for July, and all the main rainfall and wind phenomena will swing across the continent, much as they do in reality. It will be seen that the sun (marked by a black circle) appears to move north during the process, and to carry the rain-belts with it in the same direction. (Of course, the sun moves through 46 degrees, while the rain-belts move much less than this, but in general we can say that the rains follow the sun north and south.) If we investigate the problem in

[1] A movable model appears as the frontispiece to the writer's *Australian Meteorology* (Oxford, 1920).

detail we find that the rain-belts are furthest north about five weeks after the June Solstice, in other words, there is a 'lag' of this amount in the chain of events. Intermediate positions of the rain-belts, say in April, October, &c., are suggested by placing the continent at positions between the extreme months noted in Fig. 20.

Considering the seasonal rainfall in greater detail (Fig. 21) we see that the north coasts receive rain in summer (January, &c.), the south coasts receive it in winter (July, &c.), the east coasts receive it most of the year, while the centre and west have very little at any time of the year. (See also Frontispiece at B.)

It is, however, important to realize that these so-called rain-belts might more accurately be described as 'Regions favoured by Cyclones'. In summer, for instance, the rains are largely due to the prevalence of Tropical Cyclones, whose paths are now so far south that they often cross North Australia. So also in winter the rains of the south are largely associated with the more northerly path of the Antarctic cyclones in that season. The southern coasts come under the influence of the northern portions of the procession of low-pressure eddies, which is always moving round Antarctica more or less regularly from west to east.

Along the east coast there are fairly numerous cyclones passing from north to south, especially in the autumn, and these give a slight rainfall maximum in that season. To these cyclonic rains must be added in certain favourable areas the 'Topographic Rains' which occur on the scarp of the Atherton Tableland, or on the scarp of the Tasmanian Plateau.

Since the 'Polar Front' theory of rainfall has not been applied much in Australia, it is not dwelt upon in this general account of rainfall. It is, of course, largely due to the action of the heavy cold Polar air-mass streaming northward into Australia (in the south-west of a cyclone) which lifts up and chills the warm, light, moisture-laden tropical air-mass (in the north-east of a cyclone) that the major precipitation occurs along the cold 'Polar Front' (Fig. 17 at D).

Reliability of Rainfall

We may now spend a short time investigating the question of the reliability of the rain in the various parts of the continent. We can obtain a rough estimate of the great variation in Australia by considering the actual falls in several districts. At Onslow (W.A.) in April 1900 there fell 11 inches of rain; and in May 1900, 10 inches. The average for the *whole year* here is 9 inches, and in the months of April and May of the next year (1901) the total rainfall was only half an inch. Hence Onslow has a very unreliable rainfall. At Barrow Creek (N.T.) in March 1934 there fell 13 inches of rain, but in the following March only half an inch fell. At Kanowana (S.A.) there falls on an average 4 inches a year, but in November 1911 it received 6 inches, followed by 3 inches in December. All these are examples of unreliable rain, and it will be noted that they are all in the desert or semi-desert parts of Australia. All over the world these climatic regions are always characterized by low averages and unreliable rains.

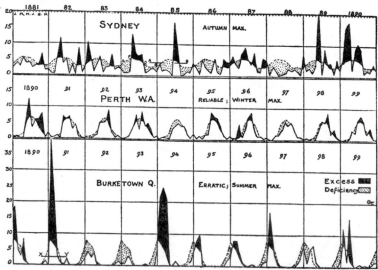

FIG. 22.—THREE TYPICAL STATIONS AND THEIR MONTHLY RAIN GRAPHS FOR TEN YEARS

Sydney has an autumn maximum; Perth has reliable rains with a winter maximum; Burketown has erratic rains with a summer maximum. Dotted areas—below broken lines—indicate *average* graphs.

(*From 'Australian Meteorology', Oxford, 1920*)

We may interpret such data quantitatively in a number of ways. In U.S.A. Kincer has decided on what constitutes a fair useful rain in a district; and he tabulates the *proportion of years* in a place, which falls short of this arbitrary criterion. Many years ago the writer used *average deviation from the mean* as a test of variability. It still seems to offer a useful picture of the reliable and unreliable rain regions. In Fig. 22 the rain regime for ten years is shown for three representative centres: Sydney, Perth and Burketown. The latter is a small town on the southern shore of the Gulf of Carpentaria.

If we look at the record for Sydney in 1881 we see that the rain was below average except in September. Next year (1882) it was well above average in April and October, as shown by the black peaks. In 1888 almost every month was below the *broken* line, which shows the average monthly rainfall. Indeed, hardly any year agrees with the *average* condition, which shows a fairly uniform rainfall, except for a maximum in autumn. We can summarize the Sydney rainfall as fairly erratic or unreliable.

Turning now to Perth, we see that most of the years graphed depart very little from the average (as shown by the broken line). Hence Perth clearly has a reliable rainfall, which repeats its pattern

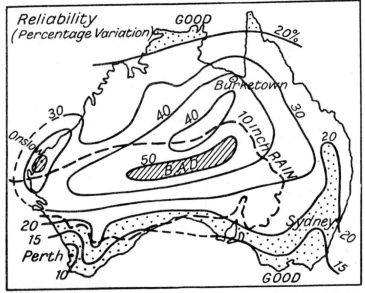

FIG. 23.—RELIABILITY OF RAIN—SHOWN BY PERCENTAGE VARIATION

of a well-marked winter rainfall, with considerable constancy. Lastly, at Burketown we see amazing divergences from the normal in 1891 and 1894; while not a single year (except perhaps in 1896) is particularly close to the average.

To obtain a quantitative picture we follow the procedure outlined below for Sydney. Here the average rainfall is 48 inches. The mean departure from this average (ignoring sign) is 9·5 inches, which is a variation of 20 per cent. This last figure is plotted on the map (Fig. 23). Perth has variation of only 10 per cent, Burketown has 40 per cent, while Onslow in Western Australia shows the large variation of 50 per cent. Drawing isopleths of variation through these figures we obtain the map shown in Fig. 23.

Generalizing a little we see that the region in the south which comes under the influence of the Antarctic cyclones, or the highlands in the south-east, are blest with the most reliable rains. So also the north coast has rains with less than 20 per cent variation. The worst places are near the North-West Cape and in the arid interior near Charlotte Waters. Here the variation is about 50 per cent. An alternative method employed by Barkley gives much the same arrangement of isopleths, except perhaps in the region south of the Gulf of Carpentaria and thereabouts, where his figures give a somewhat more favourable picture.

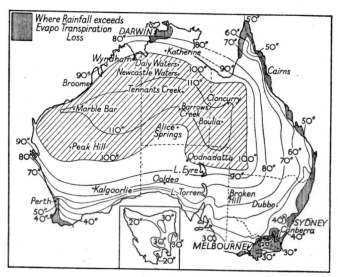

FIG. 23A.—AVERAGE ANNUAL EVAPORATION (INCHES)
The area of Humid Fringe is based on W. H. Nimmo. Tasmanian data omitted

Advantage of a specially wet rainfall is often taken to explore arid Australia. Its appearance then is not likely to resemble what it looks like in a dry season, which is likely to follow very shortly. Here we see the explanation of the conflicting accounts of the central Australian environment. Too often in the old days settlement in arid lands occurred as the result of a particularly good season, which might not occur again for a decade.

In concluding this section on rainfall attention may be drawn to a disability in arid regions which has been emphasized by Dr. Cannon.[1] He points out that the native vegetation in South

[1] W. A. Cannon, *Plant Habits in Arid South Australia*, Washington, 1921.

Australia receives little benefit from rains which barely penetrate the soil before they evaporate. Hence he states that in such an environment 'an ecologically *effective rainfall* is one consisting of 0·15 inch or more, which occurs in a distinctly rainy period'. He further shows that the percentage of what may be called non-effective rainfall increases with the decrease in the total average rainfall. At Quorn (average rain 19 inches) it is 18 per cent; at Copley (average 9 inches) it is 19 per cent; and at Oodnadatta (average 5 inches) it is 30 per cent.

The Evaporation Factor

In a dry country like Australia it is important to know the amount of evaporation which is taking place, especially in con-nexion with problems of irrigation and run-off. It is measured by cylindrical tanks 3 feet in diameter, and each is surrounded by a 6-inch water-jacket, with the water at ground level. The official map appears as Fig. 23A, but this is based on rather a limited number of stations, especially in the tropics. Over an area of 70 per cent of the continent, during no month of the year, does the rain-fall exceed the evaporation. As the map shows, only along a narrow fringe of the east coast and south of Perth does the evaporation during the *whole year* amount to less than the annual rainfall. Here of course the air is relatively humid, and here the most luxuriant vegetation occurs. To the west of Cooktown in the north—though the rainfall is heavy—the nine months' period of drought prevents the above condition from existing. The data for Tasmania are not available, but in this state most of the area has rainfall in excess of evaporation. The general character of the evaporation figures during the year can be realized from the following table:

	Jan.	Feb.	Mar.	Apr.	May	June	July
Melbourne	6·3	5·0	3·9	2·3	1·5	1·1	1·1
Boulia (Q.)	15·7	12·2	10·7	9·4	6·9	5·8	5·4

	Aug.	Sept.	Oct.	Nov.	Dec.	Total
Melbourne	1·5	2·2	3·3	4·5	5·7	38·4
Boulia (Q.)	6·7	9·3	11·7	15·0	15·6	124·5

Needless to say, for agricultural crops the evaporation is quite important. Prescott[1] has recently studied this relation in regard to possible agricultural crops in tropical Australia. He uses an index based on the ratio of the monthly precipitation to the corresponding saturation-deficiency. Where this index is as low as 5, then plants wilt; and if it is not reached during any of the twelve months in the year desert conditions prevail. Where the index rises to 35, then crops have enough water to grow vigorously. In his memoir he points out that such conditions only obtain for a

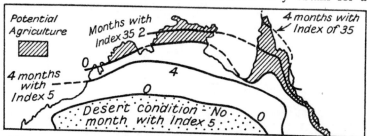

FIG. 24.—DESERT AND AGRICULTURAL REGIONS DEFINED IN TERMS OF LENGTH OF WET SEASON

The former agrees with the 15-inch annual rainfall; and the latter with the 40-inch rainfall in the tropical portion of Australia. (*After Prescott*)

limited period (up to three months) in the narrow coastal-belt shown in Fig. 24 along the north and north-east coasts.

It will be noted that the isopleth of *no months with index 5* agrees very closely with the annual isohyet of 15 inches; while the boundary of the region with 'satisfactory rains for crops' is much the same as the annual isohyet for 40 inches. Hence these botanical investigations corroborate more empirical boundaries suggested by the writer over forty years ago.[2]

Australian and Foreign Homoclimes

In a relatively young country like Australia one obvious method of assisting in the country's development is to find out where there are regions having the same climatic controls as various parts of Australia. For such places the writer many years ago suggested the word 'Homoclime', and this term is gradually being adopted. Indeed my lengthy investigations in 1916, resulting in the production of 'Climographs' and 'Hythergraphs' for much of the world, were made with this purpose, and they may now be briefly described.[3]

[1] J. A. Prescott, *Climate of Tropical Agriculture*, Roy. Soc., S. Aust., 1938.

[2] G. Taylor, *Australia*, Oxford, 1911.

[3] *Meteorological Bulletin 14*, Melbourne, 1916.

Climographs use as ordinates the monthly data for wet bulb and relative humidity. They are concerned with conditions of *comfort* in the tropics as affecting man. The *Hythergraphs* use as ordinates the monthly data of temperature and rainfall, and were drawn primarily to illustrate the possibilities of Australia for *agriculture*.

The original hythergraphs are shown in Fig. 25, where their application to the wheat crop in various hot parts of the world is shown. Thus in June at Lahore (India) the temperature is 92° F., and the rainfall is 2 inches. Plotting these data gives us the point marked 'JN', and so on for the remaining eleven months. Emerald

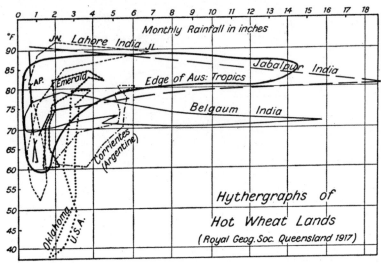

FIG. 25.—HYTHERGRAPHS ARE TWELVE-SIDED GRAPHS WHICH SHOW THE TWELVE AVERAGE MONTHLY TEMPERATURES AND RAINFALLS AT A PLACE
Most of the tropical hythergraphs for Australia fit into the boomerang-shaped area

in Queensland lies at the northern end of the wheat-belt in eastern Australia. By plotting the twelve monthly figures (for temperature and rain) we obtain the graph which is labelled 'Emerald'. Almost all similar graphs for places in tropical Australia (when charted) are found to lie within the heavy 'boomerang' line labelled 'Edge of Australian Tropics'.

Hythergraphs for wheat regions in India (such as Lahore, Jabalpur and Belgaum), or in America (such as Corrientes or Oklahoma), are added. It would seem that climates of Northern India like Lahore and Jabalpur are most akin to those found in that part of tropical Australia where wheat is at all possible. Similar comparisons with Texan wheat areas point to a homo-

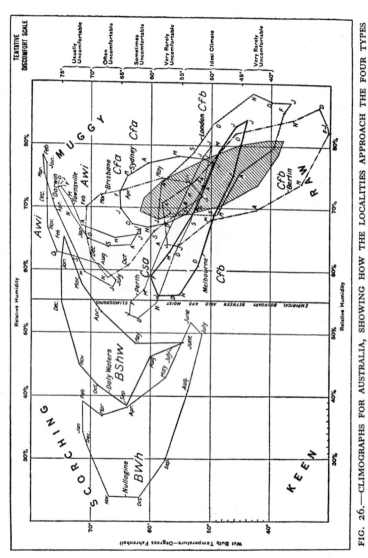

FIG. 26.—CLIMOGRAPHS FOR AUSTRALIA, SHOWING HOW THE LOCALITIES APPROACH THE FOUR TYPES OF DISCOMFORT

The shaded climograph shows the most habitable type for white settlers. The climatic formulae used by Köppen are added. The Wet-Bulb Discomfort Scale is at the right

73

HOMOCLIMES OF AUSTRALIAN REGIONS

AUSTRALIAN

Station	Lat.	Rainfall			Temperature		
		Average	Wettest month	Driest month	Average	Hottest month	Coldest month
Broome (W.A.)	18° S.	22·9	6·3	0·3	79·8	85·9	70·3
Nullagine (W.A.)	22° S.	12·7	2·7	0	76·4	89·8	59·3
Carnarvon (W.A.)	25° S.	9·0	2·8	0	71·1	79·8	60·6
Darwin (N.T.)	12° S.	62	15·3	0	82·6	84·2	77·2
Daly Waters (N.T.)	16° S.	27	6·7	0	80·4	86·9	68·6
Alice Springs (N.T.)	23° S.	10·9	1·7	0·4	69·8	84·0	52·5
Tennant's Creek (N.T.)	20° S.	14·6	3·0	0	77·3	86·0*	60·0*
Townsville (Q.)	19° S.	48·6	11·5	0·5	75·7	82·1	66·6

FOREIGN

Station	Lat.	Rainfall			Temperature		
		Average	Wettest month	Driest month	Average	Hottest month	Coldest month
Banana (Congo) Colima (W. Mexico)	26° S. 20° N.	29·0 34·0	6·0 7·0	0 0	77·9 76·1	81·5 80·9	72·5 69·5
Olukonda (S.W. Af.)	18° S.	19·5	5	0	72·5	76·6	60·9
Bathurst (Gambia) Cuttack (E. India)	13½° N. 20° N.	48 55	20·5 12·4	0 0·3	77·3 80·3	80·6 89·0	73·7 69·0
Peshawar (Punjab) Biskra (Algeria)	34° N. 35° N.	13 10	2·1 1·5	0·1 0	71·0 69·3	90·0 89·0	50 51
Calcutta	24° N.	60	12·3	0·3	77·9	82·4	65·2

* Approximate.

clime in Queensland around Taroom being suitable for further wheat extension.

The methods of drawing climographs is much the same, though here the elements considered refer primarily to human comfort. It is indeed worth noting that a hot, wet climate makes for luxuriant *plant* growth, while a cool, fairly dry climate is perhaps the best for vigorous *human* growth. In Fig. 26 a number of twelve-sided climographs are given for Australian centres. Corresponding graphs for London and Berlin are added. The *shaded* climograph is drawn from the *average* monthly figures of twelve of the chief centres of white settlement. Thus the closer the climograph agrees with this hypothetical composite graph the better it represents the conditions likely to be acceptable to white settlers in general.

The four adjectives in the corners, 'Scorching', 'Muggy', 'Keen' and 'Raw', represent conditions of discomfort experienced in places which approach such positions in the diagram. Lastly an arbitrary 'Scale of Discomfort' (based on wet-bulb conditions) is added on the right hand of the diagram. Such places as London and Melbourne are 'rarely uncomfortable', while tropical towns like Darwin and Townsville are far removed from the ideal conditions of comfort (from 45° to 55° wet bulb) and are to be classed as 'often' or 'usually uncomfortable'.

It is an easy matter to compare the climate of any locality with that of places better known to the student by using this technique. Places with well-marked *autumn rains* are 'full-bodied' like Sydney or Brisbane. Dry *Continental* climates are spindle-shaped with an enormous extension north and south. (No example is given in Fig. 26.) *Mediterranean* climates (with winter rains) have diagonal graphs like Perth. *Monsoon* climates with a hot wet summer are diagonal, but elongated in the other direction like Darwin. *Desert* graphs lie over to the left of the diagram. Since Köppen's formulae for climatic types are becoming generally known, those defining the places graphed are inserted in the diagram.

I prepared the table on page 74 in 1916 to focus the attention of Australian statesmen on the disabilities attending settlement in the arid and tropical parts of the continent. It was not difficult to make them agree that Calcutta or the mouth of the Congo were not ideal sites for white settlement; but they would not realize that Broome and Townsville are homoclimes of Banana and Calcutta respectively, as the table clearly shows.

Similar conclusions follow from a consideration of Köppen's classes. The north coast of Australia is labelled AWi, which is the same as Nigeria, Sudan, the Orinoco valley and the *campos* of Brazil. None of these is a flourishing region of white settlement in

CLIMATIC DATA FOR 20 AUSTRALIAN LOCALITIES

(Temperatures in ° F.; Rainfall in inches)

	Jan.		Feb.		March		April		May		June		July		Aug.		Sept.		Oct.		Nov.		Dec.		Year	
	T.	R.	T.	R.	T.	R.	T.	R.	T.	R.	T.	R.	T.	R.	T.	R.	T.	R.	T.	R.	T.	R.	T.	R.	Av. T.	Total R.
Broome, W.A.	86	5	85	6	85	—	83	1	76	—	72	1	70	—	73	—	77	—	81	—	85	—	86	4	80	23
Darwin, N.T.	84	15	83	13	84	10	84	4	82	1	79	—	77	—	73	—	77	—	86	2	86	5	85	10	83	62
Daly Waters, N.T.	87	6	86	7	84	5	80	1	75	—	70	—	69	—	73	—	80	—	86	1	88	2	88	4	80	27
Cloncurry, Q.	87	5	85	5	83	3	78	1	71	—	64	—	61	—	67	—	72	—	83	—	85	1	88	3	77	20
Charleville, Q.	83	3	80	3	76	3	69	2	60	1	54	1	51	1	57	1	63	1	72	1	77	1	80	2	68	20
Innisfail, Q.	79	25	79	21	78	26	75	23	71	12	67	6	66	4	67	6	70	3	73	2	75	7	78	13	73	150
Brisbane, Q.	77	7	76	—	74	6	70	4	64	3	60	3	58	2	61	2	65	2	70	3	73	4	77	5	69	47
Carnarvon, W.A.	80	—	80	1	80	—	75	1	68	3	63	3	60	2	63	1	66	2	69	—	73	—	77	—	71	9
Coolgardie, W.A.	77	—	76	1	71	1	65	1	58	1	52	1	51	—	53	—	58	1	64	1	71	—	76	1	64	9
Alice Springs, N.T.	84	2	82	2	77	1	68	1	60	1	54	—	52	—	58	—	66	—	74	1	80	1	82	1	70	11
Broken Hill, N.S.W.	79	1	78	1	72	1	64	1	57	1	51	1	49	—	53	1	58	1	66	1	73	—	77	—	65	9
Dubbo, N.S.W.	79	2	77	2	71	2	64	2	55	2	49	2	47	2	51	2	56	2	63	1	71	2	76	2	63	22
Sydney, N.S.W.	72	4	71	5	69	5	65	5	59	5	54	5	52	4	55	3	59	3	63	3	67	3	70	3	63	48
Melbourne, Vic.	68	2	67	2	65	2	60	2	54	2	50	2	48	2	51	3	54	2	58	3	61	2	65	2	58	25
Perth, W.A.	74	—	74	—	71	1	66	2	60	5	56	7	55	6	56	5	58	3	61	2	65	1	71	1	64	33
Eucla, W.A.	71	1	71	1	69	1	66	2	61	1	56	1	54	1	56	1	59	1	63	1	66	1	69	—	63	10
Adelaide, S.A.	74	1	74	—	70	1	64	2	58	3	53	3	52	2	54	2	57	2	62	2	67	1	71	1	63	20
Albury, N.S.W.	76	1	74	2	69	2	60	2	52	3	48	3	46	2	49	3	54	3	60	3	67	2	72	2	61	28
Launceston, Tas.	64	2	65	1	61	2	56	2	49	3	46	3	44	3	46	3	50	3	54	3	58	2	62	1	55	28
Hobart, Tas.	62	2	62	2	59	2	55	2	51	3	47	2	46	2	48	2	51	3	54	3	57	2	60	2	54	24

* Since the monthly totals are given in *whole* figures, the annual totals may differ slightly.

spite of the longer settlement and greater pressure of population
in the vicinity. We cannot derive much support from a consideration of the *homoclimes* of Tropical Australia for the thesis that a
numerous white population will settle the area.

Since the topography and other physical features in Australia
are rather uniform, there is no need to demarcate numerous
climatic regions. The *four major climatic regions* are based on the
seasonal rainfall, and appear in map B in the frontispiece.

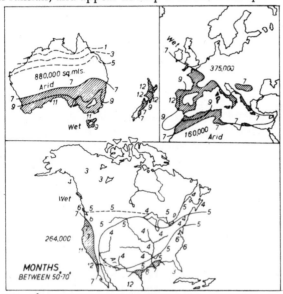

FIG. 26A.—ISOPLETHS OF COMFORT FOR AUSTRALIA, ETC.

Regions in three continents with the most pleasant climates, defined by number of months with
average temperatures between 50° and 70° F. Ruled areas have over seven such months in year.

PREDICTION OF DROUGHTS

In 1922 the writer found that drought years in the Bourke
district occurred fairly regularly during years of low solar activity;
i.e. when sunspots were few, as in 1890, 1902 and 1923. Later
Kidson, in 1925, showed that this was usually the case in the
wetter parts of Australia, while the contrary condition occurred
in the great arid region of the west and centre. Possibly the in-
tensity of the low-pressure storms along the southern littoral and
on the track from Darwin to Melbourne is increased in times
of solar activity. In the very arid regions the rain seems to be
heavier when the cyclonic storms wander from their usual tracks,
and this may occur when solar activity is low. It seems likely that
regions with clear or with cloudy skies even in the same continent
react differently to changes in solar energy. (See p. 402 of the
writer's *Environment, Race and Migration*, Toronto, 1949.)

CHAPTER V

SOILS AND NATURAL VEGETATION

PEDOLOGY, the science of soils, has only recently been studied along modern lines in Australia. A few decades ago soils were classified mainly with regard to the underlying rock formations. We learnt that siliceous rocks tended to produce sandy soils, which in general were rather sterile. Shales gave rise to clay soils, basalt to dark soils, usually of greater fertility, &c. &c. These principles are still held to be in part true today, especially if the soils are of recent origin. But where soils are mature, i.e. have been in place for long periods, it is found that the climate, especially the rainfall, has a very marked effect on the type of soil. We might perhaps say that soils *recently* derived from broken-down underlying rocks agree fairly closely with the geological map, but that *mature* soils tend to approximate in their distribution to the total rainfall map; which of course has little relation to the map of geological formations.

It seems very likely that the coastal soils in eastern Australia are of fairly recent origin. Thus the older maps, prepared by Guthrie and Jensen, are still of considerable value. The following account is based largely on the work of Dr. Jensen,[1] who was one of the first to use the Russian terms *Chernoziom* and *Podzol* for Australian soils. It deals only with the coastal soils in New South Wales. His conclusions are summarized in the map given in Fig. 27.

In general the soils of the coastal region near *Lismore* (in the north of New South Wales) are a fine series. The basalt soils are very similar to the leached soils of Madagascar and India. The *'Black Soil Plains'* are widespread near the rivers flowing inland from the northern plateau; such as the Gwydir and Namoi to the east of Pilliga (Fig. 27, inset). They also are generally of basaltic derivation, and are very sticky when wet. Organic matter in the alluvials amounts to 7 per cent. They are poor in nitrogen and

---

[1] Dr. H. I. Jensen, *Soils of New South Wales*, Sydney, 1914.

humus compared with the Russian 'Black soils', but in phosphoric acid are among the best in the world. They are uniformly deep, but have not been much utilized up to the present.

The region around *Sydney* is a hungry Triassic sandstone, which produces a very poor soil. It bears a characteristic flora which is summarized in the table on page 80. Behind Newcastle the *Hunter River Flats* (Fig. 27) are built up of a rich soil as the

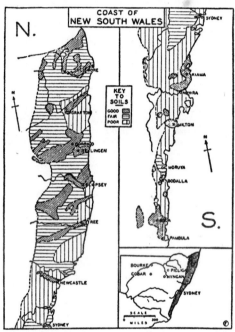

FIG. 27.—CLASSIFICATION OF THE SOILS IN THE COASTLANDS OF
NEW SOUTH WALES INTO GOOD, FAIR AND POOR TYPES

The position of the narrow strip is shown in the small map. (*After H. I. Jensen*)
(*From 'Economic Geography', 1930*)

river passes over a diverse series of rocks. The *South Coast* soils are better than those of the Southern Tablelands, for large areas of basalt occur, while the granites are less siliceous on the coast. The *South-West Slopes* are also superior, since the soils are less leached and the granites richer in useful salts than those of the Southern Tableland. But the granites of the *Northern Tableland* furnish rather better soils since they are more basic.

The *Red Soil Plains* of the Riverina (between the Murray and the Murrumbidgee Rivers) are very variable. The best are on hilly country, and are derived from basalt under oxidizing conditions. All rocks in the west which are not very poor in iron (and not situated in a basin) yield red soils, since the paucity of organic matter allows for a rapid oxidation of the iron in the clay. In the Riverina many red soils are derived from Tertiary rocks of calcareous or shaly composition.

VARIETIES OF SOILS IN NEW SOUTH WALES
(after H. I. Jensen)

Soil	District	Uses
1. Red basalt soils	(Scrublands) N. Coastal Rivers	Dairying, roots, fodder
2. Red soils	Nyngan, and red western plains	Wheat-belt
3. Saltbush country	Cobar, Bourke and west	Arid pastoral
4. Black soil plains	West slopes and plains	Agriculture, maize, pasture
5. Eucalyptus forest	Coast and tablelands	Fruit and farming
6. Drained swamps	Coast and tablelands	Pasture, crops if drained
7. Cold tablelands	Kosciusko plateau	Summer pasture

EDAPHIC CONTROL IN NEW SOUTH WALES
(H. I. Jensen)

Soil	Locality	Timber
1. Hawkesbury sandstone	Sydney	*Eucalyptus eugenoides, E. corymbosa, E. saligna, E. pilularis, Casuarina, Angophora, Acacia suavolens*
2. Wianamatta shale	Sydney	*E. hemiphloia, E. crebra, Melaleuca, Acacia decurrens, Syncarpia*
3. Rich volcanic soil	N. Coast	*Cedrela, Araucaria, Doryphora, Tristania*
4. Poor western sands	Pilliga	*Callitris, Casuarina, E. hæmostoma*
5. Black soil plains	N.W. Slopes	*Acacia pendula, E. Woolsiana, E. melanophloia*
6. Heavy red soils	Nyngan and Riverina	*Geijera, Acacia homalophylla, Casuarina, A. cambagei*
7. Poor red soils	Darling basin, Cobar	*E. populifolia, Eremophila, Dodonea, E. intertexta, Acacia aneura*

The Widespread 'Duricrust'

One of the most marked features in arid Australia is the prevalence of indurated layers on the surface to which W. G. Woolnough has given the name 'Duricrust'.[1] Where the rainfall is seasonal or even absent for almost a year at a time the following sequence occurs, to a greater or less degree, during the alternating wet and dry periods. During the rains, saturation of the dry surface-soils leads to their penetration not only by rain but also by abundant atmospheric gases. These act chemically upon the surface rocks and deeply decompose them. After this action has proceeded for some time the dry period may be supposed to commence. Capillarity causes waters to rise, carrying not only solubles but colloids. The former may form efflorescences at the surface, which sooner or later tend to be removed by the feeble surface drainage in these parts. The colloids, however, tend to be precipitated on various nuclei in the upper layers. Thus concretionary structure develops, chiefly built up of amorphous silica, alumina or iron oxide. This hard surface-layer is what is known as the *Duricrust*.

Beneath this crust is a substratum of insoluble residual constituents, such as leached sandstone or kaolin; and lower again is the more or less decomposed country-rock. At times quartz veins, &c., pass uninterruptedly through these strata into the granite or other solid rocks below, showing that the duricrust has formed *in situ*.

A classic example of varying duricrust is to be seen at the Irwin River (W.A.), north of Perth. Here the western slopes of granite are capped with laterite, the valley claystones with porcellanite and the eastern sandstones with quartzite. These formations are general throughout arid Australia, and everywhere the resulting structure is a weak one. On erosion the hard capping is breached; and then the soft leached material is easily sapped away, partly by water and partly by wind erosion. Thus mesas and buttes of the duricrust, separated from each other by wide flat valleys, are characteristic of this environment.

Another extremely interesting example is at Moolawatana, near Lake Callabonna (S.A.). Here the duricrust is beneath and older than the Pleistocene (and possibly Pliocene) lake deposits. There seems little doubt, therefore, that this continent-wide formation is a direct result of the middle Tertiary peneplanation; and Woolnough sets it down as Miocene. The general breaking down of the duricrust today seems to indicate a general change from the formative environment. Possibly the climate was less variable in the Miocene; so that the alternations of wet and dry seasons were much more regular and marked than they are in arid Australia today.

[1] Presidential Address, Roy, Soc, N.S. Wales, Sydney, 1927.

4

The Russian Classification of Soils

A modern discussion of Australian soils was published in 1931 by J. A. Prescott,[1] which was summarized by the writer in the *Geographic Review* (Jan. 1933). The following paragraphs are based on that summary. It is clear from the earlier study of topography that most of Australia has been elevated fairly recently. This is true of the Great Shield and of the eastern Highlands. Such areas of recent uplift are not, in general, favourable sites for extensive deposition of soil, since erosion tends to carry away the soils to lower levels. In the broad downfold (geosyncline), between the elevated regions, soils will naturally tend to be deposited by the

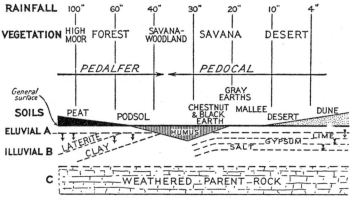

FIG. 28.—A GENERALIZED DIAGRAM SHOWING THE RELATION OF AUSTRALIAN
SOIL GROUPS TO RAINFALL

The characters of the three major profiles, A, B, C, are indicated. (*After Neustruev and Prescott with slight modification*)

('*Geographic Review*', *1933*)

main rivers. Unfortunately in Australia the main geosyncline is mostly in arid country. However, the eastern sides of the downfold (i.e. the western slopes of the highlands) have a fairly adequate rainfall, especially in the south; and here we find the largest areas of agricultural lands in Australia.

We may profitably devote a short time to the study of the Russian theory of soil development. It is summarized in the adjoining vertical section (Fig. 28). Here the soils are shown as arranged in three layers or horizons, which together constitute the 'Soil Profile'. The upper layer is the A horizon, from which rain tends to wash out the more soluble salts. It is therefore also known

[1] J. A. Prescott, *Soils of Australia, Commonwealth Research Bulletin*, No. 52, Melbourne, 1931.

as the *Eluvial Horizon.* The iron and clay portions of the A horizon, in regions of heavy rain, are carried down and re-deposited in layer B, the *Illuvial Horizon.*

In desert areas the long periods of drought and heat bring about characteristic features in the surface soil. Salts carried down to the B layer by the scanty rains are often drawn up to the surface layer in the dry periods by a sort of capillary action. Notable amounts of soluble materials are also brought to the surface from the lowest C layer (the parent rock) in the same fashion. Thus extensive deposits, of what have been called 'perspiration products', are deposited in the upper layers of the soil. Lime, gypsum and salt are transferred in this way. (See *right* side of the diagram, Fig. 28.)

Humus develops *in* the soil extensively under intermediate rain conditions. Peat grows *on* the surface in very wet areas. Sand piles up *on* the surface in very dry regions. Soils rich in iron and clay have been designated *Pedalfers* by Marbut; [1] those rich in lime *Pedocals.* The appropriate vegetation-zones are given at the top of the diagram.

Soils and Climate

To the geographer the chief interest lies in the relation of soil and climate. A second aspect of the problem of special interest in Australia deals with the bearing of the new soil data upon the widespread dunes and laterites. Let us now compare the soil map (Fig. 29) with the geological map (Fig. 12). Little correspondence appears. The outer soil-zones lie in narrow belts around a vast oval of desert-steppe soils. There is nothing on the soil map that indicates the presence of either peneplain or geosyncline; for instance, the podsols (i.e. leached grey earths) run right round the coast from the north-west along the north and down the east coast to Melbourne.

The soil boundaries agree moderately well with the annual isohyets. For instance, Prescott's podsol area is found almost universally where the rainfall is over 30 inches a year, whether the rain falls in summer, as in the north, or in winter, as in the south, or fairly uniformly, as in the eastern littoral.

It is of interest to compare the soil map with Köppen's classification of climates, so widely used as a basis of geographical discussion. Köppen's boundaries have been placed on Fig. 29. It is seen that the podsols fall in his divisions Aw, Cw and much of Cs and Cf. Hence the soil does not seem to vary very closely with

---

[1] *Scheme for Soil Classification,* 1928.

Köppen's divisions. If it did, we should surely expect soils with
Aw climates to be distinctly different from those with Cs climates.
Between the podsols and the desert-steppe soils is an interesting
series of soils. In the north and north-east are the grey earths and
the black earths. In the south are the chestnut earths, mallee soils
and laterites. The *grey earths* occur in regions with about 15–30
inches in the north, and 15–20 inches in the east. They agree

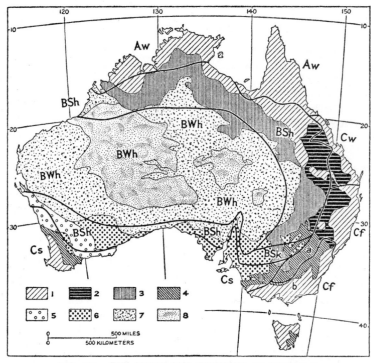

FIG. 29.—THE MAJOR SOIL DIVISIONS OF AUSTRALIA

1, podsol; 2, black earth; 3, grey earth; 4, chestnut; 5, lateritic; 6, mallee; 7, desert-steppe;
8, dunes. Köppen grades are added. (*After Prescott*)

(*'Geographic Review', 1933*)

approximately with Köppen's BSh. The *black earths* are perhaps
the most interesting of all, since they are so fertile that they offer
unrivalled facilities for prolonged agriculture. In Australia they
occupy the moderately elevated country in the central part of the
eastern highlands. Here an unusual number of Tertiary volcanoes
has enriched the soil with basalt products. It is, however, difficult
to see any adequate reason why this soil area should differ from
those immediately north or south. There is no striking climatic

difference. However, the black earths occur where the total rainfall varies from about 20–30 inches annually, is fairly uniform throughout the year, but has a definite summer maximum. This soil type is fairly equally distributed in Köppen's three regions BSh, Cw and Cf. It is the Russian *Chernoziom*.

In the southern belt of soils the *chestnut* earths may first be mentioned. These, as Prescott points out clearly, form a southern extension of the black earths, where the rainfall is mainly of the winter type. They agree fairly well with Köppen's Cfa region in the east, but in the west they form part of the Csa area.

The *mallee* soils appear to be unknown elsewhere. They are due to the combined action of a low winter rainfall, the prevalence of sandhills and the carriage inland of sea salt (*cyclic salt*) by onshore winds. They usually contain much lime, which may produce sheet-limestone surfaces if the parent rock is essentially calcareous. They agree moderately well with Köppen's BSh region.

The abundant *lateritic* soils in Australia have been discussed in many papers. Early investigators assumed that the impure earthly iron oxide was due to the evaporation of underground water, as is suggested in Woolnough's duricrust theory (p. 81). But more recent workers have found that the lateritic soils are particularly acid, and this with other evidence suggests their formation during a period of much wetter climate than at present exists in Australia.

In effect, the characteristic cappings of laterite may be *fossil* B horizons formed under conditions of greater rainfall. This hypothesis assumes the denudation of the original A horizons (Fig. 28), which would be essentially sandy in character. 'This denuded sandy material probably contributes in a major degree to the sandhills of the desert interior' (Prescott, *loc. cit.*). This interesting theory seems to the writer to be extremely suggestive, and gives us fresh evidence of the remarkable changes in climate that have characterized the last geological epoch in Australia. Possibly the widespread siliceous cappings in arid Australia have a similar fossil origin.

SECTION II

GENERAL FEATURES OF THE NATURAL VEGETATION

One of the shrewdest early students of Australian land utilization was Surveyor-General Goyder of South Australia. As early as 1865 he realized that the natural vegetation was the result of various controls of temperature, rainfall, soil and elevation; and that it would serve very well as a key to the economic possibilities of the region. Accordingly he plotted on a map the boundary of the 'saltbush, mulga and dwarf mallee country', and suggested that safe wheat-farming would be found to lie south of 'Goyder's Line'. Further experience has shown that much reliance can be placed on these zones of natural vegetation as regards man's occupation of the terrain. For instance, in Western Australia the various species of eucalypts differ considerably, in accordance with climatic and other controls. These controls are illustrated in the following table. (See also Fig. 126.)

EUCALYPT SPECIES AND SETTLEMENT ZONES IN W.A.

Region	Rainfall	Vegetation belts *	Crop	Towns and Temperature Range
A	Over 30 inches Warmer moiety	Tuart and Jarrah	Dairies Vines Oranges Sheep	Perth (January, 74°; July, 55°) Pinjarra
	Over 30 inches Cooler moiety	Jarrah Karri	Dairies Apples Sheep	Bunbury, Denmark Albany (January, 66°; July, 53°)
B	30–20 inches 20–15 inches 15–12 inches	Jarrah Wandoo York Gum York Gum	Vines, some wheat, farms Great Wheat-Belt Dry Wheat-Belt Sheep	Gingin Moora, Northam, York, Narrogin (72°, 50°) Kellerberrin (77°, 50°)
C	12–8 inches	Mallet Gum Gimlet Gum Salmon Gum	Few sheep and cattle	Carnarvon (80°, 61°), Southern Cross, Kalgoorlie (77°, 51°)

* All these trees are species of Eucalyptus.

A bird's-eye view of Australia would reveal a very simple vegetation pattern. We should see beneath us the continent with an outer zone of forest, and an intermediate zone of tree-dotted grassland, both surrounding a core of fixed dunes. But the surprising fact would emerge, after detailed examination, that almost all the trees belong to one or other of two genera (Fig. 30). In the outer zone a tremendous majority would be eucalypts, in the intermediate zone the large majority would be acacias; and nowhere would other genera bulk largely enough to be very noteworthy.

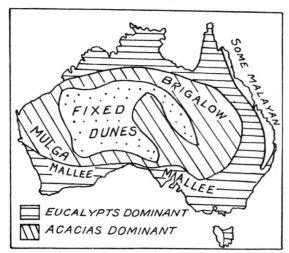

FIG. 30.—A MUCH SIMPLIFIED MAP OF THE NATURAL VEGETATION OF AUSTRALIA

to show the dominance of two genera of trees

This covering of a continent by such enormous areas of one-genus trees is, I believe, not found in the other great land-masses. Of course, there are many species both of eucalypts and acacias. Indeed, there are said to be about 365 of the former, and even more of the latter, genus.

The climatologist Köppen has introduced a generalized climate

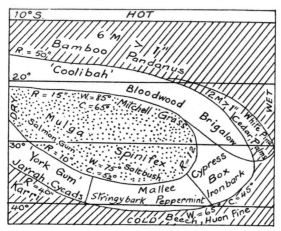

FIG. 31.—A GENERALIZED VEGETATION DIAGRAM

showing the climatic controls which determine the distribution of the main trees

vegetation graph which I have adapted to Australian conditions in the diagram (Fig. 31) on page 87. Here the commoner trees are mentioned by their vernacular names, but in the succeeding table the botanical names are also given. The diagram is zoned approximately to give latitude. The central dotted area shows the desert region, which as usual reaches the sea on the western side of the continent. The wetter regions are ruled. The limits of the various regions are given approximately in terms of the temperature of the warmest and coldest months, and of rainfall.

VERNACULAR AND SCIENTIFIC NAMES OF FLORA

Group	Species	Group	Species
Bamboo	*Bambusa* sp.	Saltbush	*Atriplex nummularia*
Screw Pine	*Pandanus* sp.	Mulga	*Acacia aneura*
Coolibah	*Euc. spenceriana*	Spinifex	*Triodia irritans*
Bloodwood	*Euc. corymbosa*	Salmon Gum	*Euc. salmonophloia*
White Pine	*Araucaria Cunninghami*	Jarrah	*Euc. marginata*
		Karri	*Euc. diversicolor*
Cedar	*Cedrela toona*	Cycad	*Macrozamia* sp.
Palm	*Livistona australis*	Beech	*Fagus Cunninghami*
Brigalow	*Acacia harpophylla*	Huon Pine	*Dacrydium franklini*
Cypress Pine	*Callitris robusta*	Stringybark	*Euc. macrorrhynca*
Ironbark	*Euc. paniculata*	Peppermint	*Euc. amygdalina*
Mallee	*Euc. dumosa*	Bluebush	*Kochia* sp.

Vegetation in Relation to the Pastoral Problem

Many attempts have been made to produce vegetation maps of Australia; among which may be mentioned those by Diels,[1] Taylor[2] and Lane-Poole.[3] The present section is based on a

[1] L. Diels, *Die Pflanzenwelt von West-Australien südlich des Wendekreises* (Die Vegetation der Erde, Vol. 7), Leipzig, 1906, map at end.

[2] Griffith Taylor, *Australia in Its Physiographic and Economic Aspects* (The Oxford Geographies), Oxford, 1911, Fig. 16 (p. 55); *idem*, 'The Australian Environment', *Commonwealth of Australia, Advisory Council of Science and Industry Memoir No. 1*, Melbourne, 1918, Fig. 10 (p. 27); *idem*, 'Agricultural Regions of Australia', *Econ. Geogr.*, Vol. 6, 1930, pp. 109–34 and 213–42, Fig. 5 (p. 114); *idem*, *Australia, Including Chapters on New Zealand and Neighbouring Islands*, Chicago, 1931, Fig. 38 (p. 71).

[3] C. E. Lane-Poole, *Commonwealth Handbook, Third British Empire Forestry Conference, Australia and New Zealand*, 1928, Canberra, n.d., map No. 6 (at end) by Commonwealth Forestry Bureau.

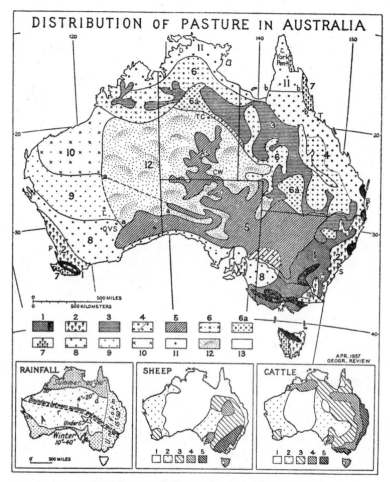

**FIG. 32.—MAP SHOWING DISTRIBUTION OF THE CHIEF TYPES OF PASTURE
IN AUSTRALIA**

Classes 1 to 12 are numbered in approximate order of value: 1, temperate grassland, with differentiation of important areas of exotic grasses (closer ruling); 2, temperate forest; 3, Mitchell Grass; 4, open eucalyptus forest; 5, saltbush; 6, sandy grassland, distinguishing as 6a areas in which acacia is more abundant; 7, rain forest; 8, mallee; 9, arid mulga; 10, west sandy grassland; 11, poor open forest; 12, fixed dunes; 13, alpine. Scale approximately 1 : 40,000,000. The three inset maps show amount and distribution of rainfall and density of livestock (1, none; 2, sparse; 3, fair; 4, good; 5, dense). (*Based in part on McTaggart*)

(*From 'Geographic Review', New York, April 1937*)

89

valuable memoir by A. McTaggart.[1] The writer summarized this in the *Geographic Review* (April 1937), and the annexed maps are derived from my summary. As the main industry in Australia is based on sheep, it is unnecessary to stress the importance of a scientific study of the pastures.

The map given in Fig. 32 differs mainly from earlier maps in three respects, due to McTaggart.[1] It defines the distribution of the two chief pasture plants of arid and semi-arid Australia: the Saltbush and Mitchell Grass associations. Furthermore, it shows where introduced exotic grasses and clovers are abundant enough to appear on a generalized map of Australian vegetation. Below the main map I have inserted three small maps for comparison, correlating the vegetation with the controlling rainfall and with the sheep and cattle industries. Our knowledge of all three is more accurate than that of the vegetation map, and therefore is a check on the latter.

The twelve main classes of vegetation are based partly on earlier maps, partly on McTaggart's map and largely on my own knowledge of the country.[2] The order of the numbers is approximately that of the value of the classes in the pastoral industry.

Most of the classes in the table on page 91 are readily differentiated; but I have separated from Class 6 some regions (6a) with much the same climate and poor sandy soils, in which brigalow and such-like acacias are somewhat more abundant than in Class 6. It is also rather hard to draw the line between Classes 9 and 10, the somewhat heavier rain in the north being balanced by the greater evaporation there.

The zone of Mitchell Grass (3) occupies a fairly definite climatic belt on the margin of the widespread semi-desert and desert areas. Its alternation with Class 6 is clearly due to edaphic (soil) control. Indeed, locally the patches of 6 in Queensland are called 'Desert'. Mitchell Grass (*Astrebla pectinata*) grows chiefly on soils resulting from the weathering of limestone or basalt. The so-called desert (6) occupies the arenaceous soils. This sharp transition from good to bad sheep-country always strikes the traveller in north-western Queensland.

The extension of the saltbush country as far north as Tennant's Creek in Northern Territory, and westward from Charlotte Waters to the very border of Western Australia, does not imply particu-

---

[1] Accompanying A. McTaggart, 'A Survey of the Pastures of Australia', *Commonwealth of Australia Council for Science and Industry Research Bulletin No. 99*, Melbourne, 1936.

[2] Descriptions of traverses made by the writer in most parts of the continent are given in his book *Australia* (1931), Chicago.

MAIN TYPES OF AUSTRALIAN VEGETATION

A. *More Important Pastoral Areas*

Class	Rain * (In.)	Stock †	Chief plants	Locality
1. Temperate Grassland	15–30 U	S	*Danthonia* sp., *Stipa* sp., now much clover, &c.	Victoria and central New South Wales
2. Temperate Forest	30–50 U & W	C	Eucalypts originally, now much exotic grass	South-east and south-west coasts
3. Mitchell Grass	15–30 S	S & C	*Astrebla* and Flinders grass (*Iseilema*)	North and east edges of central arid area
4. Open Eucalyptus Forest	20–70 S	C	Eucalypts and acacia, with grass below	Eastern Queensland
5. Saltbush	4–10 W	S (C)	*Atriplex* with *Kochia*, *Stipa* and edible acacia	Southern part of arid and semi-arid area
6. Sandy Grassland	20–40 S	C (S)	Spear grass, kangaroo grass and edible acacia	Northern hinterland alternating with Mitchell Grass

B. *Less Important Pastoral Areas*

7. Rain Forest	Over 50 U & W	C	Close-set Malayan trees in north, eucalypts in south	Small patches on coasts of little significance
8. Mallee	10–15 W	S	Close-set low eucalypts	South coasts, much now in wheat
9. Arid Mulga	8–10 W	S (C)	Scattered edible acacia; edible herbs after rains	West coast and hinterland
10. West Sandy Grassland	10–20 S	C (S)	Like 9 but with less acacia and more grass	North-west coast and hinterland
11. Poor Open Forest	Over 30 S	C	Scattered small eucalypts, useless coarse grasses	North coast
12. Fixed Dunes	9–18 S & W	None	Spinifex grass (*Triodia*), some trees	Central part of the continent

* Uniform (U), summer (S), winter (W).   † Sheep (S), cattle (C).

larly good herbage; for very few stock occupy these areas in ordinary years. In general, of course, 'saltbush' flourishes best in the region of winter rains (see inset map). In New South Wales the saltbush country is the chief habitat of the merino sheep.

In the Nullarbor Karst (limestone) region there is very little pastoral occupation, since it is so difficult to obtain permanent water owing to the permeable surface limestones. This lies north of the Bight.

In parts of the wheat and dairy country of the south and east the native vegetation has very largely vanished. McTaggart describes the planting of such grasses as Perennial Rye Grass (*Lolium*), *Paspalum dilatatum* and Cocksfoot, together with clovers in many of the wetter coastlands (see main map in Fig. 32).

Unusual Fodder Plants

Although Australia is very badly endowed with native edible fruits, the writer knowing of only two or three in the whole continent, yet there are many varieties of plants besides the grasses and saltbushes which are found to be fairly satisfactory fodder plants for stock. The value of the edible mulga (*Acacia* sp.) in the dry cattle country has been referred to several times. But many of the larger trees have great value in time of drought. For instance, the Kurrajong (*Brachychiton*) is a great stand-by in the south-east of the continent. *Flindersia* (an ally of the teaks) is readily eaten by stock. The thorny *Bursaria*, which is usually a bramble, but which grows to tree size in the south, is a fair food. In addition to the Mulga, the Wilga, of similar habit but belonging to the genus *Geijera*, is also relished. *Casuarina* (Fig. 36) grows plentifully in the interior, and its peculiar leaves are edible. *Eremophila* and *Dodonea* are useful at times. The little fern-like *Marsilea*, whose spores are eaten by the aborigines, is also devoured by stock in the Darling basin. The Wild Carrot (*Daucus*) and varieties of Portulacca are very plentiful after rains. Perhaps the most remarkable of all is the Sugar Gum. In the north-east of New South Wales branches of this large eucalypt 40 feet from the ground are cut off, so that sheep can eat the leaves in drought time. A comprehensive study of these valuable plants will be found in the *Commonwealth Year Book* for 1913 by the eminent botanist J. H. Maiden.

The Tropical Rain Forest

Australia is on the whole a semi-arid region. Hence the vegetation cover is not mainly composed of trees but of scattered shrubs and herbs. Only in the wetter parts of the outer Eucalyptus belt is there any large area of forest. There are, as we have seen, certain small areas where the coastal districts are particularly wet and have specially rich soil, and are rather well protected from the arid westerly winds. Here alone are to be found extensions of the tropical flora of northern lands (Fig. 33).

It seems very probable that this flora covered much of northern and central Australia in middle Tertiary times. We find, for instance, about 100 living *Livistona* Palms in the heart of the semi-desert at Hermannsburg. They live on the edge of a permanent water-hole in the Macdonnell Ranges. No other palms are known within several hundred miles. So also the *Flindersia* (allied to the tropical teaks) is common near Broken Hill and north of the Darling River. This cousin of many Malayan genera is almost certainly a rare survivor of former wetter conditions, but it has become adapted to its present semi-desert environment.

In north Queensland in the region of greatest rainfall (in the coastal portion of the Atherton Tableland) occur the finest

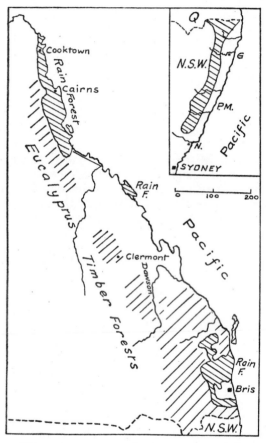

FIG. 33.—THE CHIEF AREAS IN EASTERN AUSTRALIA WHERE PATCHES OF THE TROPICAL MALAYAN FLORA PERSIST

In the large map good eucalyptus timber is shown by open ruling

examples of the Malayan flora. These are also known as the Tropical Rain-forests or 'Vine-scrubs'. They flourish best on rich basaltic soils, but also occur on rather poor granitic soils.[1] Other similar forests were once to be found near Gympie and on the

[1] Karl Domin, *Proc. Roy. Soc. Queensland*, 1911.

Macpherson Range, and there were formerly large patches of such
vine-scrubs in New South Wales. But here as in Queensland they
have mostly been replaced by dairy farms.

These vine-scrubs grow in dense formation with very little grass
as undergrowth. There are always many vines and epiphytic plants
on the branches of the trees. As is usually the case, the trees are
tall and thin, struggling up to the sun and air above the fairly
dense canopy of leaves. Domin mentions several types of scrub
near Cairns, of which those on the plains are characterized by
'Lawyer Canes' and the Climbing Bamboo. On the plateau near
Atherton the tropical trees are larger, but the epiphytes and ferns
are less numerous. Among the most characteristic trees are the
White Cedar (*Melia*), the Rosewood (*Synoum*), Red Cedar
(*Cedrela*), Maple (*Flindersia*), Bean Tree (*Castanospermum*) and
Kauri Pine (*Agathis*). Further reference will be made to these
trees in connexion with the section on the timber industry (p. 390).

Some representatives of the Malayan flora extend southward
into Victoria, and even into Tasmania. In the cooler southern
districts they are naturally much mixed with the usual 'Australian'
vegetation. At many places along the coast of New South Wales
the Cabbage Tree Palm (*Livistona*) is one such survivor. Under
the Illawarra Scarp (south of Sydney) is an association of trees
which is locally known as 'Brush'. Here the larger members are
mainly soft woods (such as *Doryphora*), linked by creepers and
diversified by ferns and epiphytes of the same type as further
north. Several species of fig-tree (*Ficus*) are found; as well as
Lilli-pilli (*Eugenia*), the forerunner of the eucalypts. The Giant
Nettle (*Laportia*) is a tree with leaves a foot across. Tree-ferns
such as *Dicksonia* and *Alsophila* add great beauty to the 'Brush';
while a true Passion Flower and the Bird's Nest Fern (*Asplenium*)
are other notable members of this forest. In the hills just east
of Melbourne are to be found glades almost filled with tree-ferns
about 6 or 8 feet high. *Dicksonia* indeed is fairly common as far
south as the hills behind Hobart in Tasmania. Diels states that
one tropical plant, *Todea*, is still found in the relatively dry Mount
Lofty Ranges behind Adelaide.

The Zone of Eucalyptus Forest

In the section dealing with Australian timbers the economic
aspects of the Australian forests are dealt with. Here we are concerned with their general character. They must not be pictured as
close-set stands of timber such as are usual in the northern coniferous forests. Nor are they usually as closely congregated as the
broad-leaf beeches. Most of the eucalypt forest is of the open type

(often called savanna woods), with considerable areas of grasslands between the clumps of trees. In wetter areas the trees grow closer together, as for instance in the Swanland region south of Perth. Here the Karri trees are some of the tallest in the world; and in

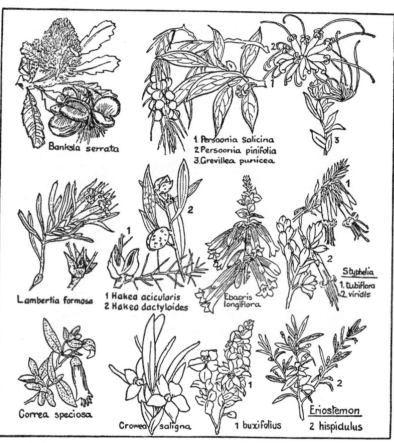

FIG. 34.—COMMON FLOWERING TREES AND PLANTS IN EASTERN AUSTRALIA; SUCH AS *GREVILLEA, CORREA, HAKEA, BANKSIA* ETC.
(*Drawn by D. R. Taylor—from F. Sulman*)

this region an undergrowth of small shrubs occurs, but annuals and grass are not so common.

In South Australia the eucalypt woods are penetrated by considerable grassy areas, and shrubs such as *Correa, Grevillea, Hakea, Exocarpus* and *Banksia* grow amid the trees (Fig. 34).

Another region of huge eucalypts occurs in Gippsland, Victoria. In New South Wales *Proteacea* and Epacrids are common amid the undergrowth. As we proceed toward the interior the savanna woods give way to grasslands or savannas. Here also are found many scattered trees of small size, and gradually the eucalypts give place to the acacias. This change of vegetation as we pass into the dry interior is well illustrated in the photographs (Plates I and II).

The Origin and Habitat of the Eucalypts

No undoubted eucalypt has been recorded from New Zealand, Fiji, New Caledonia, Borneo or Asia. Four species occur in Timor, four in New Guinea, one in New Britain and one in the Philippines. We may profitably consider the cradleland of this interesting genus.

In the wetter parts of Australia we find representatives of the Malayan flora as well as the eucalypts. Where there are rather sterile sandstones we find the sun-loving eucalypts, while the richer soils contain *Myrtus* and *Eugenia*, and other trees of the still wetter tropics to the north. The leaves of the eucalypts are often heath-like, rigid or pungent, which suggest acclimatization to arid conditions. However, eucalypts and acacias cannot compete with the Malayan flora in the wetter sites where the latter are well established.

Among the eucalypts there is a strong tendency for certain species to frequent sandy soils, while others like clay or lime soils. This seems to be connected with the type of essential oil produced in the leaves. Thus *pinene* oils occur in trees on sandy soil. 'Boxes' flourish on heavy clays, and their leaves contain much *cineol*. Peppermints and Snow Gums contain *phellandrene*, and they grow in the colder, elevated areas.

E. C. Andrews [1] is inclined to think that the Eugenias with their fleshy fruits are the ancestors of the eucalypts. The latter developed after middle Cretaceous times, as Australia was separated from Asia, and gradually became drier and more sandy. In later Tertiary time the fossil floras in Victoria show that the climate was warm enough for many Malayan types, although today the lands are higher and cooler, and the eucalypts flourish there.

All eucalypts develop a cap (*operculum*) over the young flower (Fig. 35), and with this protection it has accommodated itself to various climates and soils. The most generalized type among the 300 or more species is the Bloodwood (which includes the well-known 'Red-flowering Gum', *E. ficifolia*). Most Bloodwoods are

[1] E. C. Andrews, *Development of the Myrtaceae*, Linnean Soc., N.S.W., 1913.

found in the warmer northern parts of the continent. As stated, the Ironbarks and Boxes grow chiefly in the east, and usually on clay soil.

The Stringybarks and Peppermints are found mostly in moist

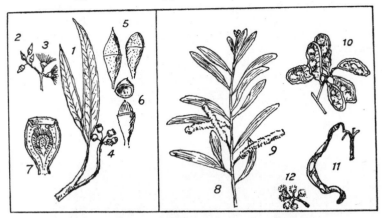

FIG. 35

1, *Eucalyptus melliodora* (Yellow Box), leaves (about 5 inches long); 2, flower-buds; 3, flowers; 4, carpels; 5, buds enlarged; 6, operculum loose; 7, woody carpel (in section), ¼ inch across; 8, *Acacia aneura* (Mulga), leaves (about 5 inches long); 9, yellow fluffy flower-spike; 10, flat pods 11, pod of *A. melanoxylon*; 12, flowers of latter

cool regions in the south-east, especially on the plateaux. In the more arid areas developed the Mallees (*E. oleosa*, &c.). The function of the characteristic oil is to form a thin spray to withstand desiccation, or to resist cold. So also the twisting of the leaf-stalk in some species and the waxy 'bloom' on the leaves both counteract aridity. (See Table, p. 390.)

The Savannas or Grasslands

Little by little the savanna woods change into pure savanna. Gradually vegetation decreases as we proceed inland until, as Diels says, the bushes and shrubs are grouped like islands in a sea of grass. In Western Australia the acacia called the Mulga is typical; but owing to the poor precipitation Diels says this 'Grass and Mulga' country is nearer desert than savanna.

In the east a much better rainfall has produced the renowned sheep and cattle 'stations' of Australia. In the Darling basin the savanna is characterized by low eucalypts, *Casuarina* (Fig. 36) and *Acacia*. There is much saltbush (*Atriplex*) in the south, as well as valuable grasses, which are relatively more widely spread in the north (Fig. 32). Among these famous forage plants are *Andropogon*

(Blue Grass) and *Astrebla* (Mitchell Grass). As Diels points out, this is an area of considerable uncertainty in the rainfall, which has made the history of Australia so rich in examples of sacrifice and renunciation.

Some notes on a journey across the grasslands in western New South Wales (made by the writer in September 1923) will give the reader a clearer impression of this characteristic Australian environment.

At Cobar the rainfall is about 15 inches a year, and here begins the true Mulga country. Some 3 or 4 inches of rain had fallen

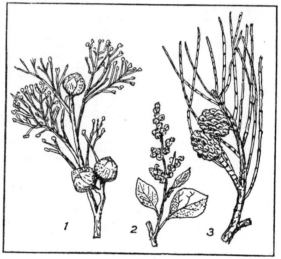

FIG. 36

1, *Callitris* ('Pine') leaves and fruit; 2, *Atriplex* (Saltbush) succulent leaves and flowers; 3, *Casuarina* (She-oak) leaves and fruit

within the last month or two, and the district was most unusually covered with herbage. In places there were acres of little yellow Compositae, while the ground beneath the scattered acacias was blue with *Scrophularia*, or covered with yellow-white everlastings. More striking still were the beautiful *Eremophila* trees, about 15 feet high, and bearing abundant pink flowers. In places were clumps of Kurrajong trees, or of glossy Bimble Box (*Eucalyptus* sp.). A dozen species of acacia could be collected, some of which were covered with golden blossoms.

The rainfall soon falls to 12 inches a year west of Cobar, and here large square reservoirs (Tanks) are cut out of the clay soil, which are of vital importance in watering the stock in this riverless region (see the photo in Plate I). Near Yoe low sandy ridges appear, though they are now 'fixed' by low vegetation and various acacias. Hereabouts also we began to meet the 'gibber' country, which consists of the layers of brown pebbles which result from wind erosion, &c. In the Sahara they are known as Serir. At Wilcannia the Darling River is incised 30 feet below the level plains. The wharf is perched up at the town level, and all navigation waits (sometimes for twelve months or more) for the floods to fill up the empty trench to the level of the wharf.

West of the Darling, eucalypts are rarer, and the acacias come into their own. The rainfall is only about 9 inches a year, but after rain one may see acres of minute yellow flowers, and a large growth of 'Barley Grass'. Leopard Wood (*Flindersia*) and Mulga are common, while scalded plains, interspersed with saltbush country, diversify the journey. About 60 miles east of Broken Hill we met a camel team dragging a large wagon. There were 20 camels in harness and four young camels ran alongside. In a few hours we reached the rocky ranges near Broken Hill, which rise some 800 feet above the general level of the western plains. Here we are in the realm of the acacia, and the general appearance of this most typical tree in arid Australia is well shown in the photograph (Plate II, photo 3).

The Desert Floras

An excellent study of the vegetation of the driest part of the continent has been published by W. A. Cannon.[1] In the vicinity of Oodnadatta, about 100 miles north-west of Lake Eyre, there is a rainfall of only 5 inches a year. Cannon writes:

In every direction the wide-spreading plains and flat-topped hills appear quite barren. The gibbers [2] glisten like polished mirrors in the sun, but otherwise a monotonous reddish-brown colour prevails. There are thus apparently no plants to enliven the scene. More careful examination, however, reveals the presence of plants. Across the lower plain are narrow ribbons of vegetation, which make grey-green bands, and mark the drainage channels. Annuals are more abundant than perennials, and *Senecio* and *Brachycome* are the commonest. Among perennials the shrub *Eremophila* is the most numerous. It grows about 3 feet high. Saltbushes and acacias are, however, not uncommon in favourable positions. On the flood-plain of the Neale's River are to be found fair-sized eucalypts, and numerous acacias, especially the Gidya and 'Dead Finish'.

---

[1] W. A. Cannon, *Plant Habitats in South Australia*, Smithsonian Institute, 1921.

[2] *Gibber* (desert pebble) pronounced with a hard 'g'.

These trees are characterized by long roots extending for as much as 22 feet, just below the surface of the ground, to make full use of the scanty rainfall.

Typical sand-hills of the Great Western Desert extend as far south as Ooldea on the East–West Railway (see photo 5). Here the rainfall is about 9 inches a year. Cannon describes eight species of acacia, of which *A. aneura* (Mulga) is the commonest. The 'oak' (*Casuarina*) is a larger tree, which helps to fix the dunes. A number of eucalypts such as *E. pyriformis* ('Ooldea Mallee') flourish here. It is a curious fact that this species bears the largest fruits (carpels) of any of the trees in this large genus. *Eremophila*, *Leptospermum*, *Hakea* and *Grevillea* are all typical Australian trees, which grow abundantly near Ooldea. Of perennials, the most interesting is *Calandrina* (Portulacca), whose fleshy leaves are much relished by stock. On the adjacent Nullarbor Plains the edible saltbushes are by far the most abundant plants (see also Chapter VIII).

In the study of the various environments of the continent, further descriptions of the natural vegetation will be found.

CHAPTER VI

DESERT LANDS IN AUSTRALIA

THE continent can be conveniently divided into three large areas, each of which has its special characteristics and problems. In the first place, we have the regions in the south and east where all the important settlement has taken place. Its boundary is the population line of one person per square mile. This may be termed 'Agricultural Australia', and to its study many chapters in this book are devoted. The remainder constitutes three-quarters of the whole continent and most of it may be termed 'Empty Australia' (Fig. 1). Here, as we have seen, *tropical* conditions are in many respects handicaps in the north, while *arid* conditions prevent settlement in the centre, west and north. There is, however, no sharp line of division, for throughout 'Empty Australia', as we have seen, heat and aridity are present during a large part of the year. Since in the whole of this tropical country (excluding the Queensland coast) there is no prospect of growing important agricultural crops, it follows that the pastoral industry is the most promising method of utilizing the land. Thus a consideration of the natural vegetation is of the first importance in assessing the best way of developing 'Empty Australia'.

It will be helpful to separate those lands of no apparent value from those where a sparse pastoral occupation is present or likely to develop. To the former we can surely give the name 'Desert'. The latter I have long been accustomed to call 'Sparselands'. Their relative importance can be learned from the following generalized table:

'Agricultural Australia', over 1 per sq. mile	A. Temperate lands climatically suitable for crops	600,000 sq. miles
	B. Tropical lands climatically suitable for crops	100,000 ,, ,,
'Empty Australia', less than 1 per sq. mile *	C. Good pastoral lands, largely tropical	1,000,000 ,, ,,
	D. Sparselands, arid with scattered pasture	700,000 ,, ,,
	E. Desert. (Dotted in Fig. 37)	600,000 ,, ,,

* In Fig. 1 the isopleth of $\frac{1}{3}$ (rather than 1) person per square mile is charted.

The figures in the above table are only first approximations. For instance, rugged country and poor soils prevent agriculture in much of section A and section B. Here also the densest occupation by sheep and cattle occurs, though in places, as we shall see, the pastoral lands are being subdivided for closer settlement. In section C is found land where stock are universal. Usually cattle are found in the rougher and also in the hotter, drier country and sheep in the wetter southern areas. In the Sparselands (ruled in

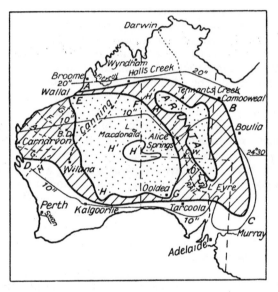

FIG. 37.—A MAP ILLUSTRATING THE LIMITS OF AUSTRALIAN DESERTS

The Sparselands are ruled. Notice the position of the 10-inch isohyet. H' is Hamada

Fig. 37) conditions are not unsuitable for stock, provided permanent water is available. Of course, only a few cattle or sheep per square mile can be grazed, and the total does not much affect the numbers in Australia. In the desert (E), the writer can see no probability of any notable settlement. It is to be remembered that the climatologist Köppen groups sections D and E together (region ABCD in Fig. 37), and calls practically all of this area 'Desert'.

Definitions of a Desert

This aspect of the problem is one to which the writer has given much attention. For half a dozen years (1921–8) Sydney newspapers [1] gave a large amount of space to controversy on 'the Australian Desert'; and it soon became clear that the scientists and the laymen had different ideas as to what constituted a desert. Indeed there is not complete unanimity among scientists, since deserts are indeed of somewhat variable types in different latitudes. It will be well therefore to devote a little time to this question of definition.

The matter is complicated for a variety of reasons. For instance, there is one group of students who accept *average* rainfall figures as sufficient criteria. Probably in any particular small region this is a fairly good test. Thus in south-west Australia (on the edge of what has been termed 'Swanland') Diels has used $8\frac{1}{2}$ inches as the limit of the desert. This seems to the writer to be fairly reasonable in that corner of the continent, but it is certainly not correct in regard to most of arid Australia. Schimper adopted a general figure of 10 inches, as did the present writer in his earliest discussions of Australia. Milham says in his *Meteorology* (p. 257), 'Below 12 inches, the country is a desert.' He is presumably referring especially to the United States. None of these absolute figures is satisfactory for large areas. Cannon uses what he himself terms the arbitrary figure of *5 inches per annum* in discussing the plants of South Australia. This is unsatisfactory in Australia, in my opinion, for some of the region with this low rainfall has been occupied by pastoralists. On the other hand, a huge wetter region (from 5 to 15 inches) is quite unoccupied in Australia. This last observation shows that it is not merely annual rainfall which determines the desert.

For many years the writer was urging, at first in vain but later with some success, that Australians should recognize that there was a very obvious limit to the regions suitable for close settlement—or even for pastoral settlement. This point of view was very obnoxious to a voluble group of boosters who roundly declared that there was no desert in Australia. [2] If one pointed out that there

[1] Of some importance in educating the public were articles on both sides in the *Sydney Morning Herald* for August 27th, 1921; November 9th, 1921; August 13th and 14th, 1924; April 4th, 1925; *Melbourne Herald*, January 17th, 1927; *Sydney Morning Herald*, May 9th, 1927.

[2] For articles of this type see *Bulletin*, May 4th, 1922; *Sydney Sun*, June 22nd, 1923; *Sydney Morning Herald*, May 10th, 1924; *Sun*, May 12th, 1924; *Herald*, July 5th, 1924; *Herald*, March 14th, 1925; *Sun*, May 25th, 1925; *Sun*, April 30th, 1926. *Hansard* for July 30th, 1924, records the desire of the Member for Darwin that the writer should 'desist from his perpetual slander on Central Australia'! A year later the same Member was lost for some days in this arid region, and was found in a semi-unconscious condition, with his mouth choked with oil from his motorcycle.

was an area of half a million square miles as empty as in the days of Captain Cook, they replied that Australia was a young nation and that the empty lands would fill up when the proper time came. I suggested that similar optimism was prevalent no doubt regarding the Sahara in the time of Tutankhamen. However, this was naturally not felt to be a satisfactory argument, and so I investigated other methods of deducing the relative values of our uninhabited regions.

One of the most useful maps in this discussion is that due to the eminent climatologist W. Köppen, which was reviewed in the *American Monthly Weather Review* for February 1922. Here the whole world was considered, and the various 'desert' regions clearly set out. I measured the various areas in an approximate fashion, and found the results as follows:

DESERTS OF THE WORLD

Region	Approx. sq. miles	Region	Approx. sq. miles
1. Sahara	2,600,000	6. Colorado (U.S.A.)	200,000
2. Australia	1,100,000	7. Gobi	180,000
3. Turkestan	900,000	8. Kalahari	90,000
4. Arabia	480,000	9. Thar (India)	74,000
5. Argentina	400,000	10. Chile	74,000

This table, after Köppen, shows that Australia contains the second largest area of extremely arid land (excluding polar regions) in the world. The figure agrees almost exactly with what I have adopted for many years as the combined area of either practically useless or inferior pastoral lands. These two areas I call *'Desert'* and *'Sparselands'* respectively (Fig. 37). It is this distinction which I propose to examine somewhat closely.

Two facts are clear from Köppen's areas. He does not base his determination only on annual rainfall, nor does he assume that a desert must contain no human beings. This latter condition is a *sine qua non* with many Australians. These folk would not (one presumes), if they were logical, use the term 'desert' for any part of the Sahara, except that seventh or eighth part which consists of living dunes (ergs).

Köppen has devised an ingenious method of determining the desert boundaries, which explains how he deduced the area ABCD in Fig. 37. Thus on the southern edge CD (with winter rain), the boundary is approximately obtained from the formula R = T; i.e. where the average *Temperature* (Centigrade) equals the average

Rainfall (in centimetres). We find that his line accordingly passes through a region with 19 cm. of rain and 19° C. On the north border AB (with summer rain) the formula is R = T + 14; thus here 39 cm. of rain occur with 25° C. Along the eastern border BC the isopleths are cut diagonally, but the rainfall is fairly uniform. Here R = T + 7. Thus Windorah has 30 cm. with a temperature of 23° C., while further south Wilcannia has 25 cm. with 18° C. Both of these satisfy his third formula. Clearly no account is taken here of edaphic (i.e. soil) characters.

In a voluminous work entitled *Australia Unlimited* (Melbourne, 1918) the writer (E. J. Brady) scorns the term 'desert' as applied to Australia. But his logic is very faulty, for it chiefly turns upon a small area near the mouth of the Murray, which has long been known, somewhat unfairly, as the 'Ninety-Mile Desert'. This region has an average and reliable rainfall of about 16 inches a year, and is of course quite different in character from the vast inland regions with which we are particularly concerned. Because, however, this southern area is being slowly occupied by wheat farmers, Brady implies that all other Australian areas described as deserts are also wrongly named. One would not discuss this type of opinion were it not that the volume in question was widely distributed by the Government!

Very different is the attitude of the Government of the United States, as may be seen in the fine *Atlas of Vegetation* published in 1924 by the Department of Agriculture. Shantz and Zon write: 'Between the Rocky Mountains on the East and the Cascade-Sierra on the West, and extending from the Canadian to the Mexican boundary, lies the great inland desert (Fig. 44), characterized largely by xerophytic shrubs.' In their accompanying map, almost all Nevada, three-quarters of Utah and half of Arizona and Idaho are characterized as desert.

It seems to the present writer that this is the type of country that might reasonably be classed as desert. The best criterion will be the natural vegetation, which results from a number of physical controls, not only climatic but also involving soil, &c. (edaphic). This type of definition is indicated by Dr. I. Bowman in his *Atacama Trails*: 'A desert has become by definition not naked sand or rock, but a place of small rainfall with a sparse and specialized plant and animal life.' Prof. J. W. Gregory, writing of South Australia (in the book thereon, dated 1909), says: 'A desert is a country with such an arid climate and such a scanty water supply that agriculture is impracticable and occupation is found possible only for a sparse population of pastoralists.'

If we use this last definition we find that it gives us much the same area in Australia as shown in Köppen's map, for it includes the uninhabited dune country (EFGH in Fig. 37) together with the arid pastoral lands (or Sparselands) of Western Australia and South Australia. These latter comprise about 700,000 square miles with a density of only 0·5 head of cattle or 5 sheep per square mile. The human population is only 28,000, surely a 'sparse population of pastoralists'. In this huge area ABCD (called desert by Köppen) graze only about 4 per cent of the sheep and 3 per cent of the cattle of Australia (Fig. 37).

As I stated before, however, I have differentiated in Australia between Sparselands and actual uninhabited Desert. The above discussion has shown that a combined climatic and economic definition is desirable. Köppen's limits are climatic, and include a much larger area than that involved by the writer's use of the word 'desert' in Australia. I would like to see the *time-factor* incorporated in a definition of desert, as in the following suggestion which covers conditions in Australia:

A desert is a region of small rainfall (usually, however, amounting to 15 inches in hot regions) with a sparse and specialized plant and animal life. It is not found capable of utilization by stationary pastoralists, even after the borders have been occupied by this class for fifty years.[1]

Characteristics of the Australian Desert. Topography

Almost the whole debatable area belongs to the Western Shield, consisting of granites, gneisses and Palaeozoic or older sediments. But the south-east corner is part of the Great Artesian Basin, capped mainly by Cretaceous sandstones. In its main features the 'Köppen Desert' (as we may term the widest area [ABCD] under review) is not directly determined by any geological characteristics. But in many parts of Australia (as in north Queensland) the term 'desert' is used for small areas with a rainfall of about 20 inches and with a strong arenaceous facies. For the adjacent districts with the same rainfall, but with shales instead of sandstones, the term 'desert' is not used. The difference to the settlers lies in the natural vegetation. The shales carry a much larger proportion of cattle-fodder, such as Mitchell Grass, while the desert carries only useless spinifex (*Triodia*) with the brittle eucalypts called 'Snapping Gum'. Often it is almost covered with the conical nests of termites.

In a secondary sense, however, we shall find that the desert is essentially determined by edaphic control, i.e. where the soil

[1] See Ann Marshall, 'Size of Australian Desert', *Aus. Geographer*, June 1948.

conditions produce only plants poor in pastoral value. We may, however, consider topography and climate before dwelling on the natural vegetation.

In many deserts the topography is the essential feature, as in the 'Rain Shadow Deserts' of the world. There is very little of this type of desert in Australia. They all belong to the class of 'Trade Wind Deserts', and are analogous to the Sahara in most essential features. Almost the whole of the Köppen Desert is

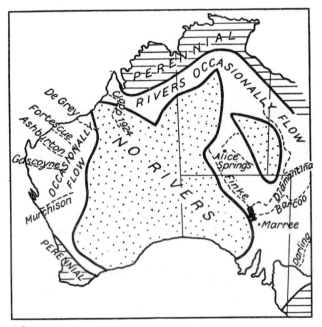

FIG. 38.—ARID AUSTRALIA, SHOWING THE CHARACTER OF THE RIVERS
The Murray very rarely ceases to flow

between 1,000 and 2,000 feet above sea level. Only three areas rise above 2,000 feet, i.e. the Macdonnells in the north-east and the Hammersley and Wiluna Uplands in the north-west. There is very little difference in the desert characters as the result of these higher elevations. Perhaps the few deep waterholes in the antecedent channels of the Finke and its tributaries (in the Macdonnells) are the chief exceptions.

No fact impresses the geographer so much as the enormous area in Australia where rivers are absent or flow but rarely (Fig. 38). De Martonne's classification into Exoreic, Endoreic and Areic regions are discussed elsewhere (Fig. 84). In the interior there is apparently an important river system flowing into Lake Eyre. It is usually many years between the periods when flood waters reach the great salt lake, either *via* the Finke, Diamantina or Barcoo. In the whole of South Australia there is really no perennial river, if we assume that the Murray approaches in character an intermittent stream. It is such data which makes the geographer realize that irrigation will never make any essential difference to the vast arid extent of Australia (p. 269).

Climate of the Desert

As Köppen has demonstrated clearly, the limits of desert lands do not depend entirely on the average rainfall. If we study the main area of uninhabited land in Australia (EFGH in Fig. 37), we find that it does not agree at all with the annual isohyets. It is roughly square in shape. The northern boundary agrees with the 16-inch isohyet approximately, the southern with the 8-inch line. But the desert boundaries in the east and west have nothing in common with them.

It might be thought that temperature or evaporation would determine this restricted desert boundary. But here again the isopleths run mainly east and west, and give us no clue to the desert boundary EH running from Wallal south to Zanthus (near Kalgoorlie) or FG from Powell's Creek south to Tarcoola (Fig. 37).

We may consider the problem in another way. Let us examine the conditions along the Tropic of Capricorn from Carnarvon on the coast to Queensland. Our traverse passes through Balfour Downs, salt-lake Macdonald, Alice Springs, the heart of the Arunta Desert and Boulia. All of these, except Carnarvon, lie at much the same elevation and in the same latitude.

| Place | Variations of country along Tropic | | | | | | Vegetation and soil |
	Elev. feet	Longitude	Charac-ter	Av. Temp. ° F.	Av. Rain inches	Evapor-ation inches	
Carnarvon	50	114° E.	Sparse stock	74	8·5	75	Scrub
Balfour Downs	1,200	120° E.	Sparse stock	74	9	100	Scrub
L. Macdonald	1,200	128° E.	Desert	70	9	120	Dunes
Alice Springs	1,800	134° E.	Sparse stock	68	10	110	Hamada
Arunta Desert	800	138° E.	Desert	70	10	120	Dunes
Boulia	800	140° E.	Sparse stock	74	10	124	Steppe

It is seen that there is nothing to choose in the conditions of the last five places. While two of them are uninhabited, yet three carry sparse stock. According to Köppen's analysis *all* these places are in the desert. From analogy with the Sahara limits, as generally accepted, this is legitimate; but even the Sahara contains several million head of stock and perhaps a million pastoral people.

Facies of the Arid Regions

We may consider the natural vegetation first in this huge region ABCD of over 1 million square miles, which extends along the north from the Indian Ocean to Wallal, to Camooweal (Q.), thence south to Broken Hill, and west to Geraldton on the Indian Ocean (Fig. 37). It is uniformly xerophytic (i.e. with drought-resisting plants). As regards the trees they are of much the same type throughout. Acacias are dominant; the species called Mulga (Fig. 35), *Acacia aneura*, is found throughout the south, centre and west, while the Brigalow (*A. harpophylla*) is perhaps most abundant in the north-east. However, scattered eucalypts occur, such as *E. rostrata*, in the centre and south, and *E. salmonophloia* in the south-west. Among smaller shrubs occur many *Eremophila* (Emu Bush), *Hakea, Grevillea*. There are large 'Corridor-trees' along the gravels of the intermittent creeks, and various clumps of the conifers *Callitris* or *Casuarina* (Fig. 36) in certain lowlands, where swamps endure for a time after occasional heavy thunderstorms.

It is in the ground-herbage that the main difference occurs. For many years the writer was trying to determine the boundary between the grass country and the saltbush country. Probably there is no sharp line of division, but it is shown approximately in the map Fig. 32, based on work by McTaggart.

In the Sparselands the stock have several sources of food besides the grasses of the north or the saltbush of the south. Thus in the western Sparselands (in the summer of 1924–5, when the writer traversed them) the stock were living on spinifex and mulga. The former is a tough spiny grass which at times grows into huge circular tussocks 20 or 30 feet across. When the spiky seed-stems arise this grass may be 5 feet high. Its scientific name is *Triodia*, and there are several species. The dwarf types are relished by sheep when nothing else offers. The larger, tougher species in the desert appear unattractive to stock except for the seeds.

More unusual is the use of several sorts of mulga (*Acacia*) as food for cattle. This 'top-feed' is eaten readily, especially in droughts.[1] The presence or absence of dwarf spinifex or mulga

[1] A valuable discussion of these edible native plants will be found in the *Commonwealth Year Book for 1913*, p. 1190.

determines largely the use of the Sparselands in Southern and Western Australia. Preference is usually given to sheep, which of late years have paid much better than cattle. But sheep cannot feed so well on the edible mulga, which is accordingly used for cattle country (see also p. 328). There are, of course, great numbers of small herbs of some value to stock. These spring up in great abundance after rains. Parakeelia (allied to *Portulacca*) is one of the best of these.

I dwell on this question of vegetation because it definitely determines the presence or absence of any population. It is not perhaps the lack of water, so much as the lack of suitable food for stock, which accounts for the half-million square miles of Empty Australia. We must now dwell briefly on the question of underground waters.

Water Supply

We have already seen that there is no question of irrigation, since there is no surface water in the whole region except for a few pools in the rocky gullies of the Macdonnells, or in such rivers as the Diamentina in the far east. Nor is artesian water likely to be of any help except in the south-east corner. Here the region east of Charlotte Waters (including Lake Eyre) has good supplies of water. Unfortunately here the rainfall is mostly only 5 or 6 inches, and the native vegetation is at its poorest. Apart from this corner, all the arid region depends on shallow ground-water. Luckily this seems to be fairly universal if not very plentiful. The best investigation is that carried out in the north-west corner of the desert. Here Canning in 1907 established a stock route from Wiluna to Hall's Creek, which cut across the corner of the uninhabited area (Fig. 37). He sank about 50 successful wells (besides many unsuccessful trials) in a distance of about 500 miles. Their average depth was about 36 feet.

But this stock route has never been found of use to the pastoralist, and expert opinion states that most of this country will never be suitable for permanent occupation. However, it seems likely that most of the huge area EFGH (Fig. 37) is not much worse than that crossed by Canning's wells, which, however, occurs in the northern wetter half of the desert (with 8–20 inches of rain). However, though the southern half receives less rain, it has less evaporation. Indeed, very little of the Australian Desert has less than 5 inches a year; and there is no area of consequence consisting of Erg or living dunes, such as cover about one-seventh of the Sahara.

The arid lands of Australia have, in fact, much the same character as the Sahara, except for the absence of living dunes. There are large areas of scrublands. These are the typical arid regions with thin sandy soil sparsely covered with mulga, spinifex and many shrubs. After a good rain a wealth of vetches with some grass, &c., springs up. Much of it is rocky and approaches *hamada*. More still is thinly covered with rock debris or gravels, and thus approaches *serir*. Patches of fixed dune occur here and there outside of the main dune area. This is indeed the character of most of the country I have termed Sparselands. It is important to note that it is very easily occupied with stock. Indeed, the original homelands of sheep and cattle in central Asia are not unlike this kind of country. Hence almost all the useful part of the Sparseland was leased from the Government by about 1880. Even in 1939 there were large areas of it quite unoccupied, especially in the Hammersley and Wiluna regions in Western Australia.

I wish here to refute the opinion that it is inaccessibility or lack of opportunity which keeps the empty lands empty. The boundaries of such country have been occupied by pastoralists for forty years. When I was in central Australia in the drought of Christmas 1924, I found that the ranchers had ridden far east into the 'Desert' hunting for feed for their starving stock. It was an unavailing effort. It is *lack of forage*, not inaccessibility, which keeps the pastoralists out of the desert. Indeed, most of the Sparselands and deserts form a single climatic unit affected by the same adverse seasons. I discuss this point in my paper on Australian and Antarctic Relations,[1] where a map shows that the area ABCD as a whole is *negative* in regard to solar energy. Accordingly the whole area tends to experience droughts in periods of marked solar energy.

The Limits of the Desert

It is amazing how little the layman uses maps in his geographical discussions. The writer was engaged in such a controversy (extending to many columns of the *Sydney Morning Herald*) in April 1925, and was long unable to get his opponent to show on a map 'those places excellent for stock which lay in Professor Taylor's so-called Desert'. When at length such a map appeared, these places were all stations known to the present writer, and of course lying outside the borders of the uninhabited desert.

The Australian is on the whole a city-dweller, and until lately it was very difficult to reach the area of our present discussion. However, two railways now run close to it. Indeed, the East-West Railway near Ooldea (S.A.) crosses over 40 miles of veritable dunes

[1] *Problems of Polar Research*, New York, 1928, p. 285.

(see the photo, Plate III). From here for 1,000 miles to the north-west there is no white settler until the Indian Ocean is reached at Wallal. No explorer has yet followed this particular route, though many explorers' tracks have crossed it.

In November 1928, Captain Holden flew over several hundred miles in the region north-west of Ooldea. He wrote, 'Forests of dead timber, areas of red sandhills and parched scrub, scorched brown and even black by the sun, passed monotonously under the plane. In my opinion the country is hopeless.'

The railway from Oodnadatta to Alice Springs places the eastern edge of the desert within 100 miles of the rail (Fig. 37). From near here the well-known explorer Captain Hurley flew north and north-west to Wyndham in the same month (November 1928). He writes:

It had ever been my ambition to see and know something of the hidden heart of Australia, and now I have seen a tract of country 80 miles wide on either side of our 2,200 mile course. I can honestly say that I am bitterly disappointed. The major portion of the country is so utterly desolate, arid and dead, as to fill one with sadness.

I quote this description because it illustrates the change in the Australian attitude toward the unknown interior. I fancy the aviator's view is not quite fair, for he is not allowing for the effect of a very bad season. On the other hand, most other descriptions are biased in the other direction. A Government surveyor or mining engineer often takes advantage of a specially good rainfall to visit uninhabited Australia, and he sees the desert after the wonderful growth which is characteristic of such regions after rain. The truth is only to be ascertained from *average climatic maps* and natural vegetation maps. These alone are not much affected by the erratic rainfall changes of desert regions.

As a matter of fact, the factor limiting the sparse population of the borderlands is the presence of the widespread dunes. No pastoralist has found this country worthy of occupation up to the present. The writer does not say that it will never be occupied by sheep or cattle, but he is sure that the total grazed, in the half-million square miles concerned, will always be negligible in comparison with those living in the better country. A desert by any other name is just as dry. The geographer is more interested in the relative values than in the nomenclature of the areas.

On all his journeys in the arid lands of Australia the writer has specially tried to obtain expert advice on the practical limits of the stock country. He has visited almost all portions of the Sparse-lands, and it is now possible to plot the limits of the fixed dunes

(Fig. 29). It is interesting that the first traverse of central Australia by McDouall Stuart in 1862 gave an unusually favourable picture of the central region. Stuart passed between the main Western Desert and the smaller Arunta Desert (Fig. 37) to the east. The least attractive part of this strip of better country lies north of Alice Springs. The stretch of 300 miles to Tennant's Creek is almost as bad as the desert. It is to be hoped that the authorities will abandon the proposal to extend the wasteful North–South Railway beyond Alice Springs. The writer opposed the building of the section from Oodnadatta to Alice Springs in many newspaper articles and geographic studies, but all to no avail. Politicians pay little heed to scientific deductions, and in 1927 blithely saddled Australia with another heavy burden in the shape of this unwarranted railway. (See p. 212.)

Character of the Desert

Carnegie gives a vivid description of the enormous sand-ridge area of the interior in his large volume *Spinifex and Sand*. Leaving the southern gold-fields in 1896, he met the first sand ridges at 26° S. They extended north for 420 miles, were from 30 to 50 feet high and ran very regularly from east-by-south to west-by-north. Belts of mulga forming dense thickets and other specimens of acacia, quandong, native poplar, &c., grew sparsely in the hollows. He describes much of it as a great undulating desert of gravel formed largely of pebbles of ferruginous sandstone (Fig. 81).

Forrest, in his traverse from west to east, in 1873 crossed near latitude 26° S. Here there seem to be larger stretches of country without fixed dunes. We may perhaps class them with the *hamada* and *serir* country of the Sahara. In specially good seasons (perhaps accompanying low solar energy and a weakening of the anticyclone belt) this hamada may temporarily be able to carry some stock (H′ in Fig. 37). Beadell's pioneer road follows this route (p. 126).

Thus the Western Desert consists essentially of three belts. A northern belt of fixed dunes, a central belt with much hamada and a southern belt of fixed dunes. In the north the dunes are apparently built up by the steady easterly Trade Winds. In the southern belt the dunes are much more confused in pattern, as we should expect, since they lie in the realm of the variable winds, far south of the Trades. In this area dunes up to 50 feet high are common.

F. G. Clapp describes the dunes in the north-west behind Wallal [1] somewhat as follows. The first sand ridge was reached

[1] 'North-west Australian Desert', *Geographical Review*, New York, April 1926.

5

130 miles to the south-east of Broome (Fig. 38). Thenceforth the ridges are practically continuous to the Northern Territory 400 miles to the east, to a similarly remote distance south-east, and to the south for about 200 miles. Although the first ridges were only a few feet high and 100 to 300 feet wide (Fig. 39), they became more formidable as Clapp proceeded south, sometimes attaining a height of 60 feet and a width of 1,000 feet. They consisted of a complex of bare sand-dunes largely devoid of vegetation, but dotted with spinifex and some bushes. The ridges, at first approximately a mile and a half apart, became closer together toward the south, until they averaged as many as four to the mile. Clapp's article is illustrated with a number of useful maps and photographs,

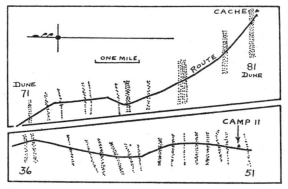

FIG. 39.—SURVEY OF TWO PATCHES AMONG THE SAND-DUNES IN
THE NORTH-WEST CORNER OF THE DESERT
Clapp's route is shown on Fig. 38
('*Geographical Review*', *1926*)

and he ends his description by the statement that the pastoral possibilities in the *unused* Western Australian Desert will not give employment to more than a score of whites for each million acres. This is at the rate of a thousand or so persons for the entire desert, and indeed he believes that not more than one or two thousand aborigines find a precarious living in this part of 'Empty Australia'.

The memoir of Davidson [1] is useful with regard to the dunes which extend far to the north-west of Barrow's Creek to the head of the Victoria River. There seems to be a stretch of bare hamada including the Macdonnells, and spreading to the north-west toward Tanami. This hamada seems to be mainly in the lee of the Macdonnells, and supports the view that the Trade Winds are the main factor in the supply of sand. From an aeroplane the present writer

[1] A. A. Davidson, *Explorations in Central Australia*, Adelaide, 1905.

saw vast stretches of the Indian Ocean off Wallal covered with
fine red sand floating on the water. This is where the Trade Wind
reaches the ocean, and a similar phenomenon occurs on the edge
of the Sahara at Cape Blanco.

A Comparison of American and Australian Deserts [1]

Every student of settlement in Australia realizes the wisdom of
using the experience of the United States to help settlers in the
younger land, but many make the natural mistake of assuming

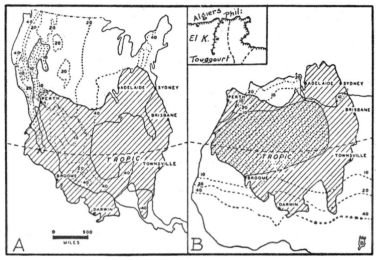

FIG. 40.—AUSTRALIA SUPERIMPOSED UPON SOUTHERN NORTH AMERICA AND
UPON NORTH AFRICA

The American and African maps show isohyets of 10, 20 and 40 inches. The two dotted areas
represent approximately the arid environments in U.S.A. and Australia. Inset is shown the
writer's traverse from Philippeville to Touggourt in the Sahara

(From 'Geographical Review', 1926)

that practices which succeed in the American arid environment
will work under Australian conditions. This section will, I hope,
help to explain certain important respects in which the two arid
regions differ. It is based in part on a traverse by car through the
southern deserts of the United States in the early summer of 1934.

In forecasting the future of settlement in Australia comparison
is often made with settlement in the United States. The areas of
the two lands are approximately the same, but unfortunately in
no other particular is resemblance close. In Fig. 40 (at A) the two
are placed in their appropriate latitudes with the drier lands to

[1] Based on an article in *Economic Geography*, Worcester, Mass., 1937.

the west in both cases. Broadly speaking, only the southern third of the United States is allied geographically to Australia, and its homologue is the southern third of Australia. But even these lands are not homoclimes (regions of similar climate), except perhaps around Sydney and Wilmington, N.C. The salient feature in the southern United States is the great area of the Gulf of Mexico running far into the land. In Australia there is an arid lowland in the same latitude, to the great disadvantage of lands still further to the west. It is often stated that Australia's arid interior will advance by irrigation as the western region of the United States has done. Apart from the great topographic differences, the irrigation regions in the United States are in very much higher latitudes —where the evaporation is relatively low and where, moreover, the rainfall in most cases is over 10 inches. Arid Mexico is perhaps a fair homoclime for the arid region (about 1,200 feet high) to the south-east of Broome.

Speaking generally, the United States has about five times as much temperate land with a rainfall over 20 inches as has Australia, and about one-fifth as much arid country (under 10 inches). These proportions largely determine the relative economic status of the two countries. A much closer homoclime for inland Australia is found in the only other large area of comparatively low trade-wind desert surrounded by an unbroken coast-line—northern Africa (Fig. 40 at B). The belts of Mediterranean flora, scrub, desert and savanna agree quite closely with the similar belts in Australia. Of course the east coast of Australia has no homoclime in the Sahara. It is in the southern coast-lands of China that we find an area with an environment much like that of eastern Australia.

It is, of course, the general arrangement of atmospheric circulation which produces deserts along the Tropics of Cancer and Capricorn. Here the dry anticyclones make their average drift *to* the east, and on their equatorial margins the steady Trade Winds blow *from* the east. We have in an earlier paragraph (p. 19) considered why Australia has so much broader a desert than has the United States. It is largely a function of the width of the continent near the tropic—but the problem is complicated by the topography. North Africa is 3,500 miles wide—and on its eastern margin adjoins the Asiatic land mass (Fig. 2). Hence no moist Trade Winds from the sea ever reach the Sahara—and in these latitudes Africa is desert from coast to coast.

In North America, Mexico is the true parallel of arid Australia, and the desert in the south-west of the States is largely of topographic origin. It is seen to lie far on the polar side of the tropic. However, as stated earlier, if the United States had a large arid

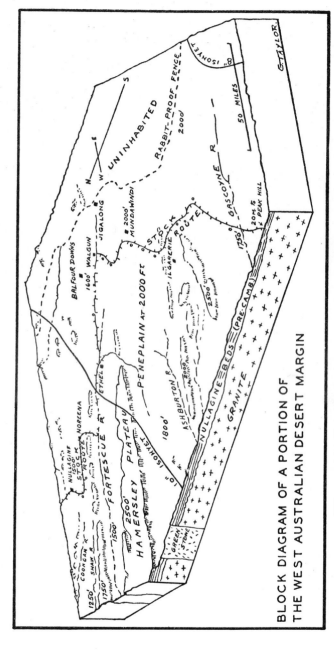

BLOCK DIAGRAM OF A PORTION OF
THE WEST AUSTRALIAN DESERT MARGIN

FIG. 41.—BLOCK DIAGRAM OF PART OF THE WESTERN AUSTRALIAN DESERT

The rivers do not contain water except after very rare heavy rains. (*Based on H. W. B. Talbot*)

land area where now is the Gulf of Mexico, there is little doubt
that much of the Mississippi Valley and adjacent states would be
as dry as the corresponding region in Australia.

The contrasts are even more strongly emphasized when we compare the 'Build' of the arid parts of the United States with that of
arid Australia. These are illustrated in Figs. 41 and 42. In Chapter
III (p. 37) I have shown that the continental build of Australia—
on the west of the Pacific Ocean—is the enantiomorph (mirror-
image) of the American continent east of the Pacific. Shield, Downfold, Young Mountains and Ocean Deep are repeated in opposite
order on different sides of the Pacific. It is true that the Austral-
asian fold-mountains are mostly drowned by the sea, and hardly
appear on the mainland of Australia (Fig. 9). In fact, they rise to
their chief height in New Zealand. However, it is of the greatest
significance that it is the *westward leeward side* of the continent
which is the arid region in both continents in these latitudes. Hence
in Australia the *Shield* constitutes the Desert, while in America it
is the high *Young Mountains* (the Basin, Range and Fold area)
which contain the desert lands. (See ends of section in Fig. 9.)
As we shall see, this entirely different build in the two types of
deserts vitally affects their environments and potentialities.

In December 1924 the writer made a traverse of the Sparselands and the margin of the Desert in Western Australia. About
200 miles of this journey, from Nullagine to Peak Hill, is illustrated in the block diagram (Fig. 41). The geology of this region
has been carefully studied by H. W. B. Talbot, and his numerous
maps have been published in Bulletin 83 of the Geological Survey
of Western Australia (1928). Reference to the block diagram will
show that we are dealing with a typical peneplain about 2,000 feet
above sea level. It consists essentially of granite capped by fairly
level beds of sediments of Pre-Cambrian age. These latter form
mesa-like structures from 200 to 500 feet above the peneplain.

The numerous 'rivers' shown in the diagram occur as vast
'senile' expanses of gravels, which rarely show any visible water.
However, some ground-water is present fairly generally, and small
wells have been dug every 10 miles or so along the stock route
for the benefit of travelling stock. These are indicated by small
circles in Fig. 41. The chief 'stations' (ranches), such as Noreena,
Ethel Creek, Mundawindi and Ilgarerie, are shown on the diagram.

In the following account of the physiography of the region
between Marble Bar (see endpaper map) and Peak Hill (Fig. 41)
it must be remembered that my journey took place in the height
of summer. In the preceding summer (1922-3) Marble Bar had
experienced 152 days in which the mean maximum was 109° F.

On Christmas Day, 1924, the writer was in Nullagine and the thermometer rose to 119° F. Indeed, it was a bad drought season, and we carried sixteen bags of grain in a trailer behind the Royal Mail, which was an old Dodge car. This fodder was brought all the way from Perth to these outback ranches in the effort to save some of the best stock.

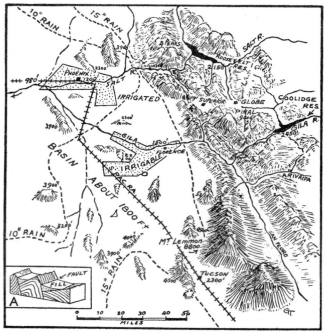

FIG. 42.—BIRD'S-EYE VIEW OF THE DESERT REGION BETWEEN TUCSON AND PHOENIX

showing the 'Block' mountains rising 5,000 to 7,000 feet above the 'infilled' basin. Inset at A is a diagram of the typical 'build' of the arid portion of U.S.A.

(*From 'Economic Geography', July 1937*)

From Nullagine southward to Noreena we traversed a stony hamada with a little 'wind grass' between the sheet waste. There was a good deal of spinifex (i.e. *Triodia*, a spiny tussock grass) and shrubs called 'kandjai'—a *Grevillea* resembling grey holly. In the shallow creek beds—all, of course, dry for many months—white gums (*Eucalyptus* sp.) were fairly numerous, their roots reaching the deep wet gravels. Mesas were numerous each side of the stock route, as shown in Fig. 41. South of Noreena we passed belts of mulga (*Acacia*) with some broombush (*Eremophila*), and then reached more spinifex and needlebush (*Hakea*). This continued to Roy Hill Station. Near Walgun we crossed Jigalong Creek (a wide expanse of drifting sand), in which the car stuck for some time. In general, however, this gravelly hamada needed only to have the bushes cut away here and there to make natural if rough motor roads. The Tropic of Capricorn runs near Jigalong, which is also right on the Rabbit-Proof fence. This famous fence is the inner (eastern) boundary of the 'Sparseland' in Western Australia. At Jigalong there was formerly a Government station for breeding camels, but this project has been abandoned.

At Balfour Downs is a fine homestead, with walls built of pisé-mud, and with the usual grass lawn kept green by constant watering from the well. In this case the lawn was about 10 feet square. The enterprising manager had little patches of lucerne, Soudan grass, onions, tomatoes and even watercress grown with the same water. His wife, with her two small children, was isolated by a hundred miles from any white woman, and I cannot refrain from expressing my admiration for such gallant pioneers.

The next station, at Jigalong, was much smaller. Here the long, low sand ridges of the uninhabited country (locally known as 'desert') could be seen from the house. As usual, they were 'fixed', or vegetated, by mulga, waxy spinifex and other scrub; but they indicate country where the feed is too poor and the water too precarious even for such sparse pastoral occupation as exists west of the boundary. Such an environment the geographer calls a desert.

From Jigalong our route crossed a number of low sand ridges, where the sand was drifting somewhat, but thence the country to Meekatharra consisted of rather poor mulga, with much rocky debris and large patches of spinifex and a little saltbush. We rejoined the great stock route, where Government wells have been sunk every dozen miles. At Mundawindi we reached the Government rest-house, and here a fee of one shilling (paid to the postmaster) gave one the use of a cowhide stretcher. 'Wild apple' bush (*Canthium*) and 'pitch bush' (*Eremophila*) were interspersed with mulga in this region. Near the Gascoyne divide another series of sand ridges was seen, with a mallee flora like that of the far south. In the evening we reached Peak Hill, now a stagnant town of about a score of houses, surrounded by bygone mines.

Australians are apt to imagine that the desert areas may be exploited by irrigation in the future. Probably they base their opinions on what has been done in the United States. The conditions are so different that no parallel exists between the two cases. In the deserts in Australia there is nothing which can be called a river; only for an hour or two after an occasional heavy thunderstorm a gully may contain flowing water. There is nothing even resembling the Mohavé River—while the longest Australian river (the Murray) does not surpass a desert-crossing river like the Colorado.

Many of the difficulties and disagreements which arise in a discussion of deserts are due to questions of definition. This aspect of the problem I have discussed fairly fully in earlier paragraphs, where the distinction between Desert and Sparselands has been stressed.

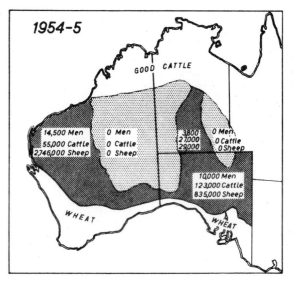

FIG. 43.—APPROXIMATE NUMBERS OF MEN, CATTLE AND SHEEP IN THE SPARSELANDS (RULED) (AFTER S. R. CARVER).

The deserts are shown dotted

Considering the area of the Sparselands (ruled in Fig. 43) about 1931, they include about 11,000 men, 150,000 cattle and 2,740,000 sheep in the Western Australian portion. In South Australia there are about 3,750 men, 56,000 cattle and 1 million sheep. In the Sparselands of the Northern Territory (between the two deserts) there are about 600 men, 130,000 cattle and a few thousand sheep. If we consider nine sheep equivalent to one cow, then the area per cow in this 700,000 square miles is about 640 acres. In the poor Winter-Range districts in arid western United States, a cow needs only 75 acres for its grazing. It is specially to be noted that the Australian Sparselands have been occupied by

ranches for 40 years, and that of late years there has been little
change in the numbers of the stock grazed there. In other words,
the pastoral industry in the Sparselands long ago reached a state
of relative saturation. Of course, large areas even in the Sparse-

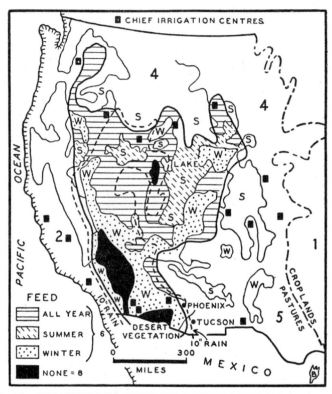

FIG. 44.—THE HEAVY LINE SHOWS THE LIMITS OF DESERT VEGETATION IN
WESTERN U.S.A., ACCORDING TO SHANTZ AND ZON

The broken line in the centre shows the 10-inch rain line. (*Data as to feed for stock based on
A. F. Potter*)

(*Map after O. E. Baker, and reproduced by permission of 'Economic Geography'*)

lands are entirely too poor for grazing, but no map, so far as I
know, has appeared which specifies such useless country.

Turning now to settlement conditions in arid America, it is not
easy to make close comparisons. We may perhaps equate the
boundary of Desert Vegetation (Fig. 44)—as given by Shantz and
Zon—with the aggregate of Deserts and Sparselands (region ABCD)
in Fig. 37. It seems reasonable to use the stock themselves as
'indicators' of land values, since neither Australia nor United

States are any longer *young* or *undeveloped* pastoral countries. Thus the black areas in Fig. 44 represent in general useless salty desert and, according to Baker,[1] total about 100,000 square miles. We may equate this with the Vegetated Sand-Dunes (and Serir or pebble country) shown dotted in Fig. 37. There is no parallel, however, in Australia for the widespread summer or winter grazing. The former is mainly found in the mountains and is largely due to the melting snows. Since there are no mountains in the Australian arid lands (except a few ranges like the Macdonnells and Musgraves, which are much too low to carry snow), there is no transhumance (shift of stock) of this kind. All the Sparseland region which is ruled in Fig. 37, where grazed at all, is used the whole year round. Hence the grazing like the topography is uniform in Australia, and very diversified in western United States.

In the earlier illustration (Fig. 42) I give a slightly generalized view of the region in southern Arizona which includes Tucson and Phoenix, together with the superb mountains to the east. The writer has done field-work in all seven continents, and no region in the world has been more interesting to him as an example of environmental control than that surrounding Tucson. The amazing rocky slopes just a few miles west of Tucson dominated by the giant cactus were of a kind totally unfamiliar to a student of desert conditions in Australia. But even more surprising—one might say incredible—were the snowclad slopes of Mount Lemmon about the same distance to the north-east. Here, above an elevation of 7,500 feet, appear thick forests of tall conifers whose bases were shrouded in snow. In May 1933 we were almost the first strangers after the winter passed to reach the outlook on the summit. Small streams dashed down the upper portions of the range but dwindled away before they had crossed the middle slopes. Similar ranges are higher and closer set still further to the east, and it is such a topography which has produced the Gila and Salt Rivers and many another like them. These rivers in turn, cutting through the 'block' formations (indicated in the inset at A, in Fig. 42), produce ideal sites for dams. Thus Roosevelt Dam was built in 1911 and Coolidge Dam in 1930, the former watering about 300,000 acres around Phoenix, and the latter some 100,000 acres near Florence (Fig. 42).

The following table shows the enormous areas irrigated by four American rivers. Only one Australian river basin, the Murray, has any large amount of water for irrigation and its quota is only about 500,000 acres.

[1] O. E. Baker, 'Agricultural Regions of North America', *Econ. Geog.*, p. 327, Oct. 1931.

CHIEF IRRIGATION AREAS IN UNITED STATES

Missouri Basin	4,185,180 acres
Columbia Basin	3,393,640 ,,
Colorado Basin	2,537,124 ,,
Rio Grande Basin	1,468,913 ,,

Thus there is little resemblance in the resources of Australia and the United States, though their areas are almost identical.

A Comparison with the Northern Sahara

For many years the writer has been interested in discovering how settlement changes in response to regular changes in the natural environment. The environment in Algeria is obviously much like that in Southern Australia, and in the summer of 1938 the opportunity arose to compare Australian conditions with those of North Africa.[1]

On this journey I made use of a technique which I have found useful elsewhere. I made my traverse *across* the rainfall lines, and halted at a number of representative localities to study in greater detail the character of the human occupation (see Inset in Fig. 40). The traverse ran from the Mediterranean at Philippeville, with a rainfall of about 40 inches, for a distance of 150 miles to El Kantara, with a rainfall of 10 inches. Here an abrupt change takes place, from wheat culture to desert. From here I traversed for 180 miles due south through the Sahara Desert to Touggourt.

I do not propose to repeat my observations of the great Algerian Wheat Belt. It corresponds closely to the similar belt, say from Cape Jervis to Quorn, in South Australia. On the southern slopes of the Atlas Mountains (here not very imposing) small clusters of date palms begin to appear a few miles north of El Kantara, and here also in the alluvial fans of the Tilatou valley are the last of the wheat patches of Algeria.

Below the Gorge of El Kantara the landscape changes entirely, for now we enter the veritable desert, where palms are almost the sole rivals of what can be described as the 'tussock' shrubs of the Sahara. Thorny bushes are fairly regularly distributed over the yellow clay soil about 30 feet apart. No sand-dunes were visible in most of the 180 miles from El Kantara to Touggourt. The characteristic hummocky vegetation of this part of the Sahara becomes common south of El Kantara. Each clump of stems tends to collect drift-soil and sand, gradually building up a mound which may be as much as a couple of feet in height. Biskra, about 35 miles south of El Kantara, is purely a desert town.

[1] 'Sea to Sahara', *Geographical Review*, Vol. 29, April 1939, New York.

The most interesting feature of the desert traverse was the presence of a regular uniform vegetation during the whole journey. Most of the way the landscape as seen in the distance seemed to be wholly vegetated, and resembled a moorland; but close at hand the tussock shrubs and plants were seen to be spaced at intervals of from 5 to 30 feet. Between the plants the yellow loam was usually bare. Since the spacing did not vary regularly as one proceeded south, it would seem that soil conditions are an important factor. I made detailed notes of the changes every mile on this long traverse, and only seven times were small dunes noticed, the largest patch being about two miles long. A number of photographs are given in my original paper.

The survey showed the expected relation between rainfall, crops and population. Where the rainfall is about 40 inches a year and where topography is favourable, vines and oranges are largely grown, just as in the similar Australian environment. Here the population is about 200 to the square mile. From 40 to 16 inches is the great wheat region of Algeria, where the population ranges from about 100 to 40 per square mile. A region of precarious wheat cultivation lies between the 16- and 10-inch isohyets, and here the population is about 20–30 to the square mile. At the 10-inch isohyet there is a sharp drop in the density corresponding to a change to a desert environment at El Kantara. (See p. 475.)

In Algeria, as in Australia, the importance of the 10-inch isohyet as limiting the desert on its poleward side is evident. The character of the desert south of El Kantara is very like the similar sparsely vegetated regions in the south of Australia. French geographers tell us that only about one-seventh of the Sahara is clothed with Ergs or *living* Dunes. I am not able to ascertain how much of the Sahara is clothed with *fixed* Dunes. But from the region which I investigated there is little to choose between the northern Sahara and the Australian deserts. Both contain a widespread vegetation. Both can support a very sparse population, whose density obviously depends largely on the standards of living required. In conclusion, Ackerman's paper on an Algerian Oasis should be read by all who are interested in the low standards of living of the desert people.[1]

In 1959 the Western Desert was opened up by a rough military road from Woomera to Wiluna—a distance of about a thousand miles. It proceeds northwest from Woomera to the opal-fields of Cooper Pedy, and so to the new weather-station at Giles (Fig. 44A). Thence the new mission to the aborigines at Warburton is reached, and a traverse of Gibson's Desert brings one to the outlying cattle

[1] *Economic Geography*, Vol. 12, 1936, pp. 250–8.

station of Carnegie. This is connected by road with the mining settlement of Wiluna, whence one can attain the railway terminus at Meekatharra, some 130 miles to the west. The road traverses mulga and spinifex country, typical of the *hamada* described by Forrest on his exploration in 1874.

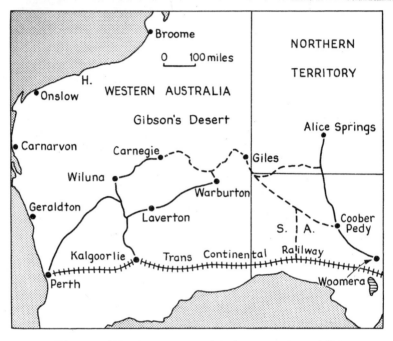

FIG. 44A. THE NEW ROAD ACROSS THE WESTERN DESERT
(*From Herald, 1959*)

At Woomera a small town has developed about nine miles north of the station of Pimba on the West–East Railway. From here are projected the rocket missiles over the uninhabited country toward 'H' (Port Hedland) (Fig. 44A).

Note.—The present chapter is wholly concerned with the main *Western* Desert in Australia. The smaller eastern or '*Arunta*' Desert is charted and described in Chapter VIII, pages 232–4.

PART II

THE NATURAL REGIONS AND THEIR
VARIED ENVIRONMENTS

CHAPTER VII

THE SEVEN REGIONS IN THE EASTERN WARP

IN a continent of 3 million square miles, there is, as we have seen, considerable diversity in build, climate, soil and vegetation, giving rise to corresponding diversity in the best form of utilization by man when he comes to occupy it. It is therefore obvious that much will be gained if the continent be subdivided into smaller units, in which there is some approach to uniformity of environment. Such units are often termed *Natural Regions*, but as is perhaps to be expected, there is no unanimity as to how uniform or how small such regions should be. No two districts, even if quite small, can be precisely alike, so that the practical answer is to decide on the number of subdivisions desired (for example about twenty), and then try to carve Australia into twenty areas in each of which the desired uniformity is approached as close as may be. In 1918 I discussed Australia in fifteen such areas,[1] in each of which the type of rainfall was perhaps the major criterion. Topography and natural vegetation were also taken into consideration. I have made this classification the basis of the present attempt to obtain a clearer picture of the characteristics of the various natural landscapes in Australia. Considerable emphasis, as in the former study, is based on the character of the rainfall. It is not only one of the main classifiers but, when considered with the natural vegetation, gives us the chief key to the future utilization of every Australian region.

It is an interesting study in deducing major Natural Regions to see how Australia can be thus subdivided into twenty unit areas. No geographer would hesitate to use the three major *structural* areas in his primary subdivision. They are of course the Shield, Geosyncline and Eastern Warp, whose boundaries are indicated on Fig. 45 by the two lines AB and CD. As our second major division we may well take the line EF, which fairly closely represents the line separating summer from winter rains, and approximately separates tropical and temperate Australia. We have thus arrived at six primary subdivisions, as suggested in the table at the top of page 131.

[1] *The Australian Environment, Advisory Council of Science and Industry*, Melbourne, 1918.

The present section dealing with the natural regions and their varying environments is, for several reasons, the longest in the book. It comprises the *regional* studies, and so gives more details of specific areas than are found elsewhere. This is especially true of Natural Regions 1 and 3, which include Sydney and Melbourne, for they contain about half the population of the whole continent.

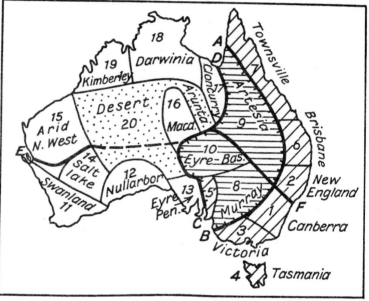

FIG. 45.—A MAP ILLUSTRATING THE DIVISION OF AUSTRALIA INTO TWENTY 'NATURAL REGIONS'

AB and *CD* are topographic boundaries; *EF* is a rainfall boundary. '5' is the Flinders Division and '16' the Macdonnells. (See the endpaper map for details)

The future possibilities of each region depend more on the rainfall than on any other factor. Hence a great deal of stress is laid on the seasonal variations of the rain. Since, moreover, the natural vegetation offers the closest response to the physical environment, and the best clue to its proper development, I have dwelt on this aspect more fully than is perhaps customary in geographies. Another good reason for this stress on vegetation is that the Australians themselves, as well as the European readers, have a very poor knowledge of the common trees and plants in Australia, and I hope that these chapters may help in this respect.

NATURAL REGIONS IN AUSTRALIA

	Temperate, mostly winter rains	Tropical, mostly summer rains
I. Eastern Warp	1. **Canberra** (N.S.W.) 2. **New England** (N.S.W.) 3. **Victoria** 4. **Tasmania** 5. **Flinders Range** (S.A.)	6. **Brisbane** (Q.) 7. **Townsville** (Q.)
II. Geosyncline	8. Murray Basin (N.S.W.) 10. Lake Eyre Basin (S.A.)	9. Artesia (Q.)
III. Western Shield	11. **Swanland** (W.A.) 12. Nullarbor (W.A.) 13. **Eyre Peninsula** (S.A.) 14. Salt Lake (W.A.)	15. Arid North-West (W.A.) 16. Macdonnells (N.T.) 17. Cloncurry (Q.) 18. Darwinia (N.T.) 19. Kimberley (W.A.) 20. Desert

Regions in **Block** type grow Crops

NATURAL REGION I: THE CANBERRA REGION

Reference to the key map (Fig. 45) shows that this region includes that portion of the Eastern Warp which lies west and south of Sydney and Newcastle. Its centre is approximately at Canberra, and it includes Sydney, the greatest city in Australia, the chief coal-fields and industrial districts, the Federal Capital, the highest mountain (Kosciusko), as well as such interesting regions as the Cassilis Gate, the Canyons of the Blue Plateau, the Jenolan Caves, Lake George and the Burrinjuck Reservoir. Hence a lengthy description of this area is justified. It extends about 400 miles along the coast, and about a hundred and fifty or more miles inland. The significant features can be made out from the block diagram, Fig. 46.

It is first of all necessary to realize that there are no striking mountain ranges, though much of the region is rugged. In truth in these uplands we are dealing with a broad warp, or with fault blocks, which do not produce jagged crests or narrow divides. The name of the best-known mountains in Australia is a misnomer. Visitors journeying to see the Blue 'Mountains' find no mountains at all. They climb up more than 3,000 feet over the gently rising slope of a broad earth fold. On the almost level

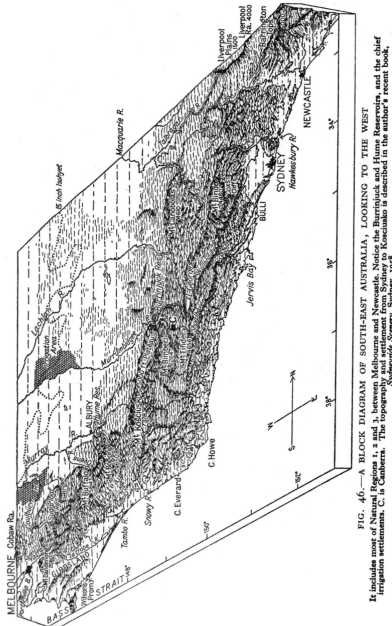

FIG. 46.—A BLOCK DIAGRAM OF SOUTH-EAST AUSTRALIA, LOOKING TO THE WEST

It includes most of Natural Regions 1, 2 and 3, between Melbourne and Newcastle. Notice the Burrinjuck and Hume Reservoirs, and the chief irrigation settlements. C. is Canberra. The topography and settlement from Sydney to Kosciusko is described in the author's recent book, *Sydneyside Scenery*, Sydney, 1958.

(*From 'Pioneer Settlement', Amer. Geog. Soc., New York, 1932*)

plateau at Katoomba (or Mount Victoria) the scenery lies *below* the town in the unrivalled canyons cut into the plateau. So also the so-called Illawarra Range behind Bulli (Fig. 46) is merely the steep scarp bounding a nearly level up-warped plateau. Indeed, the 'Great Dividing Range' itself is wrongly named, since it is in no sense a continuous ridge. The writer has tried for years to have this series of isolated plateaux and gentle warps (and in places depressions, as at Lake George) renamed 'The Great Divide' (see Fig. 14B). In Canada it would be called 'Height of Land'.

Topography around Sydney

The salient topographic feature in the vicinity of Sydney is the circular level area lying between the city and the western rugged country, which is called the 'Wianamatta Stillstand' (Fig. 46). Here the latest of the three Triassic formations (the Wianamatta Shale) has been preserved, since this area has not been warped upward in the Pleistocene folding. In the surrounding uplifted areas, this upper formation is only preserved in small cappings. To the west is the striking Monocline, which raises the Hawkesbury Sandstones from far below sea level (under the Wianamatta Shale) to nearly 4,000 feet above sea level (Fig. 120). To the north is another smaller warp, whereby the surface has been elevated about 1,000 feet above sea level. In this process the Hawkesbury River has cut the deep juvenile valley, which, on later drowning, became Broken Bay. To the south the land has risen more gradually, rising to over 2,000 feet near the Shoalhaven River, which has cut a canyon 1,600 feet deep in the rising peneplain. As the writer pointed out in 1923, Sydney lies on the axis of symmetry of these warps. Botany Bay represents a small extension of the Stillstand, which has never been elevated (hence some of its tributary valleys are not rejuvenated), but it has been drowned by the rising of ocean waters.

Sydney Harbour lies just within the southern margin of the Broken Bay Plateau. Hence the north shore of the harbour is much steeper than the south shore (Fig. 47). This difference has determined the pattern of the city. The industrial areas are mainly on the flatter south shores, especially between Balmain and Parramatta. The rugged northern suburbs offer fine sites for the bungalows and mansions, but are ill-suited for agriculture or factories.

During the 'Kosciusko Period' of uplift, the bygone 'Sydney River' cut a gorge, perhaps 400 feet deep in places. Its headwaters near Parramatta were hardly affected by the warp, and remain in a 'late mature' stage. Probably the drowning was due to the

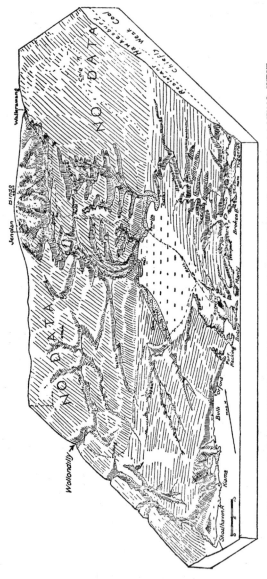

FIG. 47.—BLOCK DIAGRAM OF THE WARPED LITTORAL AROUND SYDNEY, LOOKING WEST

The strata are indicated at the right

melting of the ice caps after the last major ice age. The sea now occupies the lower 150 feet of the gorge in its eastern half.[1]

The harbour is not a typical *ria* (i.e. drowned branching valley), for its depth varies a good deal, and is perhaps due to minor faulting. Between the Heads, which exhibit cliffs 300 feet high (Fig. 49), the water is 120 feet deep; but 5 miles within the harbour (off Milson's Point) it is no less than 156 feet deep. Various valley sections near Broken Bay exhibit all stages of maturity, rejuvenescence, infilling with marine silts, &c., and even indicate a recent upward joggle of 20 feet.

Settlement around Sydney

We may now note the topographic controls which led to the choice of the site of Sydney. As I have stated elsewhere, Newcastle

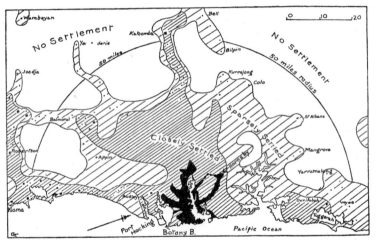

FIG. 48.—THE DISTRIBUTION OF SETTLEMENT AROUND SYDNEY

Region of city streets, *black*. Region where centres are less than about *four* miles apart, close ruling. (N.B.—Settled areas begin again somewhat to the west and north of this map)

has many advantages which are absent at Sydney, but as far as the region of our survey is concerned there are only three localities where fairly suitable sites occur. These are close together, e.g. at Botany Bay, at Port Hacking and Sydney Harbour (Fig. 48). Everywhere else the warps isolate the coast almost entirely from

[1] 'The Warped Littoral round Sydney', G. Taylor, Roy. Soc. N.S. Wales, 1923. For detailed topography from Sydney to Kosciusko, see my recent book, *Sydneyside Scenery*: 63 maps. Sydney, 1958.

the interior. Indeed, from Newcastle to Nowra (150 miles) there are only five main roads (all south of Otford) which climb these scarps.

Botany Bay offers few facilities for deep frontages, for its shores have not been rejuvenated. Port Hacking receives several large streams which carry down much silt. These render the port much shallower than Port Jackson. Finally the latter port extends so far inland that its head waters (near Parramatta) reach into the plains of the Wianamatta Stillstand, so that a much clearer path to the latter is offered behind Sydney than behind Port Hacking. One wonders what would have happened if Captain Phillip in 1788 had gone south instead of north on his arrival at Botany Bay. If the metropolis had once been located near Audley on Port Hacking (Fig. 48), should we ever have managed to change it?

Sydney has a fine site so far as its deep-water port is concerned. In passing, one may note that the Hawkesbury estuary at Broken Bay is three times as picturesque as Sydney Harbour—for its dissection is three times as deep. There is, unfortunately, only a small hinterland to Sydney, i.e. where the warping has not developed. The only really fertile regions are the small Silt-Lakes at Camden, Wallacia and Richmond along the Nepean. Here were the old 'Cowpastures' and the finest farms of the pioneers.

In every other direction Sydney is cut off by fairly sterile dissected plateaux. To the north is the barrier of the Broken Bay Plateau (Fig. 47), of very little use for primary production. The same is true to a greater degree of all the west. To the south the dissection is a little less advanced, and so we find a few small towns (Fig. 48) strung along the Great Southern Railway (such as Balmoral) before the more level land at Mittagong is reached.

If we draw a circle of 50 miles radius (see Fig. 48) about Sydney (with its million or more inhabitants) we find therefore one of the most singular dispositions of circum-metropolitan population in the world. Let us suppose that we survey this circular belt from an aeroplane. On the north our flight leaves the narrow coastal plain at Wyee. Thereafter for 80 miles along our circle we cross only one good road, which runs from Wiseman's Ferry to Wollombi, *via* St. Albans. The next 20 miles crosses Bell's Road (near Bilpin and Mount Irvine) and brings us to the Katoomba tourist belt. Proceeding south for 40 miles we notice the single settlement of the Yerranderie silver-mines, before we reach the southern line near Balmoral. Another 20-mile stretch of uninhabited water-reserves brings us to the narrow coast-plain near Kiama, and here again a closely settled region is observed. Thus, excluding the shore, during a flight of over 150 miles, we have only crossed two narrow belts of settlement (at Katoomba and Balmoral) while circum-navigating the largest city of Australia.

The actual site of the early town (within Port Jackson) was determined by the little 'Tank Stream' which entered the harbour at Circular Quay. The northern shores were much too steep for convenient roads, as noted earlier. After 1788 the town naturally grew south over the gentle slopes toward Redfern, Newtown and Waterloo. In 1880 the close-set streets had not progressed much further (Fig. 49). But military roads led to forts at the Heads

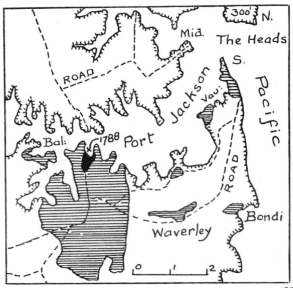

FIG. 49.—EARLY SYDNEY—FROM A MAP PUBLISHED IN 1880

The ruled areas were the chief built-up areas in 1880. The black area is the site of the first settlement in 1788

(including Middle Head), and houses soon began to spread along these roads. In 1880 there were suburbs at Waverley and Vaucluse, and to the west at Balmain. Today the city has spread its tentacles to the west far beyond Parramatta and to the south to George's River. On the rocky 'North Shore' the effect of the two railways from Hornsby in promoting building is clearly to be seen in Fig. 48.

The Blue Plateau

The so-called 'Blue Mountains' consist of a boldly warped portion of the crust, which has been elevated 3,000 or 4,000 feet. The main flexure is along the western bank of the lower

Nepean River, and here the surface rises sharply about 1,000 feet (Fig. 47). But several other parallel folds further west bring the ancient peneplain surface to a height of over 4,000 feet at Mount Bindo (near Jenolan Caves).

Marked faults have accompanied the foldings. Near Kurrajong (Fig. 48), a fault scarp of about 500 feet is a marked feature, and similar faults are probably common to the southward. The uplift dates back many thousand years, and marked rejuvenation and reversal of the streams is the result. It seems likely that the pre-

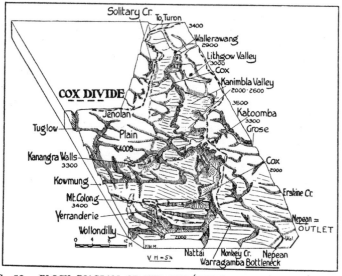

FIG. 50.—BLOCK DIAGRAM OF THE COX 'BOTTLE-NECK CANYON' ERODED IN THE BLUE PLATEAU

All the drainage reaches the lowland in the south-east corner at the Nepean River, by a narrow gorge, though the upper Cox valley is 10 miles broad

(*Survey and sketch by F. A. Craft*)

uplift drainage here was to the north-west or north, as suggested in 1911 by the writer. Such courses are still dominant in the Wianamatta Stillstand (or region of negligible uplift), which lies between Sydney and the Blue Plateau. The remarkably broad and deep gorges cut in the plateau, with their unique 'bottle-necks', where they pass through the hinge of the earthfold (Fig. 47), are due to the presence of a hard horizontal sandstone which caps softer coal measures.

The Grose Valley and the Kanimbla (Cox) Valley are classic examples of bottle-necked valleys (Fig. 50). Where the hard surface sandstones are *level*, as in the upper part or 'tread' of the monocline, the river has sapped away the softer shales below them, so that wide areas have been eroded. Where, however, the hard sandstones slope down the scarp of the monocline, the river is only able to saw a narrow gorge, and several examples of such 'bottle-necks' are evident in Fig. 47.

In some respects the valleys carved out of the great sandstone plateau of New South Wales are even more remarkable than Californian Yo-semité itself. The ravines which discharge their waters into the Cox River occupy an area of 1,212 square miles. The whole forms the basin of this mountain stream. Its main valley is 10 miles wide, and is bounded by cliffs increasing from about 1,000 feet near its outlet to about 2,500 feet near its western limits, the valley bottom being not much above sea level. Yet the only outlet is through a gorge about a third of a mile wide (Fig. 50). Thousands of tourists visit Katoomba and other plateau towns and climb down the cliffs past lovely waterfalls to the fern gullies below.

Of peculiar interest is the course of the important river known at different stages as the Wollondilly, the Warragamba, the Nepean and the Hawkesbury. At its source, its southern tributary—the Mulwaree—rises near Duck Flat just east of Lake George (see Fig. 46). This level locality is usually indicated as a *high range* on the maps, merely because it forms part of the main divide! Then it flows along the foot of a fault-scarp (which has dammed Lake Bathurst) and reaches Goulburn in the mature valley of the Upper Wollondilly. As it flows north the valley becomes incised deeper and narrower, until near Wambeyan (see Fig. 47) it makes an abrupt return on itself just after receiving the Wingecarribee from Moss Vale. The gorge becomes deeper and deeper, and the valley is practically inaccessible in the stretch called the Warragamba Bottleneck (Fig. 50). It joins the Nepean in the extraordinary gorge near Wallacia. The latter river has flowed normally through a topography which verges on senility, until at Wallacia it darts westward into the Blue Mountains scarp for 10 miles, and then returns to the easier path of the coastal plains. Thence the Nepean flows normally to its estuary, the drowned valley of Broken Bay. The last stretch is always known as the Hawkesbury River. These diverse names emphasize the difficulty of following along this river, and tell us that explorers came upon it at distant points when its continuity was not suspected. Even today there is no road along most of the course of the Wollondilly and Warragamba.

Kosciusko and the Monaro Plateau

An area of marked faulting separates the Blue Plateau from the next highland to the south. To this area of relatively low, faulted, topography the name of 'Lake George Gate' has been given. Here the former tributaries of the Yass River and other streams have been ponded back by meridional faults to form lakes like Lake George (20 miles long) and Lake Bathurst (Fig. 46). Fine 'antecedent' gorges such as the Molonglo (east of Canberra) and the Murrumbidgee (as it flows west through the horst) at Burrinjuck show the relative recency of the 'Kosciusko Uplift'.

Canberra, the capital of the Commonwealth, has been built on a small plain near the Murrumbidgee River at an elevation of 2,000 feet. To the west is the high Bimberi Range (6,264 feet),

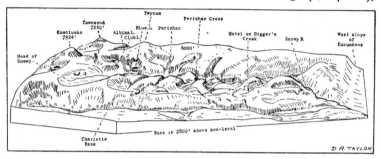

FIG. 51.—BLOCK DIAGRAM OF THE KOSCIUSKO PLATEAU, LOOKING TO THE NORTH-WEST

The sketch represents 25 miles of country. The small moraines are numbered 1 to 6. The tarns in the cirques are shown black. (See also p. 412)

where the Cotter River (supplying water to the city) has its head. Originally the Federal area of 900 square miles was used only for pastoral occupation. There were about a score of cattle and sheep stations in the area. In 1913, when the capital was named, there were 2,240 inhabitants. Now the Commonwealth Parliament and many Federal Departments are at Canberra, and the population is about 15,000 (see p. 254).[1]

The south-east corner of New South Wales contains the highest mountains in Australia. Kosciusko rises to 7,324 feet, but it is merely the summit of a crustal block or horst with a general level of 5,000 or 6,000 feet. A broad upland valley nearly 3,000 feet high separates the Kosciusko Plateau from the lower Tindery Range to the east. The whole elevated region is known as the 'Monaro'. The Kosciusko massif continues into Victoria, where the Cobboras are 6,000 feet high, while Mount Gibbo is 5,764.

In midsummer the Kosciusko Range on its sheltered eastern flank is usually covered with a chain of miniature snow-fields.

[1] *Land Classification of Australian Capital Territory*, A. W. King (Canberra, 1946), contains a fine series of maps in colour.

These have an average length of 200 yards, and are about 5 feet thick. They disappear in autumn. The range shows many features resulting from the far colder regime of the Pleistocene glaciation. Blue Lake is a cirque with walls 400 feet high (Fig. 51). Fine moraines dam Hedley Tarn and Lake May. Polished platforms with striae occur near Lake Albina. At its maximum the Snowy River glacier was perhaps 3 miles long and 400 feet thick. The whole region is deeply covered in snow during the colder months. The plateau is a summer tourist resort of some importance, while ski-ing attracts many winter visitors [1] (Fig. 128B).

Rainfall in the South-East Highlands, &c.

This highland region is obviously affected by several rainfall controls. To the north lies the *summer-rain* region; to the north-west the rainfall is very *uniform*; to the south-west it is almost wholly affected by *winter* controls. Hence we should expect a mixture of these conditions; and in fact the common feature throughout the 'Canberra' region is the presence of considerable variation throughout the year, with local maxima in each of the four seasons (Fig. 52).

Thus Queanbeyan, Moruya and Omeo have well-defined maxima in March, June, October and December. At Orbost and Bathurst the March maximum is absent. At Sydney the March and June maxima merge to give a pronounced autumn rainfall. This latter type, however, is confined to the coast from Newcastle to Jervis Bay, and does not obtain inland.

Heavy snow occasionally falls throughout the highlands. Thus a snowstorm in July 1900 extended for some 200 miles from the Hunter Valley to Condobolin, and paralysed railway traffic. Only one or two very moderate falls have occurred at Sydney, as for instance in June 1836. Melbourne has had more snow, for example in August 1849 and August 1899.

In central Victoria the constant south-west winds of the winter storms dominate the coastal highlands, as the record for Weeaproinah shows. At this place there is a wet season from April to September and a fairly dry season for the rest of the year. Something of the same type of rain regime is shown at Shepparton on the Murray in the irrigation district (Fig. 52). Melbourne, how-ever, has a quite uniform rain, since it receives about 2·3 inches in every month of the year. Much the same very uniform rain is

[1] See the paper 'Snow Country of N.S.W.', F. A. Craft, *Aus. Geog.*, 1934. See also the large contour map, *Roy. Soc. N.S.W.*, 1926, by Taylor, Browne and Jardine, on which Fig. 51 is based. See also papers by W. R. Browne (1944 and 1952) and J. A. Dulhunty (1945).

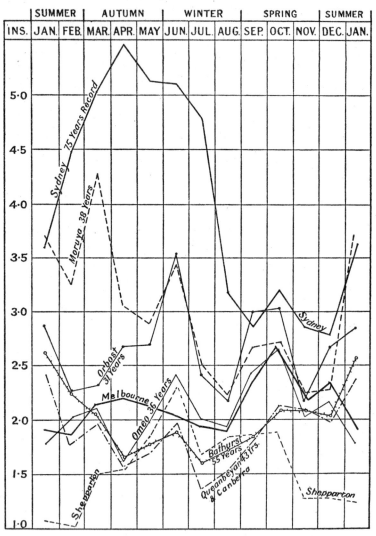

FIG. 52.—SEASONAL RAINFALL AT VARIOUS TOWNS IN OR NEAR THE
SOUTH-EAST HIGHLANDS

found along a line joining Melbourne to Dubbo (N.S.W.) by way
of Narandera.

Vegetation in the Canberra Natural Region

The eastern highlands considered in the present section are the
habitat of the chief eucalyptus forests of eastern Australia. Several
allied genera, such as *Angophora*, *Syncarpia* and *Melaleuca*, are
also abundant. The effect of the long north–south range is that it
tends to keep the western country dry by shutting off the coastal
moisture. Thus are produced the two well-known types of the
coastal and inland floras. The plateau itself, owing to its altitude,
produces a third type of vegetation, and it is the only portion of
northern New South Wales in which Tasmanian members of the
eucalypts are to be found. The moment the summit of the plateau
is reached and drier western and colder winter conditions are encountered, the jungle or brush of the coast ceases, and its place is
taken by open forest country.

The Kurrajong (*Brachychiton*), a valuable fodder tree, has penetrated far south (above the Murrumbidgee Valley) from Canberra
toward Cooma, though elsewhere it is not found in such elevated
regions. Similarly, at the 'Cassilis Gate', the flora from the western
slopes simply 'swarms' over the divide into the dry regions of the
upper Hunter Valley. It penetrates as far as Singleton, where *E.
rostrata* and *Casuarina Luehmani* reach their eastern limits.

The coastal areas of New South Wales have a rainfall varying
from 35 to 50 inches. A particular flora characterizes this region,
which is, however, also controlled to a considerable extent by the
soil conditions, for from Sydney to the west extends a belt of
sandstones. At the lower levels grevilleas, boronias and Epacris
of various species occur (Fig. 34), which are replaced by other
species higher up on the Katoomba plateau. *Eucalyptus corymbosa*
(bloodwood) extends from Sydney and up the slopes to 3,000 feet,
but not to the western sides of the plateau. *E. resinifera* and several
ironbarks are also confined to the lower regions. The turpentine
(*Syncarpia*) is a typical coastal genus flourishing from Jervis Bay
northward, chiefly on coal-measure soils. The common 'Box' (*E.
hemiphloia*) in the same region is found on shales rather than sandstones, while the *Angophora* prefers the sandstones of the lower
levels, but has crossed the divide by the Cassilis Gate to the north-
west slopes. *E. pilularis*, *E. botryoides* and *E. saligna* are also useful
coastal trees of the coastal forests.

The Hawkesbury Sandstone region of the Blue Plateau has
a peculiarly rich and beautiful flora, bright with *Boronia* and
Eriostemum, heaths and flannel-flowers, and untold multitudes of

Leguminosae, such as *Dillwynia, Pultenea, Hovea* and *Kennedya* (Fig. 53). Among shrubs the various *Proteacea* ('honeysuckle'), *Grevillea* and *Persoonia* ('geebungs') are conspicuous. Where the basalt overlies the sandstone the flora is especially rich, and in the gullies sassafras, coachwood and tree-ferns have their homes.

The mountain areas have a rainfall of about 34 inches, and are of course colder than the coastal belts, the temperature varying with the latitude. This is reflected in the vegetation. Thus the 'Snow Gum' (*E. coriacea*) grows at low level on the *coast* in Tasmania and Victoria, 'and high up on the slopes of Mount Kosciusko at 5,000 feet, where it becomes dwarfed and gnarled.

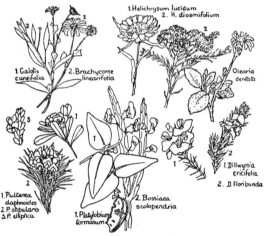

FIG. 53.—TYPICAL FLORA OF THE HAWKESBURY SANDSTONE COUNTRY
(*Drawn by D. R. Taylor, after F. Sulman*)

Behind Sydney it does not descend below 2,500 feet, and further north its lower limit is about 3,000 feet. *E. viminalis* and *E. amygdalina* are two mountain trees in New South Wales, though the latter grows on the lower slopes of the Victorian mountains. Some of the peppermints also have climatically controlled habitats. *E. dives* prefers the drier western slopes of the Blue Mountains, while *E. piperita* is commoner on the eastern side.

Near Mount Kosciusko, the tree line reaches a height of about 5,500 feet, and above this level there are morasses and boggy plains. Here appear yellow and white buttercups, fragrant swamp epacrids, forget-me-nots, the woolly daisy, woolly lily and woolly compositae. It is curious to notice how the same species alters its habits as it ascends the mountains. Below, luxuriant and smooth, above it becomes dwarfed and spreading, to support the weight of the winter snow, and covered with woolly hairs to protect it from frost in the winter and the excessive heat of the clear summer sun.

On the western slopes, with a rainfall varying from 25 to 30 inches, the 'Grey Box' (*E. albens*) is prevalent. It prefers the warmer portions of the highlands. *E. macrorrhynca* (stringy-bark) and *E. sideroxylon* are two of the more important timber trees of this belt (Fig. 124).

Homoclimes of the Canberra Region

Taking Sydney and Canberra (Queanbeyan) as representing the coastal and inland portions respectively, the following table compares them with other localities listed in Hann's *Klimatologie*:

Place	Temperature (° F.)			Rainfall (inches)		
	Average	Hottest m.	Coldest m.	Total	Wettest m.	Driest m.
Sydney	63·0	71·6	52·3	48	5·2	2·6
Queanbeyan	56·3	70·0	42·9	23	2·3	1·3
Port Elizabeth	63·0	69·4	57·0	25	2·3	1·5
Montevideo	61·3	71·8	50·7	35	4·1	1·3
Wilmington, N.C.	62·2	78·6	45·7	42	4·4	2·0
Shanghai	59·0	80·4	37·6	45	6·4	1·0

The southern homoclimes are all on the boundary between the summer and winter rainfall regions, and this is to some extent true for Carolina, as Supan's chart shows; but China is wholly in the summer rain region. I have no data to decide how far *inland* conditions in these homoclimes compare with our highland region. The inland topography is somewhat similar in Carolina and South Africa, but more rugged in China, and less so in Uruguay.

NATURAL REGION 2: NEW ENGLAND

The New England Plateau is the most extensive in Australia, though not the highest (Fig. 54). An area of about 200 miles long by 40 wide is all over or near 3,000 feet high. Three bosses between Armidale and Tenterfield (Ben Lomond, Capoompeta and Chandler's Peak) rise to 5,000 feet, while an important spur extends nearly to the east coast at Bellingen, and is called the Snowy Mountain.

The truncated coastline, with the highest land close to the ocean, is even more strikingly shown in New South Wales than in Queensland. It is only necessary to note the distance of the 500-foot contour from the Divide to the east and west respectively. From Ben Lomond to the coast at Bellingen is about 50 miles, but to Collarendabri on the west slope is 200 miles.

As is the case along almost the whole coast of Australia, the so-called mountain ranges (first seen by settlers from the coast) are usually merely the scarp-edges of uplifted peneplains. These may be relics of a former mountain range, but now are largely undulating or slightly tilted and elevated plains of erosion. Thus the

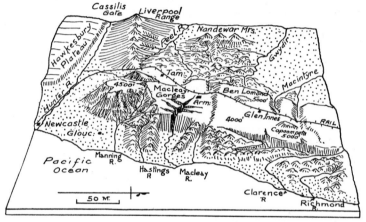

FIG. 54.—A BLOCK DIAGRAM OF THE NEW ENGLAND PLATEAU VIEWED FROM THE EAST, ALL SOMEWHAT GENERALIZED

Darling Downs in Queensland, though well marked on the east by the scarp eaten out by the Brisbane River, are ill-defined on the west, and the boundary shown on local maps (near St. George) is quite arbitrary.

Somewhat similar conditions obtain in the New England area. Along its east side are very steep slopes, which may be fault-planes. The head-waters of the Macleay and the Bellinger Rivers have eaten out stupendous gorges up to 2,500 feet deep, which head in picturesque waterfalls (Fig. 54).

It is evident that the New England Plateau must formerly have had a much greater extension than it possesses at present. The portion untrenched by canyons and ravines consists mainly of a gently warped and maturely dissected surface, above which in various localities rise other small plateaux. At the head of the

Macleay River the general plateau-surface is almost 4,000 feet in height; thence toward Armidale it possesses a very gentle dip. North of Armidale it rises very rapidly to 4,300 feet, with residuals as high as 5,300 feet on its eastern margin. The rivers descend rapidly to the coastal area by means of almost impassable gorges.[1]

Acid rocks (granite, &c.) appear to form buttresses right round New England. The long 'plateau peninsulas' of Guy Fawkes, Barrington, &c., owe their existence to the presence of huge granitoid bosses.

The conception which harmonizes most with the facts of observation appears to be that the main New England Plateau surface was developed by erosive activities near sea level, and that it has since been raised unevenly so as to form a warped and faulted surface (E. C. Andrews, *Roy. Soc. N.S. Wales*, 1912). There are three of these plateau levels: the Guyra Peneplain is at about 4,300 feet elevation, the Mole Peneplain at 4,000 feet and the Sandon and Stannifer Peneplain at 3,200 feet.

Three ancient volcanic groups are associated with New England. The Nandewar group of trachyte cones rise to a height of 4,000 feet between Armidale and Narrabri (Fig. 54). A similar group to the south-west of Narrabri is called the Warrumbungles. Its highest point is about 3,000 feet. Linking these to the main plateau is the basalt-capped highland called the Liverpool Range. For the rain graph of Armidale, see Fig. 62.

Vegetation of New England

The table on page 148 (largely due to Dalrymple-Hay) shows the geographical distribution of the chief timbers in the forest belt of northern New South Wales (Fig. 124).

In the inland belt, roughly west of the 22-inch isohyet, the trees gradually become smaller and more scattered. Westward of the ranges where the tableland sinks down to undulating country and vast plains, through which the tributaries of the Murray make their way, the vegetation changes to scrub and open forest, consisting of eucalypts, such as red gum (*E. rostrata*), along the water-courses, with several varieties of box, cypress and other pines and wattles.

Economics.—Not many studies of this region from the point of view of land utilization have been published. Readers are referred to F. R. E. Mauldon's *Study in Social Economics*, Melbourne, 1927, which deals mainly with the Hunter River Valley. The *Atlas of New South Wales* by Macdonald Holmes (1931) is useful.

[1] See the paper by F. A. Craft, *Coastal Tablelands and Streams*, Linn. Soc. N.S. Wales, 1933.

CHIEF TREES IN NEW ENGLAND

Region	Approx. rainfall	Vernacular names	Scientific names
North Coast-lands	70 to 35 in. per annum	Ironbark Tallowwood Blackbutt Sydney Bluegum Spotted Gum Red Mahogany Turpentine	*E. paniculata, sider-oxylon* *E. microcorys* *E. pilularis* *E. saligna* *E. maculata* *E. resinifera* *Syncarpia laurifoli*
New England Tableland proper	35 to 28 in. per annum	Yellow Box Manna Gum Snow Gum White Peppermint White Gum	*E. melliodora* *E. viminalis* *E. coriacea* *E. stuartiana* *E. rubida*
Western slopes of Tableland	28 to 22 in. per annum	Cypress Pine Ironbark Grey Box	*Callitris* *E. paniculata, &c.* *E. quadrangulata*

Two short papers by W. H. Maze describe the evolution of settlement in the same area. They are published in the *Australian Geographer*, Sydney, 1934. A description of the coal and steel industries near Newcastle appears later in this book. A small power station has been built on the upper Clarence River.

NATURAL REGION 3: VICTORIA

General.—The topography of Victoria may be considered in three major divisions. The *Eastern Highlands* are structurally associated with those of south-east of New South Wales. The *Northern Plains* are merely the portion of the Murray Basin which we shall consider later. In the south-east of the state is a fairly level low area which has been termed the *Great Valley* of Victoria.

The Eastern Highlands

The marked change in the direction of the main axis of the highlands near Kosciusko is of much interest (Fig. 46). Yet the Victorian highlands, like those in the south-east of New South Wales, may possibly be built up of meridional horsts of early Tertiary age, arranged parallel to each other right across Victoria. This structure is found in warps of much the same age in this latitude in New Zealand, New South Wales and South Australia.

FIG. 54A.—BLOCK DIAGRAM OF VICTORIA

showing the plateau-like Victorian Highlands, Kilmore Gate, Basalt Flows, Gippsland Faults (F.), Mallee Lands in the north-west, and the Deniliquin Horst. A cross-section from Cape Otway to Jindabyne forms the inset. (Partly after E. S. Hills.)

This theory is, however, not accepted by some geologists, since some of the scarps seem to be the edges of sheets of Devonian lava.

According to E. S. Hills, in his splendidly illustrated *Physiography of Victoria* (Melbourne, 1946), these Eastern Highlands preserve part of a Cretaceous peneplain uplifted mainly in Pleistocene times, and exhibiting a tilt downward to the west. The more resistant portions such as Mount Bogong stand out as monadnocks above the general level. Near Mansfield the plateau consists of Palaeozoic sandstones which have been eroded into table mountains and hogbacks. Further east near Buchan are widespread Silurian limestones containing many large caves. Far to the west are the Grampians and Dundas Highlands of somewhat similar character. They exhibit a somewhat plateau-like character and were probably elevated in Pliocene times (Fig. 54A with section).

The highest blocks are in the east, and Mounts Bogong (6,508 feet) and Hotham (6,100 feet) are not much lower than Kosciusko itself. The chief gap hereabouts is the 'Omeo Gate', which separates the Victorian portion of the Kosciusko massif (with the Cobboras (6,000 feet) and Mount Gibbo) from the Bogong Plateau. Lake Omeo is on a line of crustal weakness, and the head-waters of the Tambo River appear largely to have been captured by the Upper Mitta River.

The Dargo High Plains are about 4,500 feet elevation, and lie to the south of Mount Bogong. Mount Buffalo (5,645 feet) extends to the north, rising fairly abruptly above the Murray plains. Similar relics of a once continuous peneplain occur as the 'Nunyong Tableland' (4,500 feet) east of Omeo, and the Snowy Plains and Barry Mountains (5,000 feet) about 30 miles south of Mount Buffalo. The edges of this elevated peneplain have been deeply notched by the rivers to the north and south. The Goulburn has cut a deep wide valley, and has had a varied history involving several captures. Westward the highlands are somewhat lower, but Mount Howitt and Mount Wellington are about 5,000 feet. Further west again the divide becomes more ridgelike, and rapidly drops from Mount Torbreck (4,995 feet) to the 'Kilmore Gate', where it is only about 1,000 feet above sea level.

The elevated portion of the state to the west of this Gate also consists of a peneplain, in general sloping from Mount Macedon (3,324 feet) to the south-west. The level is about 2,000 feet at Ballarat, 1,000 feet at Ararat and 600 feet at Hamilton. Fault scarps, similar in origin and direction to those described near Kosciusko, seem to define the Pyrenees (3,240 feet) and Grampians (3,827 feet). These latter may also be horsts above the general level of the elevated peneplain.

The Great Victorian Valley

The whole of the Western Plains south of the Divide (in the west) has been flooded by basalt lavas. This region between Ballarat and the Otway Ranges (of Jurassic strata some 1,900 feet high) is part of the Great Victorian Valley.[1] It is about 500 feet above sea level. Small volcanic cones are common throughout, such as Mount Elephant (1,294 feet), Mount Noorat and Tower Hill. Lakes are scattered over this basalt plain, occupying depressions in the fairly lately formed surface. Port Phillip would appear to be a sunken portion of the Great Valley, which, structurally, extends to the east as the Gippsland Plains. Here the Strzelecki Ranges are of the same type and age as the Otway Ranges. On Wilson's Promontory are isolated granite hills reaching 2,434 feet (Fig. 122).

The Melbourne District

The site of the second city in Australia, with a population of 1 million, is of considerable interest, since half of the people of Victoria live in this small area. Its main features are shown in the

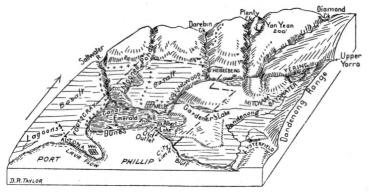

FIG. 55.—BLOCK DIAGRAM OF THE DISTRICT AROUND MELBOURNE
The broken line shows the limits of the city. Crosses show the edge of the flow of Tertiary basalt. The diagram is 15 miles wide

block diagram given in Fig. 55. In the north-east are the spurs of the highlands, mainly built up of older Palaeozoic slates, &c. The Dandenong Ranges, which bound the coastal plain on the east, are, however, built up of eruptive rocks of Devonian age. In the west the plain has been flooded by large areas of Pliocene basalt,

[1] See Front Endpaper for a map of this region. An atlas of topographic and economic maps of Victoria is included in the *Report on Regional Boundaries*, Melbourne, 1945.

which have formed a tongue of lava at Altona. Port Phillip, some 30 miles across, is a drowned portion of the coastal plain which seems to have sunk (as a graben) between two north–south faults, through Bacchus Marsh in the west and Arthur's Seat in the east.

The River Yarra is the main stream, and flows into the Melbourne area from the east. Within 20 miles of the city this stream occupies a diversified valley, which in places spreads out into flat silted basins; but it is constricted into a narrow gorge, both above and below Heidelberg. These gorges indicate that the river has cut through rising spurs of the adjacent highlands. At Collingwood the river runs along the eastern edge of the lava flow, and in process of time has filled the little bay at the head of Port Phillip with silt. Probably the river originally reached the sea *via* Albert Lake, shown in the sketch.

The first houses were built in 1835 on the north side of the Yarra just alongside some low falls, which also marked the head of tide water. Elizabeth Street was the bed of a little stream, and the Customs House was placed where Queen Street reaches the Yarra. In 1838 there were about 100 houses, almost all in the rectangle bounded by Collins, King and Elizabeth Streets. The original site is shown on the sketch. Today the city extends over almost all the area between Altona and Heidelberg.

Western Victoria

As regards the country to the west of Mount Macedon, Hart has described the whole western uplands as consisting of an early Tertiary peneplain, which has been subjected to unequal block-faulting. Thus the summit of the Pyrenees shows the same peneplain as at Ballarat, but it has been elevated 1,000 feet higher. Again the Grampians and Serra ranges are tilt-blocks, sloping to the west, with meridional creeks (such as Stony Creek and Fyan's Creek) occupying the notches between the blocks. Some geologists, however, think these ridges are due to erosion of a wide syncline folded in Upper Palaeozoic times. The hard beds stand out as the Grampians, &c.

Apart from these ridges the country does not show very striking relief, partly, no doubt, owing to the lava flows which flooded many of the Tertiary Valleys. Just as a region of recent glaciation exhibits an irregularly moulded surface without systematic drainage which soon becomes dotted with lakes and marshes, so also the enormous lava flows of Western Victoria have given rise to numerous irregular lakes. Lake Corangamite is 20 miles long, and several others are of large size. There are also smaller lakes (more closely associated with the volcanic vents), which represent areas which have subsided consequent on the extrusion of the lava.

In the north-west the dwindling rivers and shallow salty lakes are a consequence of old age, coupled with increasing aridity. The Wimmera River appears to have cut off the head-waters of the Avon and Yarriambiack, and so flows further from the hills before losing itself in the plains. Lakes Hindmarsh and Tyrrell (see map on p. 149) may be due to the removal by solution of underlying sheets of salt, as Gregory suggests. But I am inclined to attribute them to the same action as formed Lake Cowal in New South Wales. The enormous silt deposition of the Murray in earlier stages of its career has blocked the feeble waters of the tributaries. Although the Murray has now cut down below its flood plain, owing to slight elevation, the tributaries have been too feeble to be affected by this stimulus (Fig. 54A).

Vegetation of the Victorian Region

The control of vegetation by rainfall and temperature is of course as definite here as elsewhere. As a result of the mild moist winters the trees are evergreen. On the highest level is an Alpine flora, with, however, only a few exclusive species, such as *Drosera archeri*. Most Alpine plants (i.e. *Arabis perfoliata*, *Billardiera scandens*, &c.) have been but little modified, which indicates that the glacial epoch was shorter and less severe here than in Europe. (*Fide* C. S. Sutton.)

Several subtropical species, such as *Hakea dactyloides* and *Livistona australis*, extend into the state from Queensland along the coastal valleys. Here they find the same moist equable condition as in the north, even though the average temperature is somewhat lower. As in the rest of Australia, the dominant features of the vegetation are developed as protection against periodic drought and intense sunlight. Thus originate the vertical leathery leaves, which reduce transpiration, while the fleshy leaves of the saltbushes and phyllode leaves of the acacias have developed for similar reasons. To resist drought and bush-fires the seeds of the acacias are cuticularized, so that they can lie dormant in the ground for many years. To resist the sand-drift and winds in the north the mallee grows in dense scrubs, and a similar environment has led to the thick tea-tree bush (*Leptospermum*) along the coast.

In eastern Victoria the stringybark (*E. obliqua*) and messmate (*E. amygdalina*) cover almost the whole of the highlands where the rainfall varies from 30 to 60 inches, the former being the dominant species. As in New South Wales, *E. macrorrhynca* and *E. sideroxylon* are also found largely on the dry inland slopes.

In Gippsland, *E. piperita*, *E. longifolia*, *E. botryoides*, *E. corymbosa* and *E. pilularis* are common in the eastern wetter portions. with a rainfall of about 35 inches. Of the remaining three-quarters the following are the main divisions as given by C. S. Sutton:

(*a*) The thickly timbered eastern highlands, with a rainfall of 30–60 inches.

(*b*1) The 'Brushes' in the valleys of the west Gippsland and Cape Otway, &c., with a rainfall of 40 inches.

(*b*2) The 'Maqui' to the north-east of Port Phillip (25 inches).

(*c*) The open western plains (25 to 30 inches).

(*d*) The moderately timbered western uplands and northern slopes (20 to 30 inches).

(*e*) The 'Mallee' country (10 to 20 inches).

Section (*a*).—The central mountain area is clothed with thick forests, consisting largely of stringybark (*E. macrorrhynca*) and messmate (*E. obliqua*), while grey box (*E. hemiphloia*), yellow box (*E. melliodora*) and ironbark are also common. The northern slopes in Delatite and the adjoining Alpine country grow blue gum (*E. globulus*), messmate and peppermint (*E. amygdalina*) of good quality. On the higher levels are ribbon gum, woolly-butt (*E. longifolia*) and silvertop (*E. sieberiana*).

Section (*b*1).—In the Otway brushes are found blue gum, spotted gum (*E. goniocalyx*), messmate and mountain ash (*E. regnans*), with some stringybark and white gum. Here are also forest trees of other genera, such as blackwood (*Acacia melanoxylon*), beech (*Fagus cunninghami*), sycamore and cedar. Similar trees occur in the sheltered well-watered valleys of the Yarra, as well as in the characteristic tree-fern gullies.

In these fern gullies the giant eucalypts are surrounded by a thick undergrowth of smaller trees, shrubs and ferns, which is lacking in the more typical eucalypt forests of the drier country. Shaded and protected by the gums are tree-ferns such as the tall *Dicksonia* and in more open spaces *Alsophila australis*. Smaller fern genera, such as *Aspidium*, *Doodia*, *Adiantum* and *Todea*, occur near the creeks. Thickets of dogwood (*Prostanthera*), native hazel (*Pomaderris*) and cotton-wood (*Senecio*) are linked by festoons of *Clematis*. Among the smaller trees are the native cherry (*Exocarpus*), native holly (*Lomatia*), native currant (*Coprosma*) and snow bush (*Olearia*). (*Fide* Guilfoyle.)

Section (*b*2).—An interesting edaphic formation associated with the Tertiary 'red beds' is that occurring to the north-east of Port Phillip. Sutton describes it as closely allied to the South African 'Maqui'. Its development is due to the wet winters and dry summers, where the substratum is a sandy soil, liable to become parched in the dry season. This 'Sandringham flora' consists of a dominant xerophytic vegetation of dull greyish evergreen woody plants, close-set, of an average height of little more than a metre. It contains a rich admixture of species, the frequent occurrence of several epacrids being a marked feature. *Leptospermum laeviatum* forms dense thickets along the coast, associated with *Banksia*, *Casuarina quadrivalvis*, *Exocarpus* and *Eucalyptus viminalis*. In the more open maqui are *Casuarina distyla*, *Leptospermum myrsinoides*, various correas, dillwynias, styphelias and melaleucas.

Section (c).—The south-west of the state is poorly timbered. Stringybark is the prevailing tree, with red gum (*E. rostrata*) along the streams. White gum, box, lightwood and 'honeysuckle' are to be met with on the plains.

Section (d).—Along the Divide and its northern slopes there is a tendency for the trees to occur in belts, controlled by the rainfall, aspect and soil. Thus the main belt of red gum follows the Murray, and sends tongues up the tributary valleys. Sand ridges in this region grow greybox and 'cypress-pine' (*Callitris*). To the south of the Murray (and in the next belt) the prevailing trees are grey and yellow box, red and white gum, and the ubiquitous stringybark.

The foothills from Albury to Dunolly form the habitat of the red and white ironbark (*E. sideroxylon* and *paniculata*). In the Grampians the trees are only of second-rate quality; stringybark, white gum, white and yellow box occur. The growth improves in the Pyrenees, where blue gum and messmate are also abundant. Between Ballarat and Mount Macedon there are fine Government forests of young messmate, associated with peppermint and swamp gum (*E. paludosa*).

Section (e).—In the north-west of the state is the mallee scrub. Here dwarf varieties of eucalyptus (such as *E. dumosa*) form thick clumps, reaching to a uniform height, which varies from 8 to 20 feet, according to species and district. Belts of cypress-pine occur at intervals, and some red gum and box fringe the lakes and streams; but otherwise the dwarf mallee is almost universal.

Distribution of Rainfall

Although the isohyets in general run parallel to the coastline, there is no region in Australia which shows a greater control by topography, or which exhibits such examples of rain shadows and local regions of high rainfall. (See map on endpaper.) The highest rainfall (77 inches) is at Weeaproinah, near Cape Otway. Woods Point and Black Spur to the east of Melbourne have 59 inches. The rainfall decreases toward the north-west, the lowest precipitation being recorded in the Mildura region. An interesting dry tongue reaches up the Murray toward Swan Hill, where Mildura, Nyah and Tyrrell West receive about 11 inches a year.

The most noteworthy feature about the rain-distribution is the south-east prolongation of the 25-inch isohyet. This extends through the Kilmore Gate just east of Mount William as far as Geelong, and thence east almost to Kilmore. Just north of Geelong the rainfall falls as low as 19 inches. This locally dry region is related to the direction of the rain-bearing winds, which in this part of Victoria usually come from the north-west. The Geelong–Ararat belt is obviously shielded from the north-west rains by the Grampians, Pyrenees and Daylesford Hills. There is a sheltered dry area in Gippsland where the rainfall is as low as 25 inches at Sale (see endpaper).

Antarctic disturbances are much the most frequent rainbringers in Victoria, and their troughs are almost invariably preceded over Victoria by northerly winds, followed by squally winds from points between north-west and south-west. Hence the rains brought by these storms usually fall on land sloping toward these points, and only lightly on those with eastern and south-eastern aspects. That the rainfall over the southern half of the state is better than over the northern is not due, however, to the greater raininess of westerly and south-westerly winds, but to the fact that the rains in front of a tropical storm falling from clouds of greater elevation are less affected by irregularities of land height. Provided that the intercepting highlands have elevations not much over 1,000 to 2,000 feet, the rains fall almost as freely over southern slopes as over northern. South-westerly and southerly winds, on the other hand, rarely carry rain much beyond the crest of the main Divide (E. T. Quayle, 1911).

Correlation with Other Regions

There are four regions which resemble Victoria in rainfall, climate and production. These are (1) Cape Town region, (2) Valparaiso region, (3) San Francisco region, (4) Mediterranean region. (That portion of Western Australia which has been distinguished as 'Swanland' is also a homoclime, while Tasmania is very closely allied.)

In the following table Melbourne (which is too uniform to be typical) and Hamilton are quoted as representing the Victorian province; the other towns are based on Hann and Henry.

The South African homoclimes are discussed in connexion with the Swanland region (*vide* p. 198).

In my *Meteorological Bulletin on Climate and Comfort* (No. 14)

HOMOCLIMES OF VICTORIA

Place	Monthly Rainfall (inches)			Monthly Temperature (° F.)		
	Wettest	Driest	Annual	Hottest	Coldest	Annual
Melbourne	2·6 (Oct.)	1·7 (Feb.)	25·5	67·5	48·4	58·3
Hamilton	3·3 (June)	0·9 (Feb.)	26·9	66·4	46·0	55·8
San Francisco	4·5 (Jan.)	0·1 (July)	22·5	59·0	50·1	56·0
Portland	7·4 (Dec.)	0·6 (July)	45·0	67·0	39·0	53·0
Valparaiso	7·0 (July)	0·0 (Feb.)	24·0	63·5	52·7	57·7
Oporto (Portugal)	6·0 (Nov.)	1·0 (July)	48·0	67·3	47·5	57·4

it is shown that this region (represented by Melbourne) very closely agrees with the 'typical city of Anglo-Saxon settlement' (see Fig. 26). Only February is classed in the tentative 'Scale of Discomfort' as 'sometimes uncomfortable', i.e. it has an average wet-bulb exceeding 60° F. (60·3) throughout the month. Although the dry-bulb temperature increases considerably inland, this is not the case with the wet-bulb figures, so that there is no diminution of health in the warmer inland districts.

The products of this region are those of Mediterranean countries in general. Wool, meat, hides, wheat, fruit and wine are almost universally exported from the homoclimes. In Victoria, oats, barley, potatoes, hay, maize are also largely grown, while dried fruits such as raisins, from Mildura, are important products. Sawmills in the timbered southern and eastern regions, butter and cheese factories in the western and central districts give employment to many hands.

NATURAL REGION 4: TASMANIA

General.—This state, like the adjacent region on the mainland, consists essentially of lower Palaeozoic sediments buttressed by granite.[1] But over a large portion of the centre and east a basin in the Palaeozoic rocks has been filled with coal measures (and allied deposits), and these again have been overwhelmed with basic eruptive rocks. (See front edge of diagram, Fig. 57A.)

The Central Plateau.—The dominant feature is the central plateau, which falls from a general level of 3,500 feet in the north-west toward the south-east, being drained by the Derwent system

[1] A good general account of the island is given by G. L. Wood in *The Tasmanian Environment*, Adelaide, 1923. See also the excellent *Atlas of Tasmania*, published officially, Hobart, 1946.

(Fig. 56). This plateau seems to be a horst, the lowlands to the north and east having been relatively depressed by step-faulting, which has left bold scarps (locally called 'Tiers').

Along the western edge, the plateau rises to considerable heights in Cradle Mountain (5,069), Eldon (4,789) and Frenchman's Cap; while the southern wall of the Derwent Basin is crowned by Mount Field West (4,725) and Mount Wellington (4,166). The northern rim is also high (Ironstone, 4,736); but the east of the plateau is much lower and connects at Oatlands (1,350) with the east coast uplands.

North-East and South-West Highlands.—Two somewhat isolated highlands lie in the north-east and south-west respectively. The

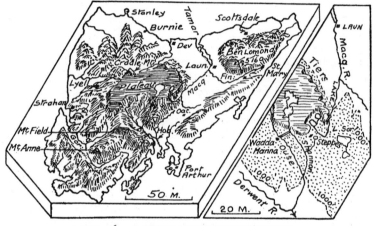

FIG. 56.—A BLOCK DIAGRAM OF TASMANIA

K., F., D. are King, Franklin and Denison gorges. At the right is a map of the region near the chief Hydro-electric station at Waddamanna. (See Fig. 128A)

highest point in the State is Legge's Peak (5,160) on the rectangular plateau of Ben Lomond. This is bounded on the west by the lowland drained by the Tamar and its tributaries. In the south-west of the island, the Gordon River flows parallel to the Tamar and Derwent. These river directions probably indicate the prevalence of 'lineaments' (ancient faults) across the plateaux forming Tasmania. The Wilmot and Arthur Highlands in the south-west are probably outlying portions of the same uplifted peneplain. Their summits are about 3,500 feet above the sea.

Evidence of Late Elevation.—The deep gorges of the western rivers (e.g. King, Franklin and Denison), the large lakes on the central plateau (e.g. Great Lake, Arthur and Sorell) and the truncated east coast (as at St. Mary's, where the South Esk rises on the coastal rim) are all features pointing to the comparatively late development of the present topography of Tasmania. Moraines and other relics of the glacial age have been described as occurring on Cradle Mountain, Mount Field, Mount Anne and other peaks.

The north-west highlands of Tasmania exhibit better than any other portion of the Commonwealth evidence of the change in climate since the Great Ice Age. The hills of the West Coast Range, of the Eldon Range and Mount Ida were covered with glaciers which discharged westward into the valley of the King River, the Macintosh River and the Henty. The lowest moraines occur at a height of about 400 feet above sea level.

Around Cradle Mountain (5,069) only the three main peaks

FIG. 57.—MOUNT ANNE, 45 MILES WEST OF HOBART
(See Fig. 56.) A typical 'Karling' in Tasmania about 8 miles across
(*From a map by A. N. Lewis*)

emerged above the ice sheet. East of Cradle Mountain Lake Rodway is the grandest example of a cirque. To the north Dove Lake seems to have been enlarged by glacial erosion, while Crater Lake has a cirque wall over 500 feet high. The moraines from the two latter glaciers cover an area 2 miles wide, and reach down to the 2,900-foot level.

The evidences of an ice age are much better shown in Tasmania than on the mainland. For instance, Mount Anne is 3,000 feet lower than Mount Kosciusko, yet there are few better examples of a rounded mountain 'scalloped' by cirque erosion (Fig. 57). This peak reminds one very much of Snowdon in Wales, and like the latter is a 'Karling', i.e. a cluster of cirques in which the process of nivation has nibbled away a large part of the original mountain. About 20 miles to the north is the plateau of Mount Field (Fig. 56), whose cirques and moraines have been described by the writer. Cradle Mountain shows less striking examples, while Kosciusko (as we have seen) has only many score of imperfect cirques and half a dozen small moraines to demonstrate that the Ice Age affected Australia. It is stated that *permanent* snow lies in the little upper cirque (Fig. 57) on the south slope of Mount Anne. If so, this is the sole area in Australia approaching the permanent snowline.[1]

Drainage.—There are two outstanding features in Tasmanian hydrography. The general relief is dominated by three great parallel valleys, and the plateau is studded with numerous lakes.

The three main valleys, which exhibit the 'grain' of the surface, are shown in Fig. 56.

(1) The Tamar–Macquarie lineament.

(2) The Lake St. Clair–Derwent lineament.

(3) The Macquarie Harbour–Gordon–Huon lineament.

All of these run parallel to the south-west coast and to the Great Western Mountains. Both of the latter are probably of fault origin, so that we may postulate extensive step- or block-faulting to account for the other features. Similar parallel faults are general on the mainland adjoining, as already described, but there the trend is north and south instead of being north-west to south-east.

The east coast would appear to be of still more recent formation, since the South Esk rises at St. Mary's, right on the coast at about 2,000 feet. In spite of the heavy rainfall and characteristic floods, the coastal creeks have not yet penetrated the South Esk basin.

The eastern edge of the plateau had been notched by coastal streams and the drainage diverted. Thus Arthur's Lake undoubtedly belongs to the Derwent Basin, but is now connected to Lake River and the Tamar. Not long ago a river bifurcation was in operation near by at Steppes, which should still be traceable.

The peculiar physiography of the Rivers Ouse and Shannon has led directly to the development of the first large hydro-electric plant in Australia. The Ouse rises in Ironstone Mountain and flows just to the west of Great Lake, gradually cutting its way into the plateau until a deep valley is formed. The Great Lake has an area of 42 square miles and is drained by the Shannon, a tributary of the Ouse. There is a difference in level of some 1,250 feet between the Shannon and the parallel course of the Ouse, which is only 3½ miles away. The hydro-electric company has built a dam which

---

[1] J. Gregory, *Q.J. Geol. Soc.*, London, 1904; N. Benson, Roy. Soc., Tasmania, 1916; G. Taylor, *Model of Mount Field*, Roy. Soc. Tas., 1922; A. Lewis, *Geology of Mount Anne*, Roy. Soc. Tas., 1923; G. Taylor, *Glaciation in the South-West Pacific*, Pan-Pacific Congress, Tokyo, 1926; *Legacy of Ice-cap*, Jennings *et. al.*, Aus. Geog. 1957.

increases the lake to 50 square miles. The water flows down the Shannon for 5 miles, and then enters a canal which leads it across the divide to the penstock. It then flows down the pipe-line to the power station at Waddamanna on the Ouse, where it generated about 70,000 horse-power in 1924. A transmission line carries the power for 63 miles to Hobart (Fig. 56). A block diagram appears on page 409.

The Great Lake is extraordinarily shallow. Although it is 15 miles long, the deepest point was originally only 20 feet below the surface. Similar features characterize most of the other lakes except Lake St. Clair, which may be in part due to glacial erosion.

These conditions of the rapid elevation of a region of heavy rainfall, combined with extensive faulting, have led to the wonderful King River Gorge, near Queenstown, which is described as being 3,000 feet deep where it cuts through the West Coast Range. A notable development of the use of hydro-electric power (*blanche houille*, as the French term it) may be expected, and should greatly enhance Tasmania's prosperity in the future. It was stated at the World Power Conference in 1924 that 700,000 B.H.P. was available in Tasmania. (See p. 408.)

Horsts and Graben near Launceston

The north centre of Tasmania is dominated by the rivers draining into the Tamar. The divide bordering the Derwent Basin is near Oatlands, at about 1,700 feet. Here, as at Hamilton, is a little town of less than 1,000 people characterized by the ancient houses built of cut stone. The scenery is mature, the surface rocks being mostly Jurassic dolerites, with inliers of Ordovician sediments. At Campbelltown we reach recent deposits, which fill the ancient lake bed between the horsts of the Central Plateau and that of Ben Lomond in the north-east part of the island (Fig. 57A). The writer has traversed this portion of the island many times, but only recently has the topography been adequately worked out. The major conclusions of Professor S. W. Carey are summarized in the accompanying diagram from his recent study (Queen Victoria Museum, Launceston, July 1947).

At the close of Palaeozoic times an extensive peneplain, consisting of Permian sediments in the west and older rocks in the east, determined the landscape. This was later intruded by wide expanses of Jurassic dolerite, in some cases 1,000 feet thick. Very extensive faulting occurred in Miocene times, which broke the region into a series of horst and graben. These still dominate the topography of the island, since they produced the major plateaux of the island (Fig. 57A).

The two lowest graben were occupied by elongated lakes, which were separated by a rather low horst, called by Carey the 'Hummocky Horst' (Fig. 57A). In Pliocene times extensive flows of basalt covered a good deal of the region, and some of these diverted the South Esk river from its direct path down the eastern graben, so that it flowed into the Macquarie. Throughout late Tertiary time erosion has been washing away the silts laid down in these graben. The Tamar Estuary now reaches far back in the eastern graben, and has captured the lower northern portion of the drainage of the western (Macquarie) graben.

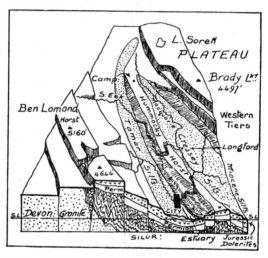

FIG. 57A.—BLOCK DIAGRAM OF NORTH CENTRAL TASMANIA
ABOUT 50 MILES WIDE (LOOKING SOUTH)

showing the horsts which build the Ben Lomond and Western plateaux.
Launceston City is black. (*Based on S. W. Carey*)

The topography of today is much like that sketched in Fig. 57A. Here we are looking south toward the Central Plateau, which consists of an elevated horst capped with Jurassic dolerites. The scarp is some 2,000 feet high, and is known locally as the 'Western Tiers'. However, the highest point of the island is found on the smaller plateau of Ben Lomond, where Legges' Peak rises to 5,160 feet. There is today little remaining of the 'Hummocky Horst', which only rises to 1,000 feet to the north-west of Launceston. The front section of Fig. 57A is of interest, since we find the same horst structure across the Bass Straits near the summit of Kosciusko, as well as in the Flinders Range behind Adelaide. It is also marked in the south of Victoria, as the later section dealing with the Morwell coal-field will demonstrate. The writer has always believed that a horst structure of this type marks the Victorian Highlands between Mount Bogong and the Grampians, but this view is not accepted by some Victorian geologists.

Natural Vegetation in Tasmania

The control of vegetation by rainfall is more marked in Tasmania than in any other state. The greater portion is a eucalypt forest, differing little from what we have seen covering south-eastern Australia. But of the west of Tasmania, Geoffrey Smith [1] (to whom I owe much of the following account) writes:

The xerophytic gums are almost everywhere replaced by the ever-green myrtles or beeches, and the undergrowth attains a rankness and density which have to be seen to be believed. If it were not for occasional patches of gum forest, with its undergrowth of wattle, honeysuckle and tea-tree, it would be difficult to believe that one were in Australia at all. There is an entire change of vegetation and scenery, so that one seems to pass right into, shall we say, Tierra del Fuego, or a lost Antarctic continent.

The distribution of the two floras, the eucalypt and the beeches (miscalled 'myrtles'), is shown in Fig. 125. Their control by the rainfall is quite striking. Even the small region in the north-east, which receives more than 50 inches per annum, has the same beech vegetation as the country on the other side of the great central plateau.

Owing to the relatively heavy rainfall in Tasmania eucalypts in general are bigger trees than in the mainland states, though not quite equal to the similarly favoured Gippsland forests. The table shown on page 164 is derived from data given by Johnstone (1892) and shows the dominant species and their range·and habit. There are four or five different types of vegetation in Tasmania, which are variations of the major divisions mentioned above. Thus the typical open eucalypt forest of the south and east becomes much more luxuriant in some of the deep valleys. The flat tops of these mountains have a flora differing from the true Alpine flora of the north-west. The open plains of the west differ again from the myrtle or beech forests in the vicinity.

The thick bush south of Mount Wellington contains huge eucalypts over 200 feet high. The undergrowth consists of a native laurel (a *Saxifrage*), acacias, sassafras (*Atherosperma*) and some beech (*Fagus*). In damp places is the tree fern (*Dicksonia*), while ti-tree is common.

On the higher portion of Mount Wellington the gums are

[1] *A Naturalist in Tasmania*, London, 1910.

TASMANIAN TREES AND RAINFALL

Species	Vernacular	Habitat	Remarks
A. Moderately Dry, 20–30 Inches			
E. amygdalina	Peppermint or Swamp Gum	Wide range up to 4,000 feet	Giant trees
E. obliqua	Stringybark	On ranges, but not Alpine	
E. viminalis	White or Manna Gum	General in east half	Biggest in deep gullies
E. Sieberiana	—	Chiefly east coast	Granite and sandy soils
E. gunnii	Cider Gum	Alpine	—
E. pauciflora	Weeping Gum	—	Dwarfed at snow line
B. Moderately Wet, 25–50 Inches			
E. globulus	Blue gum	Chiefly south	Up to 330 feet high
E. muelleri	—	South	Good forests between Huon and Derwent
Acacia melanoxylon	Blackwood	General	Largest on north-west coast
E. dealbata	Silver Wattle	—	—
C. Very Wet, over 50 Inches			
Fagus cunninghami	Myrtle or Beech	Western, 1,500–2,500 feet	Grows 200 feet high, scrubby at high levels
Dacrydium franklini	Huon Pine	SW. rivers	Best Softwood
Athrotaxis	King William Pine	West coast and valleys	Valuable timber
Phyllocladus	Celery Top Pine	Mountains of south and west	—

dwarfed, and the underscrub assumes a sub-Alpine character. Here are *Senecio* and *Bedfordia*, small trees allied to common weeds in Europe. The peculiar grass-tree *Richea* forms thick prickly masses. Many heaths, such as *Epacris*, and also *Telopea* and dwarfed *Hakea*, occur in these highlands. The native artichoke (*Astela alpina*) and cushion-plants (*Abrotanella*) are typically Alpine.

In the west the beech (*Fagus cunninghami*) is the main constituent. The forest consists of tall spars up to 150 feet high. The Celery-top pine is really a yew, and grows to 60 feet. Peculiar to Tasmania are the King William pines, of which there are three

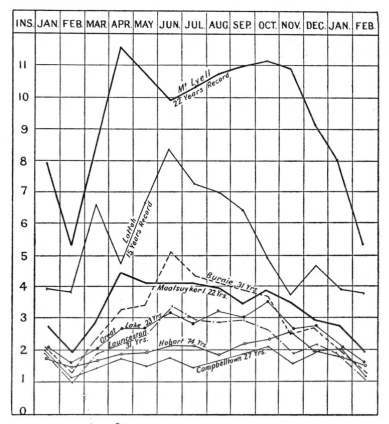

FIG. 58.—SEASONAL RAINFALL IN TASMANIA

species. The leatherwood tree is a saxifrage, and is covered with white blossom. Of peculiar interest is the 'horizontal scrub' (*Anodopetalum*) which is also a saxifrage. It builds up a tangled mass of stems and branches, forming a platform 30 to 40 feet above the ground, so closely woven that it is impenetrable, and the traveller walks over the top of it.

The rugged exposed tops of the western mountains (e.g. Mount Read), at an elevation of 4,000 feet, support a characteristic scrub, quite unlike those in the centre and south. The chief type is a small beech (*Fagus gunnii*), which is almost the sole deciduous tree in Australia. There are also two coniferous shrubs, *Pherosphaera*, allied to the yews, and *Fitzroya*, known in Tasmania and South America.

Distribution of Rainfall.—In Tasmania the control of the rainfall by the topography is very striking. The heaviest rainfall is at Mount Lyell, on the western mountains, which receives 116·7 inches a year. The lightest is inland near Ross (in the sheltered valley of the Upper Macquarie River), which receives about 18 inches a year (Fig. 58).

Season of Rain.—Tasmania belongs to the winter-rain region, but in the Hobart District the rain is almost uniform. Conditions vary somewhat, even in such a small state, as the following table shows:

REGIONAL RAINS IN TASMANIA

District	Type	Wettest month	Driest month
1. Hobart	Uniform (spring)	November	February
2. Inland	Spring (uniform)	October	—
3. West	Autumn and spring	April (October)	—
4. North-east	Winter	June (March)	—

The same features are shown in the graphs of Fig. 58. The minimum in February is common to all the graphs, but the maxima vary considerably. The special western rains occur in April and October, and the most characteristic north-eastern rains in March.

The graph (Fig. 58) shows eight localities: Burnie and Launceston on the north coast, Mount Lyell and Maatsuyker on the west coast, Great Lake and Campbelltown inland, Lottah in the north-east highland, and Hobart.

Correlation with Other Regions.—Tasmania lies on the boundary of the winter-rains region and that of 'rain at all seasons'. In this respect it agrees with New Zealand, Southern Chile, British Columbia, France, Britain and North Japan. The mean temperature of all these places is about 50·0° F.; but the low mean annual range (from 10·0 to 20·0) is only found in Tasmania, New Zealand, Chile, western Britain and western France. In Japan (50·0) and British Columbia (40·0) it is much higher.

Typical figures for these homoclimes are as shown opposite.

Character of Rainfall.—Tasmania lies south of latitude 40° S., hence it is affected by conditions differing from those controlling the other states. As a consequence the direct tropical influence is very small, though the indirect control is considerable in summer. The position of the island in the path of the 'Brave West Winds' accounts for the great number of rains throughout the year.

TASMANIAN HOMOCLIMES

Locality	Rainfall (inches)			Temperature (° F.)		
	Wettest month	Driest month	Ann.	Hottest month	Coldest month	Ann.
Launceston (Tas.)	3·4 (June)	1·1 (Feb.)	28·1	64·5 (Feb.)	44·1 (July)	54·8
Zeehan (Tas.)	9·9 (Aug.)	4·0 (Feb.)	97·9	59·9 (Feb.)	44·2 (July)	51·5
Wellington (N.Z.)	6·0 (July)	3·0 (Mar.)	50·0	62·4 (Jan.)	47·5 (July)	52·2
Ancud (S. Chile)	12·0 (May)	4·0 (Jan.)	84·0	57·4 (Jan.)	45·7 (July)	51·3
Falmouth (SW. Eng.)	6·6 (Dec.)	1·7 (May)	41·3	62·7 (July)	42·2 (Jan.)	52·4
Nantes (W. France)	4·5 (Oct.)	2·7 (Mar.)	26·0	65·7 (July)	40·1 (Jan.)	52·1

The storms are nearly all associated with Antarctic Lows. These often develop as an intensification of the isobars of low pressure to the south of the high-pressure belt. Then the high pressure may be broken through, and a trough connexion is made with the low pressures in the north of Australia. Of other types, purely tropical isobars rarely reach Tasmania, though a few such troughs and tongues may occur. 'Tongue-tip' cyclones developing from tongues and Lows off Cape Howe (SE. cyclones), occasionally give heavy rains to Tasmania, especially in the north of the island. Anticyclonic rains are not uncommon, since winds in almost any direction bring rains to an elevated island like Tasmania.

NATURAL REGION 5: THE FLINDERS REGION [1]

The state of South Australia has a rather diversified topography which can best be considered in some half a dozen separate regions. In the north-west is the south-eastern extension of the Great Peneplain. It is dominated by the residuals forming the Musgrave Ranges. To the south-west is the greater part of the Nullarbor Plains which extend into Western Australia. The eastern portion of the state has been much less stable, and the major topographic features are due to the very late buckling which has produced the Flinders Range, and also the chain of lakes surrounding this range on the north (see Endpaper map).

[1] See C. M. Hambridge on *Land Utilization*, R.G.S., Adelaide, 1945–6.

The southern part of the state is marked by the development of three peninsulas and three gulfs which constitute a type of coastline not found in any other part of Australia. The series runs as follows: Eyre's Peninsula (buttressed by the Gawler Ranges), Spencer's Gulf, Yorke Peninsula, St. Vincent Gulf, Fleurieu Peninsula (ending in Cape Jarvis, but structurally prolonged into Kangaroo Island) and the Murray Outlet gulf. The latter has largely been silted up by the immense deposits of alluvials brought down by the Murray. (See map, p. 201.)

In various papers, Howchin has discussed the elevation of the topography of South Australia. He shows from the geological

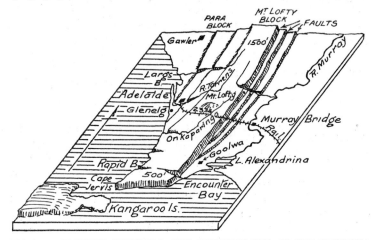

FIG. 59.—FLEURIEU PENINSULA, THE SOUTHERN END OF THE FLINDERS HORST, NEAR ADELAIDE

The map is about 130 miles wide. (*Partly after W. N. Benson*)

evidence that the Mount Lofty Range did not exist until Pliocene times, when a great continental uplift occurred (Fig. 10). The main divide in South Australia was probably much further north than it is today, and the coast extended much further south. Great north–south valleys developed, possibly leading the drainage of the Macdonnells and Musgraves to the south. These perhaps played a part in producing the large gulfs already noted.

Relics of this stage of erosion are found through the ranges in the form of flat-topped hills now about 1,500 feet high, from which rise residuals such as Mount Lofty (2,334 feet). This plateau-like area later broke into crustal blocks in the south (Fig. 59), while apparently a vast downward buckle occurred in the northern portion of the area. As a result we find a series of ranges running north and south, flanked by graben or fault-valleys now largely occupied by the sea. Mount Gambier is a small extinct volcano.

If we examine the chain of lakes which extends from the head of Spencer Gulf right round to Lake Frome, it is seen that very little depression would extend the Gulf nearly to Broken Hill (see endpaper map). From the head of the Gulf a chain of swamps and lagoons, rising only about 100 feet in 40 miles, leads to the vast salty expanse of Lake Torrens. This is 150 miles long and is separated from the Lake Eyre depression by a ridge only 175 feet above sea level. Lake Eyre is 39 feet below sea level, and flanked by ancient lake-terraces. Between Lake Eyre and Lake Gregory there are stony rises only about 100 feet high. Thence there are sandhills, about 25 feet high, separating the last lake from Lake Blanche, which at times connects with Lake Callabonna by floods in the Strzelecki Creek. A channel joins Lake Frome to Lake Callabonna, and the two latter are practically at the same level. There seems little doubt that this 'horseshoe series' of lakes has developed in a semicircular depression which accompanied the upward folding and faulting producing the Flinders Range. The latter rises sharply to 3,470 feet in Mount Benbonyathe right above Lake Frome; while St. Mary's Peak (also in this northern portion of the horst blocks) overlooks Lake Torrens from a height of 3,900 feet.

No better proof of the recency of these uplifts (of the order of 2,000 feet) could be desired than that available at Orroroo. Here we have relics of a vast river system, probably rivalling the Murray, which once drained the south-west and reached the sea near the head of St. Vincent Gulf. The Pasmore and Siccus valleys are filled with hundreds of feet of alluvial. At Orroroo on the *summit* of the ranges today a bore penetrated 591 feet of river sands and gravel without reaching bed rock. It is clear that these gravel-deposits have been buckled up to form the divide only recently, for they must rapidly disappear under the attacks of normal erosion. (See Endpaper map.)

The Mount Lofty Ranges are bounded by fault-scarps, which appear as a series of 'Steps' on both flanks of the uplands (Fig. 59). Howchin shows that there is a remarkable series of such fragmentary blocks in the Adelaide district. Thus the upper Sturt flows on a surface about 1,900 feet above the sea. Belair nearer the coast is on a broken portion of the same peneplain now about 1,000 feet above the sea; Burnside is on a fragment some 500 feet high. Under Adelaide are similar sunken areas at 220 feet and 2,000 feet (?) below sea level.

Economics.—The principal industries of South Australia have been developed in the southern portion of the state. Wheat, wool,

hides, copper, tallow, butter, meats and wines are by far the most
important products. All of these except copper are directly dependent on the rainfall. Speaking generally, the great bulk of the
sheep are south of the 7-inch isohyet, the cattle are south of the
10-inch isohyet, and the wheat is almost wholly grown south of
the 10-inch line, where a fall of 15 inches during the growing
period gives the best results.

Rain Regime

The heaviest rainfall is near Mount Lofty (47 inches), and in
the extreme south-east at Lake Leake (near Mount Gambier),
which has an average of 32·7 inches. Several areas of rather heavy

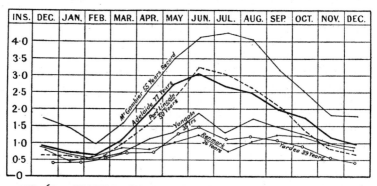

FIG. 60.—SEASONAL RAINFALL IN THE SOUTH OF SOUTH AUSTRALIA

rainfall are found elsewhere, such as east of Adelaide, west of
Kooringa and behind Port Lincoln. The Port Lincoln area, like
that of Mount Gambier, owes its heavy rain to the fact that the
land projects south into the path of the dominant westerlies. The
same factor also helps the other two areas, but there elevation is
perhaps of greater value in determining the rainfall.

A glance at the graphs shown in Fig. 60 tells us that we have
here wholly to do with a winter-rain region. At all stations the
maximum is in June except at Mount Gambier, where the rain
is slightly heavier in July. It is interesting to note that the northern
zone has a slight minimum in July, as is well shown by Yongala
(near Petersburg) and Renmark.

Vegetation of the Flinders Region

The region under consideration is in general well developed, so
that it is not necessary to appeal to the native flora to obtain a clue

to its possibilities. Although the wheat area is obviously determined wholly by the rainfall, yet it has displaced two different types of native flora. Thus the hilly country contains the open forests of the state. These consist essentially of such eucalypts as the Sugar Gum (*E. corynocalyx*), the Stringybark (*E. obliqua*) and Peppermint (*E. odorata*). The forests alternate with grasslands and small trees such as *Casuarina* (She-oak), *Xanthorrhea* (grass-tree) and various acacias are common.

The lowland regions in the east and along the west coast, although receiving a good rainfall, are often characterized by a specialized stunted vegetation known as the 'mallee scrub'. This consists essentially of eucalypts which grow to a height of about 10 feet, and form almost impenetrable masses of stems (Fig. 35). *E. dumosa* and the closely allied *E. incrassata* are common forms, but dwarfed *Casuarina* and *Melaleuca* are often present. After being neglected for many years, this sandy country is found to respond readily to the plough, and when suitably fertilized gives profitable crops of wheat.

The flora of the drier region on the northern boundary of the area differs very little from that characteristic of the arid Eyre Region to the north. Its River Gums, box flats and saltbush plains are described on page 194.

Some further mention may be made of 'Goyder's Line', which was drawn by the Surveyor-General as a result of a journey in November 1865 to the north end of the Flinders Range. He was commissioned to lay down on the map the boundary of the drought-stricken country. He writes:

The change from the country suffering from excessive drought to that where its effect has only been slightly experienced is palpable to the eye from the nature of the country itself; and may be described as bare ground, destitute of grass and herbage, the surface soil dried by the intense heat, in places broken and pulverized by the passage of stock, and formed by the action of the winds in miniature hummocks surrounding the closely cropped stumps of salt, blue and other dwarfed bushes. Those plants of greater elevation are denuded of their leaves and smaller branches as far as the stock can reach. This description generally holds good of all country upon which stock has been de-pastured and when the drought obtains. The change from that to areas where the drought has had a less serious effect being shown by the fresher and more leafy appearance of the bushes, gradually improving to those in their ordinary state, and the gradual increase of other vegetation from bare ground to well-grassed country (Fig. 96).

This line was slightly modified later, and practically agrees with the southern boundary of the distinctly characteristic 'salt-bush, mulga and dwarf mallee' country. During favourable years an immense amount of wheat may be grown outside 'Goyder's Line'; but the safe farming country lies south of this ecological isopleth. When the isohyets were adequately charted, it was found to agree closely with the 12-inch isohyet (except along the coast north of Wallaroo); and this logical method of estimating the possibilities of a new country is one which ought to be carried out in our arid central regions.

NATURAL REGION 6: THE BRISBANE REGION

The sixth region in our survey takes us north of the line dividing the winter from the summer rains. As in the northern section of Queensland, the highlands lie in the east of this division, and they are composed of much more ancient rocks than are the plains to the west. This elevated area is built up of Carboniferous rocks, both in the north and south; but from Roma to Grafton there once extended a basin now filled with later Triassic rocks. To the west of the 1,000-foot contour is the ancient Cretaceous Sea, whose sediments form the widespread Western Plains. Hence there is in this division, as in others, a close connexion between topography and geology. (See Fig. 12.)

The highland region becomes progressively more elevated to the south, but there are three or four well-marked plateaux which form dominant areas in the highlands (see endpaper map). Just east of Tambo is the Buckland Tableland, rising above 2,000 feet. About 180 miles to the south-east, the Darling Downs district is crowned by several small oval areas, which also extend above the 2,000-foot contour. Extending from the Queensland border to the Hunter Valley is the New England Plateau, of which a northern branch constitutes the Macpherson Range.

C. A. Sussmilch has recently summarized the structure of Eastern Queensland as follows:

The coast ranges and the chains of continental islands are fault-blocks (or *horsts*). These alternate with rift valleys (or *graben*), which may be drowned by the sea, thus constituting the channel which separates the island chains from the coast. The numerous small coastal plains are 'Stillstands', which have remained steady (or nearly so) in the various movements of the littoral. The period of uplift occurred so long ago (probably in early Pleistocene) that much differential erosion has taken place; and a great deal of deposition in the form of river alluvial, &c., has covered much of the lower area.

In Fig. 61 a block diagram is given of the region about 100 miles wide near Brisbane. The structure is much the same as further south. The plateau of the Darling Downs is capped by basalt lava. To the east the Brisbane River has carved out a broad valley nearly to sea level. Hence there is a steep drop in the east which is illustrated by the course of the railway from Gatton up to Toowoomba. The geology of the district is complicated, the crust consisting mainly of faulted older Palaeozoic rocks in which are small Triassic coal basins such as that near Ipswich.[1] The first settlement was at Humpybong in 1824, but was soon transferred 12 miles up the Brisbane River to the site of the present capital

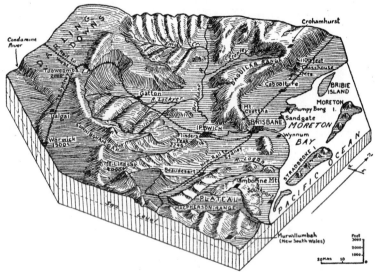

FIG. 61.—A BLOCK DIAGRAM OF THE BRISBANE VALLEY

The steep eastern scarp of the Darling Downs is also shown

(*Courtesy of Rand, McNally*)

of Queensland. In 1836 the buildings in the town were almost all used by convicts or their guards, but in 1842 squatters, moving to the coast from the Darling Downs, had changed its character. The large sandy islands off the coast contain unusually large sand dunes, up to 1,000 feet in height.

Vegetation.—The region under consideration exhibits the same subdivisions as in northern Queensland. Close to the coast and on the east slope are limited areas of 'brush timbers'. On the highlands and upper western slopes where the rainfall is satisfactory are open eucalypt forests which thin out as one proceeds westward.

[1] *Geomorphology of Eastern Queensland*, Great Barrier Reef Committee, Brisbane, 1938.

In the far west are open plains with typical 'gum creeks'. These exhibit 'corridor' trees along the intermittent streams.

A belt of scattered tropical 'brushes' extends from near Brisbane southwards nearly to Newcastle (Fig. 33). All this region receives over 30 inches of rain a year. These areas carry dense woods on the higher lands (especially on basalt soils) behind Bowen, Yandina, Tweed River, and north of the Manning River. The softwoods, often beautiful in colour and grain, comprise red cedar (*Cedrela toona*), rosewood (*Dysoxylon fraserianum*), black bean (*Castano-*

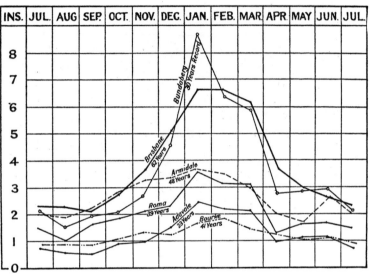

FIG. 62.—MONTHLY RAINFALL IN SOUTH QUEENSLAND AND NORTH NEW SOUTH WALES

spermum australe), silky oak (*Grevillea robusta*) and tulipwood (*Harpullia*).

The forests of eucalypts roughly occupy the country between the coast and the 20-inch isohyet. Several conifers are also of importance, such as the Moreton Bay Pine (*Araucaria cunninghamii*), Brown Pine (*Podocarpus elata*) and Bunya-bunya (*Araucaria bidwillii*). Brigalow scrub covers much good soil.

Rainfall.—Reference to the graphs given in Fig. 62 shows that all this region, and the adjacent part of New South Wales, are characterized by a marked summer rainfall. The coast has very heavy summer rains, as indicated by the graphs for Bundaberg and Brisbane. Indeed, Crohamhurst (about 40 miles north of Brisbane) is noted for heavy rains within the 24 hours. Thus on

February 2nd, 1893, this locality received 35·71 inches; while Yandina (near by) had a fall of 19·25 inches on the preceding day. The same district received falls of 26 and 19 inches on two adjacent days in January 1898. As we move away from the coast to Roma and Armidale the summer rainfall is less striking, and the rainfall approaches a uniform type. Indeed, this type is better shown at Dubbo (200 miles SW. of Armidale) than anywhere else in Australia. The rainstorms along the central east coast are due chiefly to Troughs in the summer, but in winter Coastal Lows and onshore east winds (accompanying Highs) produce more rain.

Correlation.—Similar regions are to be found in East Cape Colony, Uruguay, south-east China, and south-east of the United States of America. In all of these the mean annual temperature is about 70° F. The mean annual range of about 20° F. is true for north Uruguay and south-east China, but in the United States of America region is greater (30° or 40° F.). The annual minimum is similar in the various homoclimes, but the Australian division as a whole has a hotter maximum than any. As regards annual rainfall similar regions are China, Uruguay, south-east States of U.S.A. All have the same type of rainfall, with a mid-summer maximum, but the United States of America and Uruguay are favoured by more rain in winter. Variations in precipitation are obviously not so important as those of temperature, for the former invariably fall off with distance from the coast.

HOMOCLIMES OF THE BRISBANE REGION

Place	Temperature (° F.)			Rainfall (inches)		
	Hottest m.	Coldest m.	Ave., Ann.	Wettest m.	Driest m.	Ave., Ann.
Brisbane	77·2	58·0	68·8	6·6 (Jan.)	2·0 (Sept.)	46·9
Bourke (N.S.W.)	85·2	51·8	69·2	1·8 (Feb.)	0·8 (Sept.)	14·4
Montevideo	71·8	50·7	61·3	3·9 (May)	2·5 (Aug.)	39·0
Hong Kong	81·9	60·0	71·7	15·6 (June)	1·2 (Dec.)	83·2
Savannah (U.S.A.)	82·0	51·0	67·0	7·9 (Aug.)	2·4 (Nov.)	51·0
King Williams Town, S. Africa	73·4	55·7	65·1	3·7 (Nov.)	0·4 (July)	26·3
Durban	77·0	64·2	70·7	5·70 (Dec.)	0·6 (June)	42·2

NATURAL REGION 7: TOWNSVILLE

Topography.—Structurally Queensland consists of three longitudinal belts. There is a broad *central* belt of level-bedded plains of Cretaceous age, which contains large supplies of artesian water.

In the west (to the south of Camooweal) is an area of very ancient folded and eruptive rocks. The eastern highlands are built up of several formations (somewhat newer than the preceding area); largely granite in the north, Carboniferous sediments in the centre, and Triassic rocks to the south of Bundaberg. The more elevated portions of the highlands are largely built of basalts at the head of

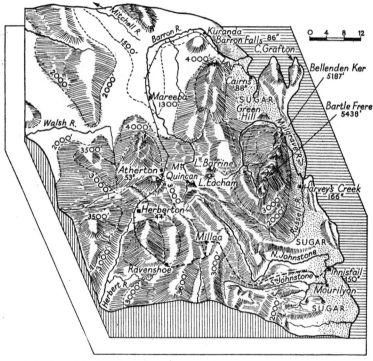

FIG. 63.—BLOCK DIAGRAM OF THE CHIEF PART OF THE ATHERTON TABLELAND IN NORTH QUEENSLAND

The heavy rainfalls in the east are noted. The heavy broken line west of Innisfail is the Palmerston Highway

the Burdekin and Belyando rivers, and of granite along the coast, in addition to the Carboniferous sediments already mentioned.

The dominant feature of the division is the way in which the highest land lies to the east, and rises abruptly from the ocean. This is especially noticeable in the north, and again near Mackay. The highest point in Queensland is Mount Bartle Frere (5,438 feet), in the Bellenden Ker Range, just south of Cairns (Fig. 63). This range forms the eastern border of the Atherton Plateau, which is probably the most favourable region in northern Australia for close white settlement. Here are about 12,000 square miles elevated considerably above 2,000 feet (Atherton 2,466 feet; Herberton 2,890 feet); and although they are only 17 degrees from the equator, many farms, including numerous dairies, have been established.

Near Cairns the river divide is only 20 miles from the coast, thus indicating the recent elevation of the plateau. As suggested by the author, it seems likely that the Barron River formerly entered the west-flowing Mitchell River (Fig. 63). The scarp facing the coast near Cairns is at times 2,500 feet high and the Barron, Russell, Mulgrave and Johnstone Rivers have cut deep gorges in the scarp. Lower coastal hills rise 2,000 feet, and are linked to the scarp by a strip of alluvial forming a low 'corridor' 4 miles wide.

Along the flat and insignificant divide between the heads of the Barron, Mulgrave and Johnstone Rivers is a very interesting series of crater-lakes and small volcanoes. Of these, Lake Eacham is the best known (Fig. 63). It fills a crater about 3,000 feet across, and its walls of ash or tuff are about 100 feet high. The lake is 226 feet deep. Just to the north is Lake Barrine, which is about 4,000 feet across. Four miles to the west is Mount Quincan, which rises 600 feet above the plateau. It is a well-preserved cone, and contains a crater 300 feet deep. From other similar small cones flows of olivine-basalt have spread over the plateau. A similar lava-flow at Green Hill in the alluvial 'corridor' seems to have deflected the Mulgrave River from its original outlet at Cairns to a much more southern entry into the sea. F. Jardine [1] is of the opinion that these volcanic activities are of post-Pleistocene age, which is of much interest in view of the absence of such action to-day anywhere in Australia. For the complex geology, see Fig. 12.

The Clarke Range region is much more restricted, and the portion over 2,000 feet forms only a narrow crescentic area. [2] The so-called 'Main Dividing Range' seems to be formed *by* (rather than separating) the rivers in many places. It rises not much above 1,000 feet, and seems merely to mark the western point to which the coastal rivers have carved their way. In other places, however, there have been large volcanic flows along the present divide, which they have undoubtedly helped to determine (Fig. 14).

A most peculiar feature of the Queensland Divide is the number

---

[1] *Drainage of the Atherton Plateau*, Roy. Geog. Soc., Brisbane (*c.* 1924).
[2] A useful block diagram of the Clarke Range, and the adjacent coast, is given in C. A. Sussmilch, 'Geomorphology of E. Queensland', *Barrier Reef Memoir*, Brisbane, 1938.

of small lakes associated with it. They are probably due to slight crustal warps. Some of these to the north-east of Longreach have been described in considerable detail by Dr. Danes, and they merit some notice in an account of Queensland hydrography. Lake Mueller has an area of 1½ square miles, and is 4 feet deep. It is fresh, and is supplied by mud springs, which are circular holes filled with muddy brackish water at 80° F. Lake Barcoorah near by is slightly larger, and overflows to the south-west in exceptionally wet seasons (Fig. 14). Lake Dunn (10 miles south of Lake Galilee) is also about two square miles in extent. It is fringed by wind-driven sand dunes and spinifex. It dried out in 1884, 1886, 1898, 1900 and 1901. Big floods occurred in 1890 and 1906. Lake Galilee has an area of about 80 square miles, and is about 20 miles long. It lies at an elevation of 1,025 feet, and on the north-west the divide from the Belyando is only about 200 feet above the lake. The lake is slightly brackish and the home of numerous game birds. Lake Buchanan is about the same area. It is the most imposing of the lakes and forms an extensive sheet of blue water. It is, however, only 5 feet deep and very salty. The divide on the west is less than 200 feet above the lake. The shores grow saltbush, and the slopes are covered with 'lancewood' (*Acacia*).[1]

The Great Barrier Reefs

Perhaps the outstanding physiographic characteristic of Australia is the unequalled series of coral reefs, which extend for 1,260 miles

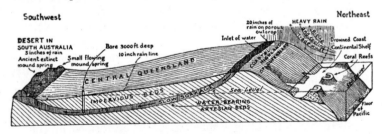

FIG. 64.—DIAGRAM ILLUSTRATING THE ARTESIAN BASIN AND THE
CORAL REEFS

The diagram is not drawn to scale, and represents a vertical section across Queensland from near Lake Eyre to Mackay—a distance of 1,000 miles. Notice the Mound Springs in the southwest, and the horseshoe-shaped coral reefs on the continental shelf.
(*Courtesy of Rand, McNally*)

northward from latitude 24°. The mean distance from the coast is about 30 miles, but this varies greatly (Fig. 64). Bryan suggests that the shelf is the drowned portion of bygone folded geosynclines, since the folds on the mainland are widest just where the shelf is

[1] Danes, *Geographical Journal*, Brisbane, 1910 (see Endpaper map).

widest. Mr. Charles Hedley and the writer made some of the earliest surveys of the individual reefs in 1906.[1] There is a well-marked continental shelf along the coast of Queensland which carried the individual coral reefs. As Jukes pointed out (from his traverse in 1843), the living coral reefs appear as 'tower-like bastions scattered over this continental shelf'. The lagoon between the outer reefs and the coast is from 100 to 400 feet deep. To the east of the reefs the ocean rapidly deepens to 14,000 feet. There has been much controversy as to the thickness of the coral limestone. Borings at Michaelmas Cay (off Cairns) penetrated over 400 feet of coral debris, and below this was found 200 feet of quartz sand and foraminifera. Hence a thickness of more than 600 feet covers the continental shelf, which may indeed be far below the bottom of the Michaelmas Cay bore. A later bore through the reef on the Tropic went down to 732 feet with much the same results.

H. C. Richards discusses the broad features of the shelf north of the Tropic.[2] In latitude 20° the Whitsunday Passage lies between drowned ranges (appearing as high rocky islands) and the coast. Similar rocky islands appear north of Townsville as far as Cairns. The shelf is 160 miles wide in latitude 22°, but is only 30 miles wide off Cooktown, where the author made his surveys. The individual coral islets (cays) are built up of coral-debris, and often resemble horseshoes in plan (Fig. 64). The steady south-east Trade Wind drives the fragments of coral, &c., to the north-west, thus building reefs which resemble *barchans* in sand. Some islets carry thickets of thorny scrub, others barely reach above high tide. The luxuriant coral growth is visible at low spring tides, but the soft brown curtains of *Alcyonaria* coral are the most notable features of the reefs.[3] Some cays are described on page 256A.

Vegetation.—The abundance of moisture and heat in the region has led to a specially luxuriant flora, and we are fortunate in that its geography has been briefly described by Dr. Karel Domin.

Along the coast occurs a dune flora characterized by *Ipomea* and shrubs like *Epacris*; mangrove scrubs (*Rhizophora*, &c.) are common in the river estuaries. But it is the 'Vine-scrubs' (or tropical rain-forests) which are of chief interest. These are found wherever good rainfall occurs, and are especially rich on basalt soils. Their chief habitat is from Cooktown to Ingham, and their optimum is in the Cairns District (Fig. 33).

They present always a dense and thick forest association, with very little grass in the undergrowth, but with plenty of vines and

---

[1] *The Great Barrier Reef*, Aust. Assoc. Adv. Sci., Adelaide, 1907.
[2] *University of Queensland Papers*, 1938.
[3] *A Year on the Great Barrier Reef*, C. M. Yonge, New York, 1930.

epiphytic plants on the trees and branches. Orchids and ferns are most numerous among them. The trees attain usually a considerable height, but their bark is regularly thin, and their tops are not too dense.

The richest type occurs on flats in deep alluvium. This is the proper home of the 'lawyer cane' and climbing bamboo. Nearly the whole space between the trees is filled with magnificent creepers climbing from top to top and drooping in wonderful festoons. Among these are *Clematis*, *Jasmine* and *Tecoma*. There are many valuable timbers, of which the chief are—*Cedrela* (red cedar), *Flindersia* (maple), *Castanospermum* (bean), silky oak, quondong, rosewood (*Synoum*), &c.

There is an extremely sharp line of division separating the above Malayan flora from the open forests or 'eucalypt flora'. This is due not only to difference in water supply and soil, but also due to relative immunity of the eucalypt forests from bush-fires. In the north this forest has a close undergrowth with high grass, with *Xanthorrhoea*, *Cycad* and 'she-oaks'. Among the representative trees which clothe the greater part of the highlands may be mentioned valuable timbers, such as ironbark, grey, spotted and red gum, black-butt, and turpentine (*Syncarpia*).

Along the main divide are several different types of forests. Where the soil is sandy and poor, a stunted forest similar to that of the Blue Plateau (New South Wales) occurs. In the centre (around Jericho) are lancewood shrubs. This is a wattle (*Acacia*), with especially straight close stems. To the west in the lower country are the gidya (*A. cambagei*) and brigalow (*A. harpophylla*) scrubs and similar trees, which in places form dense thickets, almost wholly composed of species of *Acacia*.

Rainfall in North Queensland

Regions in Australia with a rainfall of over 100 inches per annum, are found only near Cairns (Queensland) and near Mount Lyell (Tasmania). The former is an oval area about 85 miles long and 20 miles wide, which extends from Cairns to Cardwell (Fig. 63). About 40,000 square miles receive over 50 inches. Harvey Creek, near the mouth of Russell River (Fig. 63), has 165 inches of rain in a year, the heaviest in Australia. The region receiving over 30 inches is remarkably restricted along this portion of the east coast. It comprises the whole of the Peninsula, but south of Cardwell it fringes the Pacific, and is rarely more than 40 miles wide. Queensland is, however, greatly favoured in comparison with the other larger states of the Commonwealth; and the enormous areas inland receiving 15 to 25 inches are an asset which can hardly be overestimated.

Some notes on the heavy rainfall at Harvey Creek and other very wet localities on the north coast will be of interest. They are taken from the official Queensland Rainfall memoir, which should be consulted for further details of similar records. Port Douglas in April 1911 received 32 inches of rain in the 24 hours. Harvey Creek in January 1911, and again in January 1913, received 28 and 25 inches respectively, in the same period. Indeed heavy falls (over 20 inches at a time) are rather common along this coast.

Since the topography is so important a factor in the rains of this region, it is natural that rains due to elevation will occur with

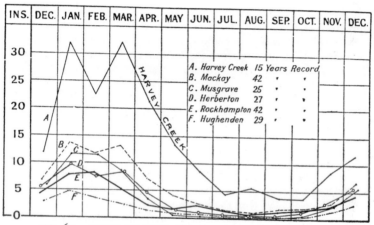

FIG. 65.—HEAVY RAINFALL ALONG THE QUEENSLAND COAST

south-east winds, no matter how the winds are produced. Hence there is a large precipitation associated with anti-cyclones lying to the south of Queensland. It is safe to say that had the Queensland coast been low-lying, these winds flowing around the northern limb of the High would have exercised very much less effect in producing rains. In fact, we have to look to the contours rather than to the distribution of the isobars for these rains. However, the dominant rain in summer is associated chiefly with tropical Lows.

It will be noticed in the graphs (Fig. 65) that the heavy rains all fall in summer. The maxima are generally in January, but February and March are nearly as wet. The heavy individual falls also occur in these months; as do the terrible hurricanes which occasionally develop from tropical cyclones, along the north-east coast.

J. J. Bradfield, who designed the great bridge across Sydney Harbour, is responsible for a scheme to divert the Tully and Herbert Rivers (south of the Atherton Plateau) into the rather dry areas west of the Great Divide. He planned to drive a 40-mile tunnel to carry the water to the Flinders and Thomson Rivers of the west. This project has been received with much enthusiasm by journalists and the non-scientific public, but most climatologists and engineers see little hope of success in view of the cost and the high evaporation in the hot inland areas. (See p. 283.)

Health.—As already stated, the North Queensland coast, especially the region around Atherton and Herberton, is especially favoured among our tropical divisions by reason of its abundant rainfall and comparatively high elevation. The climate of the actual coastline is, of course, very muggy in summer, as may be seen from the following figures for Townsville. The cooler conditions of the Herberton region (Fig. 63) are also shown in this table. It may be remembered (as Huntington points out in many of his books) that all tropical plateaux suffer from lack of variety in their climates.

Station	Mean temperature (° F.)			Mean humidity (° F.)			Mean rainfall (in.)		
	Jan.	July	Mean	Jan.	July	Mean	Jan.	July	Mean
Townsville	82·1	66·6	74·9	74	69	69	11·5	0·50	49·7
Herberton	73·4	56·7	66·7	74	78	71	10·2	0·55	43·8

I show elsewhere that the wet-bulb temperatures are above the 'comfort' line (70·0) in Townsville for the period of November to April. However, the conditions are improved by the south-east winds, which blow almost the whole year round.

In the next table it is shown that Townsville is remarkably like Calcutta.

Station	Mean temperature (° F.)			Mean wet bulb			Mean rainfall (in.)		
	Hottest m.	Coldest m.	Annual	Hottest m.	Coldest m.	Annual	Wettest m.	Driest m.	Annual
Townsville	82·1	66·6	75·7	76*	62*	69	11·5	0·5	48·6
Calcutta	82·4	65·2	77·9	80*	59*	70	12·3	0·3	60·0

* Approximate.

The Townsville division belongs to the monsoon or summer-rain 'natural regions', and is akin to east Brazil, Portuguese East Africa, and other similarly situated countries.

CHAPTER VIII

THE THREE REGIONS OF THE GEOSYNCLINE, AND THE TEN REGIONS OF THE WESTERN SHIELD

PART I

THE GEOSYNCLINE

NATURAL REGION 8: THE MURRAY BASIN

THE structure of this region is fairly simple. In the west is an out-crop of very ancient contorted sediments, which rise to about 1,500 feet (Fig. 66). They form the Broken Hill Uplands or Barrier Ranges, and the Grey Range near Milparinka. Along the east are the highlands built up of older Palaeozoic rocks. Similar material also constitutes the Cobar peneplain, which is a roughly circular region about 150 miles across, lying between the 500 and 800 feet contours (see Endpaper map for general details).

Practically the whole of the south-west portion of the area under consideration consists of alluvial deposits or marine tertiaries. These are level-bedded deposits of late geological age, and are formed of debris from ancient rivers and seas, together with a considerable amount of wind-blown material.

The Barrier Ranges appear as even-topped, undulating mulga-covered hills (Photo 3, p. 9). There is a general accordance of summit level, and an old high-level peneplain is quite evident, located about 1,400 feet above sea level. Mount Robe, Lewis Point, &c., stand out as slight irregularities in this old plain. Nearer the Queensland border, table-topped hills of Cretaceous age form a remarkably well-defined peneplain, through which rise occasional monadnocks of more ancient rocks such as Mount Brown (Fig. 66).

The plains to the east of the Barrier Ranges have an almost imperceptible inclination to the Darling River, which is about 65 miles from, and 600 feet below, the township of Broken Hill. This plain extends far to the southward, where it is continuous over the whole of south-western New South Wales. Just on the border near Minjary, there is a break in the uplands, where the plain deposits extend across the rock outcrops. Here it is probable that the Lake Frome drainage at one time had an outlet to the south-east.

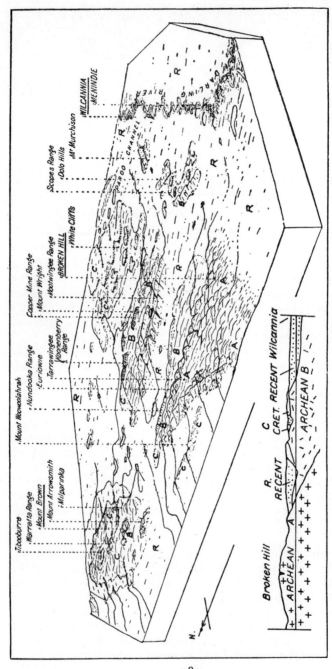

FIG. 66.—DIAGRAM TO ILLUSTRATE PRINCIPAL TOPOGRAPHICAL FEATURES OF THE WEST DARLING DISTRICT, NEW SOUTH WALES

Notice the 'Eroded Dome' about Mount Brown, with Archean rocks (B) in centre, surrounded by Cretaceous (C) and Recent (R). A section through Broken Hill to Wilcannia is inset. (*Slightly modified from E. J. Kenny.*) From Broken Hill to Menindie is 60 miles.

The Cobar peneplain has been described by Andrews (1913). Residuals rise occasionally to 500 feet above the general level, and the whole region is slightly undulating, so that it appears somewhat like a sheet of corrugated iron. All the valley-sides are covered with a decided waste-sheet. The surface rocks show very clearly the effects of the arid climate. The underground waters rise into the parched surface soils, and salts in solution are deposited when the water evaporates. Probably in this way were formed the characteristic cappings of quartzite, ironstone 'blows' and calcareous tufa. The soil characters also depend on the arid weathering. Thus the *red* soils indicate that the material has been peroxidized under a hot sun in an arid climate not subjected to periodic flooding; the *black* soils contain organic matter and fragments of lava (from New England and nearer), and generally occupy old river channels. They have not been subjected to such long periods of desiccation.

Similar soils cover a large portion of the plains surrounding the Cobar peneplain, and extend for considerable distances over the western slopes of the highlands. Andrews believes that the Cobar peneplain indicates that this portion of the State has remained above sea level since the Devonian period, and that it has slowly risen and been gradually denuded; while the adjacent areas, now covered by the red and black soil plains, have sunk to form the enormous artesian basin. The shallow valleys were formed after an uplift, at a time when the rainfall was able to keep the valleys clear. Then came the formation of the eastern highlands of Australia by the upheaval of the eastern portion of the old plain of erosion. The effect of this uplift was to increase the precipitation on the eastern seaboard, but to decrease that of the interior of New South Wales, by presenting a barrier to the winds from the sea. The effect of this has been to reduce the Cobar supply, and at the same time the precipitation is insufficient to keep the river channels open. To the south-west of a line joining Menindie to Oxley, the strata consist of the elevated bottom of an Eocene sea, into which the Murray tributaries once discharged as so many distinct rivers.

River Drainage

The drainage of these western plains is very different from that of the eastern highlands. In the place of the deep gorges and the patchwork tributaries of that troubled region of the earth's crust, we have the open plains with slow-moving rivers depositing alluvial in valleys often in an advanced stage of senility. None of the rivers is entirely permanent, though the Murray has only rarely ceased to flow, as in 1924. But the Darling and Lachlan often consist merely of a string of water-holes, while the Murrumbidgee occasionally fails to reach the Murray.

Several features in the map indicate that the river system in this region has reached a comparatively inactive stage in its cycle. The development of tributaries known as Billabongs and Ana-branches shows that it is flowing through a plain with an almost negligible slope. Thus near Wilcannia the Darling gives rise to the Talyawalka Branch, which connects with a group of shallow depressions occasionally filled with flood waters. These probably represent areas which have not been levelled up by the river deposits. Near Menindie (Fig. 66) is a series of more important basins, of which Cawndilla and Menindie can each store 17,000 million cubic feet. Other similar depressions are connected with the Darling and branches, and their flow, after the ordinary flood waters have subsided, is able to supply the river for many months. Some of these are being used as storage reservoirs.

The Lachlan gives off a distributary near Hillston, known as the Willandra Billabong (see Endpaper map). This may ultimately reach the Murray near Euston in time of high flood. The Riverina District is crossed by many such streams, such as the Moulamein, Edward and Wakool. In many cases the river alluvial has built up the banks so that they rise above the surrounding country, and this feature leads to the formation of lakes, of which Lake Cowal near Wyalong is an example. The feeble tributary from the south has been blocked as its supply has decreased with increasing aridity. In very wet seasons, as in 1870 and 1891, the Lachlan floods spread into the Cowal depression and turned it into a temporary lake 18 miles long. Meanders and ox-bow lakes are abundant along all these flood-plain watercourses, and occasionally the river is lost in a maze of swamps, as at the junction of the Lachlan and the Murrumbidgee. Further details of the physiography of this part of Australia will be found in the chapter on Irrigation.

Within South Australia the Murray has been affected by the Pleistocene uplift, and from the boundary to the outlet it exhibits signs of rejuvenation. The widespread billabongs of New South Wales are no longer to be seen, but the Murray flows in a well-defined valley; between cliffs which are steep and well marked in the harder marine beds to the west, and less marked in the softer formations in the east. River flats occupy a large part of the narrow cliffed valley, and these are marked by several terraces. Fenner has divided the lower river into three sections. The broad 'Nawait' valley from the border to Overland Corner; the 'Murundi' Gorge from Overland Corner to Wellington (near Murray Bridge,

Fig. 59), and lastly the 'Narinyeri' section from Wellington to the sea. This last includes Lake Alexandrina.[1]

It seems likely that a vast landlocked area was filled with river silts, &c., during late Tertiary times, but that this ultimately drained to the sea *via* the lower Murray. In general, the lacustrine beds cover harder marine beds. Near Renmark, the river is eroding mainly in the softer beds and its valley is about 8 miles wide. The harder marine beds deflected the Murray to the north-west from Pyap Bend to Overland Corner. Here it began to cut a trench in the harder marine rocks. The abrupt change to a southern course at Morgan may be due to the river following a fault parallel to the Mount Lofty Horst (Fig. 59). Lake Alexandrina and the adjacent sandy tongue of the Coorong are coastal lagoons akin in origin to the Haff and Nehrung types well known in the Baltic Sea. The barrages are described on page 279.

Vegetation of the Murray Basin

The Western Plains have been graphically described by Cambage and Maiden as follows. A feature of the Western Plains is the marvellous rapidity with which recovery is made from drought. During a dry period the black-soil plains especially may become reduced to dust, with not a vestige of herbage for many miles; though shrubs and trees, many species of which are valuable for fodder, may remain alive. Within a week after the rains have come, all this is changed, and the country becomes covered with a green mantle, which in a few weeks furnishes luxuriant pasture. In the springtime the most conspicuous flowers of the open black-soil plains belong to the Compositae (*Helichrysum, Helipterum, Senecio*, &c.). *Ptilotus, Goodenia* and *Salsolacaceae* are also represented.[2] The grasses, even more than the saltbush, have rendered the western plains of great value to the pastoralist. There may be enumerated many species of *Panicum*, mulga grass (*Neurachine*), Mitchell grass, blue grass and many others.

The eucalypts of the drier region are usually of the Mallee habit, consisting of numerous individuals of various species with large root-stocks, from which ascend about a dozen thin stems, each some 10 feet high. The chief species are *uncinata, oleosa* and *incrassata*. This region is noted for the abundance of the Acacia family. Since their vernacular names are much used in Australia they are given in the table on page 188.

Of considerable importance are *Callitris robusta* (white pine), bull oak and belah (*Casuarina*), the two latter resembling pines

---

[1] *South Australia*, C. Fenner, Adelaide, 1931.
[2] Allied species are sketched in Figs. 34 and 53.

ACACIAS OF WESTERN NEW SOUTH WALES

Local name	Scientific name	Local name	Scientific name
Mulga	*A. aneura*	Yarran	*A. homalophylla*
Silver Wattle	,, *decora*	Ironwood	,, *excelsa*
Currawang	,, *doratoxylon*	Brigalow	,, *harpophylla*
Waitawhile	,, *treptera*	Gidyea (Gidgee)	,, *Cambagei*
Umbrella Bush	,, *oswaldi*	Cooba	,, *salicina*
Myall or Boree	,, *pendula*	Eumung	,, *stenophylla*
Black Wattle	,, *hakeoides*		

(Fig. 36). Looking west from the Barrier Ranges the great expanse of saltbush (*Atriplex*, Fig. 36) covering the plain is seen to be threaded at intervals by meandering lines of eucalypts. These are the extension of the creeks rising in the hills. Within a few hours succeeding a fall of rain the 'gum creeks' cease to flow, and the only water remaining on the surface is contained in pools distributed at intervals along the beds.

Dune areas occur chiefly in the vicinity of Menindie; and these dunes move slowly forward across the plains, exterminating the originally scanty vegetation, and intensifying the desert characteristics. The ground vacated by a dune is hard and clayey, locally called 'hard pan'. Humus is absent, for as soon as the plant-remains decay they are swept away by the wind. Mulga scrub predominates in the hill areas, the growth ranging from 10 to 20 feet in height. The leaves form excellent feed for stock. Associated with it are wild fuschia (*Eremophila*), native peach (*Fusanus*), &c. On the plains the so-called sandalwood (*Myoporum*) and other trees replace mulga. The prevalent plants consist of bushy plants like saltbush and bluebush. Spear grass and wild carrot spring up after rains, and everlastings and desert pea flower in the spring. Swampy areas connected with the Darling River support dense growths of polygonum bush (*Muehlenbeckia*).[1]

Moving further east to Cobar (which receives about 15 inches of rain a year), we get a good picture of the vegetation from E. C. Andrews. The low average rainfall is shown by the relative absence of grasses. The country is, however, covered with beautiful shrubs and trees. A common height attained by the red box (*E. intertexta*) is 60 feet. The wilgas, mulgas, beefwoods, quondongs, &c., are especially beautiful by reason of their symmetry and umbrageous habit. When the keen winter winds have gone and the spring returns, the country becomes a veritable blaze of

[1] D. Mawson, *Broken Hill Memoir*, Adelaide, 1912.

colour. The currawangs, cassias, wattles, &c., are the most attractive of these. Many of these plants possess distinct forage values, such as currawang, kurrajong, mulga and rosebush.[1]

The following table shows that though rainfall plays the chief role, yet edaphic conditions determine the secondary distribution:

EDAPHIC DISTRIBUTION IN WESTERN NEW SOUTH WALES

Habitat	Local name	Scientific name	Habitat	Local name	Scientific name
Crushed Sandstones	Whipstick mallee	*E. viridis*	Gentle rises	Currawong	*A. doratoxylon*
,,	Verbena	*Prostanthera*	,,	Silver wattle	*A. decora*
,,	Heath	*Eriostemum*	,,	Turpentine	*Eremophila*
,,	White Pine	*Callitris*	,,	Leopardwood	*Flindersia*
			,,	Emu apple	*Pittosporum*
			,,	Rose bush	*Heterodendron*
Quartzite	Wild fuschia	*Eremophila*	,,	Beefwood	*Grevillea striata*
,,	Wattle	*A. salicina*	,,	Needle bush	*A. cyperophylla*
Alluvial flats	Bimble box	*E. populifolia*	,,	Belah	*Casuarina cambagei*
,,	Budtha	*Eremophila sp.*			
,,	Yarran	*A. homalophylla*	Gravelly country	Red mallee	*Euc. oleosa*
,,	Sandalwood	*Santalum*		White mallee	*Euc. dumosa*

Rainfall and Homoclimes

A study of the monthly rainfall graphs (Fig. 67) shows that the uniform rainfall hereabouts is due to the overlapping of the summer and winter rain controls. The graphs are remarkably flat in the east of the Murray Basin, Dubbo having about 1·8 inches each month of the year. The two western towns of Broken Hill and Milparinka, however, show a fairly well-marked peak in June.

Interior lowlands, akin in aspect and latitude to these Western Plains, occur only in two other regions in the world. The closest homoclime is northern Argentina, while the south-west Mississippi basin is also somewhat similar, though slightly wetter. In China and South Africa the inland country is either of a mountainous or plateau character. Even in United States the *drier* homoclimes most resembling our region are all so elevated that they are much colder.

[1] A valuable study of settlement in the arid Western Division of N.S. Wales (dealing especially with vegetation and erosion) by Macdonald Holmes, was published by the University of Sydney in 1938.

HOMOCLIMES OF WESTERN NEW SOUTH WALES

Place	Rainfall (inches)			Temperature (° F.)		
	Average	Wettest m.	Driest m.	Average	Hottest m.	Coldest m.
Wagga	21·3	2·6	1·3	62·2	77·5	47·5
Hillston	14·2	1·5	0·8	64·2	79·3	48·6
Broken Hill	9·7	1·3	0·6	64·7	78·4	49·4
Cordoba*	25·2	4·4	0·2	62·4	73·2	49·8
Oklahoma*	28·0	4·0†	1·0†	58·6	80·1	34·0
S. Antonio	25·2	4·0†	2·0†	67·8	82·4	51·1

* Hann.   † Approximate.

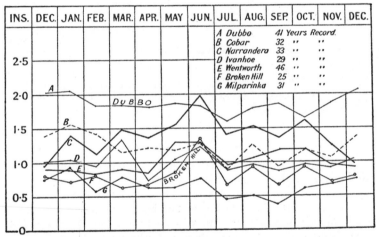

FIG. 67.—THE UNIFORM TYPE OF MONTHLY RAINFALL FOUND IN THE MURRAY BASIN

NATURAL REGION 9: THE GREAT ARTESIAN BASIN

This region includes the northern portion of the great geo-syncline, and contains the largest Artesian Basin in the world, comprising 640,000 square miles. But the south-west portion is so dry that it is advisable to consider it separately as the 'Lake Eyre Basin'. The physiography is monotonous, consisting of vast rolling plains. The chief sub-divisions seem to depend on whether the soils are siliceous or argillaceous. The former give rise to areas which are often locally called 'deserts'. The latter produce better soils, and are more fully stocked by sheep and cattle. The mound springs are charted in Fig. 86.

The surface of the region is mostly below 1,000 feet in elevation (see Endpaper map). Indeed, except along the eastern margin, nearly all of it is below 500 feet, but near Kynuna an east–west belt forms a low ridge right across the northern part of the geo-syncline. Other low ridges separate from each other the broad alluvial-filled valleys of the Diamantina, Thomson and Paroo. These rivers flow only after heavy rains, but in flood-time they are many miles wide. In some of these inland rivers 'water-holes' perhaps 30 feet deep may persist right through the dry weather. Such a pool occurs on Cooper's Creek (or Barcoo) about 30 miles east of Innamincka. The geology of this region is considered in some detail in the section dealing with the artesian water-supply of Australia (Fig. 64).

Vegetation in the Artesian Basin

The characteristic vegetation in these plains (often known as the 'Rolling Downs') is seen in the scrubs composed mainly of various acacias. The best known is *A. harpophylla*, commonly called the brigalow. In the northern and central areas are other acacias called boree and gidgee, of which the former prefers better soil, the latter growing on rather rocky ground. On the siliceous soils are also to be found large areas of the spiny desert-grass *Triodia*. In the central eastern section another of the acacias called Lancewood is common. It grows in close-set 'forests' about 30 feet high, which is not the usual habit of acacias.

In the eastern portion of the Rolling Downs, where it is drier, are grassy open plains. In the north are the valuable fodder plants Mitchell grass and Flinders grass (Fig. 32). Along the water-courses are thin 'corridor forests' of Coolibah and *Melaleuca*; while *Eremophila* and *Myoporum* are common shrubs.[1]

The rainfall is wholly of a summer type, and falls off in amount quite regularly as one proceeds away from the coast. Thus Normanton near the Gulf receives about 35 inches, Cloncurry 20 inches, and Birdsville in the south-west corner of Queensland only 6 inches (see inset in Fig. 68). However, occasionally heavy rainfalls are experienced, as at Monkira (near Birdsville), which received 12 inches of rain on February 1st, 1906. Tropical lows and troughs in summer account for much of the rain; though in the interior the proportion due to local thunder-storms (which are very prevalent here) is perhaps greater. Boulia in the west of this region experiences the highest rate of evaporation recorded in Australia. This amounts to 124 inches a year, which is but poorly

[1] K. Domin, 'Queensland Plant Associations', *Roy. Soc. Q.*, 1910.

balanced by a rainfall of 9 inches. This region belongs to Köppen's type *BSh*; and homoclimes are found in New Mexico (U.S.A.) and the Gran Chaco in northern Argentina.

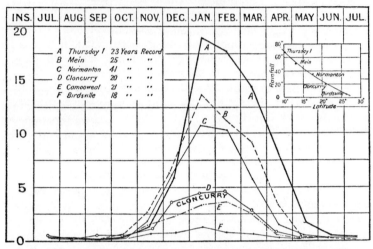

FIG. 68.—SUMMER RAINFALLS IN NORTH AND WEST QUEENSLAND

The Bradfield scheme 'for watering inland Australia' seems visionary to the writer. It is criticized by Ann Marshall in the *Journal of Aus. Inst. of Agric. Science*, Dec. 1944. See also page 283.

NATURAL REGION 10: THE LAKE EYRE BASIN

Topography

This region comprises the lower southern portion of the Great Artesian basin around Lake Eyre (see Endpaper map). A great deal of the area is below 500 feet in elevation, while the silts of the lake itself are about 39 feet below sea level. Probably, however, only a strip of shore about 10 miles wide (as well as the lake-silts themselves) would be flooded if the fantastic idea (often ventilated by the uninformed) of cutting a canal from the sea were carried out. The country is crossed by several stock-routes, notably that leading from the railway at Marree to Birdsville in Queensland. But it has negligible value for pasture (except in very wet years), and so is practically uninhabited (Fig. 43).

The Lake Eyre Basin has a watershed of nearly half a million square miles. But the lake is situated in the very driest part of Australia, its shores receiving less than 5 inches of rain a year.

The rivers entering it, though they appear to be 600 miles long, are usually dissipated in the gravels of 'distributaries' before they reach the lake itself. We owe to Dr. C. T. Madigan the best account of this interesting portion of the continent.[1] To the north-east the country consists of the deltas of the Diamantina and Cooper's Creek. Sand ridges are very common and may be 80 miles long. They are about 50 feet high, and usually occur about one-quarter of a mile apart. Between these ridges are to be seen stony or clayey flats; and in the rare wet seasons grass grows here and is sufficient to feed numbers of stock. In 1901 Professor Gregory found that only one cattle station (at Kilalpanina) was in existence. But many others had been abandoned since the country was first settled in the 'sixties. In 1927 this station also had gone, and only near Birdsville on the border were cattle being grazed (Fig. 78).

Lake Eyre is divided into two parts, of which the northern portion is 110 miles long and 40 miles wide, while the southern portion is 40 miles long and 18 miles wide. The two are connected by a narrow strait about 150 yards across. In 1929 Madigan flew over the lake, which was found to be dry, except where water was flowing from some Mound Springs. He thinks that the latter are due to the presence of a fault-plane running up the west side of the lake, which permits the escape of artesian water. He descended in the centre of the lake, and proved that the surface was a dry crumbly soil. The southern part of the floor of the lake is broken up into 'tesselations', so that the salty crust resembles the well-known 'pancake ice' of polar seas. Later in the year Madigan made a traverse of the surface of the lake for 12 miles. At the end, the salt-crust of sodium chloride was found to be 17 inches thick, 'and would have carried a locomotive'. He sank a well 13 feet deep in the lake-bed, and found that below the salt the floor was made of gypseous clay. Brine soon filled the hole nearly to the surface. Madigan concludes that water can rarely cover any large part of the lake floor. It may spread out for a depth of a few inches at the mouth of one of the northern rivers, but in a few weeks at most, this water will be evaporated. (The lake was temporarily filled in 1950.)

The original drainage scheme of the Lake Eyre region is not easily reconstructed (see Endpaper map). In the first rough maps of the explorers a vast horseshoe lake was indicated linking Lake Torrens to Lake Frome via Lake Eyre. We know that when Lake Blanche is flooded by Strzelecki Creek the water can reach Lake

[1] *Central Australia*, Cambridge, 1936. See also the description of the 'Channel Country' near the Barcoo R., by F. W. Whitehouse, Brisbane University, 1948.

Callabonna. But Lake Blanche has not joined Lake Gregory for many years, as the intervening sandhills are 25 feet high. Between Lake Gregory and Lake Eyre there lie stony tablelands from 60 to 100 feet high, and there is no appearance of these lakes having been connected.

A land surface such as that of Australia, which has been elevated since Cretaceous times, would surely (if uninterrupted) have arrived at a more symmetrical system of drainage than that exhibited by the Lake Frome–Torrens region. The steep-sided slopes of the Flinders Range seem to have risen through an ancient plain or delta, and pushed the drainage forcibly to the east. Such is my suggestion, which may seem at first sight to be rather fantastic, for the origin of the curved belt of lowlands which Eyre quite excusably covered with his 'Horseshoe Lake'.

Vegetation

The whole of this region is characterized by much the same type of flora, which is of the xerophilous kind common to all arid regions of the world. In Gregory's Tirari Desert, just east of the lake, in a bad season there may be only one needle bush to every 2 or 3 square miles, with a tuft of dead cane-grass or wild carrot to every 5 square yards. Yet in a really wet season Mackinlay found this district a 'land of lakes and meadows'.

Normally the vegetation consists of isolated clumps of acacias such as mulga (*A. aneura*), seldom growing above 25 feet, with bushes of the saltbush variety scattered at infrequent intervals. The scanty rain soaks into the sandy soil, but often finds its way to the surface along a layer of clay. At these points the flora is more abundant. 'Gum Creeks' are characteristic, and are marked out by a line of *Eucalyptus microtheca*.

Homoclimes for this type of desert occur in southern California and in Arabia. Though artesian water is obtainable, and flows freely at the surface along the south-west edge of the Artesian Basin (Fig. 64), there is too little plant growth to make the country of any importance for grazing. A small plantation of date-palms planted at Coward Springs is well known to tourists, but it has not led to any further development in this direction (Photo 4, Plate II). The character of the rainfall is indicated by the graph for Birdsville in Fig. 68.

Oodnadatta to Alice Springs

The writer flew over the desert region between Coward Springs and Alice Springs in May 1948, and some notes on this empty region will be of interest. Nearly all this country receives less than 5 inches of rain a year. The topography is nearly flat, and consists of red loamy plains with numerous dry gullies, whose dendritic pattern is well marked from the air by the black dots representing scattered acacias and small eucalypts. There were a few long dunes, running almost north–south in the vicinity of the Denison Range, whose low elevation is hardly noticeable from the air. At times we passed over broader river courses, some of which contained small pools at this time. Some 60 miles south of Oodnadatta small mesas with white cuesta cliffs appeared. Neales River contained a few waterholes dotted with dark trees, but the general impression was of a network of dry creeks in a vast plain of red loam. (Map, p. 233.)

To the north of Oodnadatta the Alberga river offers a wide sandy bed amid a landscape of ring-shaped dunes. These extend for about 60 miles north, but give place to the more common north–south dunes near Charlotte Waters. In places the dunes are somewhat crescent-shaped, with the convexity to the north-east. Occasional mesas appear near the border of Northern Territory.

North of Charlotte Waters we flew over the dry valley of the Finke River for many miles, which (in the wet season) drained the same monotonous areas of red loam. However, the topography changed about Crown Point, and much higher irregular mesas became more prominent in the view. There were still plenty of elongated dunes, running approximately NNW. to SSE., and in places anastomosing. As Ooraminna was approached—some 60 miles south of Alice Springs—*rocky* outcrops became more obvious, and one could see the definite west–east strike in these outlying portions of the Macdonnell Ranges. These new formations—largely Pre-Cambrian—became dominant as we flew north. At the same time the vegetation improved greatly, and smooth-barked 'white gums' replaced the smaller scattered acacias, &c., of the more arid region to the south.

PART II

THE WESTERN SHIELD

NATURAL REGION 11: SWANLAND

Topography.—To the temperate south-west portion of Western Australia with a rainfall suitable for agriculture and close settlement, the name 'Swanland' has been applied. It is a portion of the great peneplain, which has long been actively attacked by many rivers and streams; hence the topography is somewhat different from that of the rest of the State (Fig. 69). The western littoral is separated off by the Darling Fault-Scarp, and has dropped relatively to the inland portion. This scarp extends for (approximately) 200 miles from Moora southwards. The littoral has been dissected into wide shallow valleys in which old-looking rivers meander. It consists of clays and sands largely of fluviatile origin (which are deepest near Perth) and also of sand-dunes. The littoral has later subsided, especially near Perth, and so drowned the Swan Estuary. A small upraised block appears to account for the elevated region

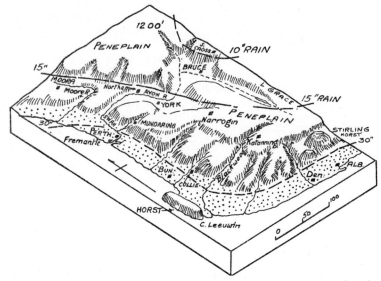

FIG. 69.—BLOCK DIAGRAM OF THE WETTER PORTION OF SWANLAND (W.A.)

The main isohyets are shown. Notice Mundaring Reservoir, which supplies gold-mines 350 miles to the east

near Cape Leeuwin. The Stirling Range is 50 miles long, and consists of quartzites which have perhaps been thrust up as a fault-block to a height of 3,000 feet. This movement seems to have occurred fairly lately, since small lakes and elevated valleys still show the disturbances which disrupted the ancient drainage. King George's Sound near Albany is, of course, a fine example of a drowned coastal valley.

A glance at the river systems of Swanland shows that the drainage scheme is somewhat complicated. The steep cliffs of the south coast are paralleled by a relatively straight steep and undissected 1,000-foot scarp behind. Very different is the shape of the same contour along the west coast. Not only is the scarp deeply dissected, so that the 1,000-foot contour winds in many convolutions, but the main trend of drainage is clearly to the north-west. This discordance is shown not only by the main valley (from Lake Grace to Toodyay), but in almost all the other rivers the dominant direction is also N. 30° W. instead of the normal south-west.[1]

Vegetation.—The south-west portion of Australia is famed for its flora, which is particularly rich in endemic forms. Along the coast is the heaviest rainfall (over 30 inches), and this area may be divided into three belts according to the dominant eucalypt. Both north and south of Perth extends the Tuart zone, where *E. gomphocephala* is the chief tree. Further south to Leeuwin is the habitat of the Jarrah, with some Wandoo and Karri. Characteristic shrubs are *Macrozamia* and *Xanthorrhea*, while of the flowering plants *Kennedya*, *Grevillea*, *Tetratheca* and *Boronia* are noteworthy. On the south coast Karri (*E. diversicolor*) is supreme, but *E. calophylla* also occurs (see Fig. 126).

In the zone from 30 to 20 inches (i.e. from York to Albany) the Wandoo (*E. redunca*) is most abundant. This is a smaller gum, and various acacias are also becoming of importance. *Hakea marginata* (Fig. 34) is also common, while such genera as *Drosera* and *Caladenia* are well represented among the smaller flowers. The 'Everlastings' (*Helipterum* sp.) in their season cover the open spaces with masses of bloom.

Another belt of more open country lies between the 20- and 10-inch isohyets. The eucalypt is still dominant, the chief being the York gum (*E. loxophleba*). Acacias, salmon gum and melaleucas are also not uncommon. In the sandy open country heaths are very abundant, with small gums, *Banksia* and *Xanthorrhea*. The well-known 'flannel flowers' and some forms of salt-bush clothe large areas in this district.

Climate and Products

The importance of the timber industry (chiefly Jarrah) may be gathered. Roughly speaking, the chief sheep and dairy regions lie between the 20-inch isohyet and the sea; while wheat is grown chiefly between the 10-inch and 20-inch isohyets. (See small book *Australian Climates* by J. Gentilli, Melbourne, n.d.)

This region belongs to the Mediterranean type of climate, but

[1] The following papers on the topography of Swanland may be consulted: J. T. Jutson, 'Physiography of Western Australia', *Geological Survey*, Perth, 1914; J. T. Jutson and E. S. Simpson, *Physiography of Albany*, Roy. Soc. W.A., Perth, 1916; M. Aurousseau and E. Budge, *The Swan and Helena Rivers*, Roy. Soc. W.A., Perth, 1920; E. de C. Clarke, 'Physiography of Perth', *A.A.A.S. Handbook*, Perth, 1926. On soils, see G. R. Bowman, *Geographic Review*, Oct. 1942.

perhaps finds its nearest homoclime in the Cape Town district. As regards temperature and humidity, the conditions near Athens (Greece) are not unlike those of Perth.

HOMOCLIMES OF SWANLAND

Place	Temperature (° F.)			Rainfall (inches)		
	Jan.	July	Year	Jan.	July	Year
Perth	73·6	55·0	64·0	0·3	6·4	33·11
Cape Town	69·2	54·2	61·3	0·7	3·4	24·11
Wynberg	69·0	55·0	62·0	0·5	7·7	40·6

As regards the maxima of rainfall these occur during the months of June and July, while the period November–February is practically rainless (Fig. 70). With a temperate climate, low summer humidity (55 per cent in January) and sufficient rainfall, the Swanland region is undoubtedly one of the healthiest in the world.

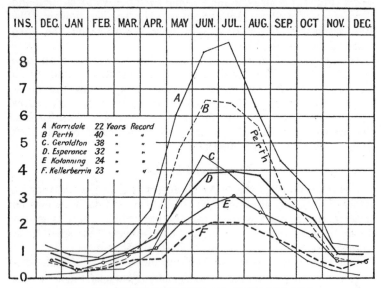

A Karridale   22 Years Record
B Perth   40   "   "
C. Geraldton   38   "   "
D. Esperance   32   "   "
E Katanning   24   "   "
F. Kellerberrin 23   "   "

FIG. 70.—WINTER RAINFALL IN SWANLAND, W.A.

NATURAL REGION 12: NULLARBOR

This region occupies the coast behind the Great Australian

Bight (see Endpaper map). It consists of a vast plateau built up of Tertiary limestones, though Cretaceous rocks outcrop on the northern edge (Fig. 12). Miocene deposits form steep cliffs 200 feet high along the coast. In many cases these probably represent lines of faulting. From the coast the plateau gradually rises to a height of about 1,000 feet in the north. The limestone is cavernous and is often 800 feet thick (see Photo 6, Plate III). The rains sink at once into the limestone, and it is this lack of surface water which has largely prevented settlement in the Nullarbor region.

The character of the region may be judged from the fact that the Transcontinental Railway runs for 330 miles across it almost without a curve, and approximately at the same level. The limestone is often covered with a foot of red soil, but rock fragments

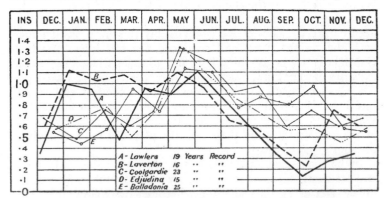

FIG. 71.—SEASONAL RAINS FOR NULLARBOR AND THE GOLD-FIELDS

are everywhere common on the surface. However, abrupt depressions or 'Dongas' are frequently met with, and numerous 'blowholes' lead to vast caves in certain areas.

The vegetation is composed chiefly of halophytes, of which saltbush (*Atriplex vesicarum*) and bluebush (*Kochia sedifolia*) are the chief. These are woody plants with grey woolly leaves, which grow to a height of 2 or 3 feet (Fig. 36). In the dongas there is a little more water preserved in the soil, and here small trees such as acacias and *Pittosporum* may grow. The typical Karst character of the topography greatly reduces the value of this region. It has about 9 inches of rainfall of a fairly reliable type, which nearly all falls in winter. The graphs for Edjudina and Balladonia (Fig. 71) resemble those for Nullarbor, since they are on its western edge.

There is some artesian water, but a good deal of it is too salty to be of use. One would imagine that the presence of the railway right across it would have greatly increased the pastoral occupation, but owing to the difficulty of obtaining permanent water this has not been the case. When the writer last traversed the Nullarbor Plains, a number of years after the line was built, settlements at the railway stations (named after the Prime Ministers Barton, Fisher, Cook, &c.) were little more than collections of huts for maintaining the railway service.

NATURAL REGION 13: EYRE'S PENINSULA

This peninsula has the form of a triangle, each side being about 200 miles long. It is fairly well marked off from the arid north by the striking series of salt lakes, Everard, Gairdner, Torrens, &c. It seems likely that the ancient rocks of the Shield have been elevated along its northern boundary in an east–west warp, which has been named the Gawler Ranges. Possibly this warp has dammed back the former rivers and produced the salt lakes, of which Gairdner is nearly 300 miles long and 30 miles wide. They are all expanses of salty mud, much as has been described for Lake Eyre. The Gawler Ranges do not rise much above 1,000 feet, and constitute a well-dissected upland built up largely of felspar porphyries. Water supplies are precarious, and the vegetation agrees with that of the arid north rather than with the plants of the peninsula to the south (see Endpaper map).

In the peninsula proper the rocks are chiefly granites and schists, and are nearly all covered with sandy soils. To the south-west an upper layer of Tertiary limestones becomes more noticeable. This region extends so far south that it comes under the influence of the Antarctic cyclones. The rainfall increases to southward, and reaches 25 inches near Port Lincoln (Fig. 60). It is typical Mallee country, though there is a good deal of saltbush in the northern portion. Much of the peninsula is now fairly prosperous wheat country. Around Flinders in the west, there are many low travertine (limestone) ridges, and in places many fixed dunes. Small swamps fill many of the depressions, where *Casuarina*, *Melaleuca* and Samphire abound. *Triodia* grass is also common. The new Tod River scheme supplies 10,000 square miles with water for stock in the north-west, from a reservoir 17 miles north of Port Lincoln. Pipes carry water to Ceduna, Thevenard and Cowell.

Iron Knob and the New Port of Whyalla

Great changes in the economy of this part of South Australia have taken place as a result of the large iron deposits at Iron Knob and Iron Monarch. For instance, water is carried some 223 miles to the nearby town of Whyalla, all the way from Morgan on the Murray. The route is shown by the heavy line in Fig. 71A. In 1944 an iron pipe (about 2 feet in diameter) was laid between Whyalla and Morgan, and this can deliver 1,200 million gallons annually. There are 27 storage tanks along this lengthy pipe line, whose construction occupied three years. Before 1944 water had been carried to the port in ships, or produced at a small distilling plant.

In June 1945 some 920 million gallons had been pumped along the pipes in the preceding twelve months. Of this amount about

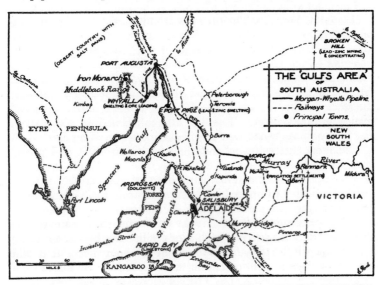

FIG. 71A.—GULFS OF SOUTH AUSTRALIA AND SITES CONNECTED WITH THE STEEL INDUSTRY

showing the mine at Iron Monarch, Whyalla and its pipe-line, Port Pirie and Broken Hill
(*From Australian Steel Industry*, by Neville R. Wills)

250 million gallons was used in Whyalla, 160 millions about half-way along at Port Pirie, 360 millions in the nearby Beetaloo District, 85 millions at Port Augusta, and about 50 millions by railways in the vicinity of the pipe line. (J. M. Holmes, *Murray Valley*, 1948.)

The growth of Whyalla, a town of 8,000 folk, in a few decades, where there are few resources and where the rainfall is only 9 inches a year, is of considerable interest (Fig. 71A). This growth is due to the presence of a low ridge of iron ore—the Middleback Range —some score of miles inland from Whyalla. The richest ore was found at Iron Knob (Fig. 117) and in 1901 a tramline from the mine to the shore 34 miles to the east gave rise to Whyalla. The hematite was used as a flux for the Broken Hill lead-zinc ores at first, but in 1913 the Broken Hill Proprietary Co. decided to build steelworks at Newcastle (N.S.W.), and to smelt iron ore from the Iron Knob area. In 1937 a blast furnace was built at Whyalla, so that the local iron ore could be smelted with coal brought some 1,200 miles from Newcastle in the holds of the otherwise empty steamers. Another new industry, ship-building, was also undertaken and in 1941 the first hull was launched.

The chief mine in the Iron Knob area is Iron Monarch, and this is charted in Fig. 117. The ore is worked in open cuts near the top of a hill of ancient schist, some 600 feet high as described on page 359. The ore contains 60 per cent of iron, and after blasting is quarried by electric shovels. It is then crushed to 4-inch size and loaded into tramcars which carry it to Whyalla. With the low rainfall of 9 inches the country is sparsely occupied by sheep ranchers, the stock feeding on salt bush which grows between the scattered mallee and mulga trees. The first pastoralists arrived about 1857, and it is now reckoned that it will carry a sheep to 20 acres.

The most interesting change in the vegetation is due to the water-supply, already described. Today, some 3 miles to the north of Whyalla, there is a remarkable oasis of 100 acres of lucerne (alfalfa) irrigated by spray lines with water from the Murray. Over 200 dairy cows are pastured here. All modern improvements are installed for cooling and bottling the milk—and the cows enter the sheds by wind tunnels in which flies are literally blown off them!

The town in 1948 had a population of about 8,000. It is laid out in an irregular grid extending westwards from Spencers Gulf along the road to Iron Knob. The residential area lies to the south of this early road, while the blast furnace and shipyards are situated along the coast to the north of the town. The main shops are naturally near the coast, but a second shopping centre has developed to the south-west beyond the Broken Hill Proprietary offices (B.H.P. on chart). The main Anglican and Catholic churches and the court house are naturally in the earlier built part of the town. In all, there are eight churches and four schools including a Technical High School. The hospital is particularly well equipped for a small town, and is largely due to the Broken Hill Proprietary Company. Many of the homes are built of stone or brick. (See the writer's map in Geog. Rev., Oct. 1950.)

The blast furnace rises 100 feet in the air, and nearly three years' work was involved in its construction, which cost a million sterling. To produce a ton of pig iron the following are fed into the furnace: ore 3,200 lb., coke (from Newcastle), 2,200 lb., limestone 600 lb.

Some 6,500 lb. of *air* is also involved in the smelting operation. The shipyard was originally a mangrove swamp, but now contains five slipways. The yard embraces all departments from platers, welders, to fitting-out. Three corvettes and nearly a dozen iron steamers (up to 9,000 tons) have already been built at Whyalla.

NATURAL REGION 14: THE SALT LAKES

The region including the numerous salt lakes of Western Australia has an elevation of about 1,200 feet (Fig. 72). It lies between the farmlands of Swanland and the 'Fixed Dunes' of the Desert division. The granite peneplain is diversified by numerous

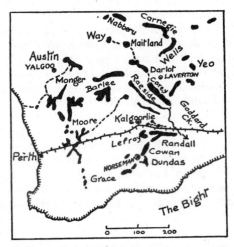

FIG. 72.—THE PLAYAS (SALT LAKES) IN THE SOUTH OF WESTERN AUSTRALIA
In rare floods Lake Austin and Lake Raeside drain some way toward the coast

mesas, and when rain falls the water collects in wide shallow depressions called 'salt-pans' if they are small and 'lakes' if they are large. The water soon disappears, both by soakage and by evaporation.

There are about 200 of these salt lakes or playas, which are large enough to appear on ordinary maps; but many of the smaller examples are not there depicted. They are almost all arranged in more or less connected strings, and after very heavy rains water may flow from one lake to the next. Thus from Yalgoo water very occasionally reaches the coastal area at Three Springs. From Lake Darlot it enters Goddard Creek, which has been known to flow across the Transcontinental Railway about 200 miles east of Kalgoorlie.

There seems little doubt that these lakes are relics of the senile rivers, which meandered over the peneplain in the wetter times before and during the Pleistocene. Perhaps slight warps during the uplift of the plateau dismembered some streams, while the increasing aridity led to many of them being dammed by drift sand. A peculiar form of arid erosion is believed by Jutson and others to have led to the actual migration of some of these lakes. Their remarkable flat rocky floors and the steeply cliffed shores favour such a hypothesis. However, in Lake Cowan silts have been proved to extend to a depth of 377 feet.

Vegetation.—Jutson describes the vegetation east of Swanland as 'far from desert', though he adds that at least half of the ground (excluding the bare areas of the salt lakes) is quite naked most of the year. The principal trees are salmon gum and gimlet gum (p. 89); while she-oak and native pine occur in small patches, as well as the graceful kurrajong-tree. The smaller vegetation consists of drought-resisting shrubs of varying heights, among which acacias, saltbush and bluebush are prominent. Grass is almost entirely absent, but small annuals thrive for a time. In the granite areas the vegetation becomes more stunted, and spinifex largely takes the place of saltbush. The country is sparsely occupied by sheep, while mining is of course very important.[1]

The region between Laverton and the eastern boundary has only been crossed by a few explorers. Lindsay in 1891–2 went from the South Australian border (latitude 26°) to the south-west near Norseman, crossing the centre of the region (see Endpaper map). At the border was poor country with low sandhills, spinifex, acacias. Even here a few large eucalypts occur. Near Mount Squires he found better country, with some Mitchell grass and saltbush. To the south of his track were high red sand ridges with some

Place	Temperature (° F.)			Rainfall (inches)		
	Average	Hottest m.	Coldest m.	Average	Wettest m.	Driest m.
Wiluna	70·0	85·0	52·0	10	2	0
Windhoek	67·0	74·0	56·0	15	4	0
Biskra	69·0	89·0	51·0	6	1	0

[1] J. T. Jutson, *Physiographical Geology*, Perth, 1914. This memoir is the most detailed source for West Australian physiography.

bloodwood and quondong. South of Queen Victoria Spring, which was dry, the country improved, and heavy Mallee was common. It may be taken as the boundary of the sandhill and spinifex areas, which runs close to Goddard Creek (Fig. 72).

Correlations.—This south-west portion of arid Australia, where the scanty rains fall chiefly in winter, is akin to Namaqua Land (Windhoek) in south-west Africa, or to Biskra in Algeria. Rainfall graphs are given in Fig. 71.

NATURAL REGION 15: THE ARID NORTH-WEST

Topography.—This region extends from the De Grey River to the Murchison River (see Endpaper map) and has been compared to the Punjab, in that it also consists (with the intervening Fortescue, Ashburton and Gascoyne) of five great river basins. The country is a peneplain rising from the coast to a height of 4,000 feet at Mount Bruce. It is crossed by fault-scarps, and merges into the sand-ridge desert in the east. The Hamersley-Ophthalmia Plateau is one of the few regions in Australia rising above 3,000 feet, and appears to be bounded by a marked fault-scarp on the north, below which flows the Fortescue River (Fig. 41). All the inland portion of the division consists of undulating (late mature) topography with large areas of plains crossed with low ridges.

The area may be subdivided into three belts, the coast, the slopes and the tableland. Each of these is about 100 miles wide and the two latter merge into each other. As is natural from the lack of rainfall, there is little dissection by streams, but Jutson[1] is inclined to assign considerable erosion to the winds. Hence the peneplain is lower in the southern drier region, where, however, Mount Augustus rises to 3,624 feet.

The two important rivers in the south are the Gascoyne and the Murchison. Jutson states that they have cut practically no trench for themselves even near their mouths, although the country which they traverse forms an elevated plateau. This is owing to the lateral erosion (largely due to the wind) keeping pace with the feeble vertical erosion due to the low rainfall. Deep water-gaps, however, occur where the Gascoyne and its tributaries leave the slopes. There have probably been numerous captures of adjoining head-waters by tributaries of the Gascoyne and Murchison.

Many of the river valleys are of the nature of Wadies, in that it is only rarely that they contain water at the surface. Thus the Shaw River had not run for nine years at the time of my visit, in

[1] J. T. Jutson, 'Physiography of Western Australia', *Geological Survey*, Perth, 1914.

1924; but its gravels gave a plentiful supply, which was carried by train 40 miles to Port Hedland. However, at Millstream on the lower Fortescue a rocky floor determines a perennial flow, which is visible for several miles until the water vanishes again in the gravels.

A further discussion of the environment on the eastern desert edge of this region will be found in Chapter VI (pages 118–20).

Season of Rain.—This region lies in the transition area between the summer and winter rains. To the north, Broome is well in the summer rain region, but Nullagine shows a slight peak in June, which becomes well marked at Onslow (Fig. 73). One point of

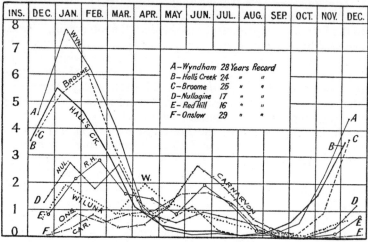

FIG. 73.—SEASONAL RAINFALL—A MIXTURE OF SUMMER AND WINTER RAINS —IN ARID WESTERN AUSTRALIA

interest is that the winter rains increase as the coast is approached, while the summer rains decrease in the same direction (Fig. 73).

The graph for Wiluna is characterized by a prominent peak (at W) in April. This is due entirely to the rain during April in 1900, when 20·7 inches fell. The total for the whole seventeen years for this month is only 33·5. Omitting this abnormal fall, the graph quite falls into line with the other stations.

Vegetation.—Along the coast is a mangrove belt, the chief genus being *Avicennia*. *Cassia* and *Mesembryanthemum* are common on the shores, while *Acacia leucospermum*, spinifex and *Atriplex* occur on the sand dunes. Further inland Mulga scrubs occur. *Eremophila* and *Helipterum* at times cover large areas with their blossoms. In the sandy country *Callitris*, *Hakea* and *Melaleuca* are typical. On the various salt-pans small varieties of *Melaleuca*, together with *Salicornia*, are characteristic.

Economics.—With a rainfall below 10 inches per annum there is no agriculture, except for some vegetables grown mainly with water from the river-gravels at Carnarvon. Considerable quantities of sheep are pastured near the coast, while inland around Peak Hill there are a few cattle stations. The gold-mining industry is of some importance, especially near Meekatharra.

Correlations.—This coastal region, where the Trade Winds blow off the continents to the sea, is represented in most of the great land masses. Yuma at the mouth of the Colorado in U.S.A. is similar. The closest parallel is with the north of South-West Africa near Cape Frio; though, owing to the stronger southern current alongside, the latter region is cooler for its latitude at Swakopmund.

Place	Latitude	Temperature (° F.)			Ann. rain (in.)
		Jan.	July	Annual	
Carnarvon	25° S.	79·8	60·6	71·1	9·05
Swakopmund	22° 42′ S.	62·6	55·2	67·1	0·7
Olukonda	18° S.	76·6	60·9	72·5	19·5

It is clear that the coastal region between Swakopmund and Olukonda in the Cunene Basin has about the same temperature as Carnarvon and a similar rainfall of about 10 inches.

NATURAL REGION 16: THE MACDONNELL RANGES

Topography.—These ranges differ a good deal from the remainder of the Northern Territory. Keith Ward has described the vicinity of Alice Springs in some detail. After the Mesozoic period, the sea retreated from continental Australia; and throughout the Tertiary period to the present day, the interior of Australia has been subjected to continuous sub-aerial denudation. The Mesozoic rocks, on elevation above sea level, formed a broad plateau region, and at the present time the remnants of this plateau slope gently towards the Lake Eyre depression, whither the drainage trends. The peneplanation of the Macdonnell Ranges was followed by an uplift, which rejuvenated the streams. They cut steep-sided gaps through the ridges of hard quartzite, which were gradually etched out in strong relief. Sometimes these gaps (as at Temple Bar) are determined by the position of fault-fractures.

The peneplain has an elevation of about 1,500 feet, and is built up of granite, gneiss and the older sedimentary series from Archean to Silurian. Three main ranges run east–west. In the north are the Davenport Ranges (in which rise the Gosse and Frew Rivers). They are only about 2,000 feet high, and are built largely of quartzite. On the Tropic is a region of parallel ranges called the Macdonnells, culminating in Mount Heughlin, 4,800 feet. The eastern portion near Arltunga is lower, but less dissected into parallel valleys. One of the latter west of Alice Springs (called the Horn Valley) runs for several hundred miles between almost continuous steep walls of rock. The salty depression of Lake Amadeus

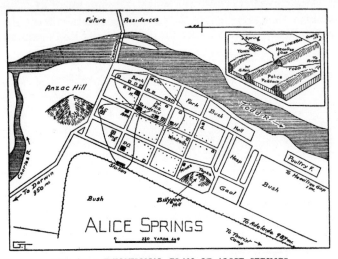

FIG. 74.—FUNCTIONAL PLAN OF ALICE SPRINGS

showing administrative and shopping centres. Inset is a view of the high parallel walls of quartzite, within 3 miles of the town, forming part of the Macdonnell Ranges

is probably about 1,400 feet above sea level (see Endpaper map). On the south the land rises again to build the Musgrave Ranges, which culminate in Mount Woodruffe at about 5,000 feet. All these higher areas are 'residuals', and are not 'young mountains' in any sense. Away from the main ranges the country is undulating, with numerous low rounded ridges, often dignified with the title of 'mountain'. Hereabouts the geology is largely masked by alluvial and windblown deposits.

The northern creeks in this area, such as the Lander, lose themselves in sand long before the lowest portion of the area is reached. Lake Amadeus in the south is said to be about 92 miles long and from 2 to 15 miles wide. It consists of a dazzling white expanse of salt, which contains a little gypsum. On each side of the lake are rows of sand hills carrying *Triodia* and sparse shrubs. The sand ridges are about 50 feet high, and are directed across the dominant direction of the south-east Trade Wind.

The Finke Basin has an area of about 80,000 square miles, with an average elevation of about 800 feet. The river rises near Mount Heughlin, and on the north of the chief ranges. It then flows through deep gorges in the Macdonnell and James ranges, and receives the Hugh, Ellery and Palmer which have traversed similar gorges (Fig. 74). South of Charlotte Waters the river has no channel, and spreads out into alluvial flats. Ultimately in time of flood the water may reach Lake Eyre *via* the Macumba, thus having a length of about 1,000 miles (Fig. 78). But in the normal state the channel is occupied by long stretches of white sand devoid of surface water. At rare intervals there may be short intervals of channel where water may be flowing gently over a rocky bed. The great part of the moisture is, of course, lost by evaporation. From 'claypans' and all shallow depressions the water disappears at an alarming rate after a fall of rain. This is to be expected with a rainfall less than 10 inches and an evaporation of over 10 feet in a year. Some of the gorges contain large pools of fresh water, which often contain fish. The picturesque saxatile vegetation is described later.

Alice Springs and the Macdonnell Ranges

In the vast peneplain which characterizes most of arid and tropical Australia, the remarkable environment of the Macdonnells has always aroused interest. Projecting above the peneplain are outcrops of ancient quartzite which rise five or six hundred feet above the general surface. They are cut through by deep narrow gorges, often containing small permanent pools with a saxatile vegetation even including *Livistona* palms. No wonder this area came as a surprise to the traveller in the interior. We know now that the curious drainage of the Todd, Finke and other rivers which cut through the 'walls' is inherited from a period when deep young Cretaceous sediments covered the whole country. Later on, erosion uncovered the almost vertical beds of far older formations, and the softer portions of the latter readily suffered erosion, while the hard bands of quartzite resisted such weathering. Simpsons Gap to the west, Heavitree Gap (Fig. 74) and Emily Gap to the east are all examples of these striking gorges to be seen near Alice Springs.

Permanent springs were found just north of the Charles River (Fig. 74), and here was built the original telegraph station of 1872. When the railway was extended from Oodnadatta to Alice Springs about 1927, the station was placed some miles south of the springs,

8

and the new settlement was called 'Stuart'. But today the old name has been transferred to the neat and flourishing little railway town almost in the centre of Australia. The Todd River is normally a flat stretch of deep sand, about 200 yards wide; and no water was visible on my visit in May 1948, although the rainy season was not long over. The town's water supply is obtained from shallow wells in the gravel just to the south of Billygoat Hill, and is stored in half a dozen tanks on that rocky knob.

As the town is approached from the Airport (inset Fig. 74) Heavitree Gap is traversed, where road and railway run along the west bank under the 500-foot cliffs. The dry bed here is 100 yards wide, shaded by large river Gums (*Euc. rostrata*). The town is 1½ miles to the north, and soon the road passes abattoirs on the east across the Todd River. Then follow many iron sheds accommodating aborigines. A successful poultry farm, a tiny Lutheran Church, and a large orange orchard are seen before we reach the hospital at the south end of Alice Springs.[1]

The town has been built in a regular gridiron between two low rocky hills. Wide sandy roads contain a few very large eucalypts, while tall hedges of pepper tree, oleander, castor-oil plant and small conifers separate the house plots. These must be watered from the wells, for there is no rain during the nine cooler months. The main road runs near the river bed, and contains six stores on each side, a bank and an hotel. The next street to the west serves another hotel, the school, a church, the Residency, and the Survey Offices. The two chief churches are in the north-west of the town, as also is the well-built post office and the station. The zones occupied by the shops and by the chief administrative offices are marked on the map.

The Residency garden contained a small green lawn, oleanders, some oranges, and vines; while tomatoes, peas, cabbages and sunflowers were growing satisfactorily with frequent watering from the wells. Many flowers such as zinnias, petunias and hibiscus brightened the garden. A number of small windmills, sunk in the river gravels, gave water to private houses in the south end of the town. At the north-east corner a concrete causeway led across the sandy bed to a new suburb under large gums, where it is proposed to build residences. Away from the river gravels the original vegetation consists of tussock grasses, small shrubs and stunted eucalypts and acacias, some 30 feet or more apart.

[1] For a lengthy description of my traverse from *Hobart to Darwin* see *Geog. Rev.*, Oct. 1950. It contains 20 maps and 8 photographs.

The Bitumen Road (Stuart Highway): Alice Springs to Barrow Creek

A journey from Leighs Creek northward must follow much the same route as that explored by Stuart, for in 1859 he found the mound springs already described, while in 1860 he reached Central Mount Stuart near Barrow Creek (Fig. 76). In 1861 he penetrated to Newcastle Waters, but was driven back by drought. Then in 1862 he crossed the continent and reached the north coast about 60 miles to the east of Darwin, in April of that year. The most remarkable episode in the early history of the Northern Territory was the construction of the overland telegraph from Adelaide to Darwin (a distance of 1,975 miles) by the small community near Adelaide numbering only 200,000 people. However, by October 1872 the line was laid, stations were built at intervals, and of course a 'bush road' connected them. For seventy years there was little change in this road, and until recently only one public vehicle—the mail—traversed the road once a month. As far back as 1889, a railway had been built between Darwin and Pine Creek, and this reached Birdum about 1928. In the south a railway as far north as Oodnadatta was built by 1891, and this was extended north to Alice Springs about 1927. Around 1942—due to the Japanese threat—the Federal Government built a tarred road of excellent quality (now known as the 'Bitumen Road') from Alice Springs to Darwin. However, over 700 miles of the central semi-desert country is served only by the Bitumen Road (or by air). The writer traversed this area in May 1948.

To the geographer this traverse is naturally of great interest, but it cannot be claimed to be replete with the features which usually attract tourists. Owing to the lack of good rains there is little in the vegetation to interest the layman, while the topography, consisting essentially of a peneplain carved in very ancient rocks, implies little variety in the landscape from end to end. There are of course no rivers of note, except perhaps the headwaters of the Roper and Katherine in the far north, which contain little water except in the wet season. We saw no wild animals except a few small kangaroos (euro) and lizards. Indeed, the chief faunal features were the innumerable termite nests, which grew larger as we proceeded north. The map is covered with 'mountain ranges'; but these are rarely more than rocky outcrops a few hundred feet high, and the very moderate hills sketched in Fig. 77A will give an idea of these 'mountains'. However, we spent a week on the journey, sleeping at the primitive but, by no means, uncomfortable hotels, which are to be found about 200 miles apart along the route.

The rocky 'walls' of the Macdonnell Ranges are soon left behind,

and a rather winding road led us towards Aileron, the next hotel
on the route. Wide plains are traversed, covered with mulga
(*Acacia*) and with a few eucalypts up to 30 feet high. There was
no sign of water in the gulleys, but bores had been put down
during the war which tapped shallow ground-water at intervals,
and shallow wells occur about 10 miles apart. Flats covered with
lance-like acacias or widespread spinifex grass (*Triodia*) characterized the route as far as the Hann Range. This rose only a few
hundred feet, and was capped by a harder layer of rock. A few
cattle were seen at intervals, and we met only two cars just as we
reached Aileron. Here is a small hotel, close to the homestead of
the station (ranche), and one or two other houses complete the
settlement.

Proceeding northwards more plains covered with shrubs or
spinifex are met. Termite nests about 2 feet high are extremely
widespread, and occasionally are built right in the margins of the
road. At Teatree Well is a small tea-house, where meals may be
obtained. It is shrouded in green Parkinsonia trees, which flourish
here, if given some well water. In the vicinity I saw an amphibian
jeep, somewhat out of place in the arid centre of Australia. It was
used with its searchlight to dazzle kangaroos, which are shot after
sundown. The hides were cured with salt scraped from nearby
salt lakes.

The road passes close to Central Mount Stuart, which is one of
a row of low rounded hills with cirque-like hollows on the slopes
(not, however, due to ice). Here we met a huge trailer-caravan
laden with steel petrol drums. (These empty containers, relics of
the war, find a ready sale in Adelaide.) At times these trailers
carry 80 bullocks or so from drought-stricken areas to those where
there is feed. The sterile soils and poor rainfall made this section
—north to Tennants Creek—the worst portion of our semi-desert
journey. Small mesas capped with rock became common, and the
well-known telegraph station at Barrow Creek is built at the base
of such a mesa (Fig. 76).

At Barrow Creek the stone buildings constructed about 1872
to withstand attacks by the aboriginals still survive, and very little
has been added to the settlement since. About a quarter of a mile
to the east is an hotel with the usual corrugated iron roof. Several
windmills (raising water from the shallow wells) and wind-motors
(to produce electric light) complete the picture. The graves of
early operators killed by the aborigines furnish an interesting
memento of distant days.

Vegetation.—The central belt contains much fair pastoral
country, though it is badly handicapped by the unreliability of the

rain. The western portion is of little value either for pastoral or mining purposes. Madigan (*loc. cit.*) gives a graphic picture of the lamentable failure of the 'Granites' gold rush, which seems to have been a glaring example of 'distance lending enchantment to the view'. Near the Gosse River there are large eucalypts, and the creek bed can be traced for over 100 miles, when it assumes the appearance of a grassy flat, and soon enters polygonum swamps. The Frew and Elkedra exhibit much the same environment (Fig. 78). The poisonous bush *Gastrolobium* is abundant in some valleys. D. J. Gordon surveyed the Frew River, and noticed all the usual xerophytic trees, such as gidji, bloodwood, tea-tree, beefwood, lancewood, &c. There were patches of Mitchell grass

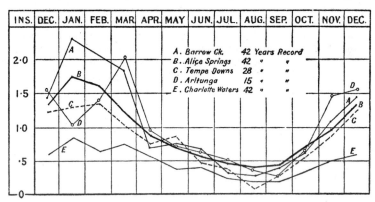

FIG. 75.—SUMMER RAINS IN CENTRAL AUSTRALIA

and many other types of valuable grasses. Notes on the trees will be found on page 228.

The west of the region is not so promising. Davidson on his survey towards Tanami travelled 300 miles without finding permanent water in 1900. The country consisted of practically useless mulga scrub. Scattered limewood, mallee, corkwood and native orange were encountered. *Gastrolobium* was plentiful near the Western Australian border. The southern portion of the region contains many plains, which are largely covered with 'gibbers' (desert pebbles) of indurated sandstone. Mallees, *Cassias* about 6 feet high, and species of *Eremophila* are common. Along the 'gum creeks' are specimens of *Eucalyptus rostrata*. *Salsola* (or 'roly-poly') grows on the lower steppes, while on the sandy slopes of the hills is the ubiquitous *Triodia*.

A special flora called *saxatile* characterizes the rocky gorges and waterholes of the region. Pines, fig-trees, *Tecoma*, cycads and even

Livistona Palms are found in favoured localities, such as Palm Creek near Hermannsburg. The best pastoral country is in the Finke basin, where there are a dozen head-stations. There are also a few in the Davenport Ranges, near the Gosse and Frew, which are intermittent rivers (Fig. 76).

The graphs in Fig. 75 show a purely summer rainfall. The amount in summer varies with distance from the northern seas, but in winter there is little difference in the amounts in all five localities. The graph for Arltunga shows a striking peak in March. This is due to one heavy fall of 13 inches in March, 1910. The average *annual* rain is only 11 inches.

NATURAL REGION 17: CLONCURRY

Topography.—The uplands west of Cloncurry are built up of ancient folded Silurian sediments, while the eastern border consists of more or less level-bedded Cretaceous sediments. The latter (as we have read) cover the great supplies of artesian water (p. 190). The more ancient deposits in the west form a peneplain about 1,000 feet high, and merge gradually into the so-called Barkly Tableland. The low-lying Gulf country is thinly forested and crossed by numerous rivers. The highest point on the Cloncurry railway is at Selwyn (1,230 feet) and the 'divide' runs north-west from here to Camooweal, which is lower. Danes has described considerable areas of Karst (limestone) country in the vicinity of Camooweal. This furthest extension of the Great Western Shield is noted for many important mining fields, of which the chief are near Cloncurry and Mount Isa (see Endpaper map).

Cloncurry is the largest town in the region, and dates back to the sixties of the last century, when gold was discovered in this part of Queensland. A mine was developed about 1 mile south of Coppermine Creek (Fig. 75A); the carrier to the mine made his camp near the creek at the spot marked 'Inn' on the map, and here the first hotel was built. Later the railway was extended to this goldfield from Townsville, and branches have been built to Mt. Cuthbert and Mt. Isa. The main stream, which flows only in the wet summer season, is the Cloncurry river, about a mile to the west; but the town was planned without reference to this inter-mittent stream. Mt. Isa is the chief mine in the district nowadays, and lies 68 miles WSW. of the town; but by rail it is about double that distance. Mary Kathleen uranium field is nearby.

The town was planned as a conventional grid centred at the Post Office at the junction of Sheaffe and Scarr Streets. The rail-way was brought in along the eastern edge of the town, and has drawn the shops somewhat in that direction, as is usually the case. The chief government offices—such as the town hall, court house, police station and the main school—are all just east of the post office (Fig. 75A). The shops form another zone, mostly along Scarr

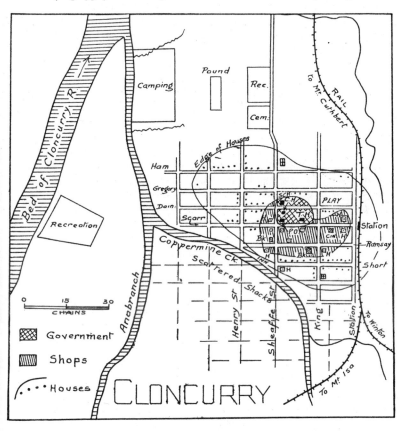

FIG. 75A.—SKETCH PLAN IN 1948 OF THE MINING CENTRE OF CLONCURRY
IN NORTH QUEENSLAND
showing functional zones. Town Hall, Court House, Banks and Hotels are shown by initials

and Ramsay Streets. The large number of hotels (H) and shops in this small town shows that it is the centre of a large mining and pastoral district. The map charts approximately the edge of built-in streets, i.e. where the *occupied* blocks are in the majority. The official town-plan includes many more streets, as shown by the broken lines; but here there are only scattered houses, usually of the nature of shacks. The better houses are to be found mainly on or near Henry Street, north-west of the shopping area. According to the author's classification, Cloncurry is in the 'juvenile' stage of evolution.

The map shows various areas set apart for Recreation and for the 'Camping' of travelling stock, &c., as they pass near Cloncurry. This area with its rather rocky soils, and a rainfall below 20 inches, is on the northern edge of the sheep areas of Queensland, but is in the middle of the beef cattle area. In both cases, however, the number of stock grazed is relatively low owing to the poor quality of the feed in this mining area.

Vegetation.—To the east of this region mulga associations occur, but open grassy plains are common in the west. The Cretaceous sandstone and shales give rise to rather poor soils, and the vegetation is rather sparse. In the uplands the soils rich in silica are locally called 'desert' irrespective of the rainfall. *Triodia* and 'snapping gum' are typical in these very poor districts. The Gulf country is largely a low-level sparsely timbered plain with stunted eucalypts. Much of it is liable to flooding, and (according to Thomson) there are 'far more termites' nests to the acre than trees'. An excellent study of the pastoral possibilities of the western portion of this region—the Barkly Tableland—by Wynne Williams, is published in the *Geographical Journal* (London), January 1928, and is discussed on page 337. In general the vegetation is similar to that found in the east of Region 18.

The purely summer character of the rain is illustrated in the graph for Cloncurry (Fig. 68).

NATURAL REGION 18: DARWINIA

Topography.—This is a convenient name, based on the sole town in the region, for that part of the Northern Territory north of latitude 19°. It has an annual rainfall of more than 16 inches, all of which falls in the summer. To the south it merges into the semi-desert lands near Tennants Creek, which connect the enormous area of the Desert to the south-west with the smaller Arunta Desert in the east of the Territory.

The region forms part of the great peneplain which was uplifted in late Tertiary times. Jensen believes that this upward movement has been continued to the present day. This is indicated by the raised beaches around most of the coastline. So also the canyons of the Katherine and the McArthur Rivers show rejuvenation by recent uplift. Inland the peneplain has not been trenched by the rivers in any general fashion. The northern part of the Territory seems to lie at an elevation between 500 and 900 feet, though considerable portions of Arnhem Land (which is not yet fully explored) may be somewhat higher. There is little evidence that much of Darwinia is above 1,000 feet, though early writers suggest this.

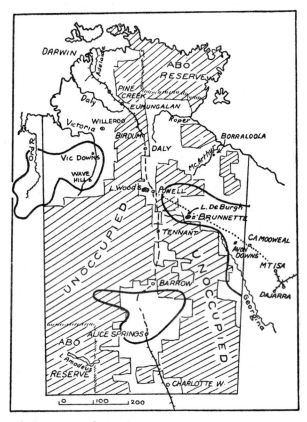

FIG. 76.—ECONOMIC ASPECTS OF NORTHERN TERRITORY, FROM THE PAYNE–FLETCHER REPORT, 1937

The ruled area is almost all desert or useless. The heavy black ovals show suggested sheep country. The dotted line shows the logical railway to the Territory as advocated by the writer since 1922.

Daly Waters is set down at 691 feet, and this station is on the local divide. Admiral Creswell wrote (far back in 1895) of the country east of Powells Creek:

From the edge of the 'jump-up' westward to Powells Creek, a distance of 300 miles, there is not a hill of any consequence. I can give you no better idea of the general level of the country than a description of what

is called Ashburton 'Range' on the map. It was only by the map that
we discovered it *was* a range, and any railway contractor would have
thought nothing of making as high a range if it were let to tender!

Drainage.—Many of the finest of Australian rivers are to be
found along the coasts of this region. The Victoria is navigable
for craft drawing 3 feet for 100 miles. The Roper can be navigated
for 90 miles by vessels drawing 14 feet; the Adelaide for 80 miles,
and the Daly (for light draught vessels) for 60 miles. Unfortunately the volume of water varies greatly. There are likely to be
heavy floods in the summer, which invade the possible agricultural
lands near the rivers. Moreover, in the winter a good deal of water
reaches the rivers from abundant springs in many areas.

In the east the Barkly Tableland appears to be well defined only
on its *northern* edge, where it drops somewhat rapidly towards the
coast. It may be about 1,100 feet high, and much of its drainage
flows into vast shallow basins, which become lakes in very wet
seasons. Thus Lake de Burgh (near Brunette Downs) may expand
to a length of about 100 miles. But generally it has disintegrated
into a series of swampy areas at the lower ends of the Playford,
Creswell and other creeks. Lake Woods, near Newcastle Waters,
is another such lake, which is also intermittent in character. It
seems logical to assume that slight warping has led to these shallow
depressions. There has been a long period of desiccation during
later Tertiary times, so that such fold-basins would not become
notched and drained as in better watered regions. Perhaps as they
dried they might be kept somewhat clear of debris by the action
of the constant winds blowing to the west.

Vegetation.—The plants of this part of the Territory are of a
more xerophytic character than might be expected from the fairly
high amount of the total rainfall. This is due mainly to two reasons.
The soils are distinctly sterile over large areas, owing to the sandy
character of many of the formations. There is a large development
of surface formations due to a process of 'sweating', whereby
magnesia, lime, iron and siliceous salts have been transferred to
the surface, and deposited there as limestone, laterite or quartzite.
The other factor is the season of the rain, which leaves nine months
of the year quite dry. Jensen and Winters have shown the edaphic
character of the vegetation in the following table. (See also notes
on the trees, p. 228.)

Rainfall.—Inspection of the graph (Fig. 77) shows that there is
only one wet season in Darwinia. Even at Tennants Creek the
presence of winter rain is almost imperceptible, though a slight
peak in the curve in July is perhaps attributable to this cause. The

VEGETATION OF DARWINIA

Formation	Composition	Locality	Rainfall	Vegetation
Cambrian	Limestone	Pine Creek to Camooweal	40–15	Excellent open pastoral country, with Coolibah, Mitchell Grass, *Bauhinia*
Cambrian	Sandstone	Narrow belts with limestone	,,	Very poor country, with messmate, spinifex, desert gum in south
Permo-carboniferous	ditto	Broad belts, S. from Borraloola and Willeroo,&c.	25–20	ditto
Granite		Pine Creek	44	Woollybutt, red gum
Basic rocks	Basalts, &c.	Upper Daly to Wave Hill	44–20	Good country, nutwood, wattle and box
Tertiary	Alluvial laterites	Coastal, along rivers	60–25	Mangroves, teatree, pandanus, &c.

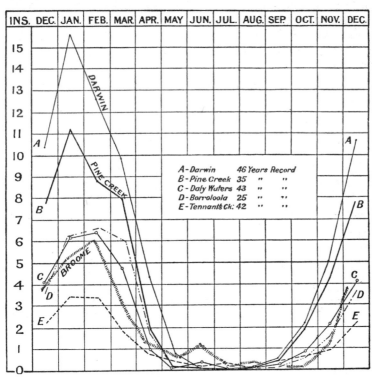

FIG. 77.—HEAVY SUMMER RAINS IN THE NORTH OF NORTHERN TERRITORY, AND IN BROOME

rain falls almost wholly in December, January and February, with the maximum generally in January. The six months from May to October are practically dry throughout, the total rainfall varying from 3½ inches at Darwin to less than 2 inches at Tennants Creek.

The changes of the monsoons at Darwin have been described by J. G. Little somewhat as follows:

The strong ESE. wind of the cooler dry season ceases in September and the weather becomes intensely hot. Thunderstorms occur every four or five days, and increase in numbers until the end of November. About an inch of rain accompanies each driving storm. In December the north-west monsoon soon blows fairly steadily, and the thunderstorms cease. The sky becomes cloudy and the air is very humid. Rain falls almost every day until the early part of February. In March the north-west monsoon dies away, and is succeeded by oppressive calms until the end of April. Then the south-east monsoon (i.e. the normal Trade Wind) sets in, giving clear skies and cool nights and mornings.

Since the colonization of this part of Australia has been a great problem throughout its history it is discussed in a later chapter dealing with population. However, the following table shows homoclimes of Darwinia, and none of these places has become an important centre of white settlement in spite of greater population pressure.

HOMOCLIMES OF DARWINIA

Place	Latitude	Temperature (° F.)		Rainfall average (inches)	Products
		Hottest m.	Coolest m.		
Australia:					
Darwin	12° S.	84·2	77·2	62	Cattle
Daly Waters	16° S.	86·9	68·6	27	Cattle
Africa:					
Bathurst (Gambia)	13° N.	80·6	73·7	48	Groundnuts, cattle
Mozambique	15° S.	82·7	73·7	37	Groundnuts, wax
Beira	20° S.	80·7	68·9	54	Cotton, sugar
Asia:					
Bangkok (Siam)	13½° N.	83·4	74·8	55	Rice, sugar, hides
Cuttack (India)	20° N.	87·0	70·0	55	Rice, jute
America:					
Uberaba (Brazil)	20° S.	74·3	65·1	64	Cattle, cotton
Quixeramobim (do.)	5° S.	83·1	78·9	28	Hides, cotton, &c.
Merida (Mexico)	21° N.	83·3	69·6	31	Sisal, tobacco, sugar

Tennants Creek and Newcastle Waters

North of Barrow Creek is the same undulating country with poor tussock grass and much bare loam. The Crawford and

Osborne Ranges, though marked on the map, were too insignificant
to be identified on the landscape. Scrub country, with bushes
3 feet high, alternated with patches of acacia, close-set and 10 feet
high. The topography became a little more hilly as we approached
the Davenport Range near Wauchope (in May 1948). I was told
that this marked the northern limit of the rabbit pest. Here some
outcrops of granite had weathered into remarkable tors—locally
known as 'The Devil's Marbles'. The range was only a few
hundred feet above the surrounding peneplain. Termites and
clumps of spinifex characterized the next section, while small termite nests were not uncommon in the bitumen road itself. White
gums became more abundant as we approached Tennants Creek.
Here small mesas and a few conical hills became visible; and a few

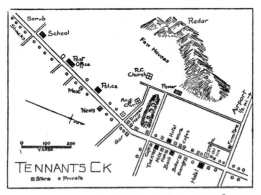

FIG. 77A.—SITE-VIEW OF TENNANTS CREEK IN 1948, THE SOLE
TOWN IN THE CENTRE OF NORTHERN TERRITORY

miles south of the little town we passed several small gold mines
which have recently shown promise (Fig. 76).

Since Tennants Creek is the sole settlement of note in the central
part of the huge Northern Territory (523,000 square miles), some
notes on its condition in 1948 should be of interest. The bitumen
road runs approximately north–south and constitutes the main
street. As the sketch plan (Fig. 77A) shows, there are only one or
two cross-streets, which lead merely to open bush for the most
part. The airport is about a mile to the north-west of the town.
The buildings of the school, post office and police quarters are
raised on short piles—indicating our approach to the hot climates
and the need for summer ventilation. There are two hotels, a bank,
a cinema, and a newspaper office. About a score of stores and
thirty private houses are arranged along the main street. The two
churches are on the main cross-street, which also leads to a power

station based on imported fuel. A few mines are to be seen in the
hills to the south-west, and a radar station crowns a nearby hill,
about 200 feet above the plain.

Proceeding north from the little town the landscape was marked
by a prevalence of thickets of small trees about 15 feet high.
Tussocks of grass were abundant but there was no underbrush.
Near Attack Creek (where Stuart was driven back in 1861) are
many small hills and juvenile valleys. Some of the poorest country
on the whole route now lay ahead consisting of rocky soil mostly
covered with tussocks of spinifex, with occasionally low mesas
capped by a hard rock layer. About latitude 18° S. new types of
trees such as Corkwood (*Gyrocarpus*), Bauhenia and Grevillea were
noted. Grey and white spotted gums and bloodwoods (both
Eucalypts) grew to heights of 30 feet, but were not very abundant
so far south. We did not pass through Powells Creek, and only
had a glimpse of Lake Woods some distance to the west. This lake
may be 20 miles long, but is usually dry by August. It was
unusually large in 1940. Near here the main road to Queensland
branches to the east, and most of it has been surfaced with bitumen
like the north–south road. We crossed Newcastle Creek (which
supplies Lake Woods) by a stony causeway, and then climbed a
low hill to Newcastle Waters.

This famous telegraph station is much less imposing than Tennants Creek, and the settlement consists of the usual hotel, a large
store and half a dozen private houses. Half a mile to the south
is the ranch, which we did not visit. Several wind motors supplied
power and light to the hotel. The Creek in May was merely a
string of shallow muddy pools. Later the main road again crossed
Newcastle Creek at a fine waterhole with numerous waterfowl, so
that a considerable improvement in the country takes place north
of Newcastle Waters, for Mitchell and Flinders grasses here replace
useless spinifex. About half-way to Daly Waters, near Dunmarra,
we crossed the continental divide, though there is no obvious topographic feature to indicate that we were now in the coastal drainage
area.

Daly Waters, Mataranka and Katherine

About 50 miles north of Tennants Creek is Dunmarra Station
where peanuts were growing in a small garden. Larger trees, scattered over the level country, gave a park-like appearance to the
landscape. The soils were, however, poor, and the termite nests
were now considerably larger, a few being 4 feet high. Thickets
of acacia were still common. As usual we met only two or three
other vehicles the whole day long. We turned off some 2 miles to

the west and reached Daly Waters. Here there are two clusters of buildings about one-third of a mile apart. The first consists of the telegraph station, and contains three or four large sheds of galvanized iron, some of which are badly infested by white ants. The dry bed of a creek (40 yards wide) lies just behind these buildings, and in front is a small garden containing a few forlorn banana and pawpaw trees. Further along the road is the hotel of the usual galvanized iron type, under some large eucalyptus trees. The Ironwood tree (*Erythrophloem*) became abundant hereabouts. Between the two sets of buildings is a dead tree with the letter 'S' carved on it. This was probably cut by Stuart in May 1862, and it is to be hoped that his memento will long be preserved. Many goats wandered below the large trees, and the hotel was draped with bougainvillea and other ornamental vines. A small airfield lies to the south-east of the telegraph station.

Much the same open woodland was now traversed with rather scrubby 'coolibah' and other eucalyptus trees, many having smooth salmon-coloured bark. Near the end of the northern railway is Larrimah, where hundreds of abandoned iron huts and sheds are relics of the war. Here the road-convoys from the south terminated their journeys. Birdum nearby is the railway terminus, but unless the line is continued on to Barkly Tableland (to the east) there seems little economic reason for the present railway connecting Birdum with the unattractive region near the coast at Darwin. The termite nests were now larger—some 5 feet high—and had pinnacled crests. A dozen miles south of Mataranka we crossed the Elsey River by the first notable bridge on our journey. Near here is the famous Elsey Station described in the classic story, *We of the Never-Never*, and the hero of the book (Aeneas Gunn) is buried in the adjacent cemetery. Alongside the river we saw the first thickets of Pandanus palms, which are typical coastal trees.

Mataranka consists of a rather large rambling hotel, half a dozen other houses, the railway station and some fine trees. Here were numerous *Sterculias* allied to the Kurrajong of the south. Poinciana and Tamarind trees had been planted nearby, and the native eucalypts were much larger than to the south. We drove a few miles to the east to the Roper River and found there a good sample of a 'Corridor forest'. In a narrow belt close to the river were various tropical trees, whose names I did not ascertain. *Passiflora* vines with edible fruit climbed through the undergrowth. In a large pool were numerous blue water-lilies, giving rise to a scene very different from anything seen hitherto. But a few yards away from the river was the usual open rather xerophytic woodland of the Territory.

From Mataranka to Katherine there were many hills and shallow valleys with the usual sparse forest-cover. We did not stop at Maranboy, where there has been some tin-mining in the past. Here the geological features changed, and ridges of limestone appeared on each side of our road. As we approached Katherine numerous abandoned iron sheds showed how important a military site this had been during the recent war. Indeed, the Japanese bombed both Katherine and Mataranka during their furthest thrusts towards Australia. This little settlement ranks second to Tennants Creek, for flanking the main road are two hotels, four stores, and a number of other shops and houses. The railway station is alongside, just on the south side of the rather deep valley of the Katherine River. There is a concrete 'ford road' some distance to the west, where the Bitumen Road crosses the valley. In the wet season cars can manage to get across on the railway bridge.

The chief interest at Katherine is the Experimental Farm a few miles to the west, close to the famous 'Springs' in the side of the river valley. Unfortunately the best land is only a narrow strip in the form of a levee along and above the sides of the deep valley of the present river. Cotton, pawpaws and bananas were being watered from the river, and were growing well. South American Lucerne (*Stylosanthis*) is a close-growing legume, whose dried leaves seem to be a valuable fodder for stock in these tropical areas. Broom millet, peanuts and tobacco are also crops which show much promise. In the vicinity are twenty Russian immigrants whose crops of peanuts are giving good returns. It is however necessary to remember that good soils are quite limited in the Territory. In the valley floors the heavy floods in the summer make it almost impossible to use these river soils for agriculture.

Katherine to Darwin

Northward from the Katherine River are limestone outcrops at frequent intervals. Long cane-grass grows in places, and Cycads soon become common in the sparse undergrowth. Edith River is another small flowing stream, near which is much granite weathering into small tors. The road becomes quite hilly in the next section, with *Callitris* trees among the eucalypts. At Fergusson River I noticed many pandanus trees near the edge of a large pool. We saw abandoned diggings on the side of a low granite hill, and soon reached Pine Creek which has been an important goldfield in days past. Today, it is a very small settlement somewhat off the Bitumen Road. There is a fairly large hotel and two stores near the station, while across the railway near the airport are the police, school and post office. An abandoned hospital is the most imposing building at the south end of the main road.

To the north of Pine Creek the country is rocky, and seems to have little pastoral value. Small palms, about 4 feet high, are very abundant in places under the larger eucalypts. Callitris and Pandanus continue to be abundant in low situations. Now deep valleys between flattened ridges appeared on both sides of the road as we neared Brocks Creek—another scene of bygone mining. The termite nests became much larger, and as we neared Adelaide River, we saw a sample about 12 feet high. Creeks containing water became fairly frequent, sometimes with huge clumps of bamboos hanging over the water. Coomallie Creek contains a flow of water, with a narrow fringe of corridor-forest as on the Roper River far to the south. We spent the night at Berry Springs—a former hospital and rest area of the Army. Here were hundreds of empty iron huts, and also a number of sheds made by the Chinese from the local bamboo. A beautiful swimming pool in the Berry River was flanked by concrete pavements, and had been a popular resort of the convalescing soldiers in the closing years of the war. It is hoped to make this a resort for folk from Darwin, since it is only about 40 miles from the large port. All this district is clothed in eucalypts up to 40 feet high, somewhat scattered and with no marked underbrush, though rough grass covers much of the surface. We passed near the large dam blocking the valley of Manton River which gives Darwin, with its 5,000 people, a plentiful supply. Indeed, it is said that ten times as large a city could be supplied without difficulty. We reached Darwin at noon of May 28, 1948.

The Functional Pattern of Darwin

Although this settlement was first established in 1868, and is one of the most widely known ports in the world, no geographic survey is known to the writer. It is situated on a typical ria named Port Darwin, which is a branching bay with half a dozen cliffed promontories projecting into it. The town has been built on the eastern 'headland' at the mouth of the bay, and though it was originally named 'Palmerston', this name has long been replaced by 'Darwin'. It will be noticed (from the inset map in Fig. 77B) that the roads and railways enter the town from the north, leading to a small horseshoe inner harbour which faces to the south-east. Here Tertiary laterites cap beds of Cretaceous shales; and cliffs of the latter rocks, some 60 feet high, surround much of the headland on which Darwin is laid out. The northern suburbs of Darwin, where the cemetery and Botanical Gardens are situated, are on lower ground than the town and its western suburbs. The open ocean has eroded sand beaches on the west side of the Darwin town area, while the shallow eastern waters (within the bay) are hidden by mangroves.

The town plan is a conventional grid consisting of six longitudinal streets crossed by six other streets. The main axis runs from SE. to NW. along the low plateau of the Darwin promontory. The Esplanade runs along the top of the cliffs on the west and

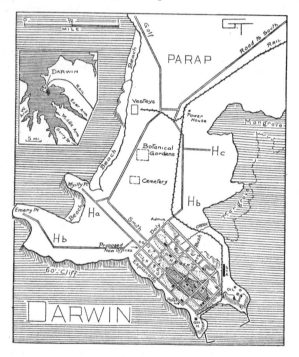

FIG. 77B.—FUNCTIONAL PLAN OF DARWIN

Ha are good houses, Hc are poor houses. Banks, Hotels, Town Hall, &c., are shown by initials. Inset is a map of the ria of Port Darwin

south sides, and contains the early government buildings just behind the inner harbour. New offices are projected in the near future, and they are to be built at the north-west end of the Esplanade. The proposed court house, town hall and post office are shown by initials in Fig. 77B.

There is an isolated cape at each side of the small harbour, and the western cape is crowned by Government House. The other is rather irregular and shelters many oil tanks on low ground near the railway station. Two long piers—served by the railway—help to shut in a portion of the bay to form an inner harbour. The wrecks of half a dozen ships, bombed by the Japanese, still lay off the promontory when I visited the town in 1948.

The functional pattern of the town is clearly charted in the map. The official buildings near the harbour were built of stone, and were badly bombed. The Anglican Church is alongside, near the Esplanade. The main street is Smith Street at right-angles to the former street, and it runs to the north-west along the axis of the promontory. It includes the banks (B), one of which was badly bombed, and most of the chief shops. The two largest hotels (H) are on the second cross-street, and the western hotel has a splendid site just above the cliffs; the eastern hotel was ruined by bombs. Behind the station was a Chinese quarter, but most of this has been demolished, and Darwin has today a neat, well-cared-for appearance in spite of its troubled history. Surrounding the shopping zone is a zone of private houses which is also somewhat oval in shape. At the northern end is the chief school (S), and the present Administrative Offices. Grass and brush clothe the slopes on the north-east and north-west corners of the 'grid', so that the little town has not yet grown to occupy all of the planned streets.

To the north of Daly Street (which bounds the grid on the north) are a number of radiating roads leading to more isolated suburbs. For instance, there are many attractive bungalows (labelled 'Hb' in the map) near Emery Point. Also near Myilly Point are some of the best houses (Ha) in the town, where military officers and senior citizens dwell. Vesteys Meat Works, which were erected at great cost near the Parap suburb, only operated for a few years and were abandoned in 1919. The Botanical Gardens contain many acclimatized tropical trees and grassy lawns, and add greatly to the amenities of Darwin. Some 4 miles to the north and well beyond most houses is the Golf Course. Several Power Houses border the railway, and the main airport lies off the map some miles to the north-east of the town.

Economic Possibilities

At the conclusion of our long traverse it may be well to summarize the economic possibilities of the Territory in the vicinity of the Bitumen Road. Mining and agriculture have not been of much importance in the past, so that we may confine our attention mainly to the cattle industry, which is the mainstay of settlement, now as in the past. It is convenient to divide our traverse into five sections, which are essentially based on the amount of the summer rainfall. (There is no rain in the nine cooler months of the year in almost all this large region.) Since the natural vegetation is the best indicator of a country's capabilities this aspect of the environment is stressed. The recent memoir by M. R. Jacobs on the Eucalypts of the Territory (Canberra, 1945) is the basis for many of the data which follow.

The first section has a rainfall from 10 to 12 inches and extends from Alice Springs to Barrow Creek. The valuable fodder, saltbush (*Atriplex*), grows sparsely in this section, and here reaches its northern limit. There are a number of cattle stations near the road, which runs between the huge western desert and the smaller Arunta Desert on the east. Among the eucalypts thicket-like Mallees are common, including such species as *gamophylla*, *morissii* and *pachyphylla*. Darker rough-bark eucalypts such as *E. intertexta*, and *polycarpa* are also to be seen.

The second section (12 to 14 inches of rain) stretches from Barrow Creek to Tennants Creek. Here the best country lies to the east of the road, where there are wet-season creeks rising in the low Davenport Range, such as the Frew and Gosse. Here are large red gums (*rostrata*) in the creek beds, bloodwoods, and other genera such as corkwood, beefwood, melaleuca, gidyea and also thickets of Acacia akin to lancewood and brigalow.

The third section (15 to 25 inches) is from Tennants Creek to Daly Waters. Very poor country lies both east and west of Tennants Creek, due primarily to the sandy sterile character of the soils. Here there is practically no pastoral occupation. But a little to the north-east is the excellent cattle country of the Barkly Tableland, near (temporary) Lake De Burgh and Brunette Downs. However, along the road in the vicinity of Lake Woods and Newcastle Waters there is a narrow belt of pastoral country, but with unoccupied country east and west (see Fig. 76). Smooth-bark eucalypts such as *aspera*, and rough-barks like *microtheca* and *terminalis*, characterize this section.

The fourth section (25 to 40 inches) extends from Daly Waters to Pine Creek. Most of this is poor stock country. Indeed, the railway was extended to Birdum mainly to bring southern cattle quickly across this area to the meat works at Darwin, which however were abandoned in 1919. The heavier tropical rain produces rank grasses not much relished by cattle, and the soil here is generally rather sterile. Rough-bark eucalypts such as *feruuginea*, *pruinosa* and *pyrophora* are abundant.

The fifth section from Pine Creek to Darwin passes through hilly country with the rainfall increasing northward to 60 inches. There are scattered cattle stations west of the road, where hybrids of cattle with zebu stand the ticks and the drought better than the usual breeds of cattle. Three white men with 40 aboriginal helpers can run a station of 200 square miles in this section. Here the common eucalypts are *grandifolia, miniata* and *latifolia*. Other types of tropical plants and trees have been mentioned in the earlier pages.

NATURAL REGION 19: KIMBERLEY

Topography.—This region differs from most of Western Australia in that it has a rainfall exceeding 20 inches (see Endpaper map). It is, however, part of the general peneplain, consisting of many different formations which have been eroded in varying degrees. The highest point is Mount Hann (2,800 feet). With the greater rainfall the older, moderately flat, surface is now broken into ridges and valleys. Some of the harder rocks stand out as steep walls, running roughly from north-west to south-east. These in part constitute the King Leopold, Napier and Geikie Ranges. The rivers in places zigzag through these walls in deep antecedent gorges. It has been suggested that the rivers originally flowed to the south-west like Sturts Creek, but have been captured by west-flowing coastal streams.

The main stream is the Fitzroy River, which is about 350 miles long, and carries enormous volumes of water to the sea after the summer rains. It drains broad grassy plains and occasionally, as in 1914, these are covered by floods over 20 miles wide. In the dry months it ceases to run, but long waterholes are common along its course.

The coast is marked by a number of deep narrow gulfs (rias) which are due to the relatively late drowning of large river valleys by the sea. A tidal rise of 25 feet is common along this coast. There is a large artesian basin in the hinterland of Broome. Several bores, about 1,000 feet deep, have been sunk in the vicinity of the town. The eastern limits of this basin have not yet been accurately determined.

The Pearling town of Broome

Broome is the capital of the Kimberley Region, although it lies in the south-west corner of this large district. It is associated with Dampier's explorations in 1699, and is in many respects one of the most interesting towns in Australia. The author's visit was made in 1924, when the number of Japanese inhabitants was near its maximum, and the map (Fig. 77C) refers to this period of its history.

Large steamers can enter the harbour only at high tide. They proceed up to the pier, and anchor about half a mile from the shore. The tide recedes and leaves them high and dry on the grey mud.

The town itself lies within the northern headland of Roebuck Bay,
so named after Dampier's ship. The streets extend along the shore
for a mile or so up to the mouth of a muddy creek among the
mangrove trees. Bungalows for the white residents are shaded by
wide-spreading Poinciana trees, but white ants destroy much of
the vegetation in the town.

The native quarter is situated in the north-east of the town. It

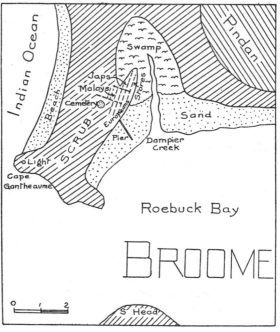

FIG. 77C.—THE PEARLING CENTRE OF BROOME (W.A.)

a sketch survey made in 1924

consists of a number of shops and houses, while three or four
warehouses belonging to white owners transact most of the pearl-
shell business. At the time of my visit Broome had a population of
about 3,000, of whom only 600 were of British birth. There were
about 1,200 Japanese, and some 600 Koepangers from Timor. All
these foreigners were indentured, and would return to their homelands when their contracts finished. Since the war all the Japanese
have left, and the pearling is carried out by Koepangers and other
coloured folk from the islands to the north of Australia. The divers
are usually Malays or Filipinos. (See p. 423.)

Vegetation.—In the southern portion of the Kimberleys there are extensive tracts of pasture land on the slopes of the rivers running into the Indian Ocean. Inland from these, are stunted bush and scrub lands with a rather widespread reddish soil. This country is locally known as 'pindan'. There is forest country near the Fitzroy River and in the King Leopold Ranges. Further east the most abundant vegetation consists of acacias and *Cassias.* Loranthaceae, Rubiaceae and Proteaceae are represented by several genera. Ferns are plentiful near the Victoria River. The distribution of the best forage plant, Mitchell grass, is indicated in the Pasture map (Fig. 32).

In North Kimberley there are large areas of basalt, which on weathering give rise to rather fertile soils. These are covered with good grass, and are lightly timbered with eucalypts such as coolibah, box and ironbark. The sandstones give rise to poor soils, but they carry a variety of spinifex which can be eaten by stock. Here the dominant trees are Woollybutt and Messmate, while *Callitris, Banksia* and *Brachychiton* are common.

Although the flow of a number of the rivers falls off a good deal in the cooler dry months, it seems likely that shortage of water will not be a serious disability to the pastoralists in this part of the Kimberleys. As mentioned elsewhere, the temperatures are very high, having an average near 84° F. The inland country rarely rises to 2,000 feet, and this is not high enough to reduce this high temperature by more than a few degrees.

Correlations.—With winter temperatures between 70° and 78° this climate is not unlike the Congo Coast and Portuguese South-West Africa, while in the northern hemisphere the west coast of Mexico is perhaps a close parallel.

HOMOCLIMES OF TROPICAL WESTERN AUSTRALIA

Place	Temperature (° F.)			Rainfall (inches)		
	Average	Hottest	Coolest	Average	Wettest	Driest
Broome	79·8	85·9	70·3	22·9	6·3	0·3
Nullagine	76·4	89·8	59·3	12·7	2·7	0
Banana (Congo)	77·9	81·5	72·5	29·0	6·0	0
Colima (Mexico)	76·1	80·9	69·6	34·0	7·0	0

Owing to the infrequent rains the humidity is not high inland; though on the more northern coasts it is unpleasant in summer, as the following figures show. Broome, January 71 per cent, July 49 per cent; Nullagine, 35 per cent and 50 per cent; Cossack, 55 per cent and 59 per cent. In winter the region is healthy and free from the danger of hurricanes, which have devastated the pearling fleets on a number of occasions. Evaporation is naturally very high, and inland rises to 100 inches a year or more.

Economics.—Pearling, mining and pastoral industries occupy the population. In the future cattle and sheep will continue to be the mainstays of the region.

It is too far from markets, too hot and, except for the far north, too dry to be suitable for tropical settlement. In a Government publication *The North-west and the Tropical North*, A. Despeissis gives a good account of tropical plants which might some day be grown in this part of Australia. But a consideration of similar regions in Africa will show that it can have little attraction for most white settlers. The rains almost all fall in summer. At Broome the maximum is in February; but there is a slight peak in June which may show that a little of the southern *winter* rain reaches as far north as this (see Fig. 77).

NATURAL REGION 20: THE DESERT

Most of this region is fully discussed in an earlier chapter (pp. 101–25). But some attention may here be given to the large area of extremely unattractive land which lies to the *east* of the Transcontinental Telegraph in the Territory and south. It is charted in Fig. 78, and comprises about 700 miles by 200 miles, which should fairly be called 'desert' if we adopt the criterion discussed on page 106. It has been known by a number of names in the past. Sturt first reached it in 1845, when he entered the Territory, and probably saw the lower part of the so-called Hay *Creek*. He called the Gibber country 'Sturt's Stony Desert'. Captain Barclay explored the upper part of the Hay Creek area in 1878, and surveyed the western edge of the sand-ridge area in 1904. Lindsay and Day also added largely to our knowledge of this arid area in 1885 and 1916.

The present writer many years ago endeavoured to chart the limits of this large uninhabited area in a number of his publications. These have appeared in various geographical publications in 1926 and later. He has made use of the name 'Arunta Desert' to define it. This name is derived from the best-known aboriginal tribe in central Australia, who lived precisely in this large area in the east of the Macdonnells. Indeed, this name (with a map) appeared in the *Commonwealth Yearbook* in 1929. However, Dr.

Madigan has since christened the central *sandridge* portion of it
'Simpson's Desert', after a citizen of Adelaide who supported his
aerial survey in 1929.

Madigan flew from Birdsville to Alice Springs across the centre
of the sandridge region. To the west of Birdsville is some sparse

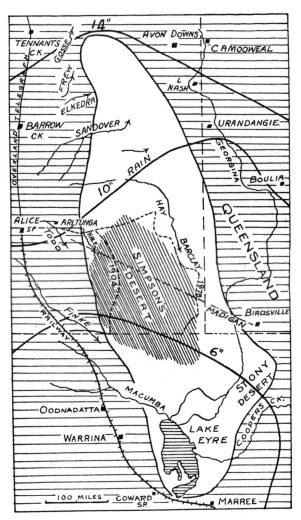

FIG. 78.—THE ARUNTA DESERT, 700 MILES LONG, EAST OF THE
OVERLAND TELEGRAPH

(*Based on the North–South Railway Report, Melbourne, 1922*)

pastoral country, though much of it is covered with sand dunes 50 feet high, and running N. 30° W. These ridges are about a quarter of a mile apart. Gidji, mulga and other acacias are scattered in the intervening clay-pans. Soon after they had entered the Northern Territory there was little to be seen but drift sand for 100 miles, though the hollow rings of the clumps of spinifex grass were numerous at times. At 140 miles from the border clay-pans appeared, where the Hale River empties its rare waters into the sandy waste. (Madigan, *Central Australia*, 1936.)

Thus the Arunta Desert forms an elongated area of uninhabited country extending to the east of such stations as Elkedra and Anacoora. It exhibits just the same variety as does the Sahara. In the north a good deal of it appears to be *Hamada*. In the centre is a fairly close approximation to the *Ergs*, or worst sandy wastes of Africa. In the south-east is Sturt's Stony Desert, which is a good example of *Serir* country. The Tirari Desert, described by Professor Gregory in his *Dead Heart of Australia*, as far back as 1906, is very like the northern portion of the Sahara as seen by the present writer in the summer of 1938.[1] It is a wide extent of loamy soil, with sparse vegetation, along the east side of (salt) Lake Eyre.

AYERS ROCK AND MOUNT OLGA, NORTHERN TERRITORY

Some 230 miles to the south-west of Alice Springs, and 33 miles south of salt-lake Amadeus (Fig. 76), are two of the most remarkable monadnocks known to the author. The journey crosses a desert area which slopes down to the playa from 2,000 feet at Alice to about 1,500 feet at the foot of the monadnocks. The geology is fairly uniform consisting of level beds of Ordovician (?) age. Ayers Rock, however, is a bun-shaped mass of felspathic sandstone, which G. F. Joklik (Canberra, 1952) believes to be the 'erosion remnant of a folded bed' rising about 1,100 feet above the level plains. The rock is a lozenge in plan, about two miles long; and the sandstone is very coarse-grained with large fragments of quartz and felspar. The dip is usually almost vertical and the strike west–east. Many caves have weathered out of the surface, and native pictures are abundant.

Mount Olga, 17 miles to the west, is another even more striking monadnock, for it is cleft by a number of deep narrow gorges along the joints in the coarse sandstones and conglomerates. The residuals in this mass of rock cover 15 square miles.

Thousands of tourists visit these interesting geological sites every year, for a fair track leads from Alice Springs to the cattle station of Curtain Springs about 50 miles east of Ayers Rock. The average rainfall is seven inches a year (Fig. 128D).

[1] 'Sea to Sahara', *Amer. Geogr. Review* (April 1939), New York. The Arunta Desert is described in *Frontiers of Settlement* by the author in *Geogr. Review*, Jan. 1926. For a useful discussion of the limits of the sand dunes, see Madigan's paper in the same journal for April 1936. (See also Fig. 29.)

PART III

THE ENVIRONMENTS AS RELATED TO MAN

CHAPTER IX

THE SPREAD OF SETTLEMENT IN AUSTRALIA

THE main feature in Australian history (prior to 1939) is the total
absence of local wars, either against the aborigines or against
white folk within or outside the continent. Probably the trifling
incident of the skirmish at the Eureka Stockade in 1854 is the
nearest Australia came to a battle. Contrast this with the history of
the settlement of Canada. For instance, the desperate wars between Indians and French; the later wars between English and
French or English and Americans; and the quite significant rebel-
lions of Riel and Mackenzie in later years. Hence the keynote of
Australian expansion is to be found in the natural spread of a
pastoral people, as it occupies new areas with its flocks and herds.
It is true that in the early decades fears of France led to isolated
garrisons being planted in various outlying parts of the continent.
But apart from these incidents, we can trace a constant relation
between exploration and environment based on economics which
gives the *leit-motif* to our present study.

We shall find that a map showing the gradual expansion of the
pastoral areas in Australia will serve as a text to our study of the
history of settlement. Such a map (based on S. H. Roberts) is given
herewith in Fig. 79. We may tabulate the early settlements in
Australia as follows. The list suggests the order of treatment
followed in this chapter.

.   SETTLEMENT IN THE VARIOUS STATES

New South Wales	Sydney	1788	Very slow expansion until 1820
Tasmania	Hobart	1803	ditto ditto
Western Australia	Perth	1828	Rather slow till 1887
Victoria	Portland	1833	Melbourne, 1835, and rapid expansion 1851
South Australia	Adelaide	1836	Rather slow till 1847
Queensland	Brisbane	1824	Toowoomba, 1840
Northern Territory	Melville Is.	1824	Macdonnells sheep stations, 1866

Early Days near Sydney

The First Fleet under Captain Phillip landed at Botany Bay in
January 1788. This site was chosen on the advice of Sir Joseph

237

Banks, who had accompanied Captain Cook in 1770. But Phillip
soon saw the greater advantages of the excellent harbour 12 miles
to the north. The first huts were erected near the south shore of
Circular Quay (Fig. 49). There were about 770 convicts and 250
soldiers in this first settlement in Australia. The structure of the
district around Sydney has been discussed earlier (p. 133). All
attempts to penetrate the rampart to the west failed, partly because
the explorers kept to the valleys. Dawes and Barallier penetrated
some distance into the dissected plateau by 1802. In 1813 Blaxland
and Evans found a stock route *via* Katoomba, by marching over

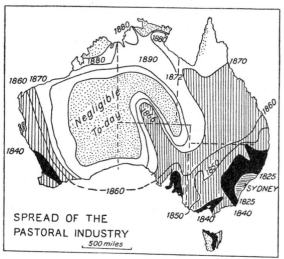

FIG. 79.—GENERALIZED MAP OF PASTORAL OCCUPATION
Black occupied about 1840, Ruled by 1870; Dotted unoccupied. Figures represent dates
(*Mainly after S. H. Roberts*)

the relatively easy surface of the plateau. This route finally led
down to the head-waters of the Cox River, and even to this day
no road follows along this river from Wallerawang (*pron.* Wal-
lèra-wang) to the Nepean River in the coastal plain (Fig. 50).
    In 1797 Shortland discovered the valley of the Hunter, and
found the outcrop of coal which determined the later growth of
Newcastle. Here is the site of a town which possesses many of the
advantages lacking at Sydney. A fine stream, the Hunter, leads
inland to a broad open valley, and this in turn penetrates into the
interior by the lowest gap in the highlands from the Darling
Downs to Western Victoria. The writer gave the name of the
'Cassilis Gate' to this feature in his discussion of the region in 1906

(*Proc. Linn. Soc. N.S.W.*). It is of interest that no railway runs through this Gate in the highlands to this day (Fig. 54).

Meanwhile by 1800 the settlement had increased to 5,000 folks. Of these one-half lived at Sydney, about 500 on the farms near Parramatta, and 1,000 on the Hawkesbury River near Richmond. The two latter places were favoured with better soils, derived either from shales or from lake silts. In 1810 Lachlan Macquarie arrived as Governor, and he soon greatly extended the area of farming by the poorer settlers. He encouraged the grazing of sheep on the newly discovered Western Plains near Bathurst. Thereafter the major industry of Australia was fairly started on the road to success. Six towns were founded and 50 miles of road constructed by 1820. When Macquarie returned to England in 1821 it was stated with much truth that 'he had found New South Wales a Gaol and left it a Colony'.

The next chapter in the history of settlement shows us explorers struggling far into the west against an unfamiliar environment characterized by an inland drainage and an erratic rainfall. In 1817–19 Hamilton Hume and Throsby found an easier route to the western plains by way of the gentle warp up to the Illawarra region in the south. It was easy to reach the Murrumbidgee Basin through the 'Lake George Gate' near the present town of Goulburn (Fig. 80).

Oxley about the same time found that the Macquarie and Lachlan Rivers leave the highlands about 150 miles from the east coast, to traverse dry plains without receiving any further supplies by notable tributaries. Gradually they decreased in volume and were lost in the marshy swamps of the interior. Oxley climbed the New England Plateau from the Liverpool Plains, and was the first to see the profound gorges of the Macleay River (Fig. 54). From here he managed to reach the coast near Port Macquarie. Cunningham started from Bathurst and crossed the Cassilis Gate in 1823. A few years later he marched up the Hunter Valley, and keeping to the west of the New England Plateau reached Brisbane in 1828. Hume and Hovell started from Lake George in 1824 and crossed the Murray near the present Hume Dam. They reached Geelong on Port Phillip by way of the Hume Range, but returned to the north by the easier 'Kilmore Gate' (Fig. 80).

Governor Brisbane opposed the rapid expansion of the pastoralists, since it was impossible to protect them with his relatively few soldiers. For a time no settlement was allowed beyond the 'Nineteen Counties'. These extended down the coast from near Port Macquarie to Bateman Bay, and westward to Wellington, Bathurst and Yass. (This area is labelled '1825' in Fig. 79.) About

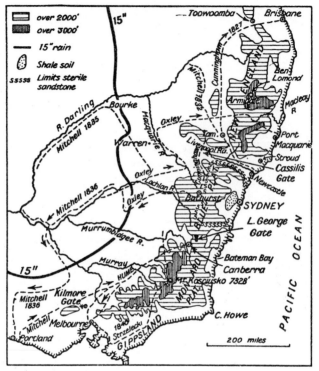

FIG. 80.—EXPLORATIONS AND TOPOGRAPHY IN NEW SOUTH WALES
AND VICTORIA

Much of the Blue Plateau is over 3,000 feet. (See Fig. 124)

1824 a new policy was inaugurated when large Land Companies
started operations in the 'Mother State'. We may now turn to
Tasmania, where settlement started nearly as soon as in New
South Wales.

Early Days in Tasmania

In 1803 Bowen was sent from Sydney to prevent the French
from laying claims to the outlying island of Van Diemen's Land.
He was accompanied by a number of convicts, and later the worst
of the prisoners at Sydney were sent to Port Arthur, a penal settlement 35 miles south-east of Hobart. In 1808 convicts from Norfolk
Island were also sent to Hobart, and founded New Norfolk to the
north of that town. For a time, especially under the able rule of
Sorell (1817–24), Hobart progressed more rapidly than Sydney.

It grew a good deal of wheat, which was of help to the older settlement; and in 1829 actually had a larger export of wool than Sydney. But land was granted very recklessly to the settlers, and by 1833 about 3 million acres of the best land had been almost given away. In 1830 there was a population of 20,000; but only 56,000 acres was under cultivation in the colony.

Capital was greatly needed in the island, and a Land Company was formed in 1824 to finance and carry out settlement on 350,000 acres in the north-west. Various explorations by Jorgensen, Hellyer and others showed that most of the hinterland was of very little value. However, holdings were occupied south of Burnie and elsewhere, while the Cressey Land Company had some success with horse-breeding near Launceston (Fig. 56).

The Australian Agricultural Company

About this same period, around 1824, a powerful group of business folk in England sent £300,000 to New South Wales to develop large areas *north* of the already settled country. At first they chose a large block on the coast near Stroud and Gloucester. The Arctic explorer, Sir Edward Parry, was sent out to control the project, and he reported very unfavourably on the designated block. Dangar successfully advocated an exchange for lands on the Liverpool Plains, about 100 miles to the north-west. From 1831 onwards the Company grazed large numbers of sheep in the region round Tamworth, and cattle to the south among the Liverpool Ranges. Moreover they acquired large interests in the coalfield near Newcastle, where they mined about 16,000 tons of coal a year (Fig. 54).

Explorations in the East, 1828–36

Before describing the early settlements in Western Australia, South Australia and Queensland, some attention may be given to the records of explorers who, in general, naturally preceded the actual settlers. Mitchell and Sturt cleared up the mystery of the drainage of south-east Australia in the period 1828–36, and showed its general resemblance to the Nile system. The Murray rises in well-watered regions, and receives many tributaries in its upper course, some of which are fed with melting snow for a large part of the year. At Wentworth, however, the rainfall is only 12 inches a year, and thereafter the Murray receives no fresh supplies in the whole lower 800 miles (p. 258).

In 1829 Sturt marched down the Bogan River and discovered the Darling, the great river of the 'Back Country' (Fig. 81). Unfortunately its stagnant waters were found to be salt, showing that

9

several years had elapsed since it had been in flood. In January 1830, he placed a whaleboat on the Murrumbidgee, and within a week reached the wide waters of the chief river of Australia, the

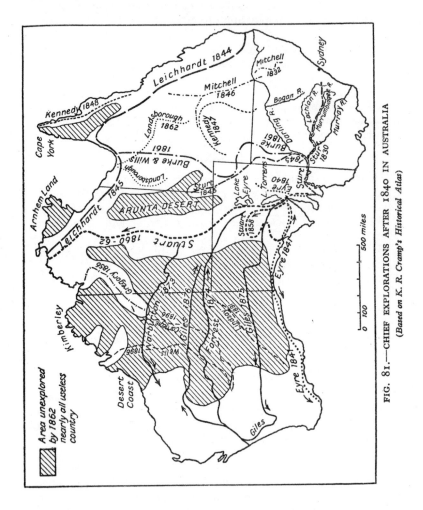

FIG. 81.—CHIEF EXPLORATIONS AFTER 1840 IN AUSTRALIA
(Based on K. R. Cramp's Historical Atlas)

Murray. Hume, of course, had already crossed it higher up in 1824. Proceeding down the Murray, Sturt reached the sea at Encounter Bay.

Mitchell, the Surveyor-General, made several expeditions, of which the first, in 1832, explored the Macintyre area near the

Queensland border. In 1835 he reached Bourke on the Darling, where he built a stockade. In 1836 he made his most famous journey, which led him to the well-grassed plains of western Victoria (Fig. 80). This region he named 'Australia Felix'. He reached the sea in July, and found a group of whalers already living there at Portland. Thence he returned to his head-quarters at Sydney, traversing excellent stock country, by a fairly direct route long known as the 'Major's Line'.

The Foundation of Western Australia

Dread of French occupation led to the planting of military garrisons at Melville Island on the north coast in 1824, from which the soldiers were removed to Port Essington (100 miles north-east of Darwin) in 1828. This also was soon abandoned for Perth; but a garrison was later maintained at Port Essington from 1838 to 1848. In the south-west corner of the continent a military post was established in 1826 at Albany, while Stirling was much impressed by what he saw of the Swan River in 1827. A few years later (1829) Stirling was appointed Governor of Western Australia, and founded the city of Perth. A Land Company under Peel had little success south of Perth; but by 1837 there were 2,000 residents in the colony, and a road had been built from Perth to Albany (Fig. 69). In the period 1837–9 Grey had made useful surveys in the Kimberleys, and further south near Shark Bay. He was wrecked near Geraldton, and made a hazardous march southward to Perth along the arid coast. In 1840 sheep were grazing along the Albany Road, and numbered about 30,000. A settlement was started in 1842 at Australind near Bunbury, but this proved abortive.

Early Settlement in Victoria

As the author has suggested elsewhere, it is not easy to explain why Hobart in Tasmania gained a thirty-year start over Melbourne. There is no comparison in the resources and present population of Tasmania and Victoria. Probably we see in the growth of Hobart a good example of what political influence can do. Hobart was started largely by officials to justify the possession of Tasmania by Britain, in view of extensive French explorations in that region. Melbourne was settled by pioneers who wished to develop new grazing lands for their increasing flocks and herds. We have seen that the Henty family settled in Portland in 1834. In 1835 another Tasmanian, John Batman, reached the site of Melbourne, and marked out large areas for himself and his friends. A little later another group under Fawkner also settled at Melbourne, and considerable rivalry developed between the two parties. In 1836 Captain Lonsdale was sent from Sydney to settle their quarrels. In 1837 the little settlement of 200 people was named Melbourne, and it grew up without much contact with the officials at Sydney 500 miles away. Hence in 1851 this region was erected into a new State and given the name of Victoria.

The Foundation of South Australia

This state was to a considerable degree affected by the theories of the English essayist Gibbon Wakefield. He strongly opposed two of the leading features of the earlier Australian administrations. They were the transportation of convicts from the homeland, and the extravagant distribution of the empty lands of the colony. He believed that the land should be sold 'at a reasonable price' and the money largely devoted to *bringing out new immigrants* when more workers were required.

In 1834 the British Government created a Crown Colony in South Australia, and a good many of the regulations of the new colony owed something to Wakefield's fertile brain. It was not till September 1836 that Colonel Light landed at Port Adelaide, having been unfavourably impressed by Kangaroo Island. The town of Adelaide was planned on a low spur of the Mount Lofty Horst (Fig. 59), and about 500 immigrants soon arrived to help to open up this new corner of Australia. Though sheep were important possessions of the settlers here, as elsewhere, wheat and copper formed a large proportion of the young colony's products from the start. In 1842 copper was found on Kapunda Station, 80 miles north of Adelaide. In 1843 Ridley and Bull invented one of the first machines for stripping and threshing wheat.

The Spread of the Pastoral Industry

As we have seen, the early Governors in vain attempted to confine the pastoralists within the 'Nineteen Counties'. The graziers pushed onwards to reach new pastures, where they squatted on the land and built their homes. At first 'squatter' was a term of reproach, meaning much the same as the 'cocky' (or cockatoo settler) of today. But gradually 'squatter' came to mean the pastoral owner in a large way, and now the further derivative 'squattocracy' means control by the wealthy pastoralists, akin to the landed aristocracy of England. So also originally the holding was known as the 'establishment' (Shann); while the small temporary folds for the sheep were called 'stations'. To-day the whole property, sometimes comprising several hundred square miles, is referred to as the 'station', though this over-loaded word also means railway station in Australia. It is interesting that Americans use 'ranch' and 'depot' for these two institutions.

By 1840 the squatters had spread throughout eastern New South Wales, and had begun to form smaller and isolated pastoral provinces based on Hobart, Melbourne, Adelaide and Perth (Fig. 79). There were about 700 stations in New South Wales and Victoria, on which were grazed about 1¼ million sheep. A temporary slump in the industry led to the development of other enterprises. Tallow was first obtained near Yass, from almost valueless sheep, and sold for 4s. an animal. In 1844 there were 44 boiling-down plants. Wine and raisins on a commercial scale were produced by a squatter near Newcastle about the same time.

Leslie, about 1840, started grazing near Toowoomba in Queensland; and four years before, sheep had been driven overland to Melbourne along Major Mitchell's Line. The Riverina (between the Murrumbidgee and the Murray) was taken up between 1840 and 1850, and then the graziers rapidly spread along the valuable water frontages of the Darling from its southern end. About 100,000 convicts had been sent to Australia, but the practice was discontinued in New South Wales in 1840. It persisted in Tasmania till 1853, and in Western Australia till 1867. But free emigration was gradually becoming more important. Indeed, by 1830 there were far more free settlers than convicts in Australia. Bounties were offered to free immigrants around 1840, and 26,000 persons were helped to enter New South Wales in 15 months. But there was at first not much chance of such immigrants advancing rapidly, though 23,000 arrived between 1848 and 1852. The discovery of gold, however, changed things for the better.

The Gold Discoveries, 1851–60

In 1823, McBrien, a surveyor, recorded gold from Fish River near Bathurst, and an early scientist in Australia, W. B. Clarke, had also found the metal near Hartley in 1841. But the authorities feared the effect of a gold-rush on their unruly settlers, and it was not till Hargraves found payable gold at Lewis Ponds near Bathurst in 1851 that the discovery attracted much attention. He had just returned from California, where rich gold had been discovered in 1849. Within a few months a thousand miners were at work near Lewis Ponds, and gold nuggets up to 4 pounds in weight had been won. In July at Turon a gold nugget weighing 1,272 ounces was dug up by an aboriginal.

The gold-fields in Victoria were discovered shortly afterwards, just at the time when Victoria was separated from the mother

colony. During 1851 gold worth over £1 million was won in Victoria. It is stated that one-quarter of the population joined in the
gold-rushes, all of which were situated in good agricultural country
already sparsely settled. In September 1852 large numbers of immigrants specifically attracted by the gold-fields reached Australia.
The number at Melbourne amounted to 94,000 in 1852, seven
times as many as the arrivals in 1851. One result of the pre-
eminence of the Victorian fields near Ballarat and Bendigo was
that the infant state within six years had a greater population than
that of New South Wales. In 1852 no less than 16 millions sterling
was won in the gold-fields. Many of the new miners were rather
rough customers, and the authorities were unable to supervise
properly the enormously increased population. A minor rebellion
on the part of the miners at Ballarat culminated in the storming of
the Eureka Stockade by the military on December 3, 1854. In the
attack five soldiers and thirty miners lost their lives. By 1861 the
palmy days of the pick and shovel men, working in soft alluvial
deposits, were largely over, and the day of the steam-engine and
the mining company had arrived.

Not only Britishers but Asiatics were attracted by the lure of
gold. Some 20,000 Chinese were mining for gold in Victoria by
1857, and there were soon about 13,000 in New South Wales.
Rioting against Chinese competition broke out at Lambing Flat,
due, as Shann frankly states, to the 'resentment of a free-spending
folk against men whose racial standards of effort and endurance
bore the marks of stern competition to survive'. The pastoral industry was at first adversely affected when all labour bolted to the
gold-fields. But the demand for meat gradually balanced these
difficulties. In Melbourne the price rose from 1½d. a lb. in 1851
to 1s. in 1854. Transport of goods to the stations and of wool to
the ports was soon greatly improved by the stimulus of mining.
The vessels bringing immigrants were eager to carry back wool,
and the price of wool doubled during the period 1851–61.

Explorations from 1840 to 1856

So far explorers had found arid but not desert lands in the interior, but they were now approaching the desert centre. In South
Australia Eyre had brought mobs of cattle to Adelaide from Victoria in 1838. Next year he explored Eyre's Peninsula, and then
turned north and discovered the great salt expanse of Lake Torrens.
In 1840 he again attacked the arid north, finding it still less attractive as he pushed towards the district of lowest rainfall near Lake
Eyre. He reached Mount Hopeless nearly at the north end of
the Flinders Range. In 1841 he determined to follow the coast

to Albany by a march of 800 miles in the hottest and driest time of the year. After losing his companion and nearly dying of thirst he was rescued by a whaling vessel at Esperance about 250 miles east of Albany (Fig. 81).

Captain Sturt was the first to reach the true desert near Lake Eyre. He travelled up the Murray and the Darling to the site of Menindie in October 1844. Then he turned to the north-west and traversed the Broken Hill Ranges to Rocky Glen near Milparinka. Here he was held up for six months till rain fell. He then pushed on to 'Sturt's Stony Desert' and perhaps reached Hay's Creek in the Arunta Desert of Northern Territory (Fig. 78). There is still practically no settlement along his track north of Milparinka, or indeed for 300 miles in this direction beyond his furthest point.

The next area to be explored lay in Queensland. A young German scientist, Ludwig Leichhardt, led an expedition in 1844 from Brisbane to the military settlement at Port Essington (Fig. 81). He marched down the Dawson River and travelled up the Burdekin nearly to the Atherton Tableland. Here he followed down the Mitchell River to the Gulf of Carpentaria. This country was not unduly rugged, and the good summer rainfall meant that he was rarely short of water. However, the aborigines of the Gulf region were unfriendly, and killed or wounded a number of his men. He then traversed the edge of the low Barkly Tableland and reached the Roper River. Here he had to abandon his botanical and other collections, but he struggled across this rather sterile region and safely reached the garrison at Port Essington. From the point of view of the discovery of valuable pastoral lands this was perhaps the most successful of all Australian expeditions. In 1848 he set out again to traverse the continent from east to west. He was last heard of near Roma (Q.); and all the seven members of his party perished somewhere in the arid interior.

Major Mitchell helped materially to open up the excellent sheep country of southern Queensland. He hoped in 1846 to find a river which would lead him to the north coast, and though he failed to reach the watershed, he first explored the Belyando and the Barcoo rivers. Kennedy in 1847 showed that the Barcoo was the same as Sturt's Cooper's Creek, which we now know flows into Lake Eyre. In 1848 Kennedy started off from Cardwell in the north, and struggled over the rugged country and through the tropical jungles which clothe much of the east coast of Cape York Peninsula. He was killed by aborigines before he reached Cape York. Owing to the sterile soil and marked seasonal rainfall this country does not equal that found by Mitchell or Leichhardt.

The northern part of Western Australia was attacked by A. C.

Gregory in 1855–6. He first explored the Victoria River (N.T.), and then crossed over to a valley which led him directly towards the interior. This was followed for 300 miles until it was lost in the great desert of Western Australia. Leaving 'Sturt's Creek' he then turned east and marched overland to Queensland and reached the coast near Rockhampton.

The Foundation of Queensland

From 1824 to 1842 a penal settlement was maintained at Moreton Bay. Limestone was discovered inland and here the town of Ipswich grew up. For a time it rivalled Brisbane on the coast as the chief centre. Oxley and Cunningham pointed out the great value of the Hoop Pine and other soft timbers, which do not grow near Sydney. In 1842 the district was thrown open for free settlement. Pastoral occupation dates from 1840, and often met with much opposition from the aborigines. For instance, in 1857 they killed eleven people on the Dawson River, and in 1861 a station near Springsure was attacked and seventeen settlers killed. Surveyor Burnett discovered the river which is known by his name in 1846, and Warwick and Maryborough were founded by 1848 (Fig. 79). Graziers settled near Rockhampton in 1853, and the hinterland was occupied by 1858. In June 1859 this north-east portion of the huge state of New South Wales was separated as the colony of Queensland.

Varying Boundaries of the States

We may here pause for a moment to consider the main stages in the sub-division of Australia. From 1788 to 1825 New South Wales included all eastern Australia and Tasmania as far west as longitude 135°. The little islands of Lord Howe and Norfolk Island were also included in the Mother State. In 1825 Van Diemen's Land was separated, and New South Wales was extended to longitude 129°. In 1829 Western Australia was founded and included all land west of longitude 129°. In 1836 South Australia was carved out of New South Wales, but it only extended west to 132°, so that a narrow strip of New South Wales still existed north of the Bight. New Zealand was officially attached to New South Wales in 1840, but became a separate colony in 1841. Victoria was marked off in 1851, and Van Diemen's Land became Tasmania in 1856. Queensland was defined as lying between longitude 141° and latitude 29° in 1859. Further additions to the west of South Australia and to Queensland in 1861–2 gave to them their present shape.

The remaining political changes may be enumerated here,

though they are rather out of order. These later changes almost wholly concern tropical territory. From 1859 until 1863 Northern Territory was presumably part of New South Wales, though Queensland and South Australia separated it from the senior state. In 1863 it joined South Australia, and in 1911 the Commonwealth.

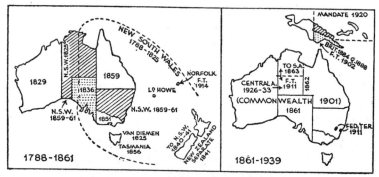

FIG. 82.—CONSTITUTIONAL HISTORY OF AUSTRALIA
(*Based on K. R. Cramp*)

Little change occurred till 1884, when the south-east of the huge island of Papua became a British protectorate. This was controlled from Queensland after 1888, and in 1902 was transferred to the Commonwealth which had been proclaimed on January 1, 1901. In 1926 the Territory was split into 'North Australia' and 'Central Australia', in the hope that this would solve some of the administrative difficulties. But in 1933 the two areas were again united as the Northern Territory.

Explorations in the 'Sixties and 'Seventies

During these twenty years exploration opened up almost the last useful land in the Commonwealth, and it was soon occupied by the energetic pastoralists. In the period 1859 to 1862 McDouall Stuart made repeated attempts to reach the northern ocean from Adelaide. In 1859 he discovered many of the mound springs near Lake Eyre (Fig. 64). In April 1860 he travelled up the Finke River and first reached the Macdonnell Ranges (Fig. 81). He was lucky in traversing the better country which contains the outflow of the artesian basin, and the steppes between the two desert regions of Australia. He pushed on to the centre of the continent, and reached the small hill now known as Central Mount Stuart. This year he attained Attack Creek in latitude 20° S. Another expedition next year only brought him to Newcastle Waters, when he was again forced to return. However, in 1862 he reached the sea at Adelaide River on July 24th. It is remarkable that within ten years a telegraph line, linking Adelaide with London, was operating along his route.

A much less successful expedition, in which most of the members lost their lives, started from Melbourne in 1860 to cross the continent to the Gulf. It was led by Burke, a police officer, and Wills, a young scientist. There were over a dozen men in the party, and they made use of 25 camels specially brought from India. In November they reached the Queensland border, and from here Burke and three men managed to attain the mouth of the Flinders River in February 1861 (Fig. 81). Burke and Wills died on the return journey, as did five other members of the expedition. All the country they traversed is now occupied by sheep and cattle stations, for it is much superior to that explored by Stuart, or by the men who crossed the Western Desert. In fact, there was not much useful country unknown after 1862, except perhaps in the Kimberleys.

No less than five traverses of the worst portion of the arid lands took place in the period 1870 to 1876. In 1870 John Forrest traversed in the opposite direction the coastlands along the Bight which Eyre had already crossed in 1841. He found a good deal of fair pastoral country, except that it was sadly lacking in any permanent water supply. Colonel Warburton was the first to cross the inland desert country in 1873 (Fig. 81). He left Alice Springs with several white men and some aboriginals in April. On June 18th they found the Waterloo Well and had to remain there a month. They tried without success to reach Sturt's Creek (p. 248); but later discovered Joanna Well, and early in December reached the basin of the Oakover River. On the 29th a party from a coastal station came to Warburton's rescue when he was almost at his last gasp. No pastoralist has yet occupied any of the country east of the Oakover, though it was traversed by Warburton 78 years ago. Yet some folk still declare that Australia contains no desert.

Forrest in 1874 and Giles in 1876 crossed the central part of Western Australia, somewhat south of Warburton's track. Here the desert seems to consist largely of rocky or gravelly plains (*hamada*), and the sandridges are not so common. Near the Townsend Range on the border of the Territory there is some sparse stock country, if it would pay to get cattle on to it. In the southern third of the great desert the sandridges are almost universal, as we learn from Giles' traverse in 1875 and Lindsay's in 1891.

Economic Expansion in the 'Sixties and 'Seventies

In New South Wales 'Free Selection' was perhaps the chief problem during the 'sixties. Sir John Robertson introduced laws to permit of alienation and occupation of Crown Lands, which made use of new principles. Anyone could select 40 to 320 acres from the Crown Lands on condition of easy payments and residence on the land. 'Dummying' and 'Peacocking' were evils in the system. The first type of lease was not held by a bona-fide settler; the second type tended to ruin a large area by isolating the vital water supplies, and so rendering intervening land of little value.

In Victoria in 1865 Grant made occupation *precede* alienation, and this prevented some of the evil effects of Robertson's Act. In Queensland Mackenzie in 1868 introduced legislation by which a squatter was encouraged to help farmers to settle on his lease. This law was a practical step towards 'Closer Settlement' in areas long used only for grazing. In South Australia 'Goyder's Line' was laid down on the map in 1865 (p. 299). It ran from Moonta north-east to Pekina and then south-east to Murray Bridge, and south of this line wheat farming was much safer. Pastoral occupation had reached Mount Remarkable east of the head of the Gulf by 1853, while agricultural settlement was at Burra in 1869 and beyond the 'Line' by 1872.

In Queensland, Landsborough found stations on the Warrego in 1862, and some of the Gulf country was occupied near Einasleigh (Fig. 79) by 1864. In the same year Jardine Brothers opened runs in Cape York Peninsula, and in 1876 the western plains near the Georgina were stocked. In 1862 Hope cleared twenty acres near Cleveland and planted them with sugar-cane. Two years later he was employing some of the South Sea Islanders (Kanakas) who had been brought to Queensland by Captain Towns to help in growing cotton. In 1876 there were 27,000 white colonists in the northern coastlands, and they strongly opposed the suppression of Kanaka labour; indeed, secession was openly advocated, and nearly attained in 1897. No less than 46,000 Kanakas were brought into Queensland to the sugar plantations, but their importation was prohibited about the year 1890.

In Tasmania in 1840 there were 27,246 convicts as against 4,043 free settlers, and by 1852 when transportation ceased about 35,000 more convicts had arrived. In 1858 there was not much good land left for the Government to alienate. In Victoria the gold-fields drew many from Tasmania, and in South Australia wheat growing was more satisfactory than in Tasmania. In 1871 'Philosopher Smith' found tin at Mount Bischoff in the west, in 1877 gold-mines were opened at Beaconsfield on the north coast, and in 1885–6 the very important silver-lead mines at Mount Zeehan and copper mines at Mount Lyell were opened. These finds awoke Tasmania from her long stagnation.

It is of interest that the early settlers in Western Australia (less than 5,000) petitioned the Home authorities for convicts. These arrived in 1850 and were used for building roads and houses for a number of years. The last convict ship arrived in 1868. In 1862 pearl shell and flour were first exported from the colony. In 1862 settlers and stock reached the district around Broome, and in 1866 the town of Roeburne was proclaimed. In 1871 a timber company opened the first railway in the south-west, but the line from Fremantle to Guildford was not finished till 1881.

The history of the Northern Territory, Australia's 'White Elephant', began in 1863, when the huge region was handed over to South Australia. The colony sold £70,000 of land before even surveyors had seen it. This money later was restored to the purchasers, when no suitable lands were found in the north within the five years specified. Grenfell Price paints a gloomy picture of the early decades. 'From 1871 to 1890 came a series of mining, pasturing, agriculture and railway booms, all of which failed. From 1890 to 1910 there followed a dreary period of stagnation, which in turn passed into a period of Federal activity, more costly, more delusive and relatively less successful than the efforts of South Australia' (p. 456).

The Last Explorations

Although Giles, Forrest and others had crossed the great desert many times along east–west tracks, no one until 1896 traversed it in a north–south direction. In that year both Wells and Carnegie made such journeys (Fig. 81). Lindsay and Hann explored smaller areas in the south-east and north of Western Australia, and the former also mapped unknown portions of the Northern Territory.

Descriptions of the country traversed by Carnegie (p. 110) and by Lindsay (p. 204) will be found elsewhere. L. A. Wells started in July 1896 from near Wiluna (W.A.) and proceeded north-east along a route about 150 miles west of that explored by Carnegie. During this 700-mile journey the first 400 miles consisted of the usual spinifex and sandridge country, and water-holes were met with when required. The last 300 miles was 'almost destitute of camel-feed or water'. Two of the party died of thirst in this region. The American geologist Clapp has given us a detailed picture of his journey in this area south of the Fitzroy basin, which is described briefly on page 113 (Fig. 39). Descriptions of recent journeys across 'unknown' Australia usually mean short journeys from one cattle ranch to another, across areas which it has never paid anyone to map satisfactorily!

The Gold-Fields of Western Australia

One interesting feature of Australian history is the way in which mining has come to the rescue of a state when agriculture may be suffering from drought and the country as a whole is stagnating. We have seen this happen in South Australia, Queensland, and Tasmania, and it is also true of the western state. But in this last environment drought was the normal condition of the gold-field, and water supply has always been a crucial problem. The first payable gold was obtained in the far north in 1883, and the Kimberley Gold-field was proclaimed in 1886. But the real gold boom started in 1887 when the Southern Cross Field, only 200 miles east of Perth, was proclaimed. In 1888 Pilbara and in 1890 Ashburton were found to contain much rich gold. In 1891 the Murchison field was discovered, and in August 1892, the richest field of all, that of Coolgardie. Here Bayley and Ford gathered 500 ounces of gold from an exposed reef in a few hours. In 1893 the Government arranged for a simple water supply along the track to the gold-fields, and 9,000 people reached the Coolgardie area in 1892 and 1893. In June of this last year Hannan discovered Kalgoorlie, about 20 miles to the east, and the deep veins of the Golden Mile have been producing gold ever since (Fig. 116).

O'Connor, Engineer-in-Chief, decided that water could be pumped from the coastal valleys at Mundaring for 330 miles to the distant gold-fields (Fig. 69). This huge work was completed in 1902, and as Shann points out, this water has been of immense value to farmers as well as to miners. In 1925–6 the railways used 8 per cent of the water, the mines 22 per cent, and gardens and farms, &c., 70 per cent of the total.

In 1898 tin was worked on a fairly large scale at Moolyella (Pilbara); and copper and coal mines were also being opened up at Phillips River (east of Albany) and Collie.

The Federation of Australia

Many suggestions of federation had been made before 1901. Earl Grey in 1849 outlined a scheme for a Federal Council. In 1881 Sir Henry Parkes made the same suggestion, and in 1890–1 a draft Constitution was drawn up. Elections to test the feeling of the people were held in 1897–8; and after some delays and amendments the required majority was gained in all the states. On January 1st, 1901, the Earl of Hopetoun, the first Governor-General, inaugurated the Australian Commonwealth. The States have handed over control of defence, tariffs and posts to the Commonwealth, and trade between states is absolutely free. As regards

justice, there is appeal from the State Courts to the Federal High
Court. The Federal Parliament, consisting of a Senate and a House
of Representatives, sat in Melbourne until 1927, when the new
Houses of Parliament at Canberra were opened by the Duke of
York.

Canberra, the Federal Capital

Although Federation came about in 1901, it was many years
before any federal buildings were erected at Canberra. By the Act
of 1900 it was provided that the Capital Territory should be situated in New South Wales (Fig. 83). But owing to the rivalry between Melbourne and Sydney it was decided that the new city
should be not less than 100 miles from Sydney. In 1899 a Commission inspected 23 sites, and reported in favour of Orange, Yass
and Bombala, of which the last (near Kosciusko) was favoured. In

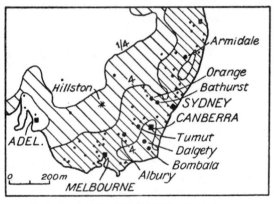

FIG. 83.—CHOOSING THE FEDERAL CAPITAL 1901–13

Dots show the towns with more than 3,000 people (except the sites of Tumut,
Dalgety and Bombala). Isopleths for ¼ and 4 persons per square mile are shown
(From the 'Geographical Journal', London, 1914)

1903 a second Commission arranged the proposed sites as follows:
Albury, Tumut, Orange, Lyndhurst, Armidale, Bathurst, Lake
George, Bombala and Dalgety. Parliament voted on these places,
choosing Tumut in 1903 and Dalgety in 1904. Hence the latter
tiny town (on the Monaro near Bombala) is given much promin-
ence in maps published about 1904. In 1908 at the final discussion
Yass-Canberra displaced Dalgety. The former unattractive name
was used to combine the factions supporting Yass, Lake George
and Canberra, which are all in the same district.

The territory around Canberra, comprising 900 square miles,

was handed over to the Commonwealth in 1909. The writer was at Cambridge University at the time, and was unable to discover Canberra on any available map, though he had written the first physiographic account of the Molonglo River (flowing through Canberra) in 1907. No one knows the origin of the word, but it is probably an aboriginal name. In 1910 the writer made a preliminary topographic survey for the Federal Government, and after his return from the Antarctic carried out (with D. J. Mahony) the geological survey. During 1913 hundreds of names for the new capital were sent in to the authorities, but it was officially announced as 'Canberra' by Lady Denman in March 1913. At the same time the pronunciation was declared to be Càn-bra, in spite of the spelling adopted.

The Canberra region consisted of a score of 'stations'. The lower plain country near the Murrumbidgee and Molonglo was used for sheep, while the rugged mountain area, rising to 6,000 feet in the south-west, was, and is, cattle country. There were about 2,300 people living in the region in 1913, which contained three or four small settlements such as Hall, Tharwa, Uriarra, &c., besides the old church at Canberra. Acton Station became the head-quarters of the Federal surveyors, Duntroon Station later developed into the Federal 'Sandhurst', and Yarralumla Station is now the residence of the Governor-General. The City was planned on the plain at 1,900 feet above sea level on both sides of the Molonglo, which flows below several hills rising steeply to 2,600 or 2,800 feet.[1] The site was chosen in fairly empty country with a rainfall of about 19 inches a year. It is about 80 miles from the coast at Jervis Bay, and here a Naval College was established on a small area of land owned by the Commonwealth, for a time removed to Flinders in Victoria. Canberra lies on the line joining the centre of population of Australia (Hillston) to the east coast of the state. It is also on the line linking the great cities of Sydney and Melbourne, and is about 170 miles by road from the former. Thus, since a special inland city had to be founded, the site was well chosen.

During the last twenty years there have been many significant changes in Australian conditions. The shift to an industrial economy has been striking, and is linked with the development of the great steelworks at Newcastle. Associated with this are a number of other developments, notably at Whyalla and Port Kembla, which are discussed in later pages. Hydro-electric power has been greatly extended in Tasmania, while in the Victorian Highlands on the Kiewa River similar power is being harnessed. Two large

[1] 'Evolution of a Capital', G. Taylor, *Geog. Journal*, London, 1914 (27 illus.).

extensions in the coal fields are to be found at Morwell (Vic.), and at Leigh's Creek far north of Adelaide. As the result of the war two lengthy tarred roads from south and east have greatly improved the access to the Northern Territory. At the mouth of the Murray five barrages have been built which have turned Lake Alexandrina into a fresh-water lake.

POPULATION OF TOWNS, IN THOUSANDS, 1954 AND 1933

	1954	1933		1954	1933
N.S.W.			Bundaberg	20	11
Sydney	1,863	1,235	Maryborough	18	11
Newcastle	178	104	Mackay	15	11
*Wollongong	91	18	A.C.T.		
Broken Hill	31	26	Canberra	28	7
Blue Mts. City	23	—	VIC.		
Maitland	21	—	Melbourne	1,524	992
Goulburn	19	15	Geelong	73	39
Wagga	19	12	Ballarat	48	37
Orange	18	—	Bendigo	37	29
Lismore	17	12	S.A.		
Albury	17	11	Adelaide	484	313
Bathurst	16	11	Port Pirie	14	12
Lithgow	15	13	Mt. Gambier	10	—
Grafton	14	—	W.A.		
Cessnock	14	14	Perth	348	207
Q.			Kalgoorlie	23	17
Brisbane	502	299	TAS.		
Toowoomba	43	26	Hobart	95	60
Rockhampton	41	29	Launceston	49	33
Townsville	40	26	N.T.		
Ipswich	39	22	Darwin	8	—
Cairns	21	12			
South Coast	20	—			

* Wollongong and Port Kembla have recently united

NEW SETTLEMENT DUE TO TOURIST TRADE

An important industry in recent years has developed in connection with tourist trade. This may be illustrated by the creation of a 'conurbation' on a small scale. The towns of Katoomba, Wentworth Falls, and others nearby have amalgamated to form the City of the Blue Mountains. It has a population of 23,000, and is the fifth in New South Wales (Fig. 50). Its growth is due to the elevation (3,000 feet) above Sydney and to the beautiful scenery in the valleys below the Plateau.

Since Australia's population is largely confined to the temperate portion, it is natural that the tropical areas, where conditions are attractive, should be frequented in winter; just as is the case with the hotter portions of the United States. From Sydney northwards to Torres Straits there extend innumerable sandy beaches, and north of the Tropic of Capricorn are some six hundred little islands more or less surrounded with coral reefs. The greatest Barrier Reef in the world stretches from New Guinea southwards to the Swain Reefs off Rockhampton (Fig. 92).

In the last twenty years an extensive tourist traffic has developed since E. J. Banfield described the beauties of Dunk Island, which is 80 miles south of Cairns. There is now a whole series of resorts usually offering bungalows, a small shop, and all facilities for boating, sailing, fishing, and observing the details of the coral reefs.

Off Cairns (17° S.) is Green Island, which is reserved as a national park. Off Townsville is Magnetic Island with coconut palms, tamarinds, and mango trees. Some 35 miles north of Townsville is Palm Island with the largest aboriginal settlement in Queensland. The scenery along the drowned coast is most striking in the Whitsunday Passage (20° S.), where there are six resorts: Daydream, South Molle, Hayman, Long Is., Lindeman, and Brampton. In some of these rocky islands the hills rise to 1,500 feet. There is a regular launch service from Cannonvale near Bowen (Fig. 92).

Heron Island lies almost on the Tropic, and is about 50 miles north-east of Gladstone. It is a famous resort for fishermen, and a biological station is maintained on the island. Quoin Island is only four miles off Gladstone, and is the most southerly of these island resorts along the Queensland coast.

South-east of Brisbane a large population has developed along the stretches of sandy beach near Southport. This is becoming known as the 'Gold Coast' from the number of attractions which appeal to great numbers of holiday makers. In some places the 'heavy sands', containing valuable minerals like rutile and zircon, are being extensively worked. Their concentrates are valued at many millions of pounds annually. They extend south to the famous beaches of Manly in the vicinity of Sydney itself. The over-burden of sand is replaced and planted with marram grass.

(For the tourist traffic to Ayers Rock, see page 234.)

Growth of Towns

In 1958 the chief changes were as follows: Sydney 2,017; Newcastle 193; Wollongong 112; Greater Cessnock 40; Brisbane 555; Melbourne 1,726; Adelaide 548; Canberra 39.

CHAPTER X

WATER-SUPPLY: WELLS, BORES AND IRRIGATION

PART I

RELATION OF RAIN TO RUN-OFF

THE distribution of rainfall has been discussed fairly extensively in earlier chapters, and it has been learnt that a large part of Australia requires much more water than is supplied by the rainfall for successful agriculture; and also that much larger resources of 'permanent water' are needed for the use of the flocks and herds than are given by the rare perennial streams or springs.

We may commence our study by a brief discussion of the character of the Australian rivers. Early explorers, familiar with the conditions in western Europe, burdened themselves on several occasions with boats to use on the large rivers which they felt sure would be encountered in the interior of the continent. Although the coastline was fairly well known by 1804, no outlet of any large river had been discovered. Of course, Australia has only one large river, the Murray; its mouth is masked by a great sand-bar, so that its outlet was not known till Sturt descended the Murray in 1830.

An interesting map, published in 1827 in the *Friend of Australia*, shows the Macquarie River entering a huge lake (about the position of the Arunta Desert, which is labelled the 'Dead Level'), and thence flowing north-west as the 'Great River', which enters the sea by way of the 'Delta of Australia' at King Sound. The actual Fitzroy River is a very humble representative of this creation of wishful thinking.

We may well adopt De Martonne's terms for the various types of river basins; for they give us a useful comparative picture of drainage in Australia and U.S.A.[1] He uses the term *Exo-reic* to indicate normal run-off, where the rivers collect the drainage and carry it to the sea (Fig. 84). *Endo-reic* means that the rain collects into streams, &c., but does not reach the sea. Thus such a region is one of internal drainage. *A-reic* means a region of such small rainfall that no real stream valleys have developed, and the rain mostly sinks into the ground or evaporates.

[1] *Régions privées d'écoulement*, Union Geog. Internat., Paris, 1928.

In U.S.A. most of the region has normal run-off, and only in the south-west corner is there any areic country. In Australia, unfortunately, the largest exoreic region is in the tropics, and most of the temperate land is endoreic or areic. The writer does not agree with minor details in De Martonne's map, but the very large area with insufficient rain to provide for normal run-off is clearly indicated.

The Lower Murray (like the Nile) flows through an areic region, since it receives no supplies from local rains. In almost all the area

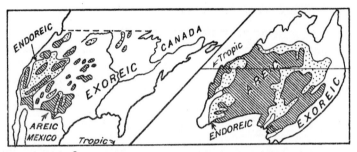

FIG. 84.—DRAINAGE TYPES IN U.S.A. AND AUSTRALIA
Exoreic means external run-off; Endoreic internal run-off; Areic no run-off
(*After De Martonne*)

labelled 'areic' or 'endoreic' extra provision of water is necessary for stock. It is true that wheat will grow in some specially favoured areic districts such as Eyre's Peninsula or the Victorian Mallee; but the supply of water for stock purposes is usually very poor, and must be increased by wells, water-holes, artesian water, or irrigation. In endoreic areas it is usually easy to dam certain intermittent streams, but here also extra watering-places are needed. Indeed it will be noticed later that irrigation is necessary for certain crops even in the *exoreic* portion of Australia.

Water-Supply from Wells

It is always an indication of permanent drought if the place-names in a region stress the water-supply. Ever since 1872, when the Overland Telegraph was laid across Central Australia, such names as Hergott Springs, Coward Springs, Alice Springs, Daly Waters, Newcastle Waters, &c., have been familiar on the map. They tell a tale of long distances between assured water, and a detailed map of most parts of inland Australia shows many such names. Luckily with a rainfall average rarely below 6 inches a year, ground-water is usually obtainable in suitable localities in most parts of the continent.

Every one knows that mines need pumps to get rid of this water, which slowly collects everywhere at the base of the zone of weathered rocks or permeable sediments and soils. This fact largely explains the popular credulity regarding water-diviners. The writer investigated such practices at Canberra in 1920 (*Roy. Soc. Vic.*, May 1921).

Many wells had been sunk (about 60 to 100 feet deep) after a period of sustained drought. Some, placed where the ground-water might reasonably be expected to collect, were successful. Others, where no collecting-ground was available, were failures. The water-diviners were responsible for both types; but neither diviner nor owner was anxious to advertise the failures, whereas the whole district heard about the successes! Many years ago in South Australia a diviner was asked to indicate *unlikely* places in his survey. Wells were sunk here also, and the proportion of successes was much

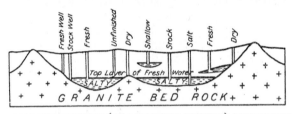

FIG. 85.—DIAGRAM SHOWING (BY A VERTICAL SECTION) CONDITIONS UNDER WHICH DIFFERENT TYPES OF WELLS OCCUR IN EYRE'S PENINSULA
(*After L. K. Ward*)

the same as in the *likely* sites! Thus a knowledge of ground-water as given in geological texts is a better preparation for well-sinking than the mysterious powers indicated by the twisting of a 'magic twig' in the hands of a diviner.

R. L. Jack gives the following directions for finding potable water in arid South Australia.[1] There should be present a channel where the surface water is collected, and shattered or jointed rocks into which the water can sink. It is found that the quality of the water will deteriorate as the distance from the heads of the various gullies increases; since then the salty ground-water of these arid regions tends to make its way into the lowest layers of drainage. Often fresh water is found as a sort of 'cream' floating on the top of the salty waters below (Fig. 85). The whole body of ground-water slowly percolates toward the lowest part of the water-table, which is usually below the lowest-lying country. Here the underground waters are usually quite salty.

[1] Bulletin 5, *Geological Survey of South Australia*, Adelaide, 1915.

The Report of the *Geological Survey* on the wells sunk in the Western Desert along the Canning Stock Route (p. 110) will give the reader a clear idea of wells in arid Australia.[1] A valuable study of fresh ground-water and its relation to underlying saline waters is contained in a recent report by Segnit and Dridan on the water-supply at Robinson in Eyre's Peninsula.[2]

Throughout arid Australia the well is a characteristic feature. In its simplest form it looks like the shaft of a small mine, with a windlass and bucket; and the water is hauled by hand. Usually only a trough can be filled by this method. A somewhat more elaborate device is the 'whip', where a horse hauls a larger bucket by a steel rope over a pulley on an inclined post. This may supply a large circular 'tank', made of vertical logs and clay. Later these may be abandoned for a powerful windmill, which keeps a large steel tank filled all the time. One may, not infrequently, see all these devices at the same place, though the earlier are no longer in use.

Water-holes and Tanks

Flowing springs are naturally rare in a country of low rainfall, though there are a few remarkable examples, as in the Barkly Tableland. Here the Gregory River rises in springs which are estimated to yield 83 million gallons daily. The Mound Springs of eastern Australia will be described in connexion with Artesian water. In the more arid parts of Australia there are semi-permanent water supplies which deserve mention. These are sometimes deep rounded hollows in solid granite, known as *Gnamma Holes*. The bare masses of rock contain patches of slightly softer rock, perhaps where two joints cross. These weather relatively quickly, and the gyratory winds of the heated desert tend to rasp out circular hollows. Rain collects here, and chemical corrosion helps to break down the granite. The cavities are widened and deepened by wild animals, and by aborigines collecting the last drops of water. Such holes are often many feet deep, and have been of great value in opening up new country, though they are rarely large enough for watering permanent stock.

The Macdonnell Ranges, with their remarkable antecedent gorges (Fig. 74), contain deep permanent pools, of which one of the best known is on Palm Creek near Hermannsburg. One of the most remarkable examples is at 'Millstream' on the Fortescue River, 80 miles south of Roeburne (W.A.). Here the river flows perennially over a rocky floor for a few miles, but all the rest of

---

[1] *Geological Survey*, Bulletin No. 39, by H. W. Talbot, Perth, 1910,
[2] *Ibid.*, Bulletin No. 17, Adelaide, 1938.

its course occurs beneath deep gravels except in an occasional flood. Unfortunately such rocky pools or flowing streams are extremely rare in arid Australia.

The most satisfactory source of water for stock in those areas where there is no artesian water is the excavated 'tank' (see Photo 2, Plate I). In Australia an artificial water-hole is given this name, though in most countries a tank indicates a large container made of metal. The 'tank', of course, depends on natural rain-water, which is led to it by long radiating ditches. Tanks are of varying sizes. A Government tank east of Kingoonya (S.A.) is 120 yards long, and holds 8 million gallons. A similar tank on Mulyungarie Station (50 miles north-west of Broken Hill) has a depth of 26 feet and a capacity of 48,000 cubic yards. On Mutooroo Station (p. 338), 70 miles south of Mulyungarie, about 200 such tanks provide water for the 3,000 square miles of the station.

PART II

ARTESIAN WATER

So far we have been dealing with water-supplies on the surface or in shallow wells. There is in Australia the largest example of an artesian basin in the world, so that a lengthy description of this feature is warranted (Fig. 86). The name '*artesian*' is derived from the region of Artois in north-east France, where flowing wells occur. Technically a well is artesian if the water ascends under considerable pressure, and flows at the surface without being pumped. There are all intermediate conditions between wells where the unrestrained water would shoot many feet into the air, and others where the water gradually diminishes so that considerable pumping is required. The term *sub-artesian* is often used in Australia, rather loosely, for a series of deep wells apparently fed from a common basin, but in which the water does not rise to the surface. For instance, the wells on the Barkly Tableland, about 200 feet deep, are usually termed sub-artesian. Such wells obviously grade into the ordinary ground-water wells already discussed. The present writer thinks that the term 'sub-artesian' should be accurately defined where it is used in scientific writings.

There are many smaller artesian basins in addition to the main Queensland basin. These are tabulated below, from the list given in Sir Edgeworth David's *Geological Map of Australia* (Sydney, 1932). The basins are found in many geological formations, though the chief are in Jurassic or Cretaceous beds. In the table the *older* basins are at the foot.

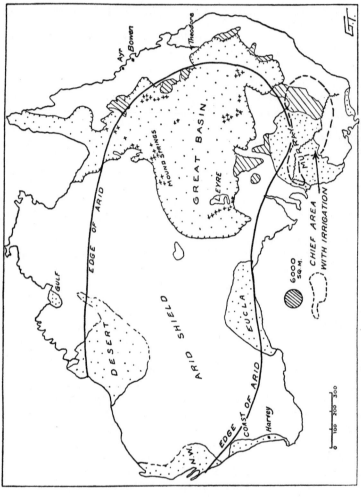

FIG. 86.—ARTESIAN BASINS IN AUSTRALIA (DOTTED)

The ruled areas are high-level water-bearing beds above the *main* permeable strata. The main region where irrigation is practised is seen to be outside the great arid portion of Australia. The small ruled circle shows to scale 5 times the area at present irrigated. (*Based on 'Commonwealth Year Book'*)

ARTESIAN BASINS IN AUSTRALIA

Name	State	Geological age	Water *	Area (sq. m.)	Depth to water (ft.)
Torrens	S.A.	Recent Pleistocene	S. & A.	4,000	up to 600
Coastal Plain	W.A.	Recent Jurassic	A.	10,000	200–2,500
Adelaide	S.A.	Recent Oligocene	S.	600	100–500
Gippsland	Vic.	Pleistocene-Oligocene	A. & S.	1,800	200–1,800
Port Phillip	Vic.	,, ,,	S.	300	up to 600
Murray	Vic.	Miocene	S.	90,000	100–900
Eucla	W.A.	Pliocene-Miocene	S.	52,000	300–2,000
Great Artesian	Q.	Cretaceous-Jurassic	A.	600,000	up to 7,000
North-West	W.A.	Tertiary-Permian	A.	40,000	400–4,000
Collie	W.A.	Permian	A.	500	—
Desert	W.A.	Permian	A. & S.	130,000?	200–3,000
Camooweal	Q.	Cambrian	S.	small	—
Gulf	W.A.	?		small	—

* Artesian (A.); Sub-artesian (S।)., i.e. like the Artesian, but needing pumping.

The Great Artesian Basin is about 1,270 miles long from north to south, and 900 miles wide from west to east. Towards the centre of the basin its strata attain a thickness of over 6,000 feet. In early descriptions the water-bearing beds were described as Cretaceous, but more accurate determinations have placed them in older beds belonging to the Upper Jurassic. The supplies are from such depths in the crust that in four bores the water is actually boiling. In the west the thermal gradient is much steeper than in the east. Thus in the bores around Lake Eyre, the temperature increases 1 degree for each 20 feet; in the centre of the basin 1 degree for 30 feet; and in the east about 1 degree for 40 or 50 feet in depth.

Origins of the Artesian Water

Long ago in geological time, say about 80 million years, occurred the period known as the Jurassic. At that time Australia had little resemblance to its present outline. Possibly the Great Western Plateau was something like it is today, but a great sea separated it from the highlands of eastern Australia, and from the vast continent which probably then covered the Tasman Sea (p. 40).

Great sheets of sand were deposited in this Jurassic sea, and over these thick beds of clay were laid which later became shales. Ultimately the whole was raised above the sea, and constituted the vast Artesian Basin. Later on some folding occurred on the eastern edge, so that the sandy beds are somewhat turned on edge. But in central Queensland these sandy beds are 5,000 feet below the surface, which is 500 feet above sea level. At its western edge the sandy layers of the basin outcrop about sea level (Fig. 64).

This great basin, which covers most of Queensland and a large area in New South Wales and South Australia, has been riddled with bores. Hence the underground structure of this portion of Australia is perhaps as well known as any similar country in the world. Valuable data have been collected as to the depth of the bed-rock (Fig. 87A) and the sandy water-bearing layers, as to the quality of the underground waters (Fig. 87B), the height to which they will rise, and as to the slow but steady decrease in amount. The most controversial aspect of the problem is the *origin* of all the water which fills the porous beds of the great basin.

One school of geologists follows J. W. Gregory, and believes that the greater portion of the water is extremely ancient, and has gradually accumulated in this basin from the extremely small original proportions which are always present in such rocks as

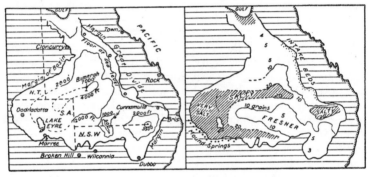

FIG. 87.—TWO MAPS OF THE GREAT ARTESIAN BASIN

showing (left) the depth below sea level of the floor; and (right) grains of sodium carbonate per gallon. (*Both after Du Toit*)

granite. This is called the *Plutonic* theory, and it is to some extent supported by the peculiar variations in temperature and salt contents. The other school, including most Australian geologists, believes that almost all the water is of recent or Pleistocene origin, and is merely rain and river water of the eastern highlands, which has been trapped by the upturned porous outcrops and so diverted into underground channels. The hydraulic grade (discussed later) seems to support this view of *Meteoric* origins.

In earlier sections I have briefly described smaller sources of water-supply which are due to rainfall, and I see no valid reason why rainfall should not supply the Artesian basin as well as those smaller sources. In all these cases if the water is to keep fresh it must have an outlet; otherwise the small percentage of salts present in all run-off waters would inevitably have become concentrated, and have ruined the waters. This has unfortunately happened in quite large areas in Eyre's Peninsula and also in the Nullarbor region. Indeed, Gregory thinks the large amounts of sodium chloride and sodium carbonate in the extreme south-west of the Great Basin have originated in this way.

If we plot on a map the height to which the artesian water will rise (if confined in an open pipe) we obtain a series of points which lie on an imaginary warped surface (Fig. 88). This surface is the

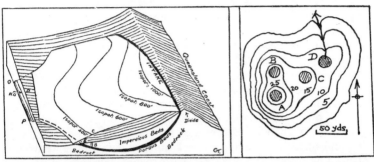

FIG. 88.—DIAGRAM ILLUSTRATING THE GREAT ARTESIAN BASIN OF AUSTRALIA

The hydraulic grade appears as a warped surface indicated by isopotential lines. At *B*, bore water would rise to *C*. At *E* (i.e. Billakalina) the porous beds (black) outcrop. Above the porous beds at *OP* (on the west) the hydraulic grade is below the surface; so that in a bore at *D* the water would rise only half-way to the surface, i.e. to the hydraulic grade *HG*. The whole is diagrammatic

FIG. 89.—CONTOUR PLAN OF THE COMPOSITE MOUND SPRING AT COWARD, NEAR LAKE EYRE

hydraulic grade, and sometimes it is above ground and sometimes below. Isopleths drawn through equal levels of this hydraulic grade give us a series of *isopotential* lines, which are graphed in Fig. 88. From this diagram (which also shows roughly the surface of the ground) we can see that the flow must be generally from east to west, for the pressure is much greater in the east. It is natural for the bores furthest from the intake to be the most saline; for the water may have been many years, perhaps centuries, flowing from the intake to the mound springs already discussed.

Outlets of the Artesian Basin

There seems little doubt that the underground water is slowly moving toward the south-west near Lake Eyre. Here the water escapes at the surface, which is in places below sea level (Fig. 64). Owing to the great evaporation it does not form a lake; and indeed there are mound springs within the salty area of Lake Eyre.

In May 1919, the writer spent some weeks on a survey of water supplies on the edge of the Great Artesian Basin. One traverse of

150 miles extended from Kingoonya on the East–West Railway to Coward Springs on the North–South Railway. Just 50 miles to the south-west of Lake Eyre is Corrie Appa, where a small flow of water seems to mark the furthest west outlet of the Great Basin. About 10 miles to the east is the first cluster of mound springs, at Billakalina. There were three mounds here, each from 15 to 20 feet high, and about 40 yards across. Each mound contained a 'crater' 12 yards across, but all were filled with sand and were dry. However, 1 mile east was a spring supplying a circular pool carefully cemented. At the time of our visit it just comfortably contained a dead horse! The adjacent spring was a gusher, and was said to give 800,000 gallons in 24 hours.

Coward Springs is on the railway (which now runs north to Alice Springs) and we happened to arrive on the day when the fortnightly train proceeded to the north. (There are more frequent services now.) There are four mound springs all close together, so much so that their bases coalesce (Fig. 89). The upper one (A) is dry, and filled with sand and black humus. It is 30 feet above the plain. The second (B) was filled with rushes, but some water was trickling into C. There was a strong stream flowing from D. Pretty willow-like trees grew near the water, but away from the latter there was only greasy saline loam in which grew a few dried-up clumps of saltbush. Four or five miles to the south are two famous springs called Bubbling Spring and Blanche's Cup, and within half a mile of these I surveyed 13 other mounds, most of which were 'extinct'.

Some of the extinct mound springs are of far greater height and area than those described. Mount Hamilton near Coward Springs is an extinct mound over 100 feet high and perhaps 300 yards across. Unfortunately I was not able to visit it. It has been noted that these ancient mounds have no aboriginal artefacts near them, whereas the flowing springs have usually been used as workshops. This indicates the great age of the large mounds. The mounds are found in many portions of the Great Basin and are indicated by the crosses on the map in Fig. 86.

R. L. Jack (Roy. Soc. S.A., 1923) has investigated the margin of the Great Basin near Lake Eyre. He finds much sodium sulphate in the artesian water near Oodnadatta, whereas to the south-east of Lake Eyre the salts are chiefly sodium carbonate. This last salt is that usually found throughout the Great Basin. Isopleths of distribution are given in Fig. 87 (right) from a valuable paper by A. Du Toit (Roy. Soc. N.S.W., 1917). This geologist supports Gregory in general, and points out that the greatest salinity is not only found in the south-west (where presumably the oldest waters should occur on the Meteoric hypothesis), but the water in the extreme south-east is also very salty. Possibly salty marine beds may occur in the overlying Cretaceous beds, and the salt may be derived directly from them.

History of Artesian Development

The Great Basin covers about 600,000 square miles, of which 400,000 are in Queensland, 100,000 in New South Wales, and 100,000 in South Australia and the Territory. The first bore was put down privately at Kallara near Bourke in New South Wales in 1879. In 1884 the Government bored successfully at Goonery in the same region. In Queensland the first bore was started at Blackall (south of Barcaldine) in 1885. By 1887 there were a number of bores, as at Thuroolgoona, Tambo and Barcaldine in the south centre of the state. It is stated that the bores have doubled the stock-raising capacity of the artesian region. Apart from local vegetable gardens near the stations there is practically no agriculture based on artesian water. Indeed, all that is available is needed for the sheep and cattle. Moreover, the water soon deposits salts which harm the plants.

The following table shows the number of bores in the various states. In Queensland these belong to the Great Basin, as do most of those in New South Wales and South Australia. The Victorian bores are chiefly in the Murray Basin (shown in Fig. 86), in which South Australia also has a share. The Eucla Basin is rather salty, and has not been of much use. In Western Australia the Coastal and North-West Basins give very good supplies, but the two northern basins have not been much exploited to date.

Though the number of bores has gradually increased, the total flow has declined since the peak flow of 351 million gallons per day in 1914. In 1956 there were 1,579 bores flowing in Queensland, with the deepest bore 7,009 feet. The total flow was 212 million gallons per day. Some 9,000 sub-artesian bores have been registered. In 1954 a government report stated that during the next sixty years the flow will decline to 110 million gallons per day.

In New South Wales there were about 1,000 bores in 1956. In South Australia the artesian water is not much utilized owing to the arid type of country in which it occurs.

The bores usually terminate above in a bent pipe with a large valve. From this the water is led into drains about a foot deep and a foot or more across. These drains may run for 10 miles or more across the stock paddocks. Since the rainfall is rarely above 25 inches and often around 10 inches, this addition to the permanent waters of a station is priceless. The cost of a deep bore is, of course, very great. For instance, in New South Wales the Government put down nearly 2,000 shallow bores at a cost of £338,000, the deepest bore being 1,307 feet. The cost worked out about 14s. a foot; but bores over 2,000 feet deep are much more expensive per foot drilled.

In New South Wales about two-thirds of the bores flow freely and one-third need pumping. Near Coonamble the bore waters decreased 8 per cent in five years. In Queensland about 33 per cent of the bores are flowing, 40 per cent are pumped and 27 per cent have failed. In some districts the flow of water is decreasing as much as 40 per cent in fifteen years. This may be due to depletion of the subterranean reservoir; but at times it results from corrosion of the steel casing. Holes in the pipes permit the waters to leak away into porous beds above the actual water-bearing strata.

PART III

IRRIGATION IN AUSTRALIA

In a distinctly arid continent like Australia the natural optimism of the man in the street leads him to suppose that Irrigation, not to mention Artesian Water, will be the antidote to Australia's lack of rainfall. Our study of artesian water shows us that only a small portion—say one-quarter—of the arid region can be at all ameliorated by artesian water. Moreover, it will only improve pastoral products, possibly doubling the stock after the region has been supplied with numerous bores. This is a fine achievement, but will do little to increase the human population in 'Empty Australia'. Irrigation, however, is another matter. Every one knows of the millions in Egypt, all depending on irrigation from the Nile. Many have heard of the remarkable changes in arid U.S.A., as at Phoenix, Arizona, where 300,000 acres of the desert have been made to bloom, and to support a population of many thousands.

Four important facts must be kept in mind in regard to irrigation. Firstly, it is expensive to initiate and maintain. Secondly, its output is usually specialized, and soon overtakes the demand. Thirdly, it is usually found of value in regions of *fair rainfall* and not in deserts, and lastly, the amount of water available is infinitely less than the amount of land which would respond to irrigation. Let us first of all examine this fourth aspect in some detail.

In Fig. 86 the large oval area of about 1,600,000 square miles would all benefit greatly by irrigation. So also would much of the better-watered land; for instance, irrigation is needed for the sugar crop at Ayr (p. 453), as we shall see. Irrigation has been practised in Australia since 1887. Fifty years later the total amount irrigated was 790,179 acres, or 1,234 square miles. Thus, less than one-thousandth part of arid Australia is benefited today by irrigation. Probably the engineers of the future will double or treble the irrigated lands, though the supplies of water are very limited. For instance, the best possible supply in Australia, the Hume Dam, will only add 310 square miles to the irrigated area in New South Wales.

In Fig. 86 I have drawn a circle including 6,000 square miles, i.e. five times the present irrigated area; which is more than will ever be irrigated, in my opinion. It is easy to compare this area with that of the arid area of the continent. The writer has no desire to belittle the work already carried out, but he does hope that we shall hear less concerning irrigation as a *cure for arid Australia*!

The main irrigation schemes in Australia are naturally found near the sole large river, the Murray. There are a number of smaller projects in other districts, but they are relatively unimportant, and will be discussed later. Thus, irrigation is confined chiefly to New South Wales, and Victoria, which contain the chief sources of the Murray, and to South Australia, through which the diminishing Murray flows after it has received its last tributary.

AREAS IRRIGATED IN THE VARIOUS STATES

(in thousand acres)

Year	Vic.	N.S.W.	Q.	S.A.	W.A.	Tas.	Total
1916	288	55	11	15?	4	—	373 (approx.)
1927	407	90	38	35	4	8	581
1954–5	863	616	139	69	36	14	1,739

The above table shows that Victoria easily obtained a marked lead in irrigation, but that New South Wales has become relatively quite important in the last decade. About 85 per cent of the irrigation is in these two states, where topography and climate are the most favourable. Tasmania is too small for large-scale rivers or irrigation.

Difficulties facing Irrigation Schemes

Let us consider for a moment various difficulties facing irrigation schemes. We may turn to U.S.A., where irrigation is on a far larger scale than in Australia.[1]

[1] See the writer's paper comparing U.S.A. and Australia, *Econ. Geog.*, U.S.A., 1937.

CHIEF IRRIGATION AREAS IN U.S.A.

Missouri Basin	4,185,180 acres
Columbia Basin	3,393,640 „
Colorado Basin	2,537,124 „
Rio Grande Basin	1,468,913 „

We may compare with these figures those of Australia's chief river, the Murray, in whose basin about 500,000 acres have been irrigated. Yet U.S.A. with all her experience knows many failures. For instance, we are told that settlers passed by the irrigation blocks in the Milk River area in Montana to reach wheat lands further west. One reason given is that dry farming in wheat is easier, even if it is a gamble; while irrigation farming, contrary to general opinion, is much harder work. Wheat farmers (according to G. Garrett, 1925) work 90 days a year, general farmers 132 days a year, but beet farmers in irrigated land in Montana have to work 178 days a year to get a crop.

In U.S.A., as in Australia, there is a tendency for the Government to build the dams and other major works in the hope that the farmers will ultimately pay off the costs of construction. Quite often the Government has to write off a considerable proportion of these costs as unrecoverable. This was done both in the Rio Grande and Salt River Projects; while Uncompahgré and Williston have failed to pay their way. But enough has been written to show that a large irrigation scheme is by no means an easy undertaking (Fig. 44).

There are a number of environmental conditions which must be met to ensure successful irrigation. Of these four may be stressed. First, the climate must be suitable for close white settlement. Secondly, the soils must be suitable, and such that they can be readily graded to the proper slope. Third, the dams can only be built where suitable buttresses and floors occur. Lastly, there must be an abundant water-supply.

The last condition clearly confines all Australian irrigation to the coastlands or to the Murray-Darling Basin. Since the Darling at times has ceased to run for eighteen months at a time, it is not a very satisfactory source for irrigation. The next large tributary towards the south-east, the Lachlan, often ceases to flow, though this is rare with the Murrumbidgee. Finally, the Murray itself has ceased to flow three times since it has been under observation.

All round the north and east coasts are numberless short rivers which will sooner or later be harnessed for purposes of power and irrigation, but there is very little land in this rather rugged littoral suitable for the large graded areas which are advisable. Some of the largest of the rivers are found on the north coast, but here the wet-bulb figures are most unattractive for many months. Here also, owing to the rather incised (juvenile) valleys, the fertile river-flats are usually flooded after the summer rains.

The best conditions in Australia are naturally found where man has already developed successful irrigation schemes, i.e. in the south-east of the continent. Here are found in close proximity the senile plains of the Riverina (so suitably graded for irrigation) and the juvenile gorges where the rivers leave the recently warped highlands (p. 132). Thus the latter offer very favourable sites for large dams; as at Burrinjuck on the Murrumbidgee, or Sugarloaf on the Goulburn. Rocky floors and buttresses are met with on most of the tributaries in this part of the basin. It will be noticed in Fig. 90 that the large dams all fringe the rugged highlands on their western side. The relation of plains to mountains is well shown in Fig. 46.

It has often been suggested that the rivers in the flat plains further west should be dammed to conserve the occasional floods. It is, however, almost impossible to dam a senile river. As the river floods, it naturally spills over the flat country, and would creep around the hypothetical dam without difficulty. It should be remembered that steamers have at times traversed these plains (as in 1870 and 1890) for a distance of 20 miles away from the Darling River. How can such rivers be dammed?

Finally, and most interesting of all, we learn from observation of other irrigated lands that it is not the deserts but the regions with around 15 inches of rain which best respond to irrigation. This is well shown in U.S.A. and in India, as well as in Australia.

RAINFALL IN CHIEF IRRIGATION AREAS IN U.S.A. (FIG. 44)

Under 10 inches	From 10 to 20 inches	
Humboldt	Okanagan	Klamath
Imperial Valley	Yakima	Shoshone
Boise	Milk River	North Platte
	Uncompahgre	Elephant Butte
	Salt River	Gila River

We find exactly the same state of affairs in Australia, as a glance at Fig. 86 will show. The region where irrigation is important is entirely outside the great arid 'oval' there delineated. In Australia, as elsewhere, irrigation converts a region of fair pastoral country, or one with precarious agriculture, into valuable croplands with assured water-supply. But in general it does not affect the desert at all.

10

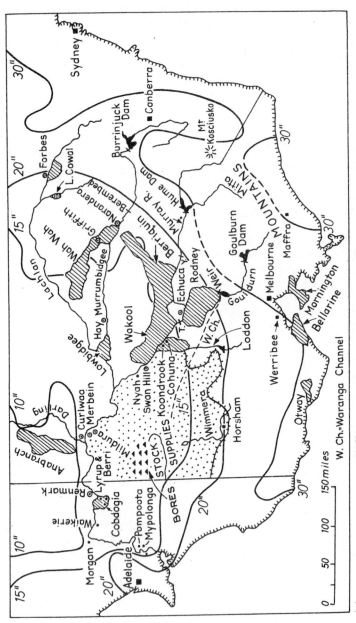

FIG. 90.—WATER-SUPPLY AND IRRIGATION IN SOUTH-EAST AUSTRALIA

Main isohyets added. Y. = Yarrawonga Weir; T. = Torumbarry Weir

The Development of Irrigation [1]

Alfred Deakin, the well-known Australian statesman, visited U.S.A. in 1884 to learn how the Americans were developing lands akin to the Mallee of Victoria. In 1886 George Chaffey, a Canadian who had achieved much success in California, came to Victoria, and investigated the Murray Valley from Echuca to Renmark (Fig. 90). As a result Renmark and Mildura were founded in 1887, as Australia's first irrigation settlements. The first pumps at Mildura, to lift the Murray water to the plains above, were fitted on a barge in the river; and this system was in use for two years. In 1888 there were 400 settlers in Mildura and 66 in Renmark. Next year 6,000 acres had been sold at Mildura and 3,000 at Renmark.

In those days the railways were about 150 miles away, reaching the Murray at Kerang near Koondrook (Vic.) or Morgan (S.A.). Only in the six months of high water (May to October) were the paddle-steamers able to voyage on the river. The Tangye engines, soon installed at Mildura, were said to be the largest pumps so used in the world; and they served Mildura for 50 years.

It was soon realized that the fruit could not be sold in the fresh state, owing to the long journey to railhead after the river traffic ceased. Moreover, the crayfish undermined the banks of the channels; and salts began to spoil some of the soils. The depression of 1893 was an evil time for the young irrigation towns where 8,000 acres have been cultivated. Expenses could not be met, and in 1895 Chaffey Brothers went bankrupt. George Chaffey returned to California, and helped to start the huge irrigation settlement of Imperial Valley, but several of his relatives stayed in Mildura.

In 1894 village settlements along the Lower Murray were initiated by the South Australian Government. In this way were started Waikerie, Holder, Pyap and a number of other small towns (Fig. 90). Most of these failed for a time, mainly owing to the ignorance and shiftlessness of the early settlers. In 1903 Mildura was connected by rail to Melbourne, and from that time the progress of this settlement has been fairly steady. In 1914 Renmark was linked to the railways of South Australia, but it was a year of phenomenal drought and 'all that was left of the mighty Murray for hundreds of miles at a stretch were a few brackish pot-holes'.[2] As an immediate result the first weirs (made of sandbags) were put across the river. An indirect result was the Interstate Commission

---

[1] *Water into Gold*, by E. Hill, Melbourne, 1937, gives a very readable popular account of Murray water development.
[2] *Ibid.*

to harness the Murray for the joint benefit of the three states involved.

Irrigation along the Lower Murray

North-east of the dry, sandy or loamy plains of the Mallee District (Fig. 54A) lies the senile valley of the Murray, before it is rejuvenated by uplift to the west of Mildura. In this eastern part the river takes a meandering course over its flood plain. No streams rise in the drier part of this corner of Victoria, and here large areas are covered with fixed dunes with a definite west–east direction. The rainfall is only about 12 inches, and large areas near the western boundary of the state are locally termed 'desert'. Between Murrayville and Mildura several areas over 50 miles long are largely covered with 'copi' or gypsum.

In the words of J. M. Holmes (*Murray Valley*, Sydney, 1948):

On the high cliffs around Mildura, Redcliffs and Merbein very intensive irrigation settlement has developed—probably the most important in the Murray Valley. One of the changes brought about by high-lift irrigation is the remarkable alteration in the land values, from a peppercorn lease to direct purchases at £250 per acre. There are now hundreds of irrigation blocks, each about 18 acres in size. . . . Mildura in 1943 had a population of 8,250 (living in 1,910 dwellings) over a total area of 5,760 acres.

In 1942 there were about 35,000 acres irrigated in this district, producing 58,465 tons of dried grapes and 450,000 bushel cases of citrus fruits.

In 1948, through the kindness of the Murray Valley Development League, I made a traverse of almost the whole of the Murray Valley below Euston (Fig. 54A). This latter town is on the New South Wales territory, and has not changed much from early days, since it only contains two hotels and four or five stores. On the southern bank is Robinvale, where sheep were grazed as early as 1847. After the first World War some 1,700 acres were found to be irrigable, and a few blocks were soon occupied. Today much of this area has been cleared by Government—who pay the prospective settlers for doing this work in a number of cases. There has long been a lock and weir at Euston across the big river, but recently a large pumping station has been built at Robinvale to lift the water up to the new vineyards and orange orchards. It is expected that 77 former soldiers will occupy these blocks in the near future. Around the pumping station an earth levee, some 15 feet high, has been built to keep out the floodwaters.

The road along the north bank to Mildura, 60 miles away,

passes through open forest of little value for timber or grazing. Hardly a house is to be seen until Mildura is approached. On the Victorian side the road passes south through Weimar and Liparoo, close to the river in places. Wheat has been grown here for twenty years, but with the low and erratic rainfall it has not been very successful, as the crop depends wholly on the rainfall. It has been found that the addition of small amounts of copper and zinc to the soil greatly improve the yield. Near Hattah are many small lakes in the old flood plain of the Murray. From here to Redcliffs the road crosses a series of west–east sand dunes, about 12 to 20 feet high, and very broad. These will grow wheat in good seasons, but the country is still largely unoccupied. At Redcliffs the main irrigation region is entered, supplied by the large pumps at or near Mildura.

Mildura (founded in 1887) is the best-known irrigation centre in Australia, as well as the earliest. Gradually population has increased, and today factories, mainly for processing fruit, have been erected at the main settlements along the river. Thus there are 31 at Mildura, 7 at Merbein, and 9 near Redcliffs; while further to the west there are 30 near Renmark, 15 near Murray Bridge and 5 at the mouth of the Murray near Victor Harbour (Fig. 90A).

Mildura is sited about 30 feet above the river, which has here cut down below its flood plain. The railway station is on the river bank, close to the pumping station. Downstream a short distance a lock has been constructed in a bend in the river, and one of the numerous weirs across the Murray holds back the waters (for the pumps) near the lock canal. The street along the top of the river bank contains the chief hotel, and avenues of large date palms enhance several of the streets. The chief shopping street runs south-west from the river, and contains the post office and municipal buildings.

Limits of space prevent any detailed description of my journey to the mouth of the Murray. From the Victorian border for 50 miles to Overland Corner there is an extensive valley, averaging about 6 miles wide, cut through red and brown, easily eroded, sediments. The fertile areas such as at Renmark, Berri and Cobdogla have been widely used for irrigation. Secondly, from Overland Corner to the lakes and islands of the mouth, there is a low gorge—averaging a mile in width—cutting through level-bedded Miocene limestones of marine origin. Many former swamps along the fringes of the valley, particularly south of Mannum, have been drained and reclaimed. Levees have been constructed, and the flats, now below river level, have provided rich lucerne-growing and dairying areas. Most of these are now irrigated, as at Cowirra,

Pompoota, Mypolonga and other settlements between Mannum and Murray Bridge (Fig. 90).

Meanwhile, irrigation on the Victorian tributaries of the Murray had long been developed. The Loddon River is actually lower than the main Murray near its junction, as is often the case with senile rivers, so that it was easy to irrigate the Loddon flats. By 1892 over 12,000 acres in the Gunbower District were being irrigated. More than half of this area was used for wheat (Gregory's *Victoria*, 1903). Higher up the Loddon River the Laanecoorie Dam was built near Bendigo. About the same time the Wimmera District was supplied with water from the Wartook Reservoir south of Horsham. The largest of the early works in Victoria was the great weir across the Goulburn River at Murchison; and about 1903 the Waranga Basin somewhat lower down the Goulburn was filled from the Murchison Weir. This southern tributary of the Murray has furnished as much as 168,000 million gallons in wet years.

The following table shows the distribution of irrigation in certain Closer Settlement Areas in 1909–10; by which time there were about 6,000 settlers at Mildura alone.

River	Town	Area irrigated
Goulburn	Rodney	32,356 acres
	Tongala	2,270 ,,
	Rochester	500 ,,
	Tragowel	20,000 ,,
Murray	Cohuna, &c.	248,000 ,,
	Swan Hill	5,400 ,,
	Nyah	569 ,,
	Merbein	202 ,,
	(Mildura	35,000?) ,,

The Murrumbidgee Irrigation Area

In New South Wales the chief irrigation scheme is connected with the dam across the Murrumbidgee at Burrinjuck, about 40 miles north-west of Canberra. This was commenced about 1906, and the dam is 240 feet high and 765 feet long. It impounds a lake of 12,740 acres, which extends 41 miles up the Murrumbidgee River (Fig. 90). The catchment of the Reservoir consists largely of the plateau north of Mount Kosciusko, and here the rainfall in places is over 60 inches a year. The water from the lake runs down the river-bed for 200 miles to Berembed, where a weir deflects it into the main supply canal. This is 44 miles long, and then reaches the irrigable areas and branches into main channels to Mirrool,

Griffith, &c. Most of the irrigation is on the northern side of the river, but later the level lands south of the river may be irrigated also. It is hoped that ultimately 200,000 acres will be supplied with water by this Burrinjuck Dam.

Until this scheme was put into operation the million acres of land involved (for much is used without irrigation) were occupied by about half a dozen sheep stations, which carried a very small population. In 1923 there were 12,000 people on 2,064 farms in the area, and six years later the number of settlers had grown to 15,000. Several small towns have sprung up, the chief being Leeton, about 12 miles from Narandera, and Griffith, 30 miles still further to the north-west.

Reference to Fig. 90 will show that the irrigation area has a rainfall exceeding 15 inches a year, and is indeed on the edge of the wheat belt. The average irrigated farm is from 15 to 25 acres, but where dairying is carried on, the farm may include as much as 200 acres, much of which is never flooded.

The chief crops have been fruit, grapes and rice, but dairy industries which are producing bacon, butter and milk also occupy the settlers. The rice industry started in 1924, and, if enough water is supplied, crops of as much as 167 bushels an acre have been obtained.

As in the case of many American projects, irrigation is expensive. The Auditor-General's Report for 1927 showed that from July 1915 to June 1927 the Government had lost £3,359,009. In establishing five settlers on reconstructed farms he stated that the Government had recently lost £8,684 on each settler.

Recent Murray River Developments

The third great project, which was carried out by the states of New South Wales, Victoria and South Australia (with considerable aid from the Commonwealth), is the elaborate and comprehensive Murray River Development Scheme. The first agreement was signed in September 1914, but work was naturally delayed by the Great War. The major work was the Hume Dam, estimated to cost $4\frac{1}{2}$ million pounds. Furthermore, storage lakes, such as Lake Victoria, near Wentworth, were to be cleared out; and 35 weirs and locks were to be built along the river. A minimum depth of 5 feet was proposed on the river as far east as Echuca, where navigation usually ended. The average flow of the Murray at Renmark is about $8\frac{1}{2}$ million acre-feet per year. In 1926-7 Victoria used 1,312,000 acre-feet and New South Wales 608,162 (chiefly from the Murrumbidgee).

Navigation on the Murray has practically ceased to-day except for a few excursion steamers. Railways reach the Murray at all the notable towns, and motor roads serve the smaller settlements. Hence the weirs will be used almost wholly for irrigation purposes. South Australia has completed 9 locks and weirs; but many of the others suggested in the original scheme may never be built, owing to changes in the method of transport.

The huge Hume Dam was begun in 1919, and was finished in November 1936. The reservoir covers 70 square miles, and is said to be the third largest in the world. The final cost was 5½ millions sterling, and it is believed that it can keep the river flowing for two years. The little towns of Bowna and Tallangatta were covered when the reservoir was filled.

Other portions of the scheme have been completed, such as the Yarrawonga Weir (above Echuca), and the Lake Victoria reservoir (50 miles west-north-west of Mildura) is ready at a cost of half a million pounds. It conserves flood water for South Australian use. At Mildura is a weir 573 feet long, while another huge structure bars the river at Torumbarry near Echuca. The latter irrigates 42,000 acres for fruit and farms.

The Barrages at the Mouth of the Murray

The most striking developments in the last twenty years are to be seen at the mouth of the Murray itself. The first Interstate Commission regarding the use of the Murray waters met in 1902. But it was not until 1930 that proposals for the erection of barrages at the mouth of the big river were considered in detail. Today there are five separate structures, connected by roads across the low intervening islands, which block the river waters in the distance of some 15 miles between Goolwa and Pelican Point (Fig. 90A). The lengths of the barrages are as follows: Goolwa, 2,075 feet; Mundoo, 2,600 feet; Boundary Creek, 800 feet; Ewe Is., 7,450 feet; Tauwitchere, 12,000 feet.

It is a curious fact that this portion of the coastline was the last in Australia to be charted. Here the survey ships of Baudin from the east met those of Flinders from the west, in what is appropriately known as Encounter Bay, in April 1802. The winds of the Antarctic Ocean have piled up for 100 miles one of the longest sandbanks, known as the Coorong, and it encloses a shallow lagoon, some 70 miles in length. The northern end of the latter reaches to Pelican Point. At times of flood the river waters may cover much of the low islands shown in the sketch.

The main purpose of the barrages—as stated in the official report—is to maintain the freshness of the river as far upstream as Wellington, 30 miles north-east of the mouth. They will also keep the waters at a sufficiently high level to permit of irrigating, by *gravity*, the areas already mentioned to the south of Mannum. Actual construction began in June 1935 and was completed in February 1940, at a total cost of £750,000. Most of the money was expended in damming the Goolwa Channel, where 70 per cent of the Murray water reaches the final mouth. Some 4,700 wooden piles, up to 40 feet long, were driven into the bottom here. Also interlocked steel sheet-piling, of about the same depth, was driven down along the whole length. On top of this is a concrete platform 3 feet thick. This supports 122 concrete piers, with vertical grooves

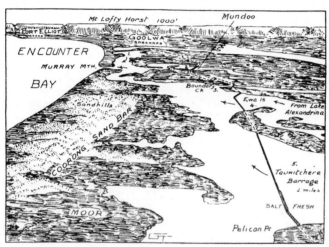

FIG. 90A.—SKETCH OF THE FIVE BARRAGES AT THE MOUTH OF THE RIVER MURRAY

They extend for 15 miles from Goolwa to Pelican Point. Looking north-west to the Mount Lofty Horst

(*From an air photo*)

to hold stop-logs. At high tides the sea may rise above the level of the impounded lakes, so that there is pressure from both sides. In general the fresh water is about 6 feet above the salt water to the west. The mouth of the river is so shallow that there has never been any navigation between the sea and the Murray. However, a canal has been suggested to link Port Elliot to Goolwa, but so far nothing has been attempted. A lock for small boats is provided in the Tauwitchere Barrage.

Modern Victorian Irrigation

Most of the irrigation in Victoria is controlled by the State Rivers and Water Supply Commission. Their report for 1936–7 shows that over 15 million acres are supplied with water for one purpose or another. There are 14,067 miles of channels used in distributing the water. The following table shows the way in which the water is utilized.

IRRIGATED CROPS, 1946, IN THE MURRAY BASIN

(*L. R. East*)

	New S. Wales		Victoria		S. Australia	
	Acres	Per cent	Acres	Per cent	Acres	Per cent
Cereals	116,228	21·3	83,155	12·4	—	—
Lucerne	27,994	5·1	65,918	9·8	—	—
Sorghum	24,105	4·4	17,135	2·6	—	—
Native pasture	163,525	30·0	112,935	16·8	10,000	24·4
Sown pasture	102,864	18·9	299,772	44·6	—	—
Vineyards	11,312	2·1	39,035	5·8	30,000	73·2
Orchards	20,226	3·8	33,779	5·0	—	—
Market gardens	15,884	2·9	11,348	1·7	1,000	2·4
Rice	32,096	5·9	—	—	—	—
Miscellaneous	30,521	5·6	8,635	1·3	—	—
Totals	544,775	100	671,712	100	41,000	100

The main dam on the Goulburn River is at Eildon near Sugarloaf Mountain, and is over 2,000 feet long and 135 feet high. The reservoir conserves about 300,000 acre-feet. The water flows therefrom down the Goulburn valley, and is used mainly between Rodney and Echuca. But the Waranga channel (Fig. 90) takes much of the water to the Loddon basin, and thence still further to the west for about 150 miles. Here it helps to provide water for stock and domestic purposes in the rather dry Wimmera and Mallee regions (which are shown dotted in Fig. 90). These latter districts do not use the water for growing crops. In the two main irrigation centres (south of Echuca and Koondrook respectively) there are about 300,000 fertile acres served by 3,000 miles of channels. There are many other small settlements in Victoria, such as those at Nyah and Merbein, where the Murray water is raised by pumping and not by gravitation. Near Melbourne is the small Werribee area, served by a reservoir at Melton; and in Gippsland there are other small irrigated districts surrounding Maffra.

An important scheme to produce 117,000 kilowatts of hydroelectric power is being carried out on the upper waters of the

Kiewa River. This tributary of the Murray rises near Mount Bogong, and the scheme when complete will be much the most important on the mainland.

Small Irrigation Settlements in Other States

In New South Wales small areas are found at Curlwaa (near Wentworth), Hay and Forbes, which are shown in Fig. 90. At Curlwaa about 10,000 acres are available, and produce oranges, grapes and lucerne. At Hay on the lower Murrumbidgee dairying is the chief industry. The Wyangala Dam on the upper Lachlan cost over 1 million sterling and was finished in 1935. It will serve several thousand acres around Forbes (Fig. 90). Suggestions have been made to dam the more northern rivers, such as the Macquarie, Namoi and Peel, and these are nearly ready. (The Namoi is being dammed near Gunnedah (1946).)

In South Australia Renmark is an early settlement whose foundation has already been discussed. The area irrigated is about 8,000 acres, and the population of the district is about 5,000. Some few years ago the crops produced were as follows: sultanas, 2,441 acres; currants, 1,335 acres; other grapes, 1,300 acres; citrus fruits, 438 acres; apricots, 292 acres; and some pears and peaches. Pumps lift the Murray waters in four flights (each about 25 feet) to the various levels where the crops are grown. The Tod River irrigation is mentioned on page 200, and the Whyalla pipe line on page 201.

In South Australia the chief irrigation regions along the Murray are devoted chiefly to vineyards and citrus orchards. Areas irrigated in 1954 were approximately as follows:

Berri, vines 5,100 acres, orchards 2,131; Renmark, 6,300 and 1,836; Loxton, 2,900 and 1,984; Waikerie, 1,700 and 1,556. Nookamba and Loveday are less important settlements.

In Queensland the more important areas are at Inkerman (near Ayr), which has been handed over to the control of the local sugar growers; and in the Dawson valley. In 1927 settlers were invited to take up farms here at Theodore, about 200 miles north-west of Brisbane. This area was stated to offer prospects of 200,000 acres of irrigable land. About 260 farms were opened for settlement.

In 1958 the total amount of land irrigated was about 180,000 acres, distributed among the following crops. Vegetables 28,000 acres; fruit 4,000; sugar 70,000; tobacco 7,000; other crops 50,000 acres. Weirs have been built near Theodore, and it is proposed to build a large dam at the Nathan Gorge on the Burdekin River, which will give a storage of $2\frac{1}{2}$ million acre-feet for irrigation.

The Lockyer valley (some 20 miles west of Brisbane) benefits from small irrigation plants, which supply much of the vegetable market for Brisbane. The Burdekin River south of Townsville offers suitable dam-sites, which will in the future give 6½ million acre-feet to the districts of Clare, Dalbeg, etc. Large crops of tobacco, sorghum, sugar and cotton would thus be obtained. Near Cairns a considerable area is being developed at Mareeba, for tobacco mainly.

In Western Australia over 13,000 acres are irrigated, depending on the small rivers of Swanland. The chief localities concerned are Harvey (6,181 acres) and Drakesbrook (1,357 acres). They are about 70 miles south of Perth, between Pinjarra and Bunbury. The water is used for such crops as green forage and pasture, and also for market gardens. The remarkable water-supply scheme linking the gold-fields with the coast has been discussed earlier (p. 253).

Production and Export

The chief product of many of the irrigation areas consists of dried fruits, mainly currants and allied dried grapes. Seventy-five per cent of these are exported, since the local demand by 7 million Australians is somewhat limited. During 1936 the various states produced dried currants, &c., as follows: Victoria, 38,000 tons; South Australia, 16,000 tons; New South Wales, 5,000 tons; and Western Australia, 3,000 tons. These dried grapes have been exported during the same year as follows: To Britain, 26,000 tons; to Canada, 16,000 tons; New Zealand, 4,000 tons; and to other countries about 800 tons.

The total value of the exported currants and raisins during the last few years has varied from £450,000 to £630,000. This considerable trade is largely due to the tariff of over 10s. per hundredweight imposed in 1932 on most dried fruits brought into the United Kingdom from alien lands.

Future Irrigation

Engineering aspects of Australian water-supply have been discussed very clearly by W. H. Nimmo in an address to the Institute of Engineers, Sydney, 1949. He states that the average rainfall of Australia is 16·5 inches, compared with an average of 26 inches for the world and 29 inches for U.S.A. He stresses the fact that the evaporation factor has been too much ignored by Australian writers. Thus in the Tasmanian Plateau a rainfall of 30 inches will yield a run-off (available for irrigation, &c.) of 15 inches; but the same rainfall in south-east Queensland would only give a run-off of 1 inch.

Nimmo gives the amount of run-off in ten subdivisions of the continent, and considers that half the total run-off of the continent is found in Queensland; but even here the total area when irrigated in the future is not likely to exceed a few million acres. He is quite sure that the plans for damming the inland rivers, such as the Barcoo and Diamantina, are quite illusionary. In times of flood this inland area, as much as 8 million acres, may produce 'a luscious growth of feed which will fatten thousands of cattle, if they can be brought without delay from the northern areas'. Sites for practical dams are rare, but at Stonehenge on the Thomson, a dam $3\frac{1}{2}$ miles long would impound 2·4 million acre-feet of water. But he continues 'because several lean years frequently occur in succession, the reservoir would not increase the flood in the worst years; and because of the great evaporation loss, would decrease the *average* flood'. There would therefore be practically no benefit from the huge expenditure that would be involved. Similar factors are found in regard to the Diamantina and Barcoo Rivers.

Diverting the Snowy River

This river rises in Mount Kosciusko—as charted in Fig. 54A— and after cutting a gorge in the plateau enters the broad valley of the Eucumbene near Jindabyne (Fig. 128B). It was proposed to build a large dam near this little town, and impound the waters of the two streams which today flow into Bass Straits, and are of little use for close settlement. The Snowy River is about 30 miles long and the Eucumbene 40 above the dam. From this dam it is proposed to drive a tunnel (over 20 miles long) to the north to reach the large *Murrumbidgee* river at Billilingera. Here a reservoir may be built from which the water can be released to increase the present supply for the extensive irrigation areas in the Leeton area and elsewhere. (This plan of 1945 is superseded by that described on pages 411–13.)

L. R. East in a paper on the 'Use of the Murray Waters' (*Murray Valley Newsletter*, January 1948) states that if one-half of the flow were granted to Victoria—by an alternative deviation into the *Murray* River—it would be possible to irrigate a further 130,000 acres in the upper Murray Valley settlements. He estimates that 27,000 persons would be engaged on the farms, and that 33,000 would also be indirectly benefited by this development. Furthermore, a very large amount of hydro-electric power would be produced by the considerable drop from the Snowy Basin to the Murray. The cost of this second plan is not mentioned, but it would certainly be much greater than the simpler plan of tunnelling the low divide between the Snowy and Murrumbidgee Rivers.

CHAPTER XI

DISTRIBUTION OF AGRICULTURE IN THE SIX STATES [1]

FROM the point of view of world agriculture Australia fills a humble place among the six continents. The writer has not been able to find an authoritative account of the totals of cropped lands in the world, but the following table gives an approximate idea:

Continent	Population	Estimate of crops
Asia	1,169 millions	800 million acres
Europe	550 ,,	570 ,, ,,
North America	182 ,,	360 ,, ,,
Africa	160 ,,	70? ,, ,,
South America	91 ,,	95? ,, ,,
Australia	7 ,,	23 ,, ,,

Thus the acreage for Australia is much less than for such European countries as Russia (285), Germany (51), France (56), Spain (56), Italy (34) and Rumania (30). It is, however, because the croplands can be considerably extended, and can everywhere be used more intensively, that Australia merits considerable attention.

The first settlers arrived in Sydney in 1788 under Captain Phillip, and endeavoured to carry on British farming in an environment more resembling that of the Carolinas in U.S.A. than that of England. Perhaps only near Lisbon or Oporto in Portugal is there a European climate something like that of Sydney.

As we have seen, the soil near Sydney is in general very poor, resulting from the weathering of Triassic Sandstones (or somewhat inland, from shales). However, at Rosehill, 10 miles from Sydney, 200 bushels of wheat and 60 of barley were harvested in December 1789. About 40 miles to the west are extensive deposits of lake and flood silt along the Hawkesbury River (Fig. 47), and here large crops of maize and lucerne are grown today; but the whole region is now known to be too wet for wheat.

---

[1] By permission of the Editor of *Economic Geography* I have made considerable use of a lengthy article which I contributed to that Journal in 1930. See also pp. 119–47 in *Australia* (G. L. Wood), New York, 1947.

There are several methods of approaching a discussion of the agricultural resources of Australia. If the continent were less uniform in character there would be a much stronger argument for treating the croplands, &c., on a *regional* basis. The fact that almost all official data are arranged in state categories also supports this approach. But since there is very little difference between conditions and technique in, for example, the wheat culture of South Australia, Victoria or New South Wales, it seems to the writer that a good deal is likely to be lost by not considering the wheat culture of south-east Australia as a unit. Clearly a better appreciation of its relation to the isotherms and isohyets will be gained by not breaking these off merely where one reaches the quite arbitrary state boundaries. Hence a compromise has been adopted. A survey will be made of the general agricultural 'pattern' of each state; but the main relations between climates and crops will (in general) be brought out by maps not limited by state boundaries. In other words, 'agricultural regions' instead of 'political regions' will be adopted as the chief determiner.

One of the differences between agriculture in Australia and in such countries as Britain (and especially in Canada) has been ably discussed by Professor R. D. Watt somewhat in the following terms. He states that the relative heat and dryness of the Australian climate, especially at the end of the growing season, will always limit the yield of wheat per acre. This yield is about 32 bushels in England, but about ten bushels in New South Wales. However, Australian wheat lands are nearer the sea than are most Canadian wheat lands, so that railway costs are less.

An advantage not realized by many is that the land is usually cheaper in Australia. Of still greater value is the fact that there is a much longer time available to prepare the land, and also for harvesting. For six months of the year the wheat land of Canada is frozen over, during which the farmer can do nothing with it. They have therefore only six months in the year to do all ploughing, sowing and reaping. In New South Wales a great deal of land can be ploughed long before it is necessary to sow it. April, May and June are regarded as comparatively safe sowing months. In many other countries the real sowing season includes only about three weeks. Horse labour is cheaper also, for the Canadian must devote much of his land to provide feed during winter.

The Australian climate is well adapted to provide wheat of fine quality, even though it has not the strength of Canadian wheat; and one man's labour will work a larger area of wheat than in most other countries. The relatively warm winters enable the Australian farmer to combine sheep-growing with wheat to a much greater degree than in North American wheat farms (Committee on Agricultural Industry, Sydney, 1923).

Agricultural Statistics

We may first of all examine how the 21 million acres under crop are distributed in Australia. This is shown in the following table, which gives *early* data for comparison.

AREA UNDER CROP

(thousand acres)

Year	N.S.W.	Vic.	Q.	S.A.	W.A.	Tas.	N.T.	F.T.	Total
1880–1	629	1,549	114	2,087	58	141	—	—	4,578
1900–1	2,446	3,114	457	2,370	201	224	—	—	8,812
1920–1	4,465	4,489	779	3,231	1,805	297	—	—	15,070
1940–1	6,374	4,467	1,734	4,254	4,027	254	1	5	21,118
1953–4	5,425	4,479	2,360	3,778	4,152	339	—	6	21,013

From this table it is clear that only 1 per cent of the total area of Australia is actually cropland; yet, owing to the small population, nearly three acres are cultivated for each inhabitant. The second point to notice is that (apart from the peak year, 1930–1) there has not been much change in the total croplands in the last ten years. Agriculture is now spreading slowly in the older parts of Australia, after a period of rather rapid growth since the early days of settlement. However, in Queensland and Western Australia the croplands have doubled in area since 1920.

Perhaps the most important table to the geographer is that which follows, for here we can see at a glance which crops characterize the various states, and also how the crops themselves vary in importance in the several states.

Since the greater portion of the hay grown in Australia consists of wheaten or oaten hay, we see that the chief agriculture (i.e. nearly 82 per cent) consists of wheat and oats. The remaining crops, in order of importance, are green forage (largely lucerne), barley, sugar-cane, maize, orchards, potatoes and vineyards. Tropical crops consist almost wholly of sugar-cane, while maize is a warm temperate crop. Oats and potatoes are found almost wholly in the cooler regions. These relations are suggested by the leading crops in the various states. Queensland, the hot state, is easily first in sugar-cane and maize. In cool Tasmania, potatoes and oats are usually more important than wheat; though the contrary is the case in all the warmer states. New South Wales is the great wheat state, Victoria stands out in hay and potatoes, while South Australia is easily first in barley and vines.

RELATIVE IMPORTANCE OF CROPS

(thousand acres in 1945–6)

	N.S.W.	Vic.	Q.	S.A.	W.A.	Tas.	N.T.	F.T.	Total
Wheat	3,774	3,251	393	2,165	1,836	5	—	2	11,425
Hay	758	1,060	69	484	281	100	—	4	2,757
Oats	617	511	40	368	396	14	—	—	1,949
Green forage	542	63	582	190	288	138	—	2	1,806
Barley	29	134	6	441	30	—¹	—	—	699
Sugar-cane	15	—	322	—	—	—	—	—	337
Maize	92	7	136	—	—	—	—	—	236
Orchards	84	69	35	27	22	32	—	—	270
Potatoes	23	63	15	9	10	56	—	—	176
Vineyards	16	43	3	57	10	—	—	—	129
Total*	6,088	5,327	1,822	3,824	2,945	412	1	9	20,429

* Including numerous small crops.

Since the agricultural regions of Australia are not yet completely exploited, it is impossible to treat the subject as systematically as in some of the older areas of settlement. Indeed, wheat is the sole crop which is so widely grown that it may be plotted as a definite 'Wheat Belt'. Oats and barley are scattered more or less in districts near the capital towns. The potato crop is even less definitely distributed. Sugar is still scattered in isolated districts along the north-east coast, and its distribution is 'sporadic', rather than suggesting a continuous *optimum* belt. This is mainly due to the low rainfall in places, but in time to come the crop may occupy more of a 'zone'.

However, if we link the sporadic centres of culture, we obtain a series of tentative optima for Australian agriculture, which will at least show us where attention should be focused for any particular crop. Such optima are charted in Fig. 91, and we see, of course, that the crops are arranged in a series of belts (as in all other continents) in the following order from hot to cold areas: sugar, cotton, maize, wheat, vines, oats, apples. Such a generalization, in the writer's opinion, should be stressed in the introduction to all similar studies.

The marginal character of Australian agriculture is obvious from the diagram. Since the isotherms run east–west, while the isohyets are concentric with the coasts, it is clear that rainfall is the dominant control. There is no agriculture in the centre and west because it is too dry. As explained earlier, the absence of crops along the north coast is due to poor soils, to a high evaporation, and to a bad distribution of the rainfall, so that nine months of the year are dry.

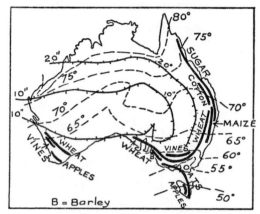

FIG. 91.—THE CHIEF AGRICULTURAL REGIONS SHOWN BY OPTIMA
(SOMEWHAT GENERALIZED)
Main climatic controls are charted

Of course, secondary factors, such as transport and lack of labour, also come into the problem; but the inherent environmental difficulties are far more important than these.

GENERAL RELATION OF CROPS TO RAINFALL AND TEMPERATURE

Rainfall	Under 65° F.	65° to 80° F.	Over 80° F.
Under 10 inches	No crops	No crops	No crops
From 10 to 20 inches	Some wheat	No crops	No crops
Over 20 inches	Good	Good	No crops

Distribution of Crops in Queensland

We may commence our survey of the distribution of agriculture in the state of Queensland, which is the sole region where tropical crops are grown on a large scale. The last survey published by the writer [1] dealt with the year 1921, and I have added the figures for comparison with the data for 1936. Figures for 1953-4 are given in the earlier table.

[1] The first set of charts for crops in Australia was produced by the writer as Bulletin 11, Commonwealth Weather Service, 1915. His study for 1923-5 appeared in *Economic Geography*, 1930.

APPROXIMATE ACRES OF CROPLANDS IN QUEENSLAND

	1921	1936
Green forage	150,000	372,000
Sugar-cane	200,000	338,000
Wheat	175,000	283,000
Maize	140,000	181,000
Cotton	—	62,000
Lucerne	70,000	58,000
Potatoes	10,000	13,000
Bananas	10,000	7,000
Pine-apples	4,000	6,000

Let us now consider how these crops are distributed in the huge state of Queensland, which contains 420 million acres. The proportions have changed very little in the last twenty years.

DISTRICTS AND AREAS CULTIVATED (1953)

Production in Various Districts (thousand bushels)

District	Wheat	Maize	Ban.	Pine-apples (doz.)	Cotton (lb.)	Tobacco (lb.)
Moreton	172	616	382	1,990	37,000	—
Darling Downs	14,993	553	—	—	51,000	1,490,000
Wide Bay	336	1,104	61	1,235	527,000	10,000
Roma	257	1	—	—	2,000	—
Rockhampton	598	126	17	208	2,917,000	8,000
Cairns	—	670	61	82	9,000	2,234,000

If we now refer to the maps where these crops are charted, their relation to the various districts (Fig. 92 at D) can be seen at a glance. The chief coastal towns are given in Fig. 92 at C. There is practically no agriculture in the western districts of Queensland. The actual figures are: South-Western District 64 acres, Central Western 308, Far Western 13, North-Western 93, and The Peninsula 681 acres (chiefly coconuts).

More than half of Queensland has over 20 inches of rainfall a year, and probably a good deal of this huge area (especially in the east where the rain is more uniform) is suited for millet, ground nuts and cotton (p. 318). At present only the more fertile parts of the coastland, with more than 30 inches of rain, are utilized.

There are five Agricultural Regions in Queensland as follows:

A. **The Brisbane Region,** which extends north to Wide Bay, while the same characteristics extend to Grafton in New South Wales. Here grow market-produce, sugar, maize, lucerne and tropical fruits like bananas and pine-apples.

B. **The Darling Downs,** where nearly all the wheat is grown and much of the lucerne. Here dairying, maize and vines, with some cotton, are also important.

C. **Maranoa.**—This region is much drier, and wheat is the only important crop. There is also a little maize and some cotton and vines.

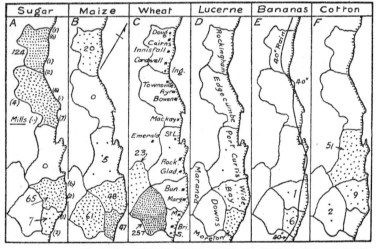

FIG. 92.—DISTRIBUTION OF THE CHIEF CROPS IN QUEENSLAND IN 1937

Each dot represents 1,000 acres. In *A* the number of sugar mills is indicated. In *C* the chief coastal towns are shown. Note that sugar is grown only in the wetter eastern portion of the areas shown in *A*; and wheat in the southern portion of Maranoa in *C*.; *M.* is Maroochy; *S.* is Southport

D. **Central Queensland Coast** (Port Curtis chiefly).—Here it is rather dry for a coastal region; but some maize, tropical fruits and much cotton are grown here.

E. **North Queensland Coast.**—This is the chief sugar region, which is all close to the coast and not scattered as suggested in Fig. 92 at A. Dairying is increasing, especially in the Atherton Tableland.

F. **Pastoral Regions.**—These comprise all the rest of the state. The sparse agriculture consists mainly of market gardens, but a little cotton and hay are grown near Emerald (Fig. 92 at C).

Agriculture in New South Wales [1]

The amount of cultivated land in the state is about 6 million acres. This is, however, distributed rather irregularly, and the densest agriculture is in the mid-south. Less densely cultivated are the central and northern portions of the 'Slopes'. There is much less land cropped in the coastlands, owing largely to their rugged character. The western portion of the state has practically no agriculture.

In the following table the crop data are given for 1920–1, 1936–7 and 1945–6. The figures represent thousand acres.

Crop	1945–6	1936–7	1920–1
1 Wheat	3,774	3,982	3,126
2 Hay	748	853	747
3 Green forage	542	645	112
4 Oats	617	236	77
5 Maize	92	116	144
6 Orchards	65	72	75
7 Potatoes	23	25	28
8 Rice	28	23	—
9 Sugar-cane	15	20	11
10 Vines	16	16	10
11 Barley	29	12	6

It will be seen that rice is a new crop, and that oats and green forage have increased greatly in importance. Other changes in the twenty-five years have not been very notable.

Now let us consider the distribution of these varied crops. The areas may be divided into five regions as in the table at the top of page 293. The regions are charted in Fig. 93 (first map), and there has been little change in the proportions since 1936.

A glance at this table shows that region A (the North Coast) contains the chief maize and millet and all the bananas and sugar-cane. Region B (the South Coast) contains a fair amount of maize and millet, and some orchards. Region C (Tablelands) is notable for hay, lucerne, orchards; and some potatoes and wheat are grown. Region D (Slopes and Riverina) is by far the chief wheat and oats belt, both for grain and for hay. It grows a fair amount of lucerne, and is the sole area notable for rice and grapes. In the Western Plains only the eastern wetter margin is cultivated, almost wholly for wheat and oats.

[1] For detailed descriptions see 'Agricultural Regions of New South Wales', J. Andrews, *Aus. Geographer*, 1934.

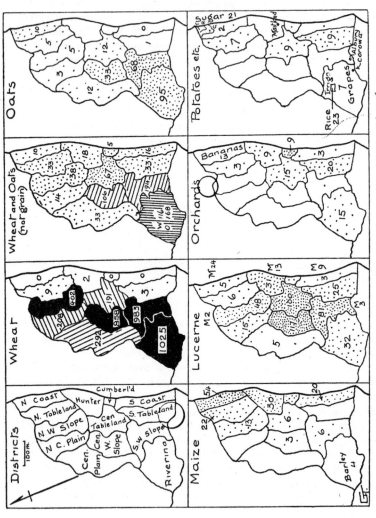

FIG. 93.—DISTRIBUTION OF CROPS IN NEW SOUTH WALES IN 1936-7

Figures represent 1,000 acres. The sugar region near the Tweed (T.), Richmond (R.) and Clarence (C.) rivers is shown in the last map. In the Lucerne map *M.* refers to Millets

CULTIVATED LAND
(thousand acres in 1953–4)

Region	Division	Acres	Chief crops
A	North Coast	104	Maize 27, Oats 10, Wheat 0·6, Lucerne 6, Bananas 21, Millet 0·6, Sugar 8
	Hunter	126	Oats 30, Maize 17, Lucerne 27, Wheat 0·5, Millet 0·4
B	Cumberland	31	Maize 22, Oats 4, Lucerne 2, Wheat 0·5
	South Coast	311	Maize 59, Oats 57, Wheat 11, Lucerne 4
C	North Tableland	114	Oats 52, Wheat 17, Maize 13, Lucerne 9
	Central Tableland	388	Wheat 184, Oats 101, Lucerne 53, Maize 3
	South Tableland	46	Oats 19, Lucerne 15, Wheat 5
D	North-Western Slopes	803	Wheat 555, Oats 156, Lucerne 64, Maize 2
	Central Western Slope	1,028	Wheat 767, Oats 181, Lucerne 66
	South-West Slope	940	Wheat 686, Oats 173, Lucerne 24
E	North Central Plain	442	Wheat 360, Oats 40, Lucerne 23
	Central Plain	244	Wheat 201, Oats 40
F	Riverina	1,091	Wheat 756, Oats 212, Lucerne 15, Rice 38

In 1953–4 the total value of the crops in the State was £68,000,000.

Agriculture in Victoria

This is the smallest state on the mainland, and is wholly in the temperate region. As mentioned, it somewhat resembles Portugal in its environment. The eastern portion consists largely of a rugged plateau, and much of the north-west of sandy heathlands (Fig. 54A). Accordingly these appear nearly empty in the crop maps. But the remainder is perhaps the chief agricultural area in the Commonwealth.

The total area of the state is 56 million acres, of which 40 million are occupied, about 3 million being devoted to the main crops. In area Great Britain and Victoria are much the same, and the wheat crops and the number of sheep in the two regions are comparable. Britain, with its winter-feeding for stock, naturally grows far more root crops like turnips, but there is no comparison in such crops as oats, barley, potatoes and hay. These latter may be expected to increase in importance in Victoria as population expands.

The relative proportions of the crops in Victoria are given in the following table (1956–7):

NUMBER OF FARMERS IN VICTORIAN REGIONS

Region	Central	N. Cen.	Western	Wimm.	Mallee	North	N.-east	Gipps.	Total
Wheat	309	258	463	3,712	2,932	3,108	361	13	11,156
Oats	232	273	574	2,539	2,238	2,523	404	13	8,796
Barley	567	79	221	828	1,031	673	35	74	3,508
Hay	5,003	1,988	5,823	3,021	971	5,072	2,821	4,883	29,582
Potatoes	2,117	596	898	36	8	65	225	953	4,898
Orchards	2,110	175	112	202	1,037	1,070	196	77	4,979

VICTORIA (thousand acres in 1956–7)

	Wheat	Oats	Barley	Hay
Central	7	11	39	129
N. Central	6	9	1	48
Western	9	41	4	202
Wimmera	458	178	1	70
Mallee	933	267	201	23
North	144	97	17	139
North-east	4	43	—	53
Gippsland	0·4	0·3	2	112

I cannot do better than repeat Dr. Wadham's remarks on the wheat crop in Victoria:

Wheat is usually the most valuable cereal in the world's market. Its bushel weight is relatively high, so the cost of shipping space per ton weight of material is lower than for the other cereals. A favourable climate and economical methods of production have contributed to make it our chief cereal export.

The principal wheat areas are found where the annual rainfall is 22 inches or less. The dark grey soils which occur in parts of the Wimmera are among the most productive of the Commonwealth [see Fig. 94, last map]. The loams of county Moira, with a relatively reliable rainfall, are also particularly valuable. The Mallee counties contain areas on which rainfall is lighter and less reliable. Here the lighter soils are cheaply worked, but the average yield is low. Wheat is also grown in various special locations south of the Divide, but in general in these areas animal husbandry is more profitable.

It is of interest that the wheat map for 1936 (Fig. 94) is very similar to that for 1923, with the chief crops in the eastern Mallee county of Karkarooc. So also in both there is no wheat along the coast except for a little in Tanjil (Gippsland), where the rainfall is rather low for such a situation.

In Victoria, as stated, a large part of the hay is oaten hay. Indeed, only a small proportion, chiefly in the coastal counties of the west and centre, is derived from grass. Not much of the hay is wheaten or lucerne (alfalfa) hay. As will be seen from the map, oats are

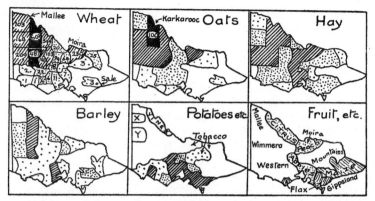

FIG. 94.—AGRICULTURAL REGIONS IN VICTORIA (AROUND 1936)

showing (by rulings) dense, moderate and sparse crops. Figures represent 1,000 acres. Districts X and Y have practically no settlers. Some place-names appear in the 'Fruit' map. (*Partly based on S. M. Wadham*)

grown in much the same region as wheat, though only to about one-quarter of the amount.

The previous table shows that there are three main agricultural regions. Of these the first is much the most important, and there is not much cropland in Gippsland.

	Regions in Victoria	
A	North-West and North Centre	Wheat, oats, barley (grapes, peaches, tobacco)
B	South Central Area	Potatoes, apples, some barley, hay
C	Gippsland	Maize, flax, some barley and potatoes

The Victorian Mallee

The north-west corner of Victoria, comprising some 13,000 square miles, consists of sand dune country which has been for the most part 'fixed' by the dwarf mallee (*Eucalyptus dumosa*). There are no creeks in this region, and the dunes run west–east in general. Some of the dunes near Hopetoun are 150 feet high, but 50 feet is the usual height. Apart from travertine, there are few rocks on the surface, but west of the Wimmera River is a pronounced rise to the west, which (according to E. S. Hills) is probably due to a subterranean scarp or monocline. This reaches nearly from Murrayville to Horsham, and is charted in Fig. 54A.

A. J. Holt in his paper on 'Wheat Farms' (Melbourne, 1947) has divided the Mallee into three belts. That north of Ouyen contains much *copi* (Gypsum); and there are large areas of *Callitris* and

Casuarina as well as the prevalent Mallee. It has been occupied
by a number of farmers since 1907, but offers only precarious
crops even in the wetter years. Holt reports that over 600 settlers
abandoned this area during the years 1920-4. The belt east of
Ouyen grows some wheat on the sand ridges, if the rains are
favourable. The Southern Mallee near Hopetoun is much more
satisfactory, and much of it was settled as far back as 1890, largely
owing to the energy of E. H. Lascelles.

There is a considerable change south of the Mallee areas (Fig.
54A) where we enter the Wimmera Districts. Here is an open park-
land type of landscape with a calcareous grey soil. It was occupied
by pastoralists in the forties of the last century, and many German
farmers took up land there in 1870-80. Warracknabeal was occupied by farmers about 1890. Near Horsham as much as 40 bushels
per acre of wheat is not uncommon. The drier portions of the
Wimmera are cut up into larger farms, many over 1,200 acres; and
near Nhill and Wycheproof many sheep are also grazed. In both
areas about 350 acres on a farm is sown for wheat, and nearly all
grow oats (for hay) also. Almost all the farms carry about 250
sheep each, producing fat lambs in the Mallee and wool in the
Wimmera. The following shows the allotment of work during the
year in the Mallee—the Wimmera being one month later.

FARM CALENDAR IN THE MALLEE

(After Holt)

April	Sow oats, lambing starts	October	Working fallow
May	Sow wheat	November	Hay cut and stacked
June	Sow wheat, lambing ends	December	Wheat stripping
July	Fallowing	January	Wheat carting
August	Trucking lambs	February	Repairs
September	Shearing sheep	March	ditto

The Mallee-Wimmera area is opened up by seven parallel railway lines, which are about 20 miles apart. By 1890 the rails had
reached Warracknabeal, while Mildura was connected by rail in
1910.

Agricultural Regions in Tasmania [1]

Only about 2 per cent of the cultivated land in the Commonwealth is found in Tasmania. Yet the island state is of special
interest, for here the *driest* portion is that most cultivated, and

[1] For a fairly complete study of this phase of the subject see *Land
Utilization Regions of Tasmania*, by Lowndes and Maze, Univ. Sydney,
1937. A very valuable official *Regional Atlas* was published in 1947.

it is the wet bleak character of the west, together with its rough topography, which repels agriculture. The area around Ben Lomond in the north-east is also empty for the same reasons.

The total land cropped in Tasmania in 1947–8 amounted to 342,311 acres, arranged as follows:

1	Hay	84,000 acres	5	Wheat	8,000 acres
2	Potatoes	40,000 ,,	6	Oats	17,000 ,,
3	Orchards	31,000 ,,	7	Peas	7,000 ,,
4	Green fodder	116,000 ,,	8	Barley	8,000 ,,

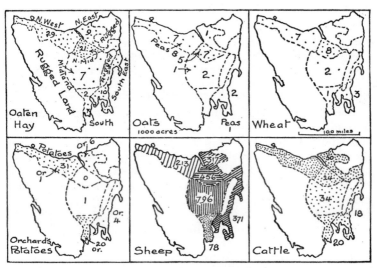

FIG. 95.—CROPS AND STOCK IN TASMANIA IN 1937
(Figures are thousands.) N.B.—Orchards and Peas shown by figures, not dots

There has been a great decline in the value of oats and wheat since 1923, as the following list shows. However, this is partly balanced by the advance in the value of potatoes and apples in the same period.

Hence in Tasmania, fruit and vegetables are of much greater importance than any single cereal, and grain crops are of less value than oaten hay and green fodder. In this southern state the three primary industries are valued as follows for 1947–8: Agriculture, £3,810,720; Pastoral, £4,332,370; Dairying, £980,300. Poultry are valued at £718,320.

VALUE OF TASMANIAN CROPS

		1947–8	1922–3
1	Apples	£2,165,000	£776,000
2	Potatoes	1,784,000	880,000
3	Hay and green fodder	1,165,000	652,000
4	Wheat	40,000	142,000
5	Hops	276,000	226,000
6	Oats	94,000	314,000

There are three agricultural divisions, whose crops are summarized in the following table:

A	The North Coast	Potatoes, oats, hay, wheat and peas
B	The Central Area	Small amounts of hay, oats and wheat
C	The South Coast	Orchards and berries, and some hay

Agricultural Regions in South Australia

The amount of land under crops in this state, on an average during the five years 1932 to 1937, was 4,783,077 acres; or if we add fallowed ground, it rises to 7,578,645 acres. No other state shows such a sharp line of division between 'closer settlement' country and that used for rather sparse pastoral purposes. Indeed, the state is generally divided into two parts, the southern smaller moiety of 56 million acres (which is divided in turn into about 50 counties), and the remainder of the state ('Outside the Counties'), which consists of 187 million acres. All the agricultural lands are in the counties (Fig. 96).

It will be gathered from the table on page 287 that the wheat crop plus wheaten hay are by far the outstanding items. The main districts are shown in Fig. 96; Central being near Adelaide, while Lower North is about 100 miles north. The semi-desert country is known as 'Beyond the Counties'; and the acres cropped therein only numbered a hundred or so in 1954–5.

AGRICULTURAL REGIONS IN SOUTH AUSTRALIA (ACRES CROPPED)

Central	910,000
Lower North	852,000
Upper North	148,000
South-east	165,000
Western	1,074,000
Murray-Mallee	734,000
Total	3,883,000

We may divide the agricultural lands into five regions as follows:

A. **East of Gulf** (Centre and Lower North) contains the main portions of the wheat and barley, and much of the vines, oats and potatoes.

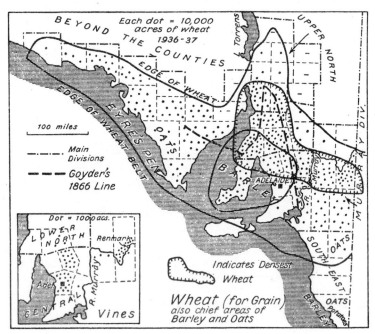

FIG. 96.—WHEAT AND OTHER CROPS IN SOUTH AUSTRALIA
Inset is a map of the vineyards

B. **The South-East Region** is cooler and wetter. It grows very little wheat, but is important for oats, barley and potatoes.

C. **The Murray Region** has increased greatly in importance for wheat and vines, the latter depending on irrigation from the Murray (p. 277).

D. **Eyre's Peninsula,** where the area of wheat has increased considerably, and where some oats are grown.

E. **The Upper North,** which grows important wheat in its southern half.

Agricultural Regions of Western Australia

This huge state contains almost 1 million square miles, or one-third of the whole area of the Commonwealth. As far as agriculture

and close settlement are concerned, only the south-west division
is of importance, for here only is there a rainfall over 10 inches
with a temperate climate. This area, becoming known as 'Swan-

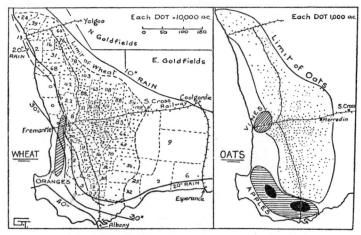

FIG. 97.—AGRICULTURAL REGIONS IN WESTERN AUSTRALIA FOR 1936–7

Chief fruit areas are charted. Annual isohyets are slightly smoothed

land', is about 150,000 square miles, a little more than that of the
British Isles. It is divided into two 'agricultural divisions' by a line
running just south of the Perth–Kalgoorlie Railway (Fig. 97). The
following table shows the areas of the various divisions of the state,
and the amount of the cropped lands in 1936.

		Square miles	Private *	Crown *	Crop-lands *	Sown grass *
Agriculture and Pasture	Metropolitan	193	21	3	2	2
	North Agric. Div.	52,723	12,017	4,886	2,130	21
	South Agric. Div.	48,302	12,393	406	1,604	609
Pastoral or Desert	E. Gold-fields	167,302	1,071	12,742	147	2
	N. Gold-fields	281,009	2	56,606	—	—
	NW. Division†	116,203	26	56,606	—	—
	Northern Div.‡	310,188	9	55,719	—	—
	Total	975,920	25,542	188,753	3,884	636

* Thousand acres.
† This division is west of the line from Yalgoo to Port Hedland (see End-paper map).
‡ This division is north of the Tropic, and west of longitude 119°.

In 1955–6 there were 5,233,501 acres used for crops, and about the same area under established pasture. About 180 million acres of land still belong to the Crown, and nearly all of this is naturally in the arid or tropical areas of the State.

In Western Australia wheat and oats constitute nearly the whole of the crops, much as in 1937, as is shown in the table below. (In 1946 wheat acreage dropped to 1,836,000 and total crops to 2,946,000.)

COMPARISON OF CROPS 1937 AND 1955–6

	Acres, 1937	%	Acres 1955–6	%
Wheat	2,575,000	66	2,889,000	58
Hay (wheat and oats)	478,000	12	269,000	5
Oats	463,000	12	1,091,000	20
Green feed	285,000	7	508,000	10
Barley	40,000	1	200,000	4
Orchards	22,000	1	22,000	1
Vines	6,000	—	9,000	—
Total	3,984,000	99	4,988,000	98

During the 15 years, 1922 to 1937, the wheat area was doubled in extent, but the chief change since has been the much greater proportion of land given to oats, barley and green feed.

A glance at the two maps shown in Fig. 97 shows that the wheat belt and the oats belt have much the same position; but there is five or six times as much wheat as oats grown in most districts. However, the optimum of the wheat seems to lie in a rather drier area than for oats. For instance, oats are grown most densely along the Perth–Albany Railway, while the densest wheat is somewhat east of this line.

Barley is found in the same belt. Near Moora, Toodyay, Meckering and Katanning are perhaps the chief centres. The distribution of orchards and vines is clearly indicated in Fig. 97. Grapes are grown in the hottest area with a rainfall of about 25 inches. Oranges do best with an average temperature from 61° to 64° F., and with a rainfall around 30 inches a year. Apples prefer the cooler wetter country of the south, where the temperature is near 60° F. and the rainfall about 30 inches. Mount Barker, north of Albany, is the chief apple-growing district, but Bridgetown, 120 miles north-west of Albany, is also very important. Pears and quinces are grown in the same region, though to a much less extent.

CHAPTER XII

FACTORS DETERMINING THE DISTRIBUTION OF THE CHIEF CROPS [1]

The Australian Wheat Crop

SINCE wheat is by far the most important crop in the Commonwealth, and constitutes 60 per cent of the area cultivated, it may well be considered first. In 1936–7 only in Queensland and in Tasmania has it a subordinate position among the crops. The production and the climatic controls in the several states are given below. The primary control is the rainfall; but it is not the *total* precipitation so much as the amount which falls during the growing period (April to October) which determines the position of the wheat belt (Fig. 98).

An official table gives a first approximation to the *temperate* areas which are more or less suitable (as far as total rainfall is concerned) for the growing of wheat; and the writer has added the areas actually cultivated in the second column.

HUMID AREAS WHICH ARE COOL ENOUGH FOR WHEAT

State	Over 10 inches annual rain	Approximate crop area
New South Wales	163,772 square miles	6,000 square miles
Victoria	74,616 ,, ,,	3,800 ,, ,,
South Australia	48,980 ,, ,,	4,800 ,, ,,
Western Australia	93,500 ,, ,,	4,000 ,, ,,
Queensland	79,247 ,, ,,	450 ,, ,,
Tasmania	26,215 ,, ,,	33 ,, ,,
Total	484,330 ,, ,,	19,083 ,, ,,

There are obviously vast areas which are climatically suited for wheat, which have not been developed. For instance, F. B. Guthrie estimated thirty years ago that the wheat area in New

[1] *Land Utilization in Australia*, Wadham and Wood, Melbourne, 1939, has just been published as this MS. goes to press. It will be found very helpful as regards agricultural and economic factors.

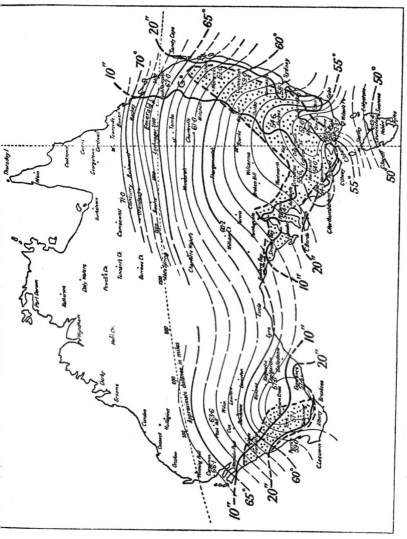

FIG. 98.—CLIMATIC CONTROL OF THE WHEAT BELT, WHICH IS SHOWN DOTTED. APPROXIMATE ISOTHERMS FOR THE WHEAT-GROWING PERIOD (APRIL TO OCTOBER INCLUSIVE)

The thick lines show the 10- and 20-inch isohyets for the same period, and enclose the chief wheat regions. Indian wheat should grow near Emerald; and Texan wheat near Gayndah (G.)

II

South Wales could be increased eightfold.[1] His result seems to me to be much too optimistic; for it is easy to show that very large areas in the first column are not suitable, from deficiencies in the soil, or from topographic disadvantages, or from distance from the railways, lack of suitable water-supply (for stock, &c.) or from poison plants. In fact, while the table takes cognizance of temperature, experience shows that rainfalls over 25 inches a year are in general too wet for profitable wheat (Fig. 98). In another section (Fig. 139) it is shown that about 30 per cent of the well-watered littoral of New South Wales is too rugged for important farming, or indeed for almost any crops at present.

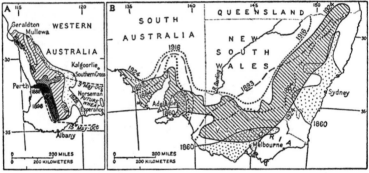

FIG. 99A.—SPREAD OF THE WHEAT BELT IN WESTERN AUSTRALIA FROM 1888 TO 1928

The isohyets for 9 inches and 15 inches (May–October) bound the actual wheat belt. (*After R. P. Roberts and E. C. Clarke*)

FIG. 99B.—FLUCTUATIONS IN THE WHEAT BELT IN SOUTH-EASTERN AUSTRALIA

The dotted areas were wheat lands in 1860, but most of this coastal land is not now used for wheat. The ruled area is the wheat belt in 1924. (*Partly after S. H. Roberts*)

(*From 'Limits of Land Settlement'*)

In the early stages of wheat-growing in Australia mistakes were made and progress was slow.[2] Cultivation was confined to the moist coastal country with its annual rainfall of 30 to 40 inches, and wheat was not a success (see Fig. 99B). The discovery that the drier districts were more suitable for wheat-growing altered the position very greatly. The bulk of the wheat is now grown in districts with a rainfall of 25 inches or under. On well-worked fallowed land it is stated that splendid crops have been gathered, although the actual *growing* crop only experienced 2 or 3 inches of rain.

[1] *Final Report on Agriculture*, 1922, Sydney (p. 44).

[2] A valuable account (in German) of the growth of various phases of Australian industry is given by A. Rühl in *Landwirtschaft-Geographie*, Univ. Berlin, 1929.

In Australian wheat districts the quantity of rain is not as important, perhaps, as the time of year in which it falls. Rain is wanted in the early autumn so that ploughing can be done, and in the spring when the wheat is heading and flowering. With rain in April and May and again in September and October, the Australian is assured of a fine crop. The summer is usually dry and warm, and this is one of the main advantages. Unless the season is unduly wet, there is no fear of rust, and nothing to interfere with the hay-making. The main crop which is kept for grain can be left standing safely in the paddocks until it is thoroughly ripe, when it is taken off with a stripper or harvester and bagged. Thus the north-east districts that have the heavy summer rain are largely unsuitable for wheat-growing.

If reference be made to the rain reliability map (p. 68) it will be seen that conditions in this respect are perhaps best in Swanland (W.A.), and least attractive in the north of New South Wales. The former has the rainfall in winter, the best season, and, though the total is low, it is reliable. The latter region has most of the rain in summer and it is rather unreliable. Furthermore, in much of the wheat area the crop depends largely on the rainfall stored in the soil from the previous year. The actual rainfall during growth may only be 7 inches or even less, but this is supplemented by the fall while the land was in fallow.

In New South Wales (Fig. 93) the practice is to plough the land in July or August to a depth of $4\frac{1}{2}$ or 5 inches, and then to let it lie for six weeks, after which it is harrowed. Subsequently the fallow receives frequent workings with the cultivator, so as to form a loose mulch which checks evaporation. This operation is repeated (until sowing time in April or May) whenever a hard crust is formed. The majority of districts enjoy an annual rainfall of 20 inches or less, and it not infrequently happens that only from 6 to 8 inches of this falls during the growing period, which is usually adequate to produce a crop of wheat of 20 bushels an acre.

In New South Wales the most productive area is perhaps in the Riverina around Corowa, and thence north to Molong (Fig. 141). The relation between the wheat isopleths and the winter-rain isopleths is extremely close (Fig. 98). The 10-inch line is very close to the *western* boundary of the wheat area except in one or two places. A rainfall of over 20 inches in the wheat period practically fixes the *eastern* boundary in this state. But until the railways are much more numerous there will be considerable areas of wheat land unoccupied. In earlier days the farthest distance from the railway to make wheat-growing profitable did not exceed 18 or 20 miles. Motor trucks are altering this condition to-day.

We owe to J. Andrews [1] an excellent study of the relation between soils and the wheat belt in New South Wales (Fig. 100). In the Riverina the soil is red-brown earth formed of sandy loam. Originally this country was used as large sheep stations, but since 1890 they have been cut up into sheep-wheat farms varying from 500 to 2,000 acres each. With the use of superphosphate some farmers in this region can produce as much as 40 bushels to the acre. The average for Australia is only 13 bushels per acre.

The mallee type of country, as we have seen, is named from the dwarf eucalypts which grow very densely there (p. 97). Near Hillston (Fig. 100A) the soils are light red, with much lime in the subsoils. Around 1890 the mallee area in South Australia was cleared by rolling down the mallee clumps. By 1898 there were

 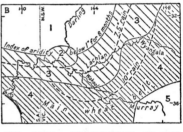

FIG. 100A.—EDAPHIC CONTROL IN THE MAIN WHEAT BELT OF AUSTRALIA

The present inner (arid) edge of the wheat belt is shown by the dotted line

FIG. 100B.—SUBDIVISIONS OF THE WHEAT BELT

The broken lines show the rainfall in inches during the cool months (April–October). Most wheat of to-day is grown in region 4; region 3 is unreliable; region 5 too wet. (*Both maps are based on John Andrews*)

(*From 'Limits of Land Settlement'*)

60,000 people in the region south of Mildura in what had often erroneously been called a desert. The somewhat similar area near Hillston (Fig. 100A) in New South Wales soon showed 100,000 acres under wheat, and represents the chief expansion of recent years in the state. The Roto area in this region has so far been reserved for stock, but it is said that there are 850,000 acres thereabouts where wheat may be grown. On the Lachlan River a large dam has been built near Wyangala, and this materially improves conditions near Roto and Hillston.

Near Roto a farm of as much as 1,600 acres is needed, so that the farmer may have 350 acres each in a rotation scheme of fallow-wheat-oats-pasture, with an additional 200 acres for horse-paddocks, &c. The total capital outlay for such a farm would amount

[1] 'Wheat-Growing Industry in South-east Australia', *Economic Geography*, Worcester, U.S.A., 1936.

to £3,780 (or about $18,000). Further figures show that only when the wheat price at country railway sidings rises above 3s. 6d. (84 cents) per bushel can the farmer receive a return on his investment.

The question of the varieties of wheat grown in the various districts is perhaps beyond the province of the geographer. But it may be mentioned that in New South Wales *Nabawa* wheat has been the favourite, producing about 27·5 per cent of the wheat crop. In Victoria *Free Gallipoli* constitutes 41 per cent of the crop and Nabawa only 3 per cent. In South Australia *Nabawa* comes first with *Gallipoli* third, while in Western Australia *Bencubbin* is first and *Nabawa* third.

In Victoria the greatest area under cultivation lies in the north and north-west (Fig. 94). The irrigation counties of Rodney and Moira are very important, though the wheat is not often irrigated. These regions fall within the rain and temperature controls specified in the table given herewith:

WHEAT CROP AND MAIN CLIMATIC CONTROLS FOR PERIOD
APRIL TO OCTOBER

	Average for ten seasons (1925–35)	Temperature (° F.)	Rainfall (in.)
New South Wales	49,732,833 bushels	61–52	15–11
Victoria	38,661,078 ,,	55–52	15–10
Queensland	3,279,029 ,,	63–61	18–12
South Australia	32,662,232 ,,	57–55	20–10
West Australia	36,084,160 ,,	62–57	20–15
Tasmania	441,155 ,,	50–47	20–15

There are several outlying regions of considerable interest in Victoria (Fig. 94). Thus around Sale is a small wheat district in the wet region of Gippsland, due to the low rainfall of a 'rain-shadow'. In the same way the rain-shadow to the west of Melbourne includes the drier coastal counties which grow wheat. In the Victorian Mallee is a large extent of sandy loam country with a light winter rainfall of from 10 to 15 inches. For a long period this land was deemed unfit for wheat, but experience has proved that it is quite profitable when properly worked. There are two empty areas (X and Y, Fig. 94) in this north-west corner of the state, where the chief objection is that the ground water is too salty for the farmers' use. To north and south of these patches the underground water is potable. In these dry Mallee areas the land is worked on the three-year rotation system of fallow-wheat-grazing.

In South Australia (Fig. 96) there is a northward bulge of the isohyets caused by the Flinders Range, and possibly also influenced by the long gulfs running 200 miles into the continent. Here the counties Fergusson, Gawler, Light, Daly, Stanley and Victoria each produced more than 1 million bushels of wheat in the 1936–7 season. Indeed, in 1932 (a much better season for wheat) Daly produced 5 million bushels, Stanley 4½ and Victoria over 3 million bushels. There is another centre of important wheat crops in the mallee south of the Murray River. Here Alfred, Albert and Chandos also produced over 1 million bushels each in the period 1936–7. The area of relatively dense crops is emphasized in Fig. 96. In all the regions mentioned, the climate is ideal for wheat culture since nearly all the rain falls in winter. Hence the production per head of population is greater in South Australia than in the eastern states, which, however, have a greater variety of crops. The 6-inch winter-rainfall line, which is about equivalent to the 10-inch annual isohyet, seems to mark the outer limit of wheat culture. This is considerably beyond Goyder's Line (Fig. 96).

In Western Australia (Fig. 97) the wheat belt receives from 12 to 20 inches of rain, and measures about 450 miles from north to south and from 30 to 120 miles from west to east. The following notes describe agriculture in the eastern wheat lands of Western Australia:

Considerable areas of the poorer sand plain which are useless for growing wheat occur in patches throughout the belt. The cost of clearing the wheat belt usually runs from 15 to 30 shillings an acre. Usually the tree roots are left in the ground, where they finally decay. The ploughing is done with a stump-jump plough, which rises over the obstructions, and greatly reduces the cost of production.

Seedtime begins about April in the earlier maturing districts, and ends somewhere in June in later districts. For fertilizers phosphates are required, but the soils usually contain enough nitrogen and potash.

A typical farm consists of 1,000 acres, and the farmer, growing from 250 to 300 acres of wheat each year, usually gets a crop every two or three years from a given area. Fallowing is managed as follows: the harvest is generally in December; then the field is cleared in January and the farmer turns sheep on the stubble. In May he seeds his next crop on another field previously prepared. He then ploughs the first field any time from June to September while the land is soft from the winter rains, and the weather is cool for his teams. In spring he works over the surface with a disc harrow, &c., and so obtains a soil mulch. Such a fallow will store up from 3 to 6 inches of rain, and crops seeded in such lands are practically independent of early rains (J. W. Paterson).

Few regions in the world exhibit the relation of rain to tree belts and to agriculture so clearly as does Swanland (Fig. 126). The

Karri forests with a rainfall of 40 inches are giving place to dairies. The next belt contains Jarrah, and this is the great apple country to-day. Then comes the wheat belt, with from 30 to 10 inches of rain, which was originally clothed with wandoo (28 inches) and York gum (25 inches) in the west; and mallet, salmon and gimlet gums in the drier east.

A glance at Fig. 97 shows that the wheat belt ends rather abruptly south of Southern Cross, though the rainfall lines would indicate that there is sufficient rain far to the east of this limit. The reliability isopleths also run east–west in this region, hence this does not explain the deficiency. The absence of a railway 'net' to collect the wheat is, of course, one factor. But it seems likely to be due to actual sterile soils for the most part. There is a great deal of salt in much of this area. I have been told also that there is rather a lot of poisonous plants which also hinder the farmer, since it is the general practice to grow both sheep and wheat.

It is very difficult to determine the lowest limit of the rainfall which admits of profitable agriculture in Australia. *Dry farming* methods of fallowing and careful tilth become increasingly important as the arid interior is approached (Fig. 141). Usually in the south of Australia a region with less than 13 inches of rain is classed as suitable for Dry Farming; but in the northern part of the wheat belt (in New South Wales) 22 inches might be so described. Here, of course, a large part of the rain falls in summer. It has been stated that every 3 inches of evaporation demands 1 inch of extra rain as an offset, so that it is found that 15 inches of rain in the south-west of New South Wales is equivalent to 20 inches in the north-west (Anderson).

This shift of the rain season from winter to summer as we move north through New South Wales (Fig. 98) puts a limit to the growth of ordinary wheat on the northern side. Of course, the temperatures are much higher in the north, even though the crop remains a winter one. In an early memoir (1916, Meteorological Bulletin 14) the writer showed that a close parallel existed between the conditions in east-central Queensland (between Mackay and Charleville) and in Central India. At Jabalpur in India the temperatures are much higher than those of the Queensland wheat belt, yet great quantities of wheat are grown. So also there would seem to be a place for the varieties of wheat grown largely in Texas in parts of Queensland north of Gayndah, which are not utilized yet.

The Oats Crop in Australia

The oats crop is of far less importance than the wheat crop in Australia. When used for grain it represents only 12 per cent of the latter crop. But it becomes of more importance when the amount of oats used for green fodder or hay is included. In New South Wales it is not unusual for the oats crop to be sub-divided as follows: oaten hay, 60 per cent; grain, 27 per cent; and green food, 13 per cent. Reference to the maps of New South Wales (Fig. 93) shows that it is chiefly grown in the middle south of the state, i.e. in the South-West Slopes and in the Riverina. The crop is usually harvested in December, and the product is used chiefly in the vicinity of Sydney and Newcastle. Usually the amount is about equal to the local demand, but sometimes a small proportion is exported; while at other times it is necessary to buy in Canada or New Zealand.

It is interesting to see how oats compare with wheat in the various states. In Queensland practically no oats are grown. In New South Wales the proportion is about 6 per cent, in South Australia 12 per cent, in Western Australia 14 per cent, in Victoria 20 per cent, and in Tasmania 22 per cent. (In some years, however, wheat is as important as oats in the island state.) Hence we see a gradual increase in importance as we move into the cooler southern croplands.

In most of the states (excluding Queensland) there is very little difference in the localities devoted to wheat and oats. In Victoria (Fig. 94) the chief county is Karkarooc (near the Murray) for both crops. In the coastlands oats is a little commoner than wheat, but neither crop is important in those regions. In South Australia (Fig. 96) the two are grown in the same districts, though here also wheat is relatively more abundant in the hotter lands, and oats in the south. Only in the extreme south-east of the state is the oats crop actually greater than the wheat crop. We see the same general arrangement in Western Australia (Fig. 97). In Tasmania the area of the Northern Midlands is the chief locality for wheat and oats, and the distribution for 1936 was the same throughout the state (Fig. 95).

Maize in Australia

The maize plant is native in much hotter countries than Britain, and so has naturally replaced wheat along the wet coastlands of eastern Australia. It has, however, never become a very important crop (as is the case in U.S.A.) for a number of reasons. Pigs and corn grow together in much of the 'Corn Belt' of U.S.A. (where 85 per cent of the maize is fed to stock); but Australians eat relatively little pork. So also the negro population of U.S.A. makes great use of 'hominy' and allied maize foods, which are little known in the southern continent. The plant is still perhaps not well understood by the majority of farmers. However, the chief objection of all is that no part of Australia agrees very well with the best maize region of U.S.A. This occurs in the cool wet east, and not in the heart of the 'corn belt' in Iowa. Thus Hartford in Connecticut produces 46 bushels per acre, while Des Moines in Iowa has 38 bushels according to Huntington.

Ellsworth Huntington has carried further the present writer's technique of the hythergraph (p. 72), to show regions where crops flourish best.[1] Thus in the adjacent figure the graph shows that in summer maize likes a climate defined by the upper oval. In winter the lower oval gives the best conditions; in autumn the right central oval; and in spring the left central oval expresses optimum

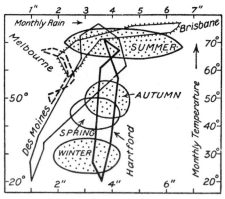

FIG. 101.—HYTHERGRAPHS OF FOUR MAIZE DISTRICTS
The four ovals show the best seasonal conditions according to Huntington

conditions. Thus a locality which exhibits such ideal climates for maize in *all four* seasons will clearly be the best suited for maize. Such is Hartford, whose climate may be summarized as having a fairly uniform rainfall of about 4 inches in each month, and a temperature ranging from 70° to 30° F. Obviously there is no such climate in Australia, since here a high rainfall (48 inches) is never found with 40° range of temperature. In Fig. 101 the graphs for Hartford and Des Moines are given, and also two centres of maize in Australia, Brisbane and Melbourne.

It is to be noted that important maize regions such as Hungary and Bulgaria also lie to the left of the four seasonal ovals. But no areas in Australia with adequate rainfall have anything like the range of temperature of the European countries. The ranges in

[1] *Economic and Social Geography*, p. 68, New York, 1933.

Australia are rarely above 20 degrees, and Melbourne (Fig. 101) is fairly typical.

In Australia almost all the maize (about 94 per cent) is confined to the two hottest states, Queensland and New South Wales. Moreover, the crop has been practically stationary for the last decade. In 1910 no less than 13 million bushels were produced, though of late the figure has been 7 or 8 million bushels. The map (Fig. 102) shows clearly that the chief Queensland maize area is found in the vicinity of Brisbane. There is a little grown near Cairns and the Atherton Tableland.

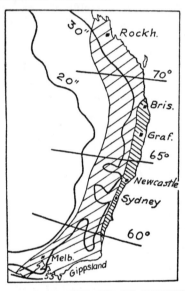

FIG. 102.—THE MAIZE CROP AND ITS CLIMATIC CONTROLS

In New South Wales the crop is found mainly on the coast, decreasing in importance as we proceed south. The extension of maize into Victoria occurs also in the coastal plain of the southeast. Here it is largely grown as green fodder. If the temperature and rainfall controls be added to the map, as in Fig. 102, we see that the chief maize is grown between the isotherms of 63° and 70° F., where the rainfall is over 30 inches a year. The average yield per acre in Australia is 26 bushels, which is somewhat higher than the world average.

Barley

This crop is of little importance in Australia, except in one region lying west of Adelaide as shown in Fig. 96. Here in about four counties, notably Fergusson on Yorke's Peninsula, is grown half of the whole barley crop of the continent. About one-fifth is found in Victoria, mostly in the Mallee, though a fair amount is grown just west of Melbourne (Fig. 94). The crop in the other states is of little importance, but the amount for Australia as a whole has been slowly increasing since 1915.

Vineyards in Australia

As in many parts of the world, there are in Australia two types of country where vineyards are successful. These depend on whether the water-supply is from rainfall or irrigation. The earliest grapes were grown with no supply added to the normal rains. For instance, in 1797 there were 8 acres of vines in the vicinity of Sydney, where the plants grow fairly well. In the Hunter valley near Newcastle grapes have been grown on a fairly large scale for a century. But it is in South Australia and Victoria that specially favourable districts for vines have been found. The acreages in the various states are somewhat as follows: South Australia 57,000 acres, Victoria 43,000, New South Wales 16,000, Western Australia 9,000 and Queensland 3,000.

In South Australia about 33,000 acres are found on the slopes of the Flinders Ranges, where a natural rainfall of about 20 inches is found to produce excellent grapes (Fig. 96, inset). Clare and Tanunda are well-known wine-producing districts. About 20,000 acres of vines are grown along the River Murray, mainly near Renmark. Here irrigation is mainly used (p. 281). In both regions the temperature varies from 75° F. in January to about 49° F. in July.

In Victoria over 80 per cent of the vineyards are found near Mildura in connexion with the irrigation areas of the Mallee (Fig. 90). The district around Albury in the north-east accounts for most of the rain-grown vines. Here the climatic controls are like those on the Flinders Range, with a rainfall of 20 to 25 inches a year. In New South Wales seven or eight thousand acres (53 per cent) are found in the Murrumbidgee Irrigation Area (p. 277). About 1,500 acres are grown with natural rainfall near Maitland in the Hunter valley. Almost all the remaining vines are grown in the vicinity of Sydney, Bathurst and Corowa (see Fig. 93, last map).

Orchards in Australia

The reasonably well-watered coastlands of Australia give every range of average temperature from 80° F. in the north to 50° F. in Tasmania. Hence most fruits of the world can be grown somewhere in this favoured belt along the east coast. Their distribution and climates are shown in the following table:

ORCHARDS AND TEMPERATURES IN EASTERN AUSTRALIA

Place	State	Lat. (° S.)	Temp. (° F.)	Rain (in.)	Bananas	Pines	Mangoes	Oranges	Peaches	Apples	Cherries	Raspberry
Cairns	Q.	17	75	90	*							
Cardwell	,,	18	75	90				*				
Bowen	,,	20	74	45		*						
Rockhampton	,,	22	70	40	*			*				
Maryborough	,,	25	70	47			*	*				
Maroochy	,,	26	68	60	*	*	*	*				
Brisbane	,,	27	68	47		*		*				
Stanthorpe	,,	29	67	32					*	*		
Murwillumbah	N.S.W.	29	67	70	*							
Erina (Gosford)	,,	34	64	45				*		*		
Orange	,,	33	65	36				*	*	*	*	
Cessnock	,,	33	65	35					*	*		
Sydney	,,	34	63	48				*	*	*		
Griffith	,,	34	62	(14)		(Irrigation)		*	*	*		
Tumut	,,	35	61	32					*	*		
Albury	,,	36	60	28				*				
Renmark	S.A.	34	63	(11)		(Irrigation)		*	*		*	*
Adelaide	,,	35	62	21						*	*	
Rochester	Vic.	36	61	(18)		(Irrigation)		*				
Melbourne	,,	38	58	26							*	
Beaconsfield	Tas.	41	55	40						*		
Hobart	,,	43	54	23						*	*	*
Port Cygnet	,,	43	53	35						*	*	*

The distribution in Western Australia is omitted from this table, but the temperatures from Perth to Albany are much like those in southern New South Wales. Reference to Fig. 97 will show that the vines, oranges and apples are distributed in much the same way as in eastern Australia.

In the following table is given the acreage devoted to the various crops in the six states. As regards the total area involved, the order is as follows: apples 102,000 acres, oranges 49,000, bananas 26,000, peaches 24,000, pears 20,000, plums 15,000, cherries 6,000 and small fruits 4,000.

AREAS OF ORCHARDS, 1945–46

(in thousand acres)

	Q.	N.S.W.	W.A.	S.A.	Vic.	Tas.	Total
Bananas	9	17					26
Pine-apples	8						8
Oranges, &c.	5	27	4	5	7		50
Peaches	1	8	1	2	15		27
Apples	5	14	13	8	22	22	84
Pears		4	1	2	13	3	22
Plums	1	5	1	2	3		12
Cherries		3		1	1		5
Raspberries					1	3	4

In 1953–4 the figures have not changed in any marked degree

A consideration of the two tables above shows that in each state the proportions of the various fruits grown are somewhat different. Queensland grows all the pine-apples and mangoes, but New South Wales, curiously enough, grows more bananas, though they are all clustered in the hot north-east corner (Fig. 93). New South Wales easily leads in the citrus fruits. They are about equally distributed near the Manning River on the coast, and in the irrigation areas on the Murrumbidgee. In plums and cherries New South Wales is also in the lead, both growing mainly in the tablelands, especially near Orange. Western and South Australia are notable chiefly for apples, but are far behind the cooler states as regards other fruit of temperate climes. Victoria (Fig. 94) leads in peaches, apples and pears; while Tasmania (Fig. 95) excels in raspberries and currants (not *grape* currants); and is nearly equal to Victoria in apples. It would seem evident that any of these crops can be widely extended when there is a greater demand, since their distribution is 'sporadic', and by no means fills the optimum areas suited for each type of fruit.

The Cotton Crop in Australia

The revival of this industry in Australia in the last thirty years offers an excellent example of the value of comparative climatology in deciding where to plant somewhat unfamiliar crops. It has long been known that cotton could be grown in Australia, and as a result of the Civil War in U.S.A., which cut off supplies, a good deal of cotton was planted in Queensland. Thus 13,000 acres were used for cotton in 1871, but by 1887 no cotton was being grown.

The new interest developed as the result of a second disturbance of the world's main crop. This was due to the invasion of the Boll Weevil, which entered Texas from Mexico in 1892. By 1916 it had spread through all the 'cotton states' except in the north-east corner. In 1911 cotton was planted again in Queensland, and during the war-years occupied 200 acres. High prices after the war led to a boom in cotton; and the farmers were assisted first by the Queensland Government and later by the Commonwealth. The immense increase in cotton-growing in 1922 is shown in the graph (Fig. 103). Without much exaggeration it may be stated that cotton

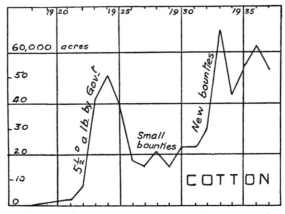

FIG. 103.—THE INCREASE OF THE COTTON CROP FROM 1918 TO 1937

was tried out by hopeful settlers in almost every district in Australia where any kind of crops had ever been grown!

The most satisfactory method, of course, is to concentrate on those districts in Australia where conditions most nearly approach to the optimum for cotton. I made a preliminary study around 1922 to discover such areas, and I summarize its conclusions here.

Somewhere about 60 per cent of the world's cotton comes from the United States of America, and much of the rest from India. In the States the cotton belt is fairly well defined and extends from Texas to North Carolina (Fig. 104). It is of interest that the best homoclime of Sydney in North America is Wilmington in North Carolina. The drier limit of the cotton belt is determined by a rainfall of 23 inches, but almost the whole is grown with a rainfall exceeding 40 inches a year. The belt lies between the average

annual temperature lines of 60° and 70° F. These limits are shown
for U.S.A. and India in Fig. 104.

Where now in Australia do these conditions occur? We have
only a narrow belt which is at all similar, and it extends along the
coast from about Sydney to Bundaberg, and inland to the eastern
slopes of the ranges. I show it approximately by the black area
around Brisbane in the map. The immense east–west extension
of the American cotton belt is due largely to the vicinity of the
Gulf of Mexico, which is represented in Australia by a large desert.
Furthermore, the soils as a whole in the Australian region are unfortunately nothing like as fertile as the rich black soils of Alabama.

If now we turn to the world's second great cotton region we find
that it is in Berar in Central India. Here conditions are very different from those in the United States, yet cotton grows nearly as

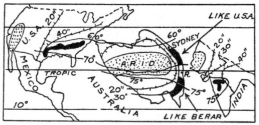

FIG. 104.—AUSTRALIA (REVERSED) COMPARED WITH U.S.A. AND
INDIA, TO SHOW CLIMATIC REGIONS AKIN TO COTTON AREAS

R. is Rockhampton. Soils are ignored

well. The rainfall is somewhat lighter, but is mostly over 30 inches.
The temperatures are much higher, the yearly average being about
75°. In Australia we have a considerable area of land in our tropics
with this temperature and between 30 and 40 inches of rain, which
extends across the root of Cape York Peninsula. Here again the
soils are on the whole much less attractive than the 'regur' of
central India, but considerable areas may yet be used for cotton.

It will be noticed that there is a gap in these cotton lands in
Australia between Cape York and Bundaberg. Since cotton luckily
flourishes with a wide range of temperatures, we can be sure that
this belt also is suited for cotton. Indeed, it is in this area, which
does not agree closely either with U.S.A. or Berar that all our
Australian cotton grows. Possibly the coastlands of Darwinia and
Kimberley, which are much hotter than Berar, but not unlike
some less important cotton areas in Southern India, may grow
cotton in the future.

In Fig. 105 the present distribution of cotton in south-east

Queensland is given. Farmers are no longer trying to grow the crop elsewhere, for in the uplands behind Rockhampton the best conditions seem to occur. All the home-grown cotton which Australia's small population needs is produced here. It will be seen that

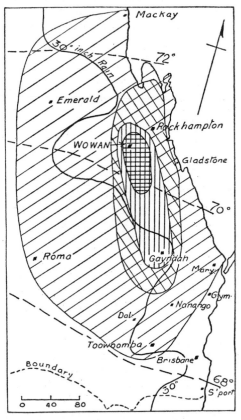

FIG. 105.—DISTRIBUTION OF COTTON-GROWING IN 1936

Over 95 per cent of the crop is grown in the three central ruled areas

Wowan is the chief centre, and it has an average temperature of about 70° F., and a rainfall of a little over 30 inches. Nearly all the crop comes from the upland region between Wowan and Gayndah, though some is grown as far west as Roma and Emerald.

Out of a total of 52,000 acres no less than 35,000 are grown around Wowan, 4,000 near by at Monto, and 5,000 near Gayndah. This only leaves 8,000 acres in the rest of Queensland. There are three ginneries—at Brisbane, Gladstone and Rockhampton. In 1936 the crop amounted to 19,198,600 lb. of unginned cotton and some 3,400 growers were concerned. In many cases crops are grown by tenants who are permitted to occupy areas of virgin land on which they grow cotton, in return for clearing the land. After picking the crop they often leave the district (*Year Book*).

The cotton crop has declined very greatly since 1943, when 41,389 acres in Queensland were under cotton. In 1946 the figure was only 7,902 acres. Australia has always imported a large amount of raw cotton, and since 1938 this has gradually increased from twice as much to ten times as much in 1945. In 1953-4 the local production of raw cotton was 2 million lb., while 44 million lb. were imported.

The Sugar Industry in Australia

Of the 786,909 tons of raw sugar produced in Australia in the 1936-7 season 95 per cent was cane-sugar produced in Queensland, about 5 per cent was cane-sugar from New South Wales, and only 0·5 per cent was beet-sugar grown near Maffra in Gippsland (Vic.). There has not been much change in the Queensland sugar production (around 300,000 acres) between 1930 and 1946, but the New South Wales crop has fluctuated considerably.

The map given in Fig. 92 (at A) shows the chief sugar areas in Queensland. (In this map the dots representing thousands of acres of sugar are scattered *equally* throughout each major division. Actually all the plantations are right on the coast.) The towns are shown in Fig. 92 at C. The relative importance of the fields can be gathered from the table at the top of page 320, which gives climatic controls.

It will be seen that the region round Mackay was the most important in 1917, but Cairns was leading in 1946. Cardwell, Ayr and Bundaberg have progressed together in the last twenty years. Generally speaking, the total acreage has doubled in every district since 1917. The relations of the sugar crop to the rainfall will be gathered from the course of the 40-inch isohyet, shown in Fig. 92 (at E). The low rainfall near Townsville and between Mackay and Bundaberg accounts for the absence of sugar plantations in these belts.

It will be seen from the foregoing table that the range of temperature is very considerable, from 78° F. at Douglas to 69° at Southport (and 68° F. at Grafton, N.S.W.). The necessity for a rainfall exceeding 40 inches confines the plantations to the coast. Even so, irrigation from shallow pipe-wells is used around Bundaberg and Ayr.

SUGAR-CANE IN QUEENSLAND, IN 1917 AND 1954

(1954 figures are in combined pairs) (thousand acres)

	Latitude (° S.)	Temperature (° F.)	Rain (in.)	1954	1917
Cairns and Douglas	16	78	85	161	24
Cardwell and Innisfail	18	77	85		34
Ayr and Townsville	19	76	50	57	22
Bowen and Proserpine	20	75	42		6
Mackay and St. Lawrence	21	72	68	172	42
Bundaberg	25	70	44		25
Maryborough	26	70	42	87	18
Maroochy	27	69	65	9	4
Southport	28	69	58		1

In Queensland sugar-cane comprises one-quarter of the agriculture of the state, and is worth about 8 millions sterling annually. There are 33 mills, the tendency being to shut down the small mills and build fewer but much larger mills (Fig. 92A). These are most numerous near Cairns, Mackay and Bundaberg (Fig. 92C). The plantations are confined to the narrow belt between the highlands and the sea. Here the constant trade winds and numerous coastal cyclones give an abundance of rain. Near Cairns at Harvey Creek (p. 176) is the heaviest rainfall in Australia.

The plantations are made in two types of country, the 'vine scrubs' and the eucalypt forest. The latter is of a more open character without vines, and contains much Bloodwood (*Eucalyptus corymbosa*). It is stated that the northern canes yield more sugar per ton than the southern. Thus in the Cairns district 8 tons of cane give one ton of sugar, while in the extreme south 10 tons are necessary.

The industry is of great interest, as the white cane-cutters near Cairns are the advance guard of such agriculture in the tropics. For instance, the coastlands of Texas have a mean temperature like that of Bundaberg, while Rio de Janeiro resembles Ayr in Queensland. I know of no white farmers outside Queensland who work at sea level in latitude 16° with temperatures such as occur at Douglas. Cane-cutting is done chiefly in June and the following cooler months, but the whole problem will be referred to later in discussing tropical white settlement (p. 455). Frost occasionally damages crops as far north as Bundaberg, while hurricanes have at times destroyed much cane in Mackay and Innisfail (as in 1918).

H. J. Easterby gives a description of the various regions in a paper he published in 1924, from which the following notes are taken.

Around Douglas the soil is nearly all alluvial, and both eucalyptus and tropical forests give place to sugar. In the Cairns district the sugar lands occur chiefly in the raised coastal plain along the lower Russell and Mulgrave Rivers [Fig. 63]. Here there are also patches of volcanic soil. The average relative humidity (80 per cent) is probably the highest in Australia, which is good for the cane but bad for the white folk.

In the Mackay district there is the greatest number of cane-farmers, and almost all the best land is ploughed. A long stretch without any sugar-fields of note separates Mackay from Bundaberg, and the latter town is well south of the tropic. Here the cane grows slower, and in times of drought, cutting may be deferred till next season. Ratoon sugar (from old roots) is more commonly grown here than in the north. Maryborough is changing from cane to dairying, and now there are only a few mills in place of 15. The same transfer has taken place in most of the sugar areas in the south.

In New South Wales all the sugar is grown along the three northern rivers, the Tweed, Richmond and Clarence (Fig. 93, last map). There are three large mills at Condong, Broadwater and Harwood Island. About 500 men are employed in these mills where the cane is crushed; and the sugar is sent to the large refinery at Pyrmont in Sydney. About 9,000 acres of cane is grown in this north-east corner of the state. The cane takes longer to mature in the south, and the production per acre is considerably less.

Many interesting byproducts are being developed in connection with the great sugar industry of Australia, which is wholly in the hands of the Colonial Sugar Refining Company. In 1936 the production of Wall-board from cane refuse (megass) was started. Later Timbrock made from local hardwoods was added. Then gypsum and asbestos resources were utilized for building materials. In recent years the Company produces many chemical products such as cellulose and acetic acid.

Minor Crops of Australia

A few words may be given to various interesting crops in Australia of minor importance. In the Northern Territory about 1,000 acres of peanuts have yielded 400 tons of that commodity. Near Somerset, at the tip of Cape York Peninsula, there are about 360 acres of coconut trees, this being the sole plantation of note. Millets of various sorts should be largely grown in central Queensland, and a large area near Emerald has recently been planted with sorghum. It is financed by British capital.

Rice is a valuable crop in the Murrumbidgee area and is discussed on page 277. Flax has been tried in Gippsland, where about 700 acres are devoted to this crop. Hops are of some importance in Tasmania, where 900 acres are grown near Hobart, but the much smaller acreage in Victoria is decreasing. Of vegetables, potatoes are chiefly grown in Victoria and Tasmania, and their distribution is shown in Figs. 94 and 95. Other root-crops are unimportant. Onions occupy 7,000 acres, chiefly in Victoria. Turnips are grown to some extent in Tasmania, and sweet potatoes in Queensland.

Large-scale experiments on the growing of rice in the river flats some 30 miles east of Darwin were started in 1955. There are said to be three-quarters of a million acres of good treeless land in the vicinity of Humpty-doo. Satisfactory crops on a few hundred acres have already been obtained, and it is hoped that eventually several thousand folk may be settled in these coastlands, when difficulties due to lack of labourers, inadequate transport and high temperatures have been met.

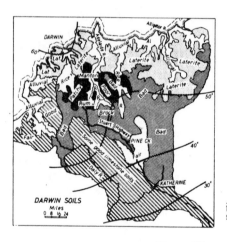

FIG. 105A.—DARWIN SOILS

Approximate Soil Map of the region between Katherine and Darwin, simplified from surveys by Christian, Stewart, etc. Isohyets are added.

Trace Elements

Remarkable improvements have taken place in various dry regions of southern Australia by the use of trace elements. At Coonalpyn (some hundred miles east of Adelaide) large areas of formerly useless heath now carry two sheep to the acre. This has been brought about by a treatment with small quantities of copper and zinc sulphates plus superphosphate. A rich covering of 'Subterranean Clover' and *Phalaris* grass has replaced the useless heath. Traces of manganese and molybdenum are often found to benefit other soils.

CHAPTER XIII

THE PASTORAL INDUSTRY IN AUSTRALIA

AN interesting table in the Commonwealth Year Book shows the
estimated gross value of production in the leading industries for
various years. We may compare the values in 1934–5 and those
ten years earlier and later. Figures represent millions of pounds
sterling.

Year	Pastoral	Agricul-ture	Dairies, &c.	Mining	Manuf.	Forest	Fish	Total
1924–5	127	107	45	25	137	11	2	456
1934–5	75	69	45	20	137	9	2	356
1945–6	86	105	50	26	352	12	3	658

It will be seen that the values have increased considerably in
the twenty years quoted. It will be noticed that the pastoral production has not reached the 1925 figure—while agriculture, dairies,
mining and forests have risen to the earlier values. However, the
chief change has been in the manufactures where the figures have
more than doubled. This indeed indicates the shift in Australian
economy. (Later data are given on page 417A.)

Some idea of the relative importance of the various sections of
the industry may be gained from the values of the pastoral products exported from Australia in 1934–5. They are given in
millions of pounds sterling in the following table. Of course, a great
deal of material is not exported, but is used in Australia itself. For
instance, about 1,000 million gallons of milk is nearly all used
locally. Slightly less butter was used in Australia than was exported,
and about twice as much cheese is eaten locally as is exported.

EXPORT OF PASTORAL PRODUCTS, 1934–5 AND 1945–6

(in millions £A)

		1934–5	1945–6			1934–5	1945–6
1	Wool	39	79	6	Rabbit skins	0·9	6·3
2	Butter	9·5	12	7	Preserved milk	0·7	4·2
3	Frozen mutton	2·6	1·5	8	Frozen rabbits	0·4	0·1
4	Sheepskins	1·8	4·5	9	Frozen pork	0·4	0·8
5	Tallow	0·9	0·3	10	Tinned meat	0·2	5·9

It is clear from the above data that the total sheep products (wool, mutton and sheepskins) are much more valuable than the cattle products (beef, butter and milk). It is, however, of interest to see (as we shall do later) which type of stock is more widely spread over Australia (p. 340).

The agricultural industries are very slowly expanding on their

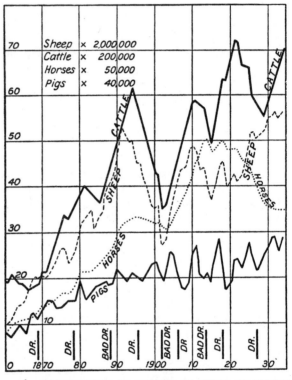

FIG. 106.—FLUCTUATIONS IN NUMBER OF STOCK IN AUSTRALIA,
MAINLY DUE TO DROUGHTS (*DR.*)

(*From 'Commonwealth Year Book'*)

inner arid margins, and will continue to do so especially in Queensland. Yet more than three-quarters of Australia is probably too dry and hot for agriculture, while on the other hand not much is too dry for some stock to be grazed. While a very large area (65 per cent) receives less than 15 inches of rain a year, only a small proportion (about 7 per cent) receives less than 6 inches. This probably accounts for the absence of drifting dunes (p. 125).

We are told that Captain Phillip arrived at Sydney in 1788 with seven horses, six cattle, twenty-nine sheep, twelve pigs and five rabbits. The graph (Fig. 106) from the *Commonwealth Year Book* shows the increase in numbers of the cattle, sheep, horses and pigs in the period 1860 to 1934. In the case of the two most important classes (cattle and sheep) there are two outstanding features. The growth of the industry was very rapid until 1891, but thereafter remarkable oscillations occurred. These correspond, of course, to widespread droughts in the main pastoral regions. In the sheep curve, however, the oscillations are becoming definitely smaller, which suggests that disturbances due to drought are being met more readily nowadays (by shifting stock, &c.) than in earlier decades.

The number of sheep was about 104 millions in 1891, but declined thereafter, and only again reached this figure about 1930. Hence the numbers of sheep have obviously not been increasing rapidly in the last forty years. Cattle also reached a peak of 12 millions about 1893 to decline thereafter (owing to drought and rabbits among other causes) until 1902. From this evil period, just as in the case of sheep, there has been a fairly rapid increase in numbers (with fluctuations around 1918). Cattle rose to a maximum of 14 millions in 1922, but a second drop, culminating in 1929, has been followed by a second rise to 14 millions in 1934.

The total numbers of stock in the Commonwealth are given in the following table. These figures are graphed in Fig. 106.

HORSES, CATTLE AND SHEEP

(in thousands)

Year	Horses	Cattle	Sheep
1860	432	3,958	20,135
1890	1,522	10,300	97,881
1920	2,416	13,500	81,976
1947	1,195	13,427	95,723
1954	850	15,601	126,924

We may obtain a general idea of the distribution of the two chief forms of stock from the following table, which gives percentage numbers in the various states in 1934.

One very interesting deduction can be made at a glance from this table. The pastoral industry, like the agricultural, is centred in the smaller eastern states, and not in the 'wide open spaces' of Western Australia, South Australia and the Northern Territory. Tiny Victoria is far more important than the three giant states

	N.S.W.	Vic.	Q.	S.A.	W.A.	Tas.	N.T.
Cattle	25	15	43	2·5	6·5	2	6
Sheep	47	15	19	7	10	2	—
Both stock*	9·1	3·8	7·8	1	2	0·5	0·8

* In this last line the figures represent millions of *large* stock, and it has been assumed that *ten* sheep are equivalent to *one* head of cattle.

together for cattle, and is nearly equal to all three for sheep. Here again we have an illustration of the principle that 'it's rain not area which matters'. The same deduction is obtained still more strikingly from the last line in the above table. Thus New South Wales is seen to be the chief pastoral state, with Queensland a close second. Victoria is about half as important as each; while the three huge areas of Western Australia, South Australia and Northern Territory are just equal (when combined) to Victoria in this connexion. (Proportions in 1954 have not varied notably.)

THE CATTLE INDUSTRY

The first imported cattle were probably brought from Bengal to provide beef for the soldiers and convicts. Later, English breeds were sent out, and as early as 1807 a Longhorn bull was sold for £86. As the population increased, Holsteins, Ayrshires and Shorthorns were imported to improve the breed. From this mixed source has evolved the Illawarra breed, which contains about one part Shorthorn, one part Ayrshire, and two parts of the old mixed breed of the country. In Queensland Devons, Shorthorns and Herefords are the common breeds. The last-named are preferred, as they are said to be hardier, stand the drought better, and travel better on the stock routes. Among dairy cows Illawarra, Jersey and Ayrshire seem to be the most popular.[1]

In Australia, as in many other parts of the world, the distribution of cattle depends on whether they are grown for beef or for dairy purposes. The latter are naturally found where pasture is rich, which confines them practically to the well-watered east coast of Australia or to the rather rare irrigation settlements. Furthermore, proximity to large towns has usually been an important factor in connexion with the distribution of milk. This is, however, becoming of less importance as better means of communication and more and more refrigeration plants and butter factories are established.

The two densest areas in the cattle distribution are found in

[1] The *Report of the Scottish Agriculture Committee*, Edinburgh, 1911, which I have used considerably in this section. See also the chapter (on Cattle) in *Australia* (edited G. L. Wood), New York, 1947.

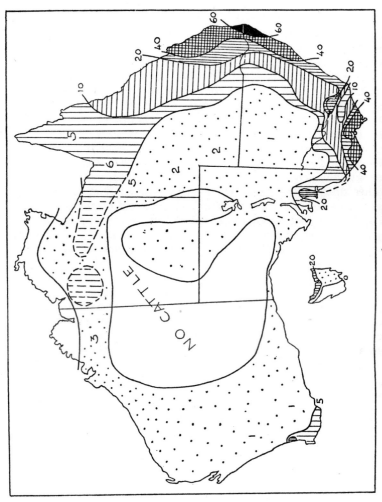

FIG. 107.—CATTLE IN AUSTRALIA IN 1936–7, SHOWING DENSITY PER SQUARE MILE

Note.—The density in Northern Territory is only approximate. Some large 'stations' carry 10 head per square mile

Southern Victoria, and near the border of New South Wales and Queensland. In the south the less rainfall is balanced by the greater coolness. In the northern area we see a correlation with the distribution of maize (Fig. 107). The second type of cattle distribution is found associated with dairies near less-important cities with fair to good pasture such as Launceston, Adelaide or Perth. The third characteristic distribution is found in the north, far from any centres of population. It extends from Townsville towards Broome in Western Australia. This is the belt of savanna or grasslands, &c., and is occupied almost entirely by *beef* cattle. It is a relatively narrow strip between the rank innutritious grasses of the coastlands and the sterile areas of the Arunta or Western Deserts.

It is of considerable interest that in temperate Australia the *important* sheep areas are found in much drier land than are any noteworthy densities of cattle. This is mainly due to the fact that, other things being equal, sheep pay far better than cattle. As a matter of fact, the really rougher and drier area on the margin of the desert (often referred to as the 'Never Never' in Australia) is given over to sparse cattle, because the latter can withstand drought, can travel further to wells, &c., and are less subject to attack by dingoes and wild dogs.

Dairy Farming

Nearly three-quarters of the dairying is carried on in the states of New South Wales and Victoria. In New South Wales the centre of the industry has migrated from the south coast to the north coast, where land was cheaper and the rainfall heavier than in the original centre of dairying in the Illawarra district. Along this coast the rainfall is fairly uniform and reliable, and hence the vegetation keeps green all the year round. There is, however, a good deal of milk and butter produced at some distance from the coast by farmers who combined dairying with wheat-growing or mutton-raising (Fig. 108).

Seventy-five per cent of the milch cows are in the coastal region; and no less than 500,000 (about half of the whole number) are found in the vicinity of Grafton and Lismore in the extreme north coast. Holstein and Jersey are perhaps the favourite breeds. Over 1 million acres are under sown grasses along the coast; including much *Paspalum*, which was accidentally brought to Australia from South America. It grows so thickly that it kills off weeds; but it tends to 'mat', and must be broken apart as it gets old. In the colder southern districts a great deal of ensilage is prepared. There are very few dairy cattle in the rugged area near Mount Kosciusko.

Victoria, however, led the way in dairying, and here it occupies a much larger proportion of the state than in New South Wales. This can be seen at a glance in Fig. 108, where the proportion of cattle used for dairying is charted. Only a very small part of the northern state has a proportion over 20 per cent, whereas the whole of Victoria exhibits this condition. Indeed, in almost every county in Victoria about half the cattle belong to the dairy class. Of course, in the north-west (Mallee) the *total* numbers of cattle are relatively unimportant.

In the southern state two-thirds of the dairy cows live in the

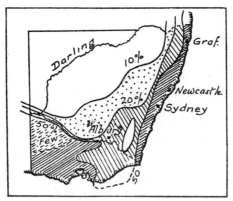

FIG. 108.—PERCENTAGES OF CATTLE USED FOR DAIRYING
IN SOUTH-EAST AUSTRALIA

coastlands. Almost every town and hamlet has its butter factory, and the rainfall throughout varies from 25 to 40 inches. In Gippsland much maize is grown, and much of this crop reaches the market in the form of butter and pork.

In Queensland there are nearly 1½ million dairy cattle, so that this rather hot state has about the same numbers as either New South Wales or Victoria. The leading districts in milk production are given in the following approximate table. Except for the highlands near Cairns, they are all to be found in or near the temperate coastlands.

DAIRY COWS IN QUEENSLAND

South Coast		Central Coast	
Moreton (Brisbane)	412,000	Rockhampton	196,000
Maryborough	372,000	Cairns	48,000
Darling Downs	285,000	Mackay	23,000
Roma	17,000	Central West	9,000
South-west	3,000	Townsville	6,000

All the above places are in the south-east corner of Queensland except Atherton, which is far north on the well-known tableland. Most of the butter comes from the vicinity of Brisbane and Maryborough or from the Darling Downs. Almost all the cheese comes from Toowoomba in the last-named district (Fig. 105).

Beef Cattle

Beef cattle on the Queensland stations are usually Devons, Shorthorns or Herefords. On many stations they are drafted as 'three-year-olds', and sent south to New South Wales or Victoria to fatten. In so doing, they must travel many hundred miles on the stock roads. These latter are broad stretches of country where the pasture is sufficient in normal years to enable travelling stock to cross the district (p. 118). About 300 cattle are sent in a mob, and they are under the charge of a head drover with 4 or 5 assistants.

There are a dozen meat factories in Queensland, the largest being at Townsville, Rockhampton, Bowen, Gladstone and Brisbane. About 90 per cent of the export goes to Britain, and its value each year is about 1½ millions sterling.

Beef cattle constitute the sole stable industry in the Northern Territory. As mentioned in an earlier section, stock was brought into the Macdonnell Ranges as early as 1866. Giles reached the Katherine River on the north coast in 1879 with 2,000 cattle and 12,000 sheep, but sheep grazing has not had much success in the Territory to date. In 1917 Vesteys opened extensive meatworks at Darwin, but they were closed about 1920. Beef is now flown from Glenroy (W.A.) to Wyndham.

Wynne Williams gives the following picture of the cattle industry in the Territory.[1] The stock fatten rapidly on the commencement of the summer rains in December and January. These rains continue intermittently till April. By June or July the green grass has lost its bloom, and the cattle lose their condition steadily as the grass becomes dry. Unless rains fall in the period September–November (Fig. 77) the cattle become weak, and if the wet season is delayed till January the mortality is heavy.

This period of stress prevents the cattle from growing rapidly and so it is almost impossible to supply the desired young cattle for the chilled-meat trade. Tick fever (p. 344) is in part responsible for these disabilities. Williams supports the proposal to cross Zebu and ordinary cattle in large numbers, since the former Asiatic cattle thrive on the coarse coastal grass and resist the attacks of tick fever.

In Northern Territory the stations are of very large size. Thus

[1] *Economic Record*, Melbourne, Vol. II.

Avon Downs, with 30,000 cattle, leases 2,000 square miles at about 2s. per square mile (Fig. 76). The leases usually run for forty-two years. The station of Victoria River Downs (Bovril Company) is about 13,000 square miles, which is larger than Belgium! It carried about 138,000 cattle in 1922. Brunette Downs runs 40,000 cattle on 4,000 square miles. Thus some of these huge marginal stations have cattle densities of about ten per square mile. Stock from some western stations in the Northern Territory travel on their hooves for three months to reach Queensland, and then go south for another three months to the South Australian Railway at Marree, where they are trucked to Adelaide. This roundabout route has better supplies of water than the more direct route via Alice Springs (C. W. Conacher).

THE SHEEP INDUSTRY

Wool may be described as the 'cash crop' of Australia. When wool is plentiful and sells at a good price, then the Australian has money to spend; and development of all sorts progresses in the Commonwealth. Its predominant position will have been gathered from the early paragraphs of this chapter. Elsewhere the gradual spread of the sheep flocks over the continent has been briefly discussed (Fig. 79). We may, however, dwell somewhat further on the early development and present characteristics of the sheep industry.

Sheep and goats are native in the drier areas of central Asia, and hence thrive well in the analogous warm dry areas of Australia. In the wild state sheep develop hair rather than wool, so that the evolution of the enormous fleece of a modern Australian ram is an example of very rapid changes due to careful breeding.

Development of the Sheep Industry

Some very interesting notes are to be found in the valuable report of the Scottish Agricultural Commission (Edinburgh, 1911). This quotes a dispatch from Governor Phillip, dated September 1788, which gives a melancholy picture of sheep grazing on the shores of Circular Quay! 'One sheep only remains of upwards of seventy which I purchased at the Cape of Good Hope. It is the rank grass under the trees that has destroyed them; for those who have only one or two sheep, which have fed about their tents, have preserved them.'

It is stated that Captain Macarthur, a member of the military corps, soon recognized that the fleece was improving in the new environment. At first the wool clip from a sheep only weighed 3½ lb., but by the year 1895 a ram produced a fleece of 23 pounds.

In 1796 Macarthur obtained some merino sheep from the Cape, and others were bought from the royal flocks at Kew. These merinoes originated in the hot dry plains of Spain; where 'merino' meant sheep controlled by an official called a 'Majorino'.

Sheep of the merino breed are much the most numerous in Australia today. In 1805 Macarthur settled at Camden near Sydney, where descendants of his early stock still survive. Cox (at Mulgoa) and Marsden were also noted early breeders. In 1821 wool sent to London by Macarthur brought 10s. 4d. a pound. After 1830 Mudgee on the drier western slopes displaced Camden as the most important sheep stud.

The Spanish were averse to other nations acquiring their noted merinoes, though a few were sent as presents to foreign rulers. But the Napoleonic wars led to considerable numbers spreading to western Europe, especially to Saxony. It was from this country that Tasmania received her chief supplies around 1830, and South Australia and Western Australia were also supplied about 1835. Merinoes, from Sussex in England, had, however, reached Tasmania before this date.

Partly as the result of the gold rushes, sheep boomed in the 'sixties and later; so much so that by 1890 the south-east portion of the continent was overstocked. Drought and rabbits accounted for tremendous losses about this time. The chief changes in the technique of the sheep industry have been the breaking up of the huge early leases. Thus in New South Wales in 1891 there were seventy-three holdings each carrying 100,000 sheep, but by 1920 only one station had flocks of such a size. The change-over from 'shepherding' to fences has been mentioned previously. Although the numbers of the sheep have not increased very much in the last fifty years, the character of the fleece has been greatly improved. The Closer Settlement policy has also been greatly extended during the last thirty years. Some amazing prices have been paid for pedigree rams in order to improve the wool clip. Thus £3,150 was given for a ram as far back as 1883, and in 1915 one sold for 2,000 guineas. So also on many stations the *average* weight of a fleece has gradually been increased from about 5 lb. to 8 lb.

The variation in the number of sheep among the various states can be gathered from the following table:

There has thus not been much change in any of the states since 1890, except in Western Australia, where the sheep have quadrupled in number. However, the leading position of New South Wales is evident at a glance, since this single state includes half the total for Australia. As pointed out earlier, the three western states combined have only the same number of sheep as tiny Victoria.

SHEEP IN THE VARIOUS STATES, 1890–1954

(in millions)

	N.S.W.	Vic.	Q.	S.A.	W.A.	Tas.	N.T.	A.C.T.	Total
1890	55·9	12·7	18·0	7·0	2·5	1·6	—	—	97·9
1910	45·6	12·9	20·3	6·3	5·2	1·8	0·06	—	92·0
1920	33·7	12·2	17·4	6·4	6·5	1·6	—	0·16	77·9
1930	53·4	16·5	22·5	6·0	9·9	2·1	0·02	0·2	110·6
1944	56·8	19·2	23·3	10·4	11·0	2·2	0·02	0·3	123·2
1954	59·6	21·4	18·2	11·8	13·1	9·4	—	0·3	126·9

Usually Australia leads the world as regards numbers, but from 1925 to 1929 U.S.S.R. owned more sheep; the total approaching 130 million. The peasants, however, in 1934 (as a protest against collectivism) slaughtered large numbers of sheep, so that the total fell to about 50 millions. The following table shows the position of the leading countries about 1938:

SHEEP OF THE WORLD

(average 1936–40)

Australia	112 millions		South Africa	40 millions
U.S.S.R.	80 ,,		New Zealand	31 ,,
U.S.A.	51 ,,		United Kingdom	26 ,,
Argentine	45 ,,		Spain (1933)	19 ,,
India	44 ,,		Uruguay	18 ,,

Leading Breeds of Sheep

The character and breeds of sheep differ a good deal according to the purpose for which they are bred, and the environments of their grazing areas. For instance, sheep reared mainly for wool may not be the best for mutton. In the very early days Macarthur favoured the former, while Marsden grew sheep largely for mutton. With the wide application of refrigeration after 1880, mutton breeds have spread extensively in Australia, and the lighter fine-woolled merino has given place in some districts to the heavier Lincolns, Leicesters or cross-breds. The *Scottish Report* states that a common practice is to mate a heavy merino ewe with a Lincoln or Leicester ram, keep the ewe lambs, and later mate them with a Shropshire ram. The wool of the first 'cross' compares favourably with that of the pure merino, and the breed is much better for producing mutton.

The principal breed in New South Wales is the celebrated short-woolled merino strain. The numbers of other pure breeds are very small, but the progeny of cross-bred ewes mated to merino rams (called 'Comebacks') are fairly numerous. English long-woolled sheep are represented chiefly by Lincoln, Romney Marsh and Border Leicester breeds. English short-woolled breeds such as the Southdown are used to some extent where the chief interest is in the production of fat lambs. The relatively few sheep in the rather wet rugged coastlands are mostly Romney Marsh breed. In New South Wales in the last decade the proportions have been somewhat as follows: Merino, 45 million; Lincolns and other pure breeds, 0·4 million; Merino Comebacks, 6·2 million; Crossbreds, 1·6 million.

Environment and Sheep

We owe to C. E. Cowley the following notes on the response of sheep to varying environments. In the elevated area of the eastern highlands fine wool is produced, but the cold conditions in winter tend to make for undernourished sheep. The open plains produce larger and more vigorous sheep, but the heat and dust has a rather bad effect on the fleece. Victoria and Tasmania are well suited for the production of attractive wool. In the hotter parts of Queensland the wool deteriorates unless the stock are continuously improved by breeding with vigorous rams imported from the south. In South Australia the dry conditions produce wool defective at the tips, but even with a rainfall as low as 14 inches the sheep are very vigorous. In Western Australia he states that long-woolled breeds meet the hot conditions better (*Australian Encyclopedia*, 1926).

Since sheep stations are so characteristic of Australian life, the following account (based on the Scottish Report) will be of interest. A sheep run of 20,000 acres in Queensland in 1911 needed a capital of about £5,000 for expenses; but by 1952 this had risen to £28,000.

	1911	1952
Fencing	£800	£4,800
Hut and sheep yard	90	350
Wool shed for five shearers	75	1,000
Wool press	35	700
Eight horses	200	250
Bore for artesian water	1,000	4,000
House and out-buildings	600	3,500
3,500 ewes	1,312	7,000
2,500 wethers	812	6,000
Sundries	130	500
Total	£5,055	£28,100

The rent of the run at 2½d. per acre would be £208. Survey fees amount to £60, and the wages of a 'boundary rider' with rations might amount to about £100 per annum in 1911. The lambs are usually kept till they are about a year old, when those not required for breeding are sold. (I owe the 1952 data to the *Pastoral Review*, Sydney.)

Shearing takes place throughout most of the year, but varies with latitude. It may begin in north Queensland as early as January, and continue in various parts of the state for many months. In New South Wales shearing extends from July to December, and in Victoria it begins in September. In Western Australia the spring is the chief shearing season, from mid-June to the end of September.

Shearing is now done almost wholly by machine shears, and the shearers are usually furnished by co-operative shearing companies. The shearers are paid so much per hundred sheep, and a man can shear from one to two hundred sheep a day. The shorn fleece is graded in the sheds by 'wool classers', who take especial note of the length and fibre of the wool, and of the amount of grease. Then the classified wool is compressed into cubical bales in the wool press. Each bale is contained in a jute cover, and weighs about 300 lb.

The limits of the sheep are due primarily to the temperature and rainfall, which in turn react on their food-supply. But these controls are not very readily interpreted. If we look at Fig. 109, where the distribution per square mile is charted, it is clear that the *optimum* belt is a fairly direct response to rainfall and temperature, but this cannot be said of the area with 'no sheep'. Let us consider the optimum area in the south-east first. Here the sheep isopleths are parallel to the isohyets, as shown in the following table.

SHEEP AND RAINFALL

	Opti-mum (in.)	Limits (in.)	Chief districts
New South Wales	20–30	10–40	New England and Western slopes
Queensland	15–22	10–40	Longreach, Darling Downs, Maranoa
Victoria	20–30	10–50	Hamilton, North-east Slopes
South Australia	20–30	5–30	Mt. Gambier, Adelaide
Western Australia	15–30	8–35	Swanland
Tasmania	20–30	20–60	Central east

We may summarize this table by placing the optimum of the sheep as lying between the 20- and 30-inch isohyets, with a maximum density along the 25-inch isohyet. This is considerably wetter than the corresponding optimum for wheat, though most

12

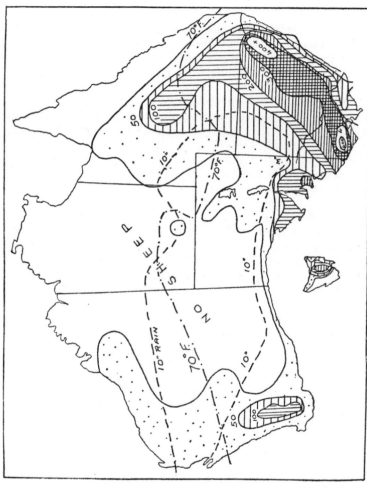

FIG. 109.—SHEEP IN AUSTRALIA IN 1936-7—SHOWING THE DENSITY PER SQUARE MILE

The main climatic controls are indicated. There are very few sheep where the rainfall is below 10 inches or the temperature above 70° F. There are only 20,000 sheep in the Territory. M. = Mutooroo

folk believe that the densest sheep belt is in drier country than the optimum for wheat (Fig. 141).

Sheep in the Arid Lands

Turning now to the inner edge of the sheep belt, the control is mainly edaphic (soil, &c.) in the south. There are no sheep in the 'fixed dunes' shown in earlier maps (Fig. 29). Given a reasonable rainfall, the noteworthy sheep stations seem to be bounded at present by a temperature of 72° F. in Queensland. There are only a few sheep in northern Western Australia. There are experts who firmly believe that sheep will extend in considerable numbers into

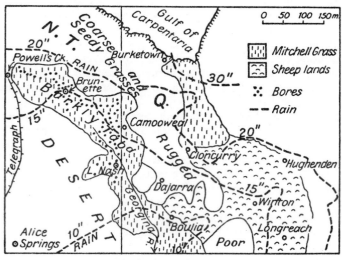

FIG. 110.—SHEEP DEVELOPMENTS IN NORTHERN TERRITORY ON THE
BARKLY TABLELAND
(*Based on Wynne Williams*)

the Barkly Tableland, where they are negligible at present. We may examine this suggestion in some detail, since it is vitally concerned with the major geographical problem in Australia. What can we do to extend settlement in the arid and tropical areas?

In a valuable paper in the *Geographical Journal* (January 1928) Wynne Williams shows that sheep may profitably displace cattle in the Barkly Tableland. This area lies on the border of Northern Territory and Queensland. It is well within the tropics, and has an average rainfall of 15 inches a year (Fig. 110). The rainy season is in the warmer months, and the graph for Daly Waters is given in Fig. 77. Only 2 inches out of a total of 26 inches falls in the six cooler months (May to October). The average temperature is about 80° F., which seems very hot for wool-bearing animals.

The character of the feed seems to depend on the amount of the rainfall. Thus in the lands with more than 20 inches of rain the grass is rank and sour, and is of little value for fattening stock. On the drier side the grass is more nourishing, and valuable plants allied to saltbush are present also; but this gives place to desert lands fairly soon on the south-west side. This is vegetated by spinifex, mulga and turpentine, and is of no value for stock.

It is of interest to note that the three vegetation belts in this region *cut across* the isohyets. Thus the latter are not the direct control. Mitchell grass—the best forage—grows with as little rainfall as 10 inches near Boulia, and as much as 30 inches near Burketown (Fig. 110). The intervening country is largely useless for stock, primarily because the soils are so sandy or rocky that a poor vegetation of spinifex and 'snapping gum' takes the place of the nourishing Mitchell grass. Furthermore, the ticks which give rise to Tick Fever are much less dangerous in the drier country south of the 20-inch isohyet.

In the early days of settlement several thousand sheep were grazed on Avon Downs (near Camooweal) in the Territory, but they were given up later. The disadvantages were that the paddocks were too large, and the watering facilities too scattered. Sheep need water within about 5 miles of their grazing area, while cattle will readily graze 10 miles from water. There is very little surface water in the Tableland, but over a hundred bores have been put down about 200 feet into water-bearing strata. From this level the water is lifted by steam-pumps.

Much of the lower ground in the Tableland is flooded after the rains. Lake De Burgh (Fig. 76) is sometimes 150 miles long and 50 miles wide, though the water disappears in a few months. Williams thinks that areas of this type can be drained, and that as much as 18,000 square miles can be made available for sheep. If the grasses are somewhat improved it may carry from 100 to 200 sheep to the square mile, adding 3 million sheep to Australia's total. This will displace many beef cattle, which, however, have not been a paying proposition in many areas, as already stated. Several other possible sheep regions are suggested in Fig. 76.

Probably the greatest 'advance on the arid lands' will result from a much larger outlay in constructing reservoirs. The example of Mutooroo is often cited in this connexion. This sheep station is in South Australia about 50 miles to the south-west of Broken Hill (Fig. 109). The rainfall is about 7 inches a year, and produces a good cover of saltbush, but there are no surface or artesian waters.

However, by an expenditure of £100,000 (chiefly used in excavating water-holes and drains leading thereto) an adequate water-supply has been provided, and the station carries about 33 sheep to the square mile.

Where the natural vegetation is satisfactory this practice can be followed in many areas in the south. But it is obvious that a large outlay of capital is needed, and that such expenditure does not lead to much human settlement. Another example leads us to the same conclusion. One of the largest ranches in Australia was Ord River (in east Kimberley, W.A.). Originally it comprised 4,400 square miles and carried 80,000 cattle. But at that time 40 white employees (with 70 aboriginal helpers) constituted almost the whole population in this large area, nearly half the size of Belgium (Fig. 76).

A grim picture of the deterioration of the 'saltbush country' in the north-east of South Australia is painted by Pick and Alldis in their booklet *Australia's Dying Heart* (Melbourne, 1944). In much of this region they state that nine-tenths of the saltbush has disappeared owing to drought and over-stocking by sheep. Rabbits have also been responsible for great losses, and though the trade in rabbit skins, &c., is worth some 3 millions a year, the loss to the sheep industry through the presence of the rabbits in their opinion amounts to ten times as much. They believe that twenty rabbits eat as much herbage as one sheep, so that the countless millions of the pest are responsible for grave damage.

The Wool Trade

The nation's prosperity is largely dependent on the sale of the wool clip. This varies not only according to good and bad seasons in Australia, but also with the varying prices offered in the world market. Thus in 1932–3 the average price (Australian currency) was only 8·7d. per pound for greasy wool. In 1933–4 it rose to 15·8d. per pound, but next year fell to 9·75d.; to rise to 92d. in 1951. Half the fine-wool merino of the world comes from Australia, and though the number of local woollen mills has increased to 103, so far they only use about 6 per cent of the clip. The amount of wool produced varies around 1,000 million lb. of greasy wool per annum. (If the grease is removed by scouring, 1 lb. of clean wool is obtained from $2\frac{1}{6}$ lb. of greasy wool.) Nearly all the wool is exported in the greasy state. In 1953–4 the export figures were 990 million lb. 'greasy', and 81 million lb. scoured.

It is interesting to see how the export of wool has varied among the nations in the last thirty years. Japan has become of recent years almost as large a purchaser as Britain, spending nearly 15 millions sterling on wool for clothing her troops. Italy, Germany and U.S.A. have fluctuated a good deal.

EXPORT OF GREASY WOOL

(million lb. weight)

	1901	1931	1935–6	1951–2	1957–8
United Kingdom	235	257	245	239	251
France	55	116	65	134	179
Germany	51	81	27	25	66
Belgium	33	64	103	59	102
U.S.A.	8	9	25	130	21
Italy	3	57	5	86	130
Japan	0·2	186	234	96	203

The Pastoral Index

One always thinks of Australia as a great sheep country, with cattle coming a very bad second. Some few years ago I attempted to find out whether cattle or sheep utilized more of the natural vegetation of Australia. To do this I chose a rather arbitrary relation, i.e. that 100 sheep ate as much as 10 cattle. In the map (Fig.

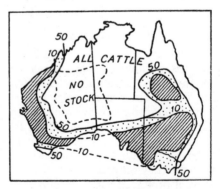

FIG. 111.—THE PASTORAL INDEX

Figures show *number of cattle* per 100 sheep. Sheep are more important in ruled areas

111) the numbers represent the numbers of cattle in any area *compared with* 100 *sheep*. Thus near Longreach (Q.) a certain area carried 55,000 cattle and 820,000 sheep. Here there were about 7 cattle for each 100 sheep. Thus the figure 7 was plotted on the map. So also near Sydney there are 60 cattle for each 100 sheep.

All these figures form the basis of Fig. 111; isopleths are drawn through the places where there are 50 and 10 cattle (per 100 sheep). The latter isopleth (10 cattle) shows where cattle and sheep are eating *equal* amounts of the natural vegetation. Ignoring the main desert area (where no stock graze) we see that, as far as area is concerned, cattle are more important than sheep; which was a somewhat surprising conclusion to the writer when he constructed this chart about twenty years ago.

The Distribution of Horses

With the great increase in motor-cars and in farm tractors, the number of horses has greatly decreased in the last twenty years

FIG. 112.—DENSITY OF HORSES PER SQUARE MILE

(Fig. 106). The maximum number of $2\frac{1}{2}$ millions was reached around 1918; and the distribution at that date is given in Fig. 112. In recent years the figure has remained steady around one million horses.

HORSES IN 1918, 1934 AND 1947

(thousands)

	N.S.W.	Vic.	Q.	S.A.	W.A.	Tas.	N.T.	F.C.T.	Total
1918	721	524	759	269	180	41	31	1	2,527
1934	535	358	448	199	162	31	35	1	1,768
1947	380	227	343	109	81	24	30	1	1,195

As in other forms of stock, the wetter eastern states contain by far the larger number of horses. Thus New South Wales has about 30 per cent, Queensland 25 per cent, and Victoria 20 per cent. However, in proportion to the population, the figure is highest in the Northern Territory, where there are 7 horses for each settler. In Tasmania there is only one horse for each eight persons. The map (Fig. 112) shows a very close resemblance to the distribution of farming and of population as a whole. This is what we should expect, since horses are used on dairy farms on the coast, as well as on wheat farms in the drier interior. Draft horses in Australia are usually crosses of Clydesdale and Shire blood. In most districts they live almost exclusively on the natural grasses, though a little chaff may be given occasionally. This consists generally of wheat and sometimes oats and lucerne, harvested green, and cut when dried into short lengths (*Scottish Report*). There is not much foreign trade in horses. Four or five thousand are exported each year, chiefly to India. But the import of several hundred valuable race-horses (or of breeding stock) sometimes gives an adverse balance of trade.

Distribution of Agricultural Pests: Rabbits

Since the latter part of the nineteenth century Australia has been menaced with agricultural pests. Of these the rabbit has been much the most costly, for one rabbit is said to consume and destroy 2 lb. of feed every 24 hours. Some rabbits were carried to Australia in the ships of the First Fleet, for in 1788 they are recorded at Sydney. In 1859 twenty-four were brought to Geelong in Victoria, and about 1863 a large warren was established near Castlemaine (Vic.). When the fence at the latter site was destroyed by fire, the rabbits escaped and overran the central and western districts of Victoria (Fig. 113). About 1880 the first long fence was constructed in the north-west of Victoria; and in 1887 a longer fence against rabbits and wild dogs was built between Victoria and South Australia. But it was found almost impossible to supervise these fences and to prevent fires from destroying them, and the rabbits soon spread as far west as the Murray River in South Australia.

In South Australia they seem to have spread independently from Adelaide to Peterborough and Renmark about 1881. They reached Beltana by 1886, and Fowler's Bay and Lake Eyre by 1891.

In New South Wales the menace was well developed by about 1883, and in the next five years nearly £1 million was spent to counteract it. Thus the rabbits reached Tilpa (near Bourke) in 1882 and Coonamble in 1898. In 1887–8 a fence was built across the state from Bourke to Corowa, and in 1890 another fence, 648 miles long, was erected between New South Wales and Queensland. This latter costs £11,000 a year to maintain. Soon, however, the rabbits crossed into Queensland, and in 1886 they had penetrated 30 miles into the state. In 1895 there were many at Thargomindah, and in 1899 they reached Charleville. In 1906 they were seen near Camooweal, and in 1922 they reached Longreach, but they are still largely confined to the south and south-west of Queensland. A tremendous network of fences characterizes southern Queensland.

West Australia was the last state to become infested, for the wide desert-stretch isolates it from the rest of Australia everywhere

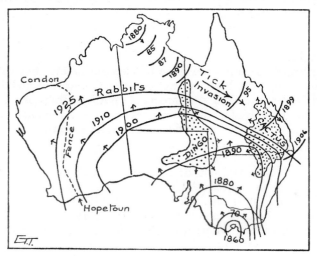

FIG. 113.—SPREAD OF VARIOUS AGRICULTURAL PESTS ACROSS
AUSTRALIA, ALL NOW UNDER CONTROL

except in the north. Two great fences were erected. One runs from near Geraldton to Yalgoo, and thence south to Albany. It was built in 1904 and 1905. The larger runs from Condon on the north-west coast to Hopetoun, 150 miles east of Albany (Fig. 113). This is a distance of over 1,000 miles, and the fence was built from 1902 to 1907. Rabbits were first noted at Kalgoorlie in 1901, at Peakhill in 1913, York 1916, and Albany in 1918.

When the writer motored along this great fence (in the heart of Western Australia) he found that it was not of much value, for the rabbits had passed from the desert westward into the huge unfenced stations. Since 40 rabbits are said to eat as much as a sheep, the damage done by the millions of rodents can readily be imagined. Upon three stations (aggregating 1 million acres) in New

South Wales the carrying capacity between 1880 and 1890 was reduced by 120,000 sheep. But with poisoning, trapping, digging-out and closer fencing, the rabbit menace is gradually becoming controlled in the chief pastoral districts of Australia. It has been noted that there is a valuable trade in rabbits for flesh, fur and felt (p. 323); but this does not by any means balance the loss to the wool clip. The introduced disease *Myxomatosis* has destroyed them in many areas.

The Wild Dog Pest

For a decade or two the pastoralists on the borders of the arid country have been greatly troubled by the dingo and by crosses between the dingo and the larger forms of European dogs (Fig. 113). Indeed, the dingo is very close to the wild dog of Syria, and was probably brought from Asia by the early migrations of Aborigines.

Netted fences similar to those to keep out rabbits, but with a larger mesh, have been erected between Queensland and New South Wales, and along the borders of South Australia, &c. For a time the dingo lived on the rabbit, but by degrees drought and the dog killed off many of the rabbits in this semi-desert land, and then the dogs moved eastward into New South Wales and Queensland. Here they killed the lambs in thousands; so that it is reported that north of Broken Hill one station lost 22,000 sheep, and another 45,000 sheep in one year. A bonus is paid for dingo scalps varying from £1 to £10 per scalp; and this menace is now largely a thing of the past. Four of the western pastoral districts in New South Wales (Wilcannia, Milparinka, Wanaaring, and Menindie) recorded bonuses for 9,502 dingoes in the period 1919–24 (Fig. 66). But the result was a considerable shift from sheep to cattle in much of the wild-dog area, which is indicated approximately in Fig. 113.

The Cattle Tick

This pest has caused grave losses in northern Australia, especially during the period from 1894 to 1900, when cattle worth 3½ million sterling died. Many herds lost 90 per cent of their numbers. It started near Darwin in 1880, and by 1900 it had reached Brisbane, as shown by the isopleths in Fig. 113. By suitable dipping methods the ticks are eradicated, and so the 'Texas Fever' (due to protozoan parasites transmitted by the tick) did not spread far south of the Queensland border. It is now also well under control in Queensland. From Darwin tick fever spread down the western cattle lands as far as Perth, but it has not caused such serious damage in that part of Australia as in Queensland.

The Prickly Pear Pest

This has been a grave disability in much of the best agricultural land in south-east Queensland. Over 50 million acres have been invaded by this large cactus plant (*Opuntia* sp.), which was introduced from America. For a time it was spreading at the rate of 800,000 acres a year. Much of the Black Earth region has been covered with this pest, to the great loss of the sheep and wheat industries. However, after a long period of scientific investigation, in which 150 insects were examined, the caterpillar of a moth (*Cactoblastis*) from South America was found to destroy the cactus rather rapidly. In 1925, 3,000 million insects were distributed, and within ten years they had virtually eradicated 22 million acres of the *Opuntia*, and had stopped its spread. The whole of the badly infested area has now been reclaimed (Fig. 113).

CHAPTER XIV

THE MINERAL INDUSTRY; METAL MINES

IN the section dealing with the geology of the continent I have pointed out some of the factors which control the distribution of metals in the earth's crust. Since they are almost wholly derived from deep-seated sources, it is logical to expect that they will be found either in formerly deep-seated rocks, or in rocks which have been permeated by solutions (liquid or gaseous) emanating from such rocks. In certain portions of the world, as in British Columbia, the presence of widespread plutonic and volcanic rocks of relatively late origin has given rise to ore deposits of correspondingly late formation. But in Australia the crust has been relatively stable and free from extensive igneous action in later periods. In the words of Sir Edgeworth David, 'but little in the way of primary ore-deposition has occurred since the close of Palaeozoic time'.

The geological map given in Fig. 12 indicates pretty clearly where it will be wise to look for valuable ores. As stated earlier, we may omit the huge areas of Triassic, Cretaceous and Tertiary rocks, as well as the region almost wholly hidden by Fixed Dunes. However, a few non-metallic minerals such as opal, gypsum and salt, which are all due to surface waters of *late* origin, occur in young deposits; and perhaps alluvial gold and stream-tin may be classed in this category.

The areas where metals are most likely to occur are in the Great Shield. Here deep-seated rocks were peneplained far back in the geological record, and have often never been covered since. A second favourable site is in association with widespread igneous activity. A third is in the 'cores' of sharply folded layers of the crust. Here in the cores the older layers are necessarily found, and such 'eroded anticlines' often contain metallic ores. In Australia, however, we have few typical examples of such structures (see, however, Mount Brown in Fig. 66), though they are common in other continents. Lastly, Palaeozoic rocks as a whole are so old that they may have had many chances of receiving ore solutions.

In modern text-books (e.g. Tarr's *Economic Geology*) a hypothetical section of the crust is given, showing a gigantic batholith (or boss) of igneous rock covered by layers of other rocks. The highly heated batholith is supposed to be the source of vapours or heated solutions which carry various metals towards the surface. Thus mercury and antimony are very volatile, and so are found furthest from the batholithic source. Silver, lead and zinc tend to occur in an intermediate belt. Gold and copper are readily precipitated on cooling, and form an inner zone. Tin, wolfram and molybdenum often seem to crystallize out in the margins of the granite batholith itself.

Many years ago L. K. Ward showed that something of the same sort occurred around the granite bosses of west Tasmania. These granites intruded the crust in Devonian times, and the ores in this rich metalliferous area are arranged somewhat as follows: the lodes of tin, tungsten and bismuth at Mount Heemskirk occur *within* the granite bosses or close to them; but the lodes containing lead, zinc and silver are found at some distance from the granite areas. (*Mining Bulletin* 8, Hobart, 1910.)

A second type of ore-deposit occurs without any apparent connexion with batholiths of deep-seated origin, though far below the surface there may be such a connexion. Often enough metallic ores are found along the junction of two *dissimilar* rocks, such as limestone and an igneous rock. Or they may occur, as at Ballarat, where layers of somewhat *carbonaceous* slate are cut across by cracks. In both cases it seems likely that chemical precipitation from heated waters has occurred at these favourable positions.

There is a considerable tendency for the weathering of surface rocks (due partly to air, to water and to weak acids such as carbonic or humic acid) to have a considerable effect in concentrating the metallic contents of a lode or vein. The upper ores are dissolved and redeposited lower. Such concentration is called 'secondary enrichment', and it is obviously more likely to occur in the upper portions of a large lode than in the deeper portions of the deposit.

Finally, a third type, which is of considerable importance in many mineral fields, is due to the actual normal erosion of rocks containing insoluble ores such as gold or tin oxide, &c. The lighter portions such as the quartz (gangue) are carried slowly down the gullies and streams, but the heavy gold or tin tends to collect below (but near) the site of the original vein or lode. Such deposits are called *alluvial* or *placer* deposits; and since they are easily mined they are sometimes described as 'Poor Man's Fields'. Examples of all these types, as well as many others, are to be found in Australia.

A Brief Summary of Mining Development

In the general description of Australian settlement in Chapter IX, the manner in which mining discoveries have come to the rescue of a state undergoing general trade depression has been referred to. It will, however, be useful to collect in a table the dates of the first working of some of the main mining fields of the continent. In this table the mines are arranged in the separate states and the oldest discoveries are to be found at the foot of the table on the next page. Mary Kathleen and Weipa are mentioned on p. 417B.

Some Commercial Aspects of Mining

Before describing the distribution of mines for metal, it will be well to consider certain other factors besides the mere presence of metallic ores, which must be considered in developing a mine. I quote freely from a valuable discussion of this aspect of the mineral industry by L. Keith Ward (S. Aus. Chamber of Manuf., Adelaide, 1922).

The geographical position is very important, especially with regard to low-value ores such as those of iron. The Yampi Sound (W.A.) deposits right on the coast (p. 365) are far more valuable than a similar amount at such a position as Wilgie Mia far inland in Western Australia (Fig. 114). Rates of transport for ores, fluxes and concentrates have all to be considered, and depend essentially on the proximity of roads, railways or ships. In New Guinea aeroplanes have helped to solve this problem in mining (p. 425).

The character of the ore is of course very important. For many years the intimate mixture of lead and zinc sulphides at Broken Hill handicapped the cheap production of the pure metals. Often small quantities of sulphur and phosphorus make iron ores much less valuable than they would otherwise be.

Size of the ore body is important, especially for low-value metals such as iron, or in the case of deposits of limestone for fluxes. The Australian, being most interested in gold-mining, is apt to have erroneous ideas as to what is a workable deposit of less-valuable materials. The writer, while making a geological survey, has often been told of 'enormous deposits' of limestone, which turn out to be narrow bands among shale, &c., and of no value for the purpose required. So also small quantities of radio-active ores might be workable, whereas similar indications of copper and silver would have little value. The price of metals varies greatly, and this often determines the closing or working of a known mine. The recent rise in the value of gold has made many deposits worth working which have been neglected for many years.

The accessories of mining, such as fuels and fluxes, if any concentrating is to be done near the mine, are also to be carefully considered. Sometimes iron ore, limestone and coal are in close proximity, as in southern U.S.A. The Newcastle iron foundries

APPROXIMATE DATES OF SOME OF THE CHIEF MINERAL FIELDS

C. = copper; CL. = coal; G. = gold; I. = iron; S. = silver; T. = tin

Year	N.S.W.	S.A.	Vic.	Q.	Tas.	W.A.	N.T.
1920	Coorabin (CL.)	Salt	—	Mt. Isa (S.)	—	Yampi (I.)	—
1915	—	—	Morwell (CL.)	—	—	—	—
1910	Ardlethan (T.) Carcoar (I.) Yeranderie (S.)	Phosphates	Wonthaggi (CL.) Poseidon (G.)	—	—	Bulfinch (G.) Collie (CL.)	Maranboy (T.)
1905	Canbelego (G.)	Iron Knob (I.)	Mt. William (G.)	Dawson (CL.)	—	Moolyella (T.)	—
1900	Wyalong (G.)	Tarcoola (G.)	—	Wide B. (CL.)	—	Kanowna (G.)	Arltunga (G.)
1895	—	—	—	—	—	Coolgardie (G.)	—
1890	Broken Hill (S.)	Teetulpa (G.)	—	Callide (CL.)	Mt. Nicholas (CL.)	Ashburton (G.)	—
1885	—	—	—	Cloncurry (C.)	Zeehan (S.)	Yilgarn (G.)	—
1880	—	—	—	Mt. Morgan (G.)	Lyell (C.)	—	—
1875	Inverell (T.) Hill End (G.)	—	—	Heberton (T.)	Beaconsfield (G.)	—	—
1870	Cobar (C.)	Echunga (G.)	—	Charters T. (G.) Clermont (CL.)	Bischoff (T.)	—	—
1865	—	Barossa (G.)	Dunolly (G.)	Gympie (G.)	—	Roeburne (C.)	Pine Ck. (G.)
1860	Young (G.)	Moonta (C.)	Bendigo (G.)	—	—	—	—
1855	—	Wallaroo (C.)	Ballarat (G.)	—	—	—	—
1850	Summer H. (G.)	—	—	—	—	—	—
1845	Mittagong (I.)	Burra (C.)	—	Ipswich (CL.)	—	—	—
1840	Molong (C.)	Kapunda (C.)	—	—	—	—	—
Before 1840	Newcastle (CL.)	—	—	—	—	—	—

in New South Wales are obviously working under a considerable handicap; since their iron ore comes from a thousand miles away, the limestone from some other distant locality, and only the coal is near the blast-furnaces. Often enough in Australia the mines are situated in quite arid regions. Here the problem of fuel and water for the smallest mine often demands considerable thought. Indeed in the arid parts of Western Australia the 'dry blower' has to a large extent replaced the cradle or dish as a simple method of extracting gold from powdered rock.

Relative Values of Australian Metal Mines

There are two ways of looking at the value of a mineral deposit. We may consider its past production or its present and future possibilities. If we add the total production to date of the various minerals in Australia, the gold total far surpasses any of the other minerals. But in recent years (1915–35) the annual value of the humble mineral coal has often surpassed the value of the gold won each year.

MINERAL PRODUCTION

Value to the end of 1945 (millions sterling)

	N.S.W.	Vic.	Q.	S.A.	W.A.	Tas.	N.T.	Total
Gold	72	**317**	99	2	276	11	4	**782**
Silver-Lead	**171**	—	15	—	2	13	—	202
Copper	17	—	**34**	33	2	28	—	116
Iron	9	—	—	**38**	—	—	—	49
Tin	19	1	14	—	2	**21**	1	57
Zinc	**31**	—	3	—	—	1	—	40
Coal	**287**	24	37	—	12	6	—	**363**
Others	12	1	3	10	—	3	—	33
Total	619	344	207	84	296	87	6	1,645

Block type shows the chief region for each metal.

Referring to the last column, we see that gold has been by far the chief value won from the earth, with coal next and silver-lead third. It is of interest that only four fields of the thousands in Australia have been primarily concerned in the pre-eminence of these minerals. They are (1) the central gold region of Victoria during the 'fifties and 'sixties; (2) the gold-fields around Kalgoorlie in Western Australia around 1900; (3) the Newcastle coal-field; (4) the Broken Hill silver-mines. These vital mining resources will be described at some length shortly.

Let us now look at the production today, and we shall see that the relative values have changed a good deal. The Western Australian gold-mines today approach the Newcastle coal-mines, Broken Hill comes third, and the gold-mines of Victoria are no longer pre-eminent in Australia.

MINERAL PRODUCTION FOR 1925, 1935 AND 1945

(thousands sterling)

		N.S.W.	Vic.	Q.	S.A.	W.A.	Tas.	N.T.	Total
Gold	1925	82	201	197	3	1,874	15	2	2,375
	1935	439	768	904	64	5,677	73	44	7,971
	1945	461	661	676	3	5,012	139	77	7,031
Silver-Lead	1925	5,320	—	241	2	115	302	—	5,982
	1935	3,189	—	755	—	12	63	—	4,022
	1945	4,625	—	—	—	—	—	—	4,625
Copper	1925	30	—	254	36	18	436	—	775
	1935	30	—	101	11	—	464	—	606
	1945	305	—	1,500	12	—	463	4	2,285
Coal	1925	9,303	596	1,038	—	363	70	—	11,370
	1935	4,887	282	843	—	318	86	—	6,416
	1945	8,694	1,136	1,759	14	573	126	—	12,302

Referring to the last column, we see that coal produced in 1945 is by far the largest total of the values quoted. But in 1935 it had dropped from 11 to 6 millions, while gold had jumped from 2 millions to 8 millions in the same decade. Silver-lead has not fluctuated much in the same time. Copper is far behind as the fourth mineral product, but has increased greatly in value lately. Both tables suggest that New South Wales is the chief state as regards mineral wealth, Western Australia is second, while Queensland is today a long way ahead of Victoria.

General Distribution of Metallic Minerals

The two maps shown in Figs. 114 and 115 give the localities of most of the important metal-mining fields. The chief empty areas are stressed in Fig. 114. The large artesian basins in the east have been laid down relatively lately, say in the last 60 million years; and have not been folded or faulted, nor have they been much affected by igneous action. For all these reasons they are poor prospects for metals; and speaking generally, none has been found in them. Opal, at White Cliffs and elsewhere, did not of course originate in the same way as metallic ores. The large areas of

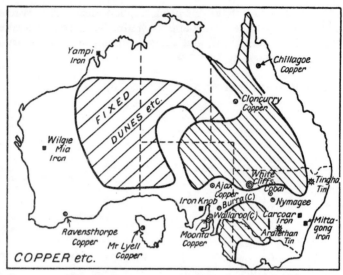

FIG. 114.—THE CHIEF MINING FIELDS FOR COPPER, IRON AND TIN

Ruled areas show regions where metals are not likely to be found

dunes indicated in the west cover the Shield, and undoubtedly hide valuable ore deposits beneath their sandy cover. But in places large areas of rocks are at the surface, so that there may be metal-

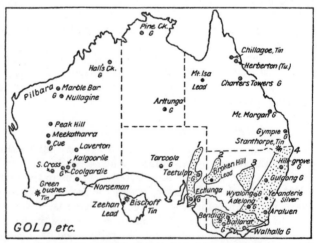

FIG. 115.—THE CHIEF MINING FIELDS FOR GOLD, SILVER, LEAD AND TIN

The numbers 1, 2, 3, 4 indicate anticlines or horsts with metals (see Fig. 10)

bearing deposits available in this region. But apart from small 'shows' like Tanami or Tennants Creek, nothing of value has been discovered in the century of prospecting which Australia has just about completed. Perhaps magnetic or electric detection may solve the problem, but at present we can safely rule out the major dune area as hopeful for mining.

The remainder of Australia consists of Shield or Palaeozoic rocks. All the metallic minerals in Western Australia are associated with the Shield, while those of South Australia and the Territory are partly in the Shield (Fig. 12), and partly in Palaeozoic or allied rocks. In the east all the metal mines are in the older rocks of the warps constituting the four 'waves' of the last period of mountain-building. These are labelled 1, 2, 3, 4, in Fig. 115. After such folding the *tops* of the waves are soon eroded, and are kept free from the deposits of large rivers. In such positions metallic ores may come to light. The *depressions* (between the folds) on the other hand preserve the upper newer layers of their sediments, and are also covered with much alluvial; and minerals are rarely discovered in them. Hence the mines occur in the Flinders Range (1), in the Barrier Ranges (2), in the Cobar Peneplain (3), or in the Eastern Highlands (4). This upward warping of course extends north into Queensland and south into Tasmania; so that the minerals of Queensland and Tasmania are in extensions of the uplifted region labelled (4) in Fig. 115.

Typical Mining-Fields: Poseidon Nuggets

Before we describe the mining-fields as a whole it will be well to discuss in more detail the origin of the ores in some of the more famous fields. A number of metals and metallic ores are so heavy that they are often found in the alluvial deposits in rocky gullies, where they have been preserved after the mother rock was eroded by rain and rivers. Such is the case with alluvial gold, including the famous nuggets, with stream tin, with platinum, &c. It was the writer's good fortune to be present in the last of the more famous alluvial 'gold rushes' in Victoria. This occurred in Poseidon, late in 1906. A description of the occurrence should make clear to the reader the difference between alluvial (placer) gold and vein (or lode) gold.

Poseidon is close to Dunolly, near which place the famous 'Welcome Stranger' nugget (worth £9,000) was dug up. It is about 20 miles south-west of Bendigo (Fig. 115) on the banks of the Loddon River. Here a low ridge of slate with numerous quartz veins projected above the level clay plains which were clothed with grass and dotted with eucalypts. These veins had been worked profitably for gold for some years, but the mine had been abandoned. (See the *Section*, at top of Fig. 116.)

Poseidon is a farming district, and a local farmer used to spend some of his time boring through the clay with a long auger to find the gullies in the slates below the clay. He found such a gully alongside the reefs mentioned previously. He sank a shaft about 30 feet deep, and came on several nuggets lying in the clay-filled creek-bed of earlier times. His farmer friends immediately 'pegged out' all the adjacent land hoping to share in his good luck.

The sketch-map (Fig. 116) shows the distribution of the nuggets which were ultimately obtained from the Poseidon Gold Field. The floor of the underground gully dipped down from the quartz veins on the top of the slate ridge. The nuggets were found distributed according to size down the rocky gully. Within a few feet of red clay were found three nuggets weighing 953, 675 and 502 oz. Lower down the gully was a cluster of nuggets around 40 or 50 oz., and still lower down the gold was in smaller pieces or in gold dust. The four isopleths in the map include the four sizes of nuggets; they are not contours.

Away from the narrow gully the claims were worthless. But it must be realized that the paddock above was nearly flat, and the underground topography was only discovered by boring or by sinking shafts. The various other famous Victorian fields where nuggets were found near Ballarat, Maryborough, Dunolly, &c., had somewhat the same features as those described for Poseidon.

Kalgoorlie

We may now turn to one of the most valuable fields for *vein* gold in Australia. In the gold-fields around Kalgoorlie the Shield consists mainly of granites and schists, which have been crushed and altered in various ways. Often these are intersected by igneous dykes of newer rock, and by quartz veins which represent the last products from a once molten magma of rock below. The gold usually occurs in narrow belts running north-west to south-east. It is often associated with tellurium (as tellurides) or with iron and copper pyrites and with stibnite.

The chief gold-field in Western Australia, and indeed in all Australia, lies south-east of the town of Kalgoorlie (Fig. 116). Here the original rocks consisted of sedimentary strata which were deposited on a granitic and gneissic floor. Lava flows were associated with these strata, which were probably of Pre-Cambrian age. By earth movements these were tilted into their present highly inclined positions, and were subsequently intruded by large masses of basic and ultrabasic rocks. The latter have also been invaded

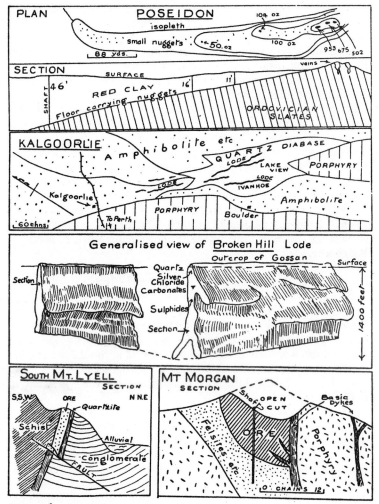

FIG. 116.—DIAGRAMS ILLUSTRATING THE ORE DEPOSITS AT FIVE FAMOUS MINES

by a series of acidic rocks. Slight further earth movement has then taken place causing considerable shearing and faulting, the shearing resulting in the formation of the lines along which the auriferous lodes of the field occur.

The class of deposit is that known as a 'lode deposit'. This is a more or less vertical zone of rock usually continuous with the surrounding rock, but distinct from it in that it carries metallic ores disseminated through it in payable quantities, and is as a rule characterized by strong foliation. The main mines at Kalgoorlie and Boulder occur in *quartz diabase*. This rock has been chemically altered into a greenstone, or at times into an indefinite mixture of lime, iron and magnesium carbonates with some residual silicates and quartz. In this series the rocks where the alteration is greatest are the most highly auriferous. The less altered gabbros at the western end are practically non-auriferous, whereas the highly altered chloritic diabases are extremely rich. The lode channels are very persistent in length, and have frequently been known to continue without break through several leases. The lodes thus occur as nearly vertical sheets—which are shown in plan in Fig. 116. Their width varies, but reaches a little over 100 feet in places, the whole carrying payable gold values. The tellurides occur as somewhat irregular crystalline masses. The gold may have been derived from vast bodies of granite, which have not reached the surface at Boulder, but make a prominent feature north of Kalgoorlie.[1]

The Broken Hill Silver-Lead Mines

Perhaps the best-known field of all is that at Broken Hill, which is in an arid upland region in the extreme west of New South Wales (Fig. 115). For many years it was only linked with Adelaide, but in 1928 the railway connexion was completed with Condobolin and Sydney. Some silver ore had been found in the Barrier Ranges in 1876; but the famous outcrop of brown 'gossan', which stood out as the 'broken' hill, was pegged out by Charles Rasp in September 1883.

The rocks consist of very ancient mudstones and sandstones, which have been intruded by igneous rocks (porphyrites, &c.) in the form of flat 'sills'. Folding occurred, giving rise to asymmetric arches. The alteration of the original minerals is greatest around Broken Hill and decreases with distance therefrom. High-temperature zinc minerals are found near the centre, but are absent in outlying portions of the field. Further compression formed 'Zones of Flowage', and along these the igneous emanations carried the valuable metals which constitute the huge lode of Broken Hill.

The outcrop of the lode is $3\frac{1}{2}$ miles long, and varies in width from a few feet to 200 feet. The main trend of the lode is north-easterly, and the dip is nearly vertical. The enormous lode of galena (lead sulphide) and zinc-blende has been fancifully compared to a somewhat ragged 'sword-blade' 3 miles long, which has been just buried (on its edge) in the crust of the earth. The 'blade'

[1] A. G. Maitland, *The Gold Deposits of Western Australia*, Perth, 1919.

extends about 1,000 feet deep, but it is rather irregular. A large model has been made of the ore body; and Fig. 116 shows a small portion of this model, with the different minerals which occur at various levels. There are still large reserves of ore.

Underneath the ironstone outcrop (gossan) and between it and the sulphide ore, vast quantities of 'oxidized' ores occurred. They were due to the action of air, water, &c., on the original sulphide ores, and consisted mainly of carbonate ore. This was a loose aggregation of carbonate of lead, and a gangue composed of siliceous and aluminous material impregnated with iron oxide. The silver in this ore occurred chiefly as native silver and chloro-bromide of silver. This class of ore contained from 5 to 80 oz. of silver per ton, and from 20 to 60 per cent of lead.

There was a zone of enriched 'secondary sulphides' below the carbonate ores, due to descending surface waters. This contained up to 250 oz. of silver to the ton. The vast body of the ore is, however, found in the unaltered sulphide zone, and is an intimate mixture of galena and zinc-blende. In the central part of the lode there is also much rhodonite, while at the ends calcite is more common. The average value of all ores concentrated at Broken Hill during 1918 was: Lead 14·5 per cent; zinc 12·68 per cent; silver 8·36 oz. per ton. This colossal mass of sulphides has produced by 1946 metals worth approximately 207 millions sterling.

E. C. Andrews considers that the lode appears to have originated from igneous emanations, which rose along the zones of strain causing the gap between the two walls of the lode. The ore may also have replaced certain folded silts and slates, which originally occupied the space now filled with the somewhat crumpled 'sword-blade' of sulphides.[1]

The Mount Lyell Copper-Field

We may now turn to a representative copper-mine, Mount Lyell in the north-west mountains of Tasmania, which has been one of the chief producers for many decades. Twenty miles to the north-west is the famous silver-lead mine of Mount Zeehan, and 40 miles to the north is Mount Bishoff (tin).

The Mount Lyell mine is situated on a ridge of schists, but there are large areas of conglomerate, perhaps of Devonian age, in the vicinity. The payable ore is found close to the junction of the two formations (Fig. 116). There are great lens-shaped masses of very pure sulphide ore, and in places the soil was so shallow over the chief ore body (the 'Iron Blow') that the water-courses had cut down to it and exposed fresh unoxidized pyrites.

[1] *Broken Hill Guide*, Pan-Pacific Science Congress, Sydney, 1923.

The ore-body trends north-west, and its length at the surface
was 800 feet, the width being about 200 feet. The ore consists
almost wholly of iron pyrites containing copper, gold and silver.
The latter metals are richer near the lower wall of the lode, and
sometimes shoots of rich ore are found.

Gregory believes that the Great Fault which crosses the region
enabled thermal waters to carry metallic solutions towards the
surface.[1] They deposited the sulphides near the junction of the
two rocks, and in places replaced the original rock by masses of
pyrites. The different theory of L. K. Ward has been briefly
referred to earlier (p. 347).

The Mount Morgan Gold-Mine

The next illustration is a section across the most famous gold-
mine in Australia, now unfortunately nearly worked out (Fig. 116).
Mount Morgan is about 25 miles south-west of Rockhampton (Q.).
The cap of the hill when discovered consisted almost entirely of
a white spongy sinter (mainly quartz), which was at first believed
to have been deposited by a geyser or mound spring! For many
years this sinter gave fabulous returns of gold of remarkable purity.
But at deeper levels the sinter gave place to masses of pyrites, and
the mine became almost as notable for copper as for gold. It still
produces about £40,000 worth of copper a year.

Practically all the upper part of the lode was removed by an
open cut. As the sketch-section shows, the old porphyries and
felsites (fine-grained rocks allied to granite) have been intruded
by basic dykes. Later, granite intrusions seem to have mineralized
the rock, apparently largely by replacement with sulphides.

In the Recent geological era the upper portion of the pyrites
was almost completely oxidized and dissolved, leaving behind the
spongy quartz (which ramified through the pyrites) and the insoluble gold. The lower part of the pyrites was enriched by the
solutions seeping from above, and this process produced 'bonanzas'
of great value. The change from the completely oxidized ore to
solid pyrites occurred with apparent suddenness at varying levels,
perhaps due to the varying surface of the ground-water. The lower
pyritic ore had somewhat the following composition: Iron 15 per
cent, Sulphur 15 per cent, Silica 67 per cent and Copper 1·4 per
cent. This mine illustrates the origin of gold deposits from large
sulphide masses. It also suggests why mines are usually richer
near the ground-water levels. Apart from bonanzas (due to
secondary enrichment), mines usually exhibit less valuable and
less extensive ores at greater depths.

[1] J. W. Gregory, Aust. Inst. Mining Engineers, 1905.

The Iron Mines at Iron Knob (S.A.)

I close this description of typical mines with a plan of Australia's sole large iron-mine. The Iron Knob ore was first used as a flux for Broken Hill ores, which were smelted at Port Pirie; but about 1914 the Iron Monarch alongside began to be quarried for the production of steel at Newcastle (N.S.W.). These two deposits are 33 miles from the coast, and a port has developed on Spencer's Gulf at Whyalla [1] (Fig. 71A).

The iron ore occurs in a north–south ridge about $1\frac{1}{2}$ miles long, which rises 600 feet above the adjacent plains. The southern portion of this ridge constitutes Iron Monarch, the centre is a mass of

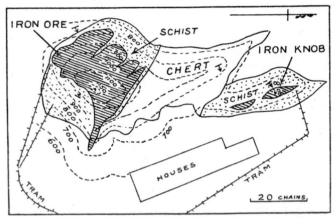

FIG. 117.—CONTOUR PLAN OF IRON DEPOSITS AT IRON KNOB (SOUTH AUSTRALIA)

showing Iron Monarch deposit on the left. (*After R. L. Jack*)

ferruginous chert (or quartzite), and in the northern third is the mass of iron ore called the Iron Knob (Fig. 117).

The ore body is surrounded on all sides by decomposed chloritic schist. The Iron Knob deposit is tabular in form, with a length of 26 chains; and it has been worked by two open quarries on the east face. It is estimated that it will yield about $2\frac{1}{2}$ million tons of ore, containing 60 per cent of metallic iron.

The deposit at Iron Monarch is much larger, and seems to occupy a wide trough (in the schists) which pitches steeply to the north. It is not a simple vein, but is due to replacement on a large scale. It is estimated to contain 130 million tons of good hematite above the level of the plain; and probably there are large masses

[1] Water is now pumped from the Murray River to this port.

below this level.[1] In 1939 nearly 2½ million tons of ore (valued at 2·9 millions sterling) were raised from the quarries at or near Iron Knob. The works at Newcastle and Port Kembla produce annually about 698,000 tons of pig iron, 696,000 tons of steel ingots and 586,000 tons of steel rails, &c. (See also pp. 201 and 416.)

The Gold-Fields of Australia

Victoria.—A description of one of the gold-fields of the state has already been given in the case of Poseidon. It may be mentioned that 12 nuggets of gold, each over 1,000 ounces, have been discovered in similar deposits in Victoria. Many other mines occur in the state, which may be classified in three groups. The *Western* are chiefly in Lower Ordovician rocks, and have usually involved the exploitation of deep quartz veins. Under the basalt-flows in this region many 'Deep Leads' have been worked. The *Central* area is associated with Silurian rocks as at Walhalla and Woods Point. The *Eastern* area is largely in Upper Ordovician or metamorphic rocks, as at Bright and Bethanga.

The *Ballarat* mines are famous for the 'indicators', which are a dozen thin pyritic or carbonaceous layers, which cross the quartz reefs fairly regularly. Rich deposits of gold often occur at the junctions of the indicators and the quartz reefs. The field is crossed by well-defined faults (called 'leather-jackets'), and these are also often associated with rich deposits. Much of the Ballarat district is covered by 400 feet of basalt lava. The rocky gullies which were buried under the lava often contain alluvial (Deep Leads), which have been found to be very rich in gold.

The *Bendigo* Gold-Field is about 15 miles long and 3 miles wide (Fig. 118). It is specially noted for its Saddle Reefs, in which the strata in the field are folded into corrugations along north–south axes. There are about 14 of these ridges in the Bendigo area, and the saddles occur along the ridges. In some shafts twenty-four such saddles have been found, one below the other in a vertical distance of 2,200 feet. The saddle reefs in the upper part of Hustler's shaft are illustrated in Fig. 118 (left). Several of the shafts at Bendigo are over 4,000 feet deep.

Another famous mine was Cohen's Reef at *Walhalla*. A 'gold shoot' here extended to a depth of 3,000 feet, and had produced gold worth 2½ millions by 1913. Maryborough, Clunes and Wood's Point are other mining towns where similar ore deposits in folded Palaeozoic rocks occur. At Ararat and Rutherglen 'deep leads' have been extensively worked, some of them as much as 700 feet below the present surface.

[1] R. L. Jack, *Iron Ore Resources of South Australia*, Adelaide, 1922.

Western Australia.—The earliest gold-field discovered in this state has never been very important; though there are still a number of mines in the *Hall's Creek* district, of which Ruby Creek and Brockman are the chief. In both areas gold occurs associated with large quartz reefs (Fig. 115).

The Pilbara Field contains many well-known mining townships, such as Marble Bar, Nullagine and Bamboo Creek. *Marble Bar* is the centre of the field, and is named from the remarkable bar of variegated jasper which crosses the Coongan River. The auriferous reefs occur in a belt of greenstone schists, which runs north—south adjacent to a large area of granite.

Nullagine is somewhat different, for here the gold is found in an

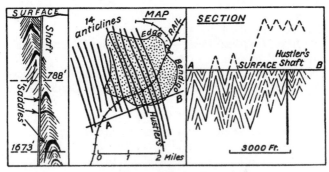

FIG. 118.—BENDIGO GOLD-MINES

showing in the centre a map of the main fold-ridges (anticlines) crossing the city. On the right a vertical section through seven of the ridges. On the left a section showing half a dozen of the saddles cut by the Hustler's Shaft.

(*B.A. Handbook for Victoria*)

ancient conglomerate, which resembles the famous 'Banket' of Johannesburg. At *Peak Hill*, north of Cue, the ore consists of a mass of indefinite country-rock, with much kaolin, traversed by a network of interlacing veins of auriferous quartz.

Meekatharra is one of the most important mining towns in the centre of the state. The ore deposits are confined to the marginal zone of granite masses and their metamorphosed borders. These are penetrated by quartz veins which often contain gold. It is also found disseminated in the highly altered schists. At *Day Dawn* is the Great Fingal Reef, a mass of solid quartz 40 feet thick and 2,000 feet long. The remaining gold-fields, near Yalgoo, Lawlers, Laverton, &c., are of somewhat the same character as those mentioned above. The chief deposits at Kalgoorlie have been mentioned above.

The following table shows the order of importance of the various Western Australian gold-fields some few years ago.

1. East Coolgardie (Kalgoorlie)	5. East Murchison (Wiluna)
2. Murchison (Meekatharra)	6. Coolgardie
3. Mount Margaret (Laverton)	7. Yilgarn (Southern Cross)
4. N. Coolgardie (Menzies)	8. NE. Coolgardie (Kanowna)

New South Wales.—In this state gold is of much less importance than in Western Australia. Lack of space prevents more than a brief reference to the type of ore-deposits. The following classification due to Pittman (*Mineral Resources*) summarizes the data:

A. *Reefs in Sedimentary Rocks*—(a) Silurian age: Cobar, Hargraves, Hill End, Wyalong. (b) Carboniferous age: Hillgrove.

B. *Impregnations in Sedimentary Rocks*—(a) Silurian: Mount Drysdale; (b) In tuffs: Lyndhurst.

C. *Reefs in Eruptive Rocks*—(a) In granite: Young, Araluen; (b) In felsite: Pambula.

D. *Alluvial Gold*—(a) Permian age: Gulgong; (b) Cretaceous, Mount Brown, Tibooburra; (c) Tertiary Deep Leads: Gulgong: Corowa.

Queensland.—In this state *Charters Towers* was for many years a large producer. The chief rock is granite intersected by basic and acidic dykes. Later fissuring allowed the ascent of quartz and metal-bearing solutions, which gave rise to the auriferous reefs mined to-day. Another famous field at Mount Morgan has been described. The Great Fitzroy Mine near Rockhampton is noted for copper as well as gold.

South Australia has no gold-fields of note, though Tarcoola and Teetulpa have produced large amounts of gold in the past.

Tasmania produces some gold in the Beaconsfield district on the north coast.

Northern Territory has so few important settlements that such small fields as Arltunga and Tennants Creek receive more attention than they would elsewhere.

Silver Mines in Australia

Broken Hill has already been fairly fully described. It is the chief silver-producing district, and has produced silver-lead, &c., to the end of 1935 valued at £159 millions. In this year (1935) large dividends were paid by the chief mines along the great lode, as follows: Zinc Corporation, £116,000; North Broken Hill, £385,000; Broken Hill South, £320,000; and Broken Hill Proprietary, £336,000.

In New South Wales *Yeranderie* (42 miles west of Camden) has produced silver worth 1½ millions sterling in the past, but it has been shut down for some time. The ores occur in fissures in porphyry. Captain's Flat produces lead, zinc and silver.

In Queensland *Mount Isa* near Cloncurry has been an important source of silver in recent years. Mount Isa is sometimes described as a second Broken Hill. It is stated that the lode is over a mile long, and is extensive enough to keep the huge mine busy for eighty years. Hatfield in his book *Australia through the Windscreen* (Sydney, 1938) gives an interesting account of the technical and social aspects of the mine, which in his opinion are unrivalled in Australia. During 1935 this mine produced 2½ million oz. of silver and 33,000 tons of lead.

In Tasmania *Mount Zeehan* is the chief field, and produced about 200,000 oz. But the blister copper from Mount Lyell was the source of silver totalling 133,000 oz. in 1935.

Copper Mines in Australia

The chief field is *Mount Lyell* in Tasmania, already briefly described. In 1935 this Company produced 13,000 tons of copper worth £464,000. Queensland contains the remaining important mines, which are located at Cloncurry, Herberton and Mount Morgan. A little copper is produced from the silver-lead ores of Broken Hill; and from the once famous field of Moonta in South Australia. Mount Isa has extensive ores of copper.

Zinc Mining

One of the world's greatest sources is *Broken Hill*, which gives Australia fourth place among zinc countries. U.S.A. is easily the first producer, followed by Belgium, Canada, Australia and Germany, which are of about equal importance in the zinc market. The zinc-blende is separated from the galena by grinding the ore very fine, and then mixing it with a frothy scum of eucalyptus oil. By this 'Flotation Process' the separation is effected. It could not be done by the ordinary jigging methods, since the two sulphides have much the same specific gravity. Some of the zinc concentrates are sent to electrolytic works near Hobart, and the rest is exported overseas.

Zinc products worth £283,000 were produced from various mines near Mount Zeehan, Tasmania, in 1936.

Tin Mining

Mount Bischoff in Tasmania is perhaps the chief mine in Australia. It was discovered in 1870 and has been working ever since. The tin workings are on the south-east slopes of the hill, and consist of open cuts and quarries excavated in porphyry. The ore is found in decomposing porphyry dykes, and is associated with various minerals such as tourmaline, quartz and calcite. Sometimes the tin occurs in very rich pockets, one such example yielding £60,000 worth of tin. The tin oxide also occurs in lodes which cut through the porphyry and adjacent slates. In 1935 the tin produced at Mount Bischoff was worth £258,000.

In New South Wales the tin deposits in the granites of New England have been known since 1860. The first mines were worked near Oban and Vegetable Creek. Tingha (Fig. 114) is the chief producer today. The heavy tin oxide is largely obtained by dredging processes, which grab and sift the alluvials in the modern and ancient drainage channels cut in the granite. In 1935 Tingha yielded 424 tons of concentrates and Emmaville 257 tons. A later tin-field was discovered at Ardlethan in the southern portion of New South Wales (Fig. 114); and here 269 tons were obtained in the same year.

Iron Mines in Australia

Coal and iron are the two chief products required for building up the so-called 'heavy industries'. Australia has plenty of coal, but she is not so well endowed with iron. A fairly recent survey of world resources (in the *Engineering and Mining Journal*, 1926) lists the visible iron ore resources as follows:

THE WORLD'S IRON ORE RESOURCES

(million tons)

1	U.S.A.	10,450	6	Newfoundland	4,000
2	(U.S.S.R.*	10,300)	7	India	3,326
3	France	8,164	8	Cuba	3,160
4	Brazil	7,000	9	Sweden	2,203
5	Britain	5,970	10	Germany	1,307

* From American-Russian Chamber of Commerce, New York, 1936.

Estimates of Australia's total vary from about 200 up to 990 million tons. It may be noted that U.S.A. uses about 70 million tons of iron ore in a year, so that the 130 million tons found at *Iron Knob* would not go far in America. This field has already been fairly fully described (p. 359). There are several other small deposits in South Australia such as the Middleback Range near Iron Knob, and Koolka and Cutana both to the west of Broken Hill.

Another valuable field is located on a small island off the north-west coast of Western Australia. *Koolan Island* in Yampi Sound is about 8 miles long, and contains two large seams or lodes. They seem to be inter-bedded with layers of quartzite, and dip about 50° to the south. The south lode is about 2 miles long, and varies in thickness from 4 to 50 feet. Another lode parallel to it to the north is 25 feet wide. The ore is said to contain 65 per cent of iron, and it is now being developed on a small scale (Fig. 114).

LESS IMPORTANT MINERALS

(Values to end of 1945)

	Chief Locality
Alunite	Bullahdelah (N.S.W.), £226,000
Antimony	Hillgrove (N.S.W.), Costerfield (Vic.), £435,000
Arsenic	Bellingen (N.S.W.), £212,000 (West Aus., £679,000)
Asbestos	Barraba (N.S.W.), Wittenoom (W.A.)
Barytes	Queenstown (Tas.) (and South and West Aus.)
Bauxite	Emmaville (N.S.W.), Weipa (Q.)
Bismuth	Glen Innes (N.S.W.), £257,000 (Qu., £146,000)
Chrome	Barraba (N.S.W.), £143,000
Cobalt	Cloncurry (Q.), £158,000
Diamonds	Tingha (N.S.W.), £151,000
Gems	Anakie (Q.), £655,000
Gypsum	Penong (S.A.), £1,718,000
Magnesite	Tamworth (N.S.W.), £764,000
Manganese	Grenfell (N.S.W.)
Mica	Arltunga (N.T.)
Molybdenite	Glen Innes (N.S.W.), Rum Jungle (N.T.), £232,000
Opals	White Cliffs (N.S.W.), £1,639,000 (Q., £188,888; S.A., £236,000)
Osmiridium	Savage R. (Tas.), £657,000
Phosphates	West Australia; South Australia, £188,000
Platinum	Fifield (N.S.W.)
Radium	Mary Kathleen (Q.), Rum Jungle (N.T.), Olary (S.A.)
Salt	Lake Hart (S.A.), £6,134,000
Scheelite	King Is. (Tas.), £553,000 (N.S.W., £243,000)
Wolfram	Tasmania and Queensland

At *Wilgie Mia* (40 miles from Cue, W.A.) there is another good supply of iron ore, said to contain 26 million tons; but it is far inland and is not likely to be mined for many decades. Mount Gibson near Yalgoo contains about 10 million tons of haematite inter-bedded with schist.

In New South Wales the old stone blast-furnace at *Mittagong* near Sydney was a well-known landmark some decades ago. This interesting relic was built about 1860, and used intermittently until 1886, but it was unfortunately torn down a few years ago. The iron ore at Mittagong consists of two or three small deposits in the form of mounds around chalybeate springs.

In this state there are also a number of small deposits such as Tallawang ($\frac{1}{2}$ million tons) and Carcoar (3 million); and one larger deposit at *Cadia* of 39 million tons (L. F. Harper). Cadia is 12 miles north-west of Carcoar, and the iron ore is chiefly hematite inter-bedded with augite-andesite. It is 3,000 feet long and 80 feet wide, and contains from 57 to 65 per cent of iron. All these were exhausted in the last war.

Queensland has some useful supplies at *Mount Leviathan* near Cloncurry, but this source is 481 miles inland. It has been proposed to build works at Bowen, and use the ore from Koolan Island.

Summary of the Less-important Minerals

There are numberless other minerals of value produced in Australia; and some of them are given in the preceding list, which also indicates the value of the materials produced to end of 1945.

Uranium

Until recent years only small deposits of radio-active ore had been found in South Australia near Olary (west of Broken Hill) and at Mt. Painter. Carnotite and Torbernite have been found here in Pre-Cambrian rocks. But in 1949 substantial deposits were found at Rum Jungle, about 60 miles south of Darwin. Other deposits have been found near Pine Creek. At Mt. Isa (Q.), associated with copper and zinc ores, some uranium minerals occur. Indeed, such ores have been discovered (by geiger-counters, etc.) near Tenterfield and at Myponga, south of Adelaide. No doubt other deposits will be found in the widespread ancient rocks of Australia—as is the case in other parts of the world.

It was reported in the *Sydney Morning Herald* of the 8th March 1957 that 1,000 long tons of Uranium Oxide were produced at Mary Kathleen. Elsewhere, U.S.A. produced 7,000 tons, South Africa 4,500, Canada 4,000, and Belgian Congo 1,000 tons.

Further references to modern mines will be found on pages 417 to 417D in the section on Rapid Industrial Expansion.

CHAPTER XV

THE COAL-MINING INDUSTRY

The Origin of Coal

SOME general notes on the origin of coal will enable us better to understand the distribution of the coal deposits of the continent. Coal is derived from plants which have been grown under suitable circumstances, and have subsequently been subjected to pressure and chemical changes. All stages of the process of evolution are found in nature, from the early peaty stage through Brown Coal (lignite), Cannel Coal, Bituminous Coal to the final stage of Anthracite.

The most favourable conditions seem to have been forest, fern or algal growth in swampy ground, which subsequently subsided. In most cases this sinking was so gradual that the new peaty plants grew continuously on the sinking peat. Some such uniform subsidence is necessary to explain the solid deposit of Brown Coal at Morwell (Vic.) which is over 700 feet thick. The Great Dismal Swamp in south-east Virginia (38 by 25 miles) gives us an idea of a peaty area which in long ages might be converted into a large coal deposit.

The pressure of subsequent deposits of sand, &c., consolidates the peaty material, which slowly loses much water and gas. But the ash, representing the lime, silica, &c., in the plants, as well as accidental inclusions of soil, is not altered by the pressure. However, the proportion of carbon steadily increases with the age of the coal deposit. It is stated that peat can be artificially converted into hard brilliant coal merely by subjecting it to a pressure of 6,000 atmospheres (D. Powers).

The somewhat generalized table on next page gives approximate percentages (in the various types of coal) of water, ash, gas and fixed carbon. The latter component is much the same as the *coke* portion of the coal remaining after the gas has been removed.

It seems likely that bacteria help to change peat into a brown pasty mass, which binds the plants into a compact material, ultimately becoming lignite. In Pennsylvania and Belgium it has been noticed that the same seam may appear as bituminous coal or anthracite according to the amount of earth folding which has

	Dried peat	Lignite	Bituminous	Anthracite
Specific gravity	Variable	1	1·3	1·5
Fixed carbon	24%	36%	55%	95%
Gas	60 ,,	41 ,,	32 ,,	2 ,,
Ash	10 ,,	9 ,,	10 ,,	2 ,,
Moisture	up to 90%*	14 ,,	2 ,,	1 ,,

* Before drying.

affected the coal. Volcanic heat also produces the same change sometimes, as in the Clermont seam in central Queensland. Some authorities, however, believe that anthracite results from peaty materials which have been unusually oxidized or have been altered considerably *before* their final burying and compression.

Caking (or coking) coals are low in oxygen, and contain 25 to 30 per cent of gas. They soften when heated, so that the fragments coalesce and yield a compact coke. This makes them specially suitable for use in blast-furnaces, for air can penetrate the coke better.

Since coal is mainly derived from swamp plants, it is not likely to be found earlier than Carboniferous times, for a land flora on a large scale had not evolved before that age. *Psilophyton* (from Gaspé in Quebec) is said to be one of the earliest land plants, and it started in Silurian times. Numerous plants allied to the ferns developed in Devonian times, but no notable coal-fields are due to their remains.

The Carboniferous period, about 250 million years ago, was peculiarly suited to produce coal. Vast peaty swamps, undergoing slow subsidence, have produced the enormous coal-fields of the northern hemisphere. It is of interest that there is very little coal of this age in Australia. It was in the earliest portion of the Permian period, say about 200 million years ago (the so-called Permo-Carboniferous times), that coal-producing plants flourished in the vicinity of Sydney, Australia, and produced the chief coal-field of the southern hemisphere.

In general, older coals approach anthracite, and the youngest coals resemble peat. But the geological history differs in various districts. Thus, the Ipswich coal in Queensland is quite bituminous; while the Leigh's Creek coal of the same age in South Australia is much nearer lignite, because it has been involved in much less earth-folding. So also some of the older coals such as Collie (W.A.) and Coorabin (N.S.W.) retain a large amount of moisture, because they have been subjected to relatively much less compression.

The probable coal resources of the world are given in the recent report of the Commission on the Coal Industry (Sydney, 1930) as follows:

WORLD'S COAL

(in thousand million tons)

North America 5,073 (including U.S.A. 3,838, and Canada 120)
Asia   1,279 (,,   Siberia 174,* China 995)
Europe   784
Australasia   170 (,,   New Zealand 3)
Africa   57 (,,   South Africa 56)
South America   32 (,,   Colombia 27)

* Some estimates put the coal of Siberia as high as 1,260 × 10⁹ tons.

Thus Australia contains only about 2½ per cent of the world's coal resources. Recent calculations have greatly reduced the figures for the available coal reserves of New South Wales, and increased those of Victoria. The same report gives the following data:

DISTRIBUTION OF AUSTRALIAN COAL

State	Black coal	Brown coal
New South Wales	13,929 million tons	
Victoria	40 ,, ,,	37,000 million tons
Queensland	2,238 ,, ,,	67 ,, ,,
South Australia		57 ,, ,,
Western Australia		3,500 ,, ,,
Tasmania	244 ,, ,,	
Totals	16,451 ,, ,,	40,624 ,, ,,

The table on next page shows the chief coal-fields of Australia arranged so that the oldest beds are at the foot of the table. The reserves mentioned (in million tons) are those which are highly probable. Much larger figures are given in some tables.

History of the Newcastle Coal-field

The Government started to obtain coal from mines at Newcastle in 1804, and here the seams actually outcrop in the cliffs along the shore. In 1828 the Australian Agricultural Company (p. 241) acquired the sole right to work this coal, but they relinquished their privilege in 1847. In 1850 steamers began to call at Newcastle to fill their holds. In the southern portion of the field (at Mount Keira near Bulli) coal-mining began in 1857. In 1860 there were three

AGE, COMPOSITION AND RESERVES IN THE CHIEF DISTRICTS

Age	District	State	Reserves (million tons)	Composition				Characters
				H₂O	Vol.	F.C.	Ash	
Tertiary	Morwell	Vic.	5,000	42	29	26	2	Brown coal, hydrous, briquetted
	Traralgon	,,	5,600	21	36	37	6	At Morwell, 700 feet of solid coal
Jurassic	Wonthaggi	,,	30	8	28	56	8	Rather thin seams, friable
	Outtrim	,,	—	5	30	60	5	,, ,, ,,
Triassic	Leigh's Ck.	S.A.	—	27	25	34	14	400 miles inland, clinkery
	Mt. Nicholas	Tas.	134	4	21	52	23	Good coal
	Callide	Q.	20	7	26	54	12	Not used, 20-foot seam
	Waterpark	,,	3	10	41	41	7	Brown coal, 60-foot seam
	Ipswich	,,	242	1	27	59	14	Good coal
	Clarence R.	N.S.W.	—	—	—	—	—	Much ash, little used
P. Carbs.	Mt. Mulligan	Q.	15	3	24	57	16	Used in mines
	Mackenzie R.	,,	112	1	14	77	8	'Mammoth' seam, 20 feet thick
	Clermont	,,	208	5	32	58	6	One 90-foot seam
	Dawson	,,	10	1	10	80	9	Excellent coal
	Collie	W.A.	3,500	25	26	?	6	Hydrous, non-caking
	Coorabin	N.S.W.	?	—	—	—	—	Sub-bituminous, 8- to 36-foot seams
	Ashford	,,	10	—	—	—	—	Little used, Greta coal 27-foot seam
	Bulli	,,	⎫ 14,000	1	24	64	12	Much used for coke and export
	Lithgow	,,	⎬	2	32	53	13	Much used for smelting
	Newcastle	,,	⎭	2	41	51	6	Chief export in Australia
Carbonif.	Stroud	,,	—	—	—	—	—	Very poor, not used

mines in the Newcastle district, the A.A. Company, the Coal and Copper, and the Minmi mine, but these are no longer working. About 1861 two mines, which are still working, were opened (Fig. 121); namely the Wallsend and Old Lambton. South Bulli mine started in 1862, and in the west some of the Lithgow mines about 1869.

In 1886 Sir Edgeworth David discovered the invaluable Greta seam in a creek bed where the Abermain colliery is now working (Fig. 121). About this time nearly 2 million tons of coal were exported from Newcastle, chiefly to Victoria, U.S.A., New Zealand and South Australia. East Greta (20 miles west of Newcastle) opened in 1889, but most of the big mines on this field were of later date. Thus Stanford Merthyr dates from 1901, Pelaw Main from 1902, Hebburn 1903, Abermain 1904, and Aberdare 1905. In 1901 a shaft sunk at Balmain (Sydney), in the centre of the great Coal Basin, reached coal at a depth of about 3,000 feet.[1]

The Newcastle mines are rather unfavourably known for widespread strikes, such as those in 1896, 1909 and 1913–14. These in part led to the development of the easily won brown coal of Morwell, Victoria, but this did not begin on a really large scale until 1925.

The Newcastle Coal-field

This enormous basin occupies an area of about 16,550 square miles. It extends along the coast to the north and south of Sydney, which is in the centre of the basin, and 2,884 feet above the upper (Newcastle) seams. The position of the capital city is well shown in the block diagram (Fig. 120). The western outcrop of these same coal seams is found at Lithgow; the southern outcrop becomes visible in the cliffs near Bulli; and the northern shows at Newcastle.

The upper series of Coal Measures is 1,500 feet thick at Newcastle, where it contains 13 seams of coal, of which six seams are 6 feet thick or more. The Borehole and Burwood seams are worked in 15 and 7 mines respectively. This series is about the same thickness in the south, and there are a dozen mines (chiefly working the Bulli seam) at Bulli, Coal Cliff, Mount Kembla and other towns (Fig. 120).

In the west at Lithgow these coal measures are only 600 feet thick, and the bottom (Lithgow) seam is 6 feet thick. It is worked in 20 mines at Lithgow, Kandos, Wallerawang and other towns. In Sydney itself the coal is worked by a shaft nearly 3,000 feet

[1] *Official Report on the Coal Industry*, Sydney, 1930.

deep, as already mentioned. Coorabin in the Riverina is an outlying patch of the same coal measures.

There is a series of layers of intermediate coal (Tomago seams)
about 3,000 feet below the Newcastle seams. These are not worked
at present. Below these come 6,400 feet of marine sediments, and
then a very valuable series of layers of coal called the Greta seams.
These latter are the chief worked in Australia to-day, in a string
of mining towns such as Aberdare, Cessnock, &c. (Fig. 121), to the
south of Maitland. As the block diagram shows, the Greta seam

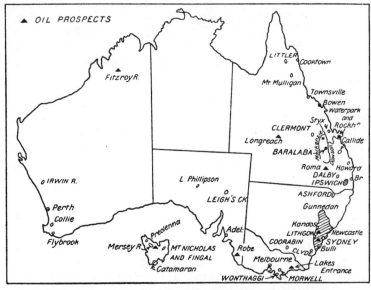

FIG. 119.—DISTRIBUTION OF COAL-FIELDS IN AUSTRALIA
The sites where petroleum has been found or suspected are indicated by black triangles

has been much folded and fractured near Muswellbrook to the
west of Maitland.

At Clyde River, in rather deep valleys in the far south of the
coal basin (Fig. 119), some rather poor seams of coal outcrop.
They belong to the Greta series.

In the Maitland district there is a geological 'dome' (or upthrust) which brings the Greta series to the surface. The upper or
Newcastle seams necessarily outcrop in an *outer ring* to the south-
east of the 'dome' (Fig. 120). The Greta coal occurs in a 22-foot
seam, without interruption by clay bands, in the Stanford Merthyr
Colliery near Maitland. The coal is very hard, and can therefore
be worked more economically than some of the more friable coals.

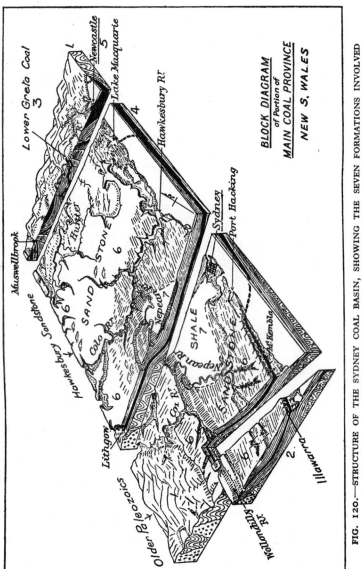

FIG. 120.—STRUCTURE OF THE SYDNEY COAL BASIN, SHOWING THE SEVEN FORMATIONS INVOLVED

1 = Older Palaeozoic rocks containing the Basin; 2 = oldest coal measures; 3 = Lower Greta Coal; 4 = Middle Coal Measures; 5 = Upper Newcastle Coal; 6 = Triassic Sandstones; 7 = Triassic Shale

(From the Royal Commission on the Coal Industry, Sydney, 1930)

373

It is of excellent quality, and can be used equally well for gas-making, steam-raising or household purposes. It makes too much black smoke, however, to be used by the Navy.

One disadvantage is that the Greta coal has a rather high percentage of sulphur, especially in certain of the top layers. These have much iron pyrites in them, called 'brassy tops' by the miner. Usually this part of the seam is left unworked in the roof of the mine. There are over 36 mines at work on the Greta coal between Maitland and Cessnock (Fig. 121). Some of the oldest are East Greta, Stanford Merthyr, Pelaw Main, Abermain and Aberdare.[1]

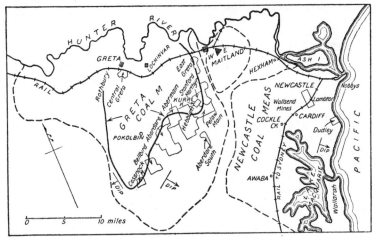

FIG. 121.—THE CHIEF COAL-FIELD IN AUSTRALIA BETWEEN NEWCASTLE AND GRETA

Many of the coal-mines are indicated. The Greta coal (black) forms an incomplete circle about the Pokolbin-Lochinvar 'Dome'

The Greta coal is below the Newcastle in the basin, hence in the Newcastle district both coal measures are dipping somewhat to the south-east, *away from the upthrust 'dome'*. Thus the coal in the Aberdare South mine (Fig. 121) is reached at 1,481 feet below the surface, though it *outcrops* in the mines just to the west. This feature in the structure of the field can be made out in the northern section cutting across the block diagram (Fig. 120).

It will have been gathered that mining conditions are rather favourable in this field, since the seams are so thick and in many

---

[1] F. R. E. Mauldon gives an excellent study of this region in his book *Social Economics* (Melbourne, 1927). He shows that the population in the vicinity of Cessnock grew from 500 in 1886 to 40,000 in 1927. His account of the decline of Wollombi near by is also illuminating.

cases so near to the seaboard. In some of the Newcastle mines, however, such as the Dudley (Fig. 121), it is impossible to work far to the east under the sea, since the solid rock between the sea and the coal soon becomes too thin. Igneous dykes have spoilt some of the coal in Illawarra (in the south); but in general this is not a common disability.

A more detailed account of the reserves of coal in this very important mining district is contained in the following table from the same report:

COAL RESERVES IN THE NEWCASTLE-BULLI FIELD

(million tons)

Field	Town	Actual	Probable
Northern	Newcastle	825	1,441
	E. Maitland	88	201
	Singleton	19	120
	Gunnedah	49	17
	Muswellbrook	366	257
	Maitland	1,714	940
Central	Sydney	97	470
Southern	Illawarra	1,291	2,177
	Wollondilly	—	1,841
	Moss Vale	178	403
Western	Lithgow	573	192
	Kandos	55	98
	Talbragar, &c.	—	135
	Total	5,257	8,672

In addition to the areas given in the table, whose geology is fairly well known, there are almost 15,000 square miles of coal measures buried less than 4,000 feet deep, where no accurate data of the coal has yet been obtained. It has been suggested that the water may have been *too deep* for plants to grow in the centre of this basin; but it may be that there is here a larger amount of coal available for the future than the amount indicated in the estimate above.

We may obtain a clear idea of the relative values of the Australian coal-fields by considering the following table, which deals with conditions in 1927–8:

RELATIVE PRODUCTION OF CHIEF FIELDS

(thousand tons)

State	Field	Production	State	Field	Production
New South Wales	Greta Seam	4,254	Queensland	Ipswich	583
,,			,,	Bowen	161
,,	Newcastle Seam	1,724	,,	Darling Downs	98
,,	Illawarra Field	1,817	,,	Maryborough	94
,,	Lithgow Field	1,652	,,	Clermont	55
Victoria	Morwell (Yallourn)	1,500	West Australia	Collie	501
,,	Wonthaggi	684	Tasmania	Mt. Nicholas	112

Victorian Coal-Fields. The Brown Coals

Second to the Newcastle Field in production, but perhaps not far behind in actual reserves, is the Morwell (or Yallourn) deposit of brown coal. Thick beds of lignite (brown coal) occur in the Oligocene (mid-Tertiary) strata of the Latrobe valley in Gippsland. There are other less-abundant deposits of the same age at Altona, Lal Lal and elsewhere, which are indicated in the map (Fig. 122). These Tertiary beds contain fossil plants such as *Banksia* and *Gingko*.

At Yallourn in southern Victoria coal seams almost 1,000 feet thick have been discovered by drilling along the Latrobe valley. For some 70 miles along this river, from Warragul in the west to Sale in the east, bores have shown that vast deposits of coal are present, but the country has been much faulted, and in many places the coal is too far below the surface for its winning to be payable (Fig. 123). Mines are now operating in three areas, the chief being the Yallourn open cut, operated by the State Electricity Commission. The seam here is about 200 feet thick, and about 5 million tons a year of the early Tertiary coal is won annually. A small amount is obtained from another open cut about half a mile north.

The chief interest to the geographer, however, lies in the proposals for exploiting the coal some 6 miles south of Yallourn at Morwell, where similar geologic conditions obtain. The Latrobe river flows to the east as appears in the sketch map (Fig. 54A). It occupies a somewhat complex graben, whose northern margin is an extensive fault running along the foothills of the Victorian Highlands. These are formed of older Palaeozoic rocks and rise to 6,000 feet. Its southern margin would seem to be about 10 miles away, where another parallel fault bounds the cretaceous rocks of the low South Gippsland Hills (2,366 feet). In the vicinity of Morwell, however, at least three other faults occur which complicate the structure. Thus along the north of the Latrobe valley is the Yallourn Basin. South of this is the Morwell Dome (or horst) in which the coal is close to the surface. South again of this is the Traralgon Graben, where the coal is depressed far below the present surface. Along the southern edge of the main Latrobe

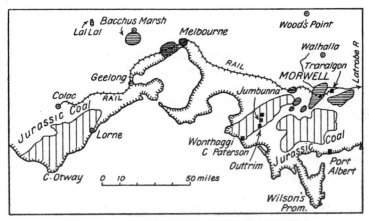

FIG. 122.—CHIEF COAL RESOURCES IN VICTORIA
Brown coal areas shown by horizontal lines

valley is the Hazelwood graben, where the coal is workable, since this 'step' is only depressed to a small amount.

The Yallourn-Morwell field was first developed after 1918 when it came under the control of the chief electricity commissioner, Sir John Monash. In 1925 the Yallourn field began producing briquettes of dried compressed coal. The raw material is essentially steam-coal with a high moisture content, ranging from 33 to 66 per cent; and most of it is of an earthy character. The water content is less in the compressed deeper deposits, decreasing about 1 per cent for each 100 feet of descent. In the Latrobe seam, moisture is under 33 per cent, volatile hydrocarbons about 43 per cent, fixed carbon about 26 per cent and ash 2·5 per cent. In the vicinity of Morwell there are three thick seams totalling over 1,000 feet of coal, which have been warped into a dome by converging fault movements of the bedrock. In the central part—the Morwell Dome—erosion has removed the upper Yallourn seam, and the top 250 feet of the second or Morwell seam.

The new developments at Morwell will produce coal from a new open cut, about 5 miles south of the earlier Yallourn site. Ground in 1950 has only just been broken for this project, in which the coal is to be used almost wholly for making briquettes. The overburden here is about 44 feet thick, beneath which is an unbroken layer of coal 380 feet thick. It is proposed to excavate 320 feet of this coal, and it is expected that the final output of coal will be about 4 million tons of raw coal a year. At the older Yallourn works nearly 6 million tons of coal is won annually, two-thirds going to the power station and one-third to the briquette factory. In the future a full train load of briquettes will be run to Melbourne about every three hours, in addition to the four briquette trains which proceed daily to Melbourne from Yallourn today. The little town of Morwell will double in size as the result of these new industrial developments.

The quality of the brown coal varies, some showing much woody matter, while near by none is apparent. So also the amount of water varies a good deal. The ash content is low, which suggests that the plants grew in *wide* lagoons, without much drainage to carry silt from adjacent shores. As stated earlier, the largest reserves are found at Morwell and Traralgon (Fig. 122).

The Black Coals of Victoria

The black coal is older than the brown coals, but not so old as the seams at Newcastle. It is intermediate in character as well as in age. The coal occurs in rather steeply dipping sediments (of Jurassic age) which seem to be due to currents from different directions. The plants apparently grew in a number of isolated shallow swamps, but subsequent faulting has disturbed the geological structure a good deal.

The mines are in South Gippsland (Fig. 122); partly on the coastal plain near Wonthaggi, and partly in the hills at Outtrim, Jumbunna and Korumburra. The coal is bituminous, and of moderately good quality, but it yields much slack. The seams are often wedge-shaped, so that one portion may be 9 feet thick, while a mile away the coal has thinned out to a few inches. At Wonthaggi State Mine it has been necessary to sink twenty pits to maintain an output of about 3,000 tons a day. The seams have an average thickness of about 3 feet.

The Coal-Mines of Queensland

In this state there are useful coal-seams representing all four periods when coal-forming plants flourished. Thus there is Permo-Carboniferous coal at Mount Mulligan (near Atherton), at Collinsville (near Bowen), at Clermont, and in the large Dawson-Mackenzie coal-field (Fig. 119). The Triassic rocks contain the best-known seams near Ipswich in the south; the Jurassic seams (akin to those of Victoria) are found in the Darling Downs (near Dalby); while the Cretaceous fields are at Styx River (near Rockhampton), and the Howard-Burrum area near Maryborough.

Of all these the Mackenzie and Ipswich probably contain the biggest reserves, as shown in the table on page 370. At present the Ipswich field is the largest producer, chiefly owing to its geographical position. The fifty mines are all small, and their total output does not equal that of two large mines in the Maitland district (*Coal Report*).

There are four main seams yielding coal near Ipswich. Of these the Aberdare seam is about 6 feet thick, and contains coal which is rather friable, and with a high ash content of 16 per cent. However, it is much used for various industrial purposes. The other three seams are the Four-foot, Bluff-Aberdare, and the Seventy-foot (so-called because it is 70 feet below the 4-foot seam).

The Darling Downs coal area extends from Toowoomba to Warwick and to Chinchilla in the north-west. The seams are a little younger in age than those at Ipswich, but have a higher proportion of volatile matter (38 per cent), so that they are largely used for gas-making. There are seven mines working these seams, mostly at depths not exceeding 150 feet.

The Wide Bay (Howard-Burrum) field supplies seven or eight mines, and the coal is chiefly used by sugar mills and butter factories in the vicinity. However, the railways take some supplies, and there is a small amount exported from Maryborough and Urangan.

The mines near Rockhampton have varied in production a good deal, but in 1935 there were four mines at work. Styx River, 84 miles to the north, and Baralaba, on the Dawson River, have been important producers. The Blair Athol mines at Clermont have a main seam said to be over 90 feet thick in places, and only covered by 70 feet of over-burden. There were four mines at work in this field in 1935. There are also several collieries at work on the Mackenzie River, about 100 miles west of Rockhampton. The 'Mammoth' seam, about 20 feet thick, is worked on this field. Since the coal is low in volatile products it is not used for gas production. The combined Dawson-Mackenzie basin is stated to contain far more 'probable reserves' (612,000 million tons) than all the other fields of the state added together (*Coal Report*).

Proceeding north, there is a good deal of coal mined at Collinsville (53 miles from Bowen), and the coal is used chiefly on the railways. Mount Mulligan (46 miles south-west of Cairns) is worked by the State, as are some of the mines at Styx River and Collinsville.

Coal in South Australia—Leigh's Creek

All the coal in this state is so inaccessible that it has not been much utilized. At Robe (Fig. 119) a seam 3 feet thick was discovered in a bore, but its depth 3,000 feet below the surface makes it practically useless. Of surface deposits the best is at Leigh's Creek, but this is 170 miles inland (Fig. 119). There is a similar bed of coal at Lake Phillipson still further inland. Beds of lignite from 12 to 20 feet thick are known at Coffin's Bay and Pidinga. These may be used in the future.

About 100 miles to the south of Lake Eyre the ancient pre-Cambrian and Palaeozoic rocks of the Flinders Horst have subsided, and in Triassic times large swamps occupied these areas, which ultimately became coal. At Leigh's Creek there is a marked unconformity between the coal measures—some 1,900 feet thick—and the underlying Pre-Cambrian bedrock which consists of clay slates with ancient tillites (glacial beds). There are three coal-bearing basins in this region; but the workings are mainly confined to the central larger basin. In the southern (Copley) basin the coal is interlaminated with silts; but the coal seams are much thicker in the other two basins. The coal is sub-bituminous, and contains 32 per cent moisture, 22 per cent volatile matter, 30 per cent fixed carbon and 17 per cent ash.

Several features are of considerable interest in the Leigh's Creek deposit. Firstly, it is the sole important source of coal in South Australia; secondly, it occurs far in the interior and in a desert region, where thick seams of coal are rarely found. Furthermore, although it has been known since 1888 that there was coal at this point (373 miles north of Adelaide) yet it was assumed to be of little value. Thus W. Howchin in his authoritative *Geography of South Australia* (1909) states: 'The main coal (as shown by a bore in 1891) occurs at a depth of 1,500 feet . . . but the inferior quality of the coal and distance from a market made the venture unremunerative.'

In 1918–19 further surveys were made, and it was recommended that the coal in pulverized form be used in railway locomotives.

However, little was done as the result of this report. Owing to the high cost of imported coal further work was carried out in 1941, and largely owing to the advice of the Government geologist (L. K. Ward) *shallow* coal was discovered in October which revolutionized the future of Leigh's Creek. The bore struck a seam of coal 40 feet thick only 66 feet below the surface, and an open cut has been developed in recent years to work this deposit. The coal dips on all sides towards the centre of the main basin, which is roughly circular in shape and 4 miles across.

It is estimated that the two seams of the northern basin contain 20 million tons of coal. The larger central basin has not been so thoroughly explored by bores, but it is believed that it contains 360 million tons; so that in summary it is thought that the field has 30 million tons which can be reached by open-cut, and 350 million which will require underground mining. It is quite possible that other similar coal seams will be discovered to the north, between Leigh's Creek and Marree on or near the railway line.

Coal in Tasmania

Seams both of Permo-Carboniferous and Triassic age occur, the latter being much the more important. The former seams are found near Preolenna and Latrobe in the north-west littoral. The coal is of good quality, but the seams are so thin, seldom over 20 inches, that it does not pay to work them. Similar coal up to 3 feet in thickness, but high in ash, occurs at Port Cygnet in the extreme south.

The later coal seams have been worked for many years near St. Mary's in the east. Fingal and Mount Nicholas are the two chief centres, and Catamaran (in the far south) is of the same type (Fig. 119). The coal is rather high in ash, and is all used in Tasmania. In most years a good deal of coal is imported from the mainland. In 1935 the fields near Mount Nicholas produced about 99,000 tons of coal.

Coal in Western Australia

By far the most important field in the state is near Collie, 124 miles south of Perth. This field lies in a depression in the granite tableland. It is connected by rail with Bunbury 41 miles away. The area occupied by coal measures is about 50 square miles, and the town of Collie is about 700 feet above sea level (Fig. 123). The Collie field seems to be faulted down into the ancient Shield, and is therefore a sort of graben.

The coal measures are about 2,000 feet thick, and contain seams

aggregating 137 feet of coal. There are three main sets of seams.
The upper is the Cardiff series, with three seams of which several
are as much as 12 feet thick. The middle series is Collie Burn with
eight seams of the same type. The lower Proprietary seams are six
in number. They all dip about 10 degrees to the south (Fig. 123).

These seams seem to have been deposited by a river in a valley,
and this has given rise to many bands, and to the large percentage
of ash (8 to 10 per cent). The coal is hydrous (19 per cent of water),
semi-bituminous, non-caking, and approaches lignite in places even

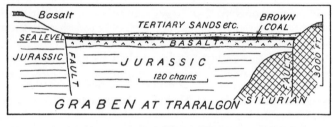

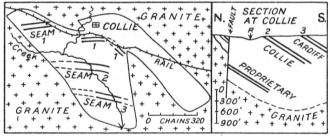

FIG. 123 (*above*).—VERTICAL SECTION ACROSS BROWN COAL AT THE
MORWELL FIELD IN VICTORIA (SOMEWHAT SIMPLIFIED)

(*below*).—MAP AND SECTION OF COAL-FIELD AT COLLIE, WESTERN
AUSTRALIA

though it is Permo-Carboniferous in age. One peculiarity is that
the ash of the Collie Burn seams contains 14 per cent of aluminium
phosphate, so that it may have some value as a fertilizer. The total
resources reach the high figure of 1,500 million tons.

Another smaller basin of similar character is found in the upper
reaches of the Collie River at a place called Wilga. At Flybrook,
south of Collie, there are several seams of coal, of which the thickest
is about 5 feet thick (Fig. 119). At Irwin River 200 miles north of
Perth, a seam 5 feet thick has been prospected, but this coal is not
yet utilized. In the far north, in a well at Liveringa near Derby, a
seam 12 feet thick was found about 50 feet below the surface. This
suggests that there may be a large amount of coal in the wide-

spread Permo-Carboniferous strata of the Kimberley region, south-west of the Fitzroy River.

Coal Export

Owing to the abundance of coal in the northern hemisphere, it is clear that Australia's chief foreign market will be in the Pacific Isles and the adjacent coasts. The total export trade amounted to about 3·5 million tons in 1912, but as a result of the war it fell to 1 million tons in 1918. A quick recovery then occurred to 3·2 million tons in 1921. But since that date there has been a steady drop to 1933, when the export total was about 800,000 tons.

In recent years about 66 per cent of the New South Wales coal was used in the state, 23 per cent was exported to the other Australian states, and 11 per cent was sent overseas. Nearly all the coal which is exported is sent from the port of Newcastle. In 1935 the export from New South Wales was 2·7 million tons, divided as follows:—

(in thousand tons)

	Interstate	Overseas
Cargo	1,584	323
Bunker (for ships)	305	553

The figures for various countries overseas do not seem to be officially published; but Dr. F. R. E. Mauldon has given the salient data (up to 1927) in his pamphlet *Problems of Australian Coal*, 1928. The figures are thousand tons:

	1913	1918	1923	1927
New Zealand	500	250	420	400
Dutch East Indies	over 160	10	80	70
Philippines	—	10	90	45
Fiji	30	40	30	30
Ceylon	—	—	15	—

Mauldon points out that New Zealand is pushing ahead her hydro-electric schemes, and developing more fully her own coal supplies. The Dutch Indies are taking much larger supplies from South Africa, and also exploiting their own coal. Japan is turning to China rather than to Australia. Chile is placing heavy duties on all coal brought from abroad. He further adds that there are too many coal-mines in Australia, and he believes that three-fifths of the existing Newcastle fields could meet the demand there.

Strikes among the miners have led to exasperating delays in the loading of ships, and have helped to send vessels to other coaling ports. Some of these disabilities cannot be overcome; but the gradual growth of a large and prosperous industrial population in the regions surrounding Sydney and Morwell—based on the best coal resources south of the equator—would seem to be within the bounds of reasonable expectation.

Petroleum Prospects

The search for oil in various parts of the world has been so persistent, and the prize if successful so great, that we may be sure that Australia has been surveyed for petroleum. So far the result has been very disappointing. It has been pointed out that Australia resembles Africa in the small development of young folds, and in the relatively large extent of Shield. Africa contains no petroleum field of note, though a small field is being worked south of Suez.

In Australia a little oil has been found in Gippsland, but nothing on a commercial scale, though many thousands of pounds have been spent in official and private investigations. It is worth noting that the pronounced earth-folds of the Pacific (which miss Australia, but pass through Papua and New Zealand) are associated with oil-fields of some value at Purari and Taranaki.

There are many theories as to the origin of petroleum; but most authorities seem to believe that the oil is derived from organisms, probably marine plants or animals, whose tissues have gradually been converted by pressure and moderate heat into liquid hydrocarbons. To produce an extensive 'deposit' of petroleum it is necessary to have an underground reservoir. This usually consists of a series of porous strata (such as coarse sandstones) sealed between impermeable rocks.

Perhaps the most interesting feature to the geographer—who is interested primarily in distribution—is the fact that these reservoirs often have the form of domes or anticlines. These naturally are best developed in regions of moderate folding; and often the space in the cap of the anticline contains a layer of petroleum floating on water. Here we see a reason why the main oil-fields of the world are found along the margins of the folded mountain systems.

In the Old World we can follow the course of the great oil-fields along the margin of the Carpathians (Rumania), the Caucasus (Baku), the Persian folds (Iraq), Burmah, the East Indies, and so by Purari (in Papua) to New Zealand. There are no fields of importance far from this line of major folding, which seems to be clearly connected with the production of the helpful domes or anticlines. The African, Siberian and Australian Shields are devoid of oil. It is amusing to note that the *whole* of Western Australia was 'pegged out' for oil in 1922 (*Sydney Mail*, July 5th). In the New World the relation is somewhat the same, though the early fields of Pennsylvania border the *old* Appalachian folds rather than those of the *young* Rockies. Oil reservoirs do not usually occur where sharp over-folding or faulting has occurred, for this would crack or destroy the domes.

In Australia we have, of course, some areas of simple foldings, and it is not impossible that oil may yet be found on a commercial scale. David has pointed out, however, that there are few examples of rocks rich in the remains of marine organisms. Traces of oil and asphaltum (which is a dense product of allied origin) have been found in a number of places in Australia, usually as the result of boring for water.

Asphaltum occurs in bores at Mount Wynne in the Kimberleys (W.A.) in rocks of Carboniferous age. More favourable indications come from Roma in south-east Queensland (Fig. 119). Here natural gas and even a little oil have been obtained in a number of bores put down into Jurassic rocks. A waxy hydrocarbon has been met with in several bores near Longreach (Q.). Near Robe in South Australia deep bores have yielded some natural gas.

It is, however, only in Gippsland that actual oil has been tapped in appreciable quantity. At Lakes Entrance sands of Oligocene (mid-Tertiary) age were reached in a bore about 1,300 feet deep. These sands contain the tests (shells) of foraminifera, and contain 0·067 per cent of mineral oil. 'Up to June, 1930, about 350 barrels of oil had resulted from many months of seepage into several bores.' [1] These are small figures compared with some American results. For instance, the Cushing Well in Oklahoma in 1914 gave 320,000 barrels a day for several months. In recent years the production in Victoria has increased somewhat. In 1935 about 4,200 gallons were obtained, and the total product of the Gippsland bores to the end of that year was 87,148 gallons. The Commonwealth is endeavouring to locate favourable structural formations by aerial surveys carried out by competent geologists.

Oil Shales

Australian prospects are much more hopeful in regard to another source of petroleum. Oil Shales are known in many parts of the world, but the process of producing oil is rather costly; so that as long as sufficient liquid petroleum pours out from the oil wells the

[1] Sir T. W. E. David, *Geological Map of Australia*, Sydney, 1932.

shales will not be exploited on a very large scale. However, shales have been worked for many years in New South Wales and Tasmania.

In the former state they occur in lenses (rarely a mile long) in the Coal Measures of the Newcastle-Clyde Basin (Fig. 119). Newnes, Hartley Vale and Joadja, which are all about 60 miles to the west or south-west of Sydney, are the best-known areas.

The composition of the shale at Joadja is as follows: moisture, 0·5 per cent; volatiles, 68 per cent; fixed carbon, 15 per cent; ash, 16 per cent. The yield of crude oil per ton of 'Kerosene Shale' ranges from 75 to 120 gallons for the better classes of shale. Near Newnes in the Capertee Valley one tunnel has exposed a seam of oil shale over 3 feet thick for a distance of 4,000 feet. In the Capertee area it is estimated that the shale reserve could produce 50 million barrels of petroleum. For the whole state the total is said to be about 3,500 million barrels. During 1942 oil to the value of £142,343 was won from the shales near Newnes (N.S.W.).

In Tasmania there are two fields, one near the Mersey River (Fig. 119) which may contain 36 million tons of shale, and a smaller field near Oonah. The shale is about 4 feet thick, and gives about 40 gallons of oil per ton of 'Tasmanite'. As in New South Wales, the deposits are of Permo-Carboniferous age. In 1934 about 3,800 gallons of oil were distilled from Tasmanian shales.

Owing to the discovery, late in 1953, of a small flow of petroleum at Rough Range, some 650 miles north of Perth (W.A.), an oil boom started in Australia. In spite of millions spent in trial bores, etc., no further flow had been discovered in 1954–7. However, very large refineries to process *imported* oil have been built at Kwinana (Perth), Corio (Geelong), and Kurnell (Sydney).

CHAPTER XVI

FORESTS, FISHERIES, TRANSPORT AND MANUFACTURES

THERE are a number of minor industries which do not readily fit into the earlier chapters, and yet cannot be ignored. Among these may be included Forestry, Fisheries, and Transport by water, land and air.

PART I

FORESTS OF AUSTRALIA

The distribution of forests has been discussed in considerable detail in Chapters VII and VIII. In the present section the problem of the *timber* supply will be taken up. Only in those regions where the rainfall is good will large trees flourish. In temperate Australia this includes the narrow coastal fringe with 30 or more inches of rain a year. In the tropics there is not much good timber where the rainfall is below 50 inches a year.

The main timber areas may be classified as follows:

	Region	Rainfall
1	Swanland area, from Perth to Albany	Over 30 inches
2	South and south-east of Victoria	,,
3	Mountain forests of Victoria and New South Wales	,,
4	Coastal districts of New South Wales and Queensland	,,
5	Most of Tasmania	,,
6	The forests on the Murray, &c., near Echuca	15 inches
7	'Cypress Pine' forests in plains of south-east	15–30 ,,

It will be noted that the last two regions have lower rainfalls than are found in the other timber forests. The Murray forests, of eucalypts largely, grow in damp river flats; while the 'cypress' (*Callitris*) never grows into a very large tree.

It is usually assumed by foresters that a prosperous temperate country should have about 25 per cent of the area under forest. This is about the case in Germany, France, U.S.A., Poland and

Canada. Australia has such large arid areas that it cannot approach this standard, and a figure of 1 per cent of the area is what she may hope to attain.

Very little of Australia's forest can yet be described as properly cared for, but great improvements are taking place now that the Commonwealth and states are realizing how valuable are the country's forests. Expert foresters consider that approximately 30,000 square miles represent the possible limit for permanent reservation; and if this is properly cared for, it will yield enough hard and soft woods for a population of $22\frac{1}{2}$ millions. The following table shows the amount of land reserved as forests (much not cared for yet) in the various states.

ESTIMATED FOREST AREAS

State	Forest area	Percentage of state	Density of people
New South Wales	4,000,000 acres	2·02	8·67
Victoria	5,500,000 ,,	9·78	21·07
Queensland	6,000,000 ,,	1·40	1·46
South Australia	500,000 ,,	0·21	1·55
West Australia	3,000,000 ,,	0·48	0·46
Tasmania	500,000 ,,	2·98	8·97
Total	19,500,000 ,,	1·02	

It is interesting to note that the percentage of forest land in the state fluctuates in somewhat the same way as the density of population. This results, of course, because both series of figures depend primarily on the proportion of good rainfall.

E. H. Swain in his book on Queensland timbers (Brisbane, 1928) states that Australia uses four sorts of wood, as follows: (a) Constructional hardwood, (b) cabinet woods, (c) constructional soft woods, (d) special purpose woods. He affirms that there are ample resources of the first two classes, but the last two must be imported in very large amounts. The following table shows the amount paid to foreign countries in 1946–7 for imported timber.

It is clear that about $3\frac{1}{2}$ millions sterling is paid by a pioneering nation for imported timber. Much of this should ultimately be grown in Australia; but at present the native *softwoods* are so restricted in quantity that they hardly affect the demand for this commodity.

The import of dressed timber listed above consists mainly of

IMPORTED TIMBER, 1946-7

Country	Dressed timber	Undressed timber
Canada	£A.72,078	£A.2,537,499
New Zealand	15,861	170,072
U.S.A.	67,299	525,515
Norway	1,215	—
Philippines (1939)	—	72,921
Sweden	61,045	36,488
Total (with others)	£A.217,665	£A.3,367,164

deal and pine used for linings, floors, doors, box-making, &c. The undressed timber is oregon, redwood and other softwood coniferous timbers from America; and Kauri, Rimu and White Pine from New Zealand. There is, of course, an export trade of the dense and exceptionally strong timbers of various eucalypts; but the excess of imports over exports for 1935-6 amounted to £1,451,973.

D. E. Hutchins, in his book on Australian forestry (Perth, 1916), is insistent that the forests of Australia would have been of at least double value if the trees had been *softwoods*. It is curious that the valuable pines of the Northern Hemisphere did not migrate south of Nicaragua in America, or south of Timor in the Old World.

Fairly large plantations of the European pine, *Pinus insignis*, have been made in Victoria and South Australia, where the timber is used chiefly for box-making. Hutchins thinks that *Pinus pinaster* (Cluster Pine) and *Pinus canariensis* are likely to do better in Australia. The Portuguese Cypress and the Californian Redwood (*Sequoia sempervirens*) are in his opinion some of the best softwood trees to transplant to the southern continent.

Character of Australian Timbers

There are said to be more species of eucalypt than there are days in the year. These many kinds can be classified in various ways, but the popular method is based on the barks, and is due, I believe, to R. H. Cambage. Most of the important features of the timber trees of Australia are given in the following lengthy table on next page.[1]

All the eucalypts have thick barks, which are said to have

[1] See Carter, C. E., *Distribution of Eucalypts*, 1947; Anderson, R. H., *Trees of New South Wales*, Sydney, 1947; Boas, I. H., *Commercial Timbers of Australia*, Melbourne, 1947.

CLASSIFICATION OF AUSTRALIAN TIMBERS [1]

A. EUCALYPTS

Class	Vernacular name	Botanical species	Locality	Uses
Smooth Barks (Gums)	Sydney Blue Gum	*saligna*	N.S.W. and South Q.	Ship-work and road blocks
	Tasmanian Blue Gum	*globulus*	Victoria and Tasmania	Decking, piles, exported trees
	Scribbly Gum	*haemostoma*	East coast	—
	Murray Red Gum	*rostrata*	Murray, Lachlan, interior	Mine-props, sleepers
	Spotted Gum	*maculata*	East Coast	Planks, bends well
	Sugar Gum	*corymocalyx*	Flinders Range	Sleepers, piles, top feed
	Karri	*diversicolor*	Near C. Leeuwin	Heavy, tough, flooring, &c.
Half Bark (Boxes)	Yellow Box	*melliodora*	W. slopes of Highlands	Honey producer
	Coolabah	*microtheca*	Dry inland plains	—
	Grey Box	*hemiphloia*	South-east	Sleepers, props
	Tuart	*gomphocephalus*	Perth coast	Very strong, hard, framework
Wrinklebarks (Bloodwoods)	Bloodwood	*corymbosa*	East coast	Resists ants, much kino
	Red flowering Gum	*ficifolia*	Denmark, W.A.	Ornamental tree
	Blackbutt	*pilularis*	East coast	—
Stringybarks	Tallowwood	*microcorys*	N.S.W. and South Q.	Floors, girders
	Red Stringybark	*macrorrhynca*	SE. Australia	Fence posts, splits well
	Messmate	*obliqua*	SE. Australia	Weather-boards
	Jarrah	*marginata*	Swanland, W.A.	Piles, sleepers, blocks
Ironbarks	Ironbark	*paniculata*	East highlands	Girders, sleepers, wagons
Peppermints	Peppermint	*piperita*	N.S.W. coast	Over 300 feet
	Mountain Ash	*regnans*	Victorian Highlands	
Mallees	Red Mallee	*oleosa*	Southern plains	Rich in oil; 12 feet high

B. MOSTLY SOFTWOODS (NOT EUCALYPTS)

Class	Vernacular name	Botanical species	Locality	Uses
	Hoop Pine	*Araucaria*	S. Queensland	Lining boards, cases
	Cypress	*Callitris*	Inland plains	Resists white ant
	Red Cedar	*Cedrela.*	Eastern Brush	Beautiful timber easily worked
	Rosewood	*Dysoxylon*	" "	Furniture, &c.
	White Beech	*Gmelina*	" "	House fittings
	Silky Oak	*Grevillea*	" "	Furniture, boxes
	Kauri Pine	*Agathis*	S. Victoria	Linings, framework
	Blackwood	*Acacia* sp.	" "	Furniture
	Evergreen Beech	*Fagus* sp.	S. Tasmania	Furniture, Joinery
	Huon Pine	*Dacrydium*	S. "	" "
	Sandalwood	*Fusanus*	Semi-desert in south	Fragrant wood"

[1] In part based on the useful little manual, *The Tree Book*, D. G. Stead, Sydney, 1933.

developed in response to bush fires. The *'Gums'* have a smooth grey
bark on which it is quite possible to write with a pencil. These
barks usually split off in spring in long strips. The *'Halfbarks'* have
smooth bark on the limbs and upper part of the trunk, but rough
fibrous bark near the ground. In the *'Stringybarks'* the fibrous bark
splits and frays as the girth increases, but does not fall off in sheets.
In *'Ironbarks'* the bark is several inches thick, and it becomes
seamed with deep furrows as the trunk increases in girth.

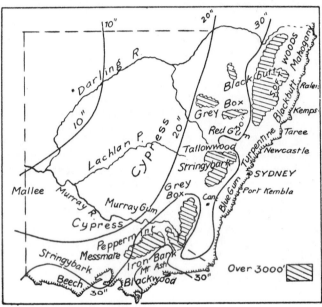

FIG. 124.—SOME OF THE TIMBER TREES OF NEW SOUTH WALES AND VICTORIA
The relation of highlands to isohyets is indicated, heights approximate

The *peppermints* are akin to the stringybarks, but the leaves are
specially rich in essential oils with a smell like peppermint. The
Mallees are small trees with many branched stems, which grow in
regions of rather low winter rainfall.

Distribution of Saw-mills

The following table shows the amount of sawn timber produced
in the various states in 1935–6 (figures represent 1,000 'super'
feet).[1] (The amount cut had doubled in N.S.W. and Vic. by 1946.)
The saw-mills are found scattered through the forest country,
chiefly in the eastern littoral and in Tasmania. In Queensland the

[1] A 'super foot' is a foot square and 1 inch thick.

State	Timber amount	Hardwood (%)	Softwood (%)	Saw-mills
New South Wales	133,000	65	35	445*
Victoria	106,000	100	—	315
Queensland	125,000	37	63	317
South Australia	13,000	26	74	60
Western Australia	109,000	100	—	93
Tasmania	76,000	100	—	213

* 665 mills in 1946.

mills are most abundant in the south-east, and in the forests near Cairns. As will be seen in the table, the state is noteworthy for its supply of softwoods.

In New South Wales the north coast contains most of the saw-mills, especially near Raleigh, Kempsey, and Taree (Fig. 124). In Victoria they are most numerous in Gippsland and in the mountain behind this district. Here are found the giant eucalypts called mountain ash (*E. regnans*). C. W. Robinson has measured one of these giants which was 342 feet long to the 'die-back' at the top. He believes that another 20 feet should be added for this loss. The tallest redwood measured by a Californian expert was 340 feet.

In Tasmania saw-mills are found on the north-east coast and in the south of the island. The Huon pine and the red beech are two interesting trees cut fairly extensively in this state (Fig. 125). South Australia has not much of a supply of timber; but she has planted relatively large areas of foreign pines at Bundaleer and Wirrabara, which are already giving fair supplies of soft wood.

Timber in Western Australia

In this state the jarrah and karri timbers are very important, and give rise to a large export (Fig. 126). There is very little, if any, softwood available in this state, and there is said to be about twenty years' supply of the original jarrah available yet. Jarrah is not a tall tree, those used for timber being about 60 feet high; while one of the largest known is only 145 feet high (Hutchins). It has about 91 per cent of the strength of karri, but is relatively easier to work.

Of all the Australian timbers Queensland brigalow (an acacia) is said to be the strongest. Then comes the Western Australian tree yate (*E. cornuta*). This timber is a little stronger than ironbark, which is much the same as karri in this respect. Karri is 14 per cent stronger than Tasmanian blue gum, and 31 per cent stronger than English oak.

Karri matures in about forty years, and is especially abundant near Denmark in Swanland (W.A.). Many specimens grow to 300 feet, and one is said to have reached 342 feet. Indeed, it is stated that one cut for the Paris International Exhibition was 432 feet high, but this figure lacks corroboration.

Hutchins' Report gave the areas of marketable timber in 1916 as follows: Jarrah 8 million acres, karri 1·2 million, tuart 200,000, wandoo 7 million, York gum, &c., 4 million. All these distributions are clearly shown in Fig. 126.

In addition to the timber values there are many other uses for

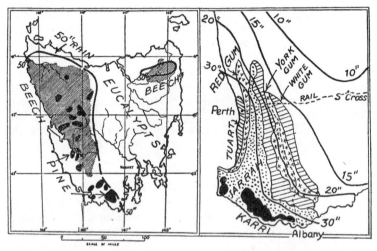

FIG. 125.—FORESTS IN TASMANIA   FIG. 126.—FORESTS IN WESTERN
Huon and other Pines are black   AUSTRALIA

the eucalypts. The bark of some species is quite useful as a thatch for simple buildings. The exudations (or kinos) from the bark have some value as drugs. Some of the barks contain an unusual amount of tannin, the best being the mallet gum (*E. astringens*). Two of the acacias (*pycnantha* and *decurrens*) are also of use in this connexion; so much so that 25,000 tons of bark are exported annually. The plantations of golden wattle (*A. pycnantha*) in Natal have been made from Australian seed. There are notable essential oils in some of the eucalypts, the silver leaf mallee being perhaps the best for this purpose. These oils are used as drugs, as perfumes, and in the flotation process in metallurgy (p. 363).

Sandalwood and sandalwood oil to the value of £67,000 are exported to the east of Asia from the semi-arid regions of the south. Geraldton is one of the chief ports for this trade. There has been a great deal of experiment in connexion with the production of pulp for paper. It is reported that a large factory is to be started immediately at Maryvale (Victoria) for this purpose.

The fishing industry is not of great importance in Australia for a number of reasons. In general, cool waters give the largest supplies of fish, as witness the prolific areas off Canada, Japan and the British Isles. Moreover, the Australian eats very much less fish than the Britisher, the ratio being 13 lb. to 42 lb. per annum. However, it would seem that this industry might readily be greatly extended, since the value of imported fish-products amounts to $1\frac{1}{2}$ millions sterling. This is just about the value of the fish caught in Australian waters. The chief imports are tinned salmon from Canada, tinned herrings from Britain, and tinned sardines from Norway. There are about 8,000 men employed in fishing in Australia, of whom about one-third come from New South Wales.

Marine Fisheries

The marine fishes of eastern Australia belong to two distinct groups; a northern and a southern.[1] Owing to the presence of a south-flowing current, the so-called *Notonectian Current*, many of the tropical types are brought south to Sydney or thereabouts. But the common edible fish caught off Sydney belong to the southern types. The fish in the deeper cooler water near Sydney are often found in the surface waters of Tasmania, since they tend to keep to a water layer of equal temperature. Thus the southern Barracouta is found off Sydney more often in winter than in summer. Trumpeters, leather-jackets, trevally, sweep and flathead are all representatives of the southern genera. The fish usually marketed are shallow-water types, often being caught in the estuaries of New South Wales. Such are the jew-fish (*Scioena*), black bream, snapper (*Pagrosomus*), flathead (*Platycephalus*), whiting (*Sillago*), mullet (*Mugil*), and garfish (*Hemirhamphus*). Great shoals of anchovies, herrings and pilchards pass up and down the coast, but are ignored by the fishermen, although large sums are paid for similar fish imported from foreign lands.

Investigation of the waters off New South Wales has revealed several good trawling grounds between Sydney and Bass Straits.

[1] Based on an interesting account by A. MacCulloch, *Brit. Assoc. Handbook*, Sydney, 1914.

The initial research was done by Government vessels from 1915 to 1923; but since that date private enterprise has employed 15 steam trawlers, which in recent years have caught 10 million lb. of flathead annually.

On the south and south-west coasts of Australia the fish sold in the markets are much the same as those listed for New South Wales. Oysters are of increasing importance in the estuaries of New South Wales and Queensland. About 700 men are engaged in this trade, which is worth about £90,000 a year.

Fresh-water Fisheries

The eastern rivers of Australia, including the Murray system, contain large numbers of Murray cod (*Oligorus*) and Australian perch (*Percalates*). The former may grow to a length of 6 feet, and they are caught in large numbers for the metropolitan markets. The perch can live in brackish waters, and so has a wider range than the Murray cod.

Trout have been successfully acclimatized in many of the streams in the south-east of the continent. The chief centres in New South Wales are Cooma for the Snowy River; Tumut for the Yarrangobilly; Tarana for the Fish River; and Walcha for the Namoi tributaries. In Victoria and Tasmania the Government operates hatcheries, from which trout have been released in many of the mountain streams.

The most remarkable of Australian fish is the Burnett River salmon or lung fish. Its skeleton is well known in Triassic rocks in Europe, but it was first found alive in 1870 in the rivers near Maryborough (Q.). This fish (*Ceratodus*) has paddle-like fins, and is covered with large scales. Its chief peculiarity is that it carries an air-sac, which seems to be the ancestor of the lungs of land vertebrates. During dry seasons it lives in the foul water of shallow pools, and comes to the surface every 30 minutes or so, to empty and refill its lung. This method of breathing enables it to live after most other life in the pool has been poisoned. Some specimens may measure 6 feet in length, but this is exceptionally large.

Another interesting fish is the eel-gudgeon (*Galaxias*), which is only 7 inches long. It is a fresh-water fish found in many of the mountain pools of the southern hemisphere; in South America and South Africa as well as in New Zealand. Its wide distribution is some slight evidence for a former land connexion between the continents by way of a warmer Antarctica than we see today.

In the northern waters of Tasmania is found the largest crayfish in the world (*Astacopsis*). This creature may grow to a length of 2½ feet, and weigh 8 or 9 lb. It is not widely known, since it is difficult to catch. The so-called Lobster (*Jasus*) is common in the south-east of Australia, but it is really a marine crayfish, and this genus is sold extensively in the city markets. In Queensland there are several canneries engaged in catching and utilizing turtle (*Chelone*) from the adjacent coral reefs.[1]

Pearl Shell, Trochus, &c.

The pearl shell (*Meleagrina margaritifera*) lives in the tropical waters from Cape York to Shark Bay (W.A.), a distance of 2,000 miles. The industry is based on the supply of shell rather than on the pearls, though at times fine specimens of the latter are discovered. Thus in 1911 a pearl weighing 178 grains and worth £3,000 was obtained.

Some notes on the pearling industry at Broome, which the writer visited some years ago, will be of interest. The little town has a population of 3,000, of whom only about 600 are of British descent. All the rest are 'aliens', but without them the pearling industry would collapse. Each pearling lugger (really a small schooner) has a crew of about six men. There is a white skipper, two Japanese divers,[2] a Japanese engineer,[2] and usually several sailors from Timor.

The pearl shell is found all down the coast from Derby to Cossack. It is obtained at all depths down to 120 feet, which is about as deep as ordinary diving suits will permit operations. The diver collects the shell from the floor of the ocean just where the Trade Winds produce a continuous supply of sand from the desert. The shell is stored in the shallow well of the boat, and above this are the cramped quarters of the crew. Since they stay at sea in this very hot region for several months at a time, the industry must rank high among the unpleasant trades of the world (p. 230).

After a long spell of calm weather the shell tends to become lost in the sand and weed, but a storm tears away the weed and exposes fresh areas of shell. The terrible hurricanes along the coast, which have wiped out scores of fishermen, usually occur from Christmas to the end of January. The luggers therefore return to Broome about the middle of December for two months' refitting.

There are other centres at Cossack, Onslow and Sharks Bay, as well as at Thursday Island off Cape York. For a time there was pearling at Darwin, but the high tides and muddy waters soon caused the pearling to be abandoned here. In 1953 there were 87 boats engaged in pearling in Queensland, 27 in West Australia, and 10 in Northern Territory.

[1] A good account of the tropical fish will be found in the article by D. G. Stead in the *Australian Geographer*, November 1929.
[2] Replaced by Malays and Filipinos since 1939.

DATA OF THE PEARLING INDUSTRY, 1935

	Boats	Men	Value of shell	Value of pearls
Western Australia	87	529	£45,000	£2,816
Queensland	98	1,203	123,000	2,515
Northern Territory	30	259	71,000	700

The large conical shell *Trochus* is exported to Japan, and cut into pieces for the manufacture of 'pearl buttons'. In 1935–6 the value of the shell obtained from the coral reefs in tropical waters was about £42,000. The sea-slug, *bêche-de-mer* or trepang (which is really a holothuroid allied to the starfishes) is a sluggish creature about a foot long. It is dried and used in China for soup. It is found crawling among the coral reefs, and the 'catch' was worth about £15,000 in 1935, though a few years ago its value was £48,000.

AUSTRALIAN WHALING

Whaling was very lucrative in the seas bordering Australia in the early days. In 1790 a sperm whale invaded Sydney Harbour, and later was stranded on Manly Beach. Sea elephants and seals were common on Tasmanian coasts, but were soon killed off by the sealers. In 1841 there were 35 whaling stations in Tasmania, but by 1896 the last whaler ceased to operate in these seas.

In the 'forties Boyd at Twofold Bay (N.S.W.) and Mossman and Berry in Sydney Harbour made large sums through the whaling industry. This slowly decreased in importance, and whaling from Sydney was given up about 1891. The sole station of any importance today is at Point Cloates, north of Carnarvon (W.A.). A few years ago about 600 humpback whales were caught off North-West Cape, from which 3,000 tons of oil and 400 tons of fertilizer were extracted. At Byron Bay (N.S.W.) is a new whaling station.

PART III

TRANSPORT IN AUSTRALIA

Early Roads

As in all pioneer settlements transport by water was used in the early days wherever possible. Indeed, the outstanding feature of Australia today is the way in which important settlements cluster *near the coasts*, so that coastal navigation still bulks importantly in the transport of heavy goods. In Canada by contrast, since the settlement is concentrated in a narrow inland belt fringing the United States, railways are far more important.

However, roads soon became necessary, though little was done to construct permanent roads till 1850. Stage-coaches ran regularly out of Sydney about 1838 carrying mail and passengers to Bathurst and Goulburn. They performed the journey to and from these places in two days. About the same time coastal trade had grown to such an extent that two steamboats were regularly employed in the traffic between Sydney and Newcastle. No less than 35 sailing vessels were required to carry on the trade between the various ports from Moreton Bay to Hobart, and there were as many more engaged in the whaling industry (R. P. Thomson).

Lennox built numerous fine stone bridges in the 'forties, not only in New South Wales but later also in Victoria. Cobb & Company founded the famous coaching transport to the gold diggings about 1853. Later, as the locomotive appeared on the main lines, Cobb & Co. went further out. In 1924 the last coach was taken off the road to Surat (Q.), and placed in the Queensland Museum.

The writer owns a detailed County Atlas, published by Basch, which shows the roads in New South Wales about 1870. The whole littoral for 150 miles from the sea was criss-crossed with roads. In the northern interior roads reached west to Goondiwindi, Mungindi, Walgett and Bourke. Between the Bogan River and the Murray only one road crossed the western plains, going from Hay to Wilcannia. But another road paralleled the Darling from border to border (i.e. from Mungindi to Wentworth). In the south, roads followed the Lachlan and Murrumbidgee to Hay; and there were roads leading from Deniliquin to Wagga, Albury, Hay and Balranald.

Roads were developed at about the same rate in the other colonies, and we may realize their slow development by what happened in South Australia. In 1839 Gawler was constructing three main roads; one north-east to Morgan, another south-east to Lake Alexandrina, and a third easterly over the horst of Mount Lofty. At the end of 1839 a regular mail was running to Encounter Bay. In 1841 the necessary bridges were finished on the Morgan road and it was passable for carts *via* Gawler and Barossa. The road up Glen Osmond and over the horst necessitated many deep cuttings and embankments, and was not finished till 1845.[1]

By 1867 roads extended north to the end of the Flinders Range and along the Murray to the border; and there were, of course, roads to the mines at Wallaroo and Moonta. But Yorke's Peninsula

[1] Grenfell Price, *Foundations of South Australia*, Adelaide, 1924.

and Eyre's Peninsula had no roads according to Whitworth's map, though there were small settlements between Port Lincoln and Flinders.

By 1887 there were 2,000 miles of 'metalled', i.e. macadamized, road in South Australia; while the total length of roads open for traffic in the same state in 1936 was 50,000 miles (D. V. Fleming).

In Fig. 127 is represented (by the *thin* lines) the state of transport about 1926, before flying became of much importance in the

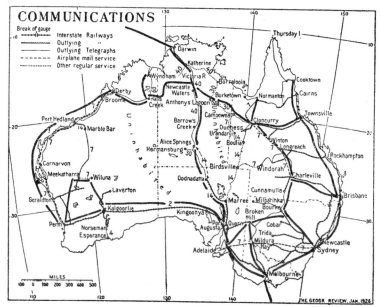

FIG. 127.—COMMUNICATIONS IN THE FRONTIER REGIONS OF AUSTRALIA AND THEIR MAIN CONNEXIONS

Figures along the routes give the days intervening between services in 1926. The heavy lines added to the map show air services in operation in June 1937. Air routes in 1954 reach all parts except those labelled 'Uninhabited'

'outback' areas. The chief interest centres in the routes connecting the pioneer districts with the closely settled coasts. Between Queensland and the Indian Ocean, a distance of 1,200 miles, only two routes crossed the continent which were served by public transport. One of these ran along the Overland Telegraph through the Territory. Although this route was permanently occupied by the telegraph stations as early as 1872, there was so little traffic in 1926 that only one public motor-car (carrying mails) crossed from Alice Springs to Katherine every six weeks.[1] Alice

[1] A military road was built here during the war (p. 211).

14

Springs was connected with Oodnadatta (then the rail-head) by a
service which met the fortnightly train.

Further to the west there was a similar mail-route, which fringed
the western desert on its other margin. This car was subsidized
by the Government, and carried the mail from Marble Bar to
Meekatharra once a week. A lengthy description of this journey
has been given previously (p. 118).

A mail service went every month in winter from Wyndham to
Hall's Creek, and every two months in the wet summer. Coaches
or pack-horses carried the mail from Marree to Boulia (Q.) every
fortnight; while one of the most isolated services was by packhorse
every month from Camooweal to Borraloola (on the Gulf of
Carpentaria), whence one could reach Katherine every six weeks.
Of course these arid lands were crossed by rough but serviceable
tracks which connected every 'station'. But no regular mail or
passenger vehicles served these places.

Inland Navigation

A brief description of the traffic on the Murray and Darling
Rivers must be included in a study of Australian geography, though
now it is a moribund industry. Since South Australia controlled
the outlet of the Murray this state has always been concerned with
navigation. New South Wales and Victoria border the upper waters
only, and they have always been more interested in the irrigation
aspect of the rivers. All three states are controlled by capitals which
are separated from the Murray Basin by fairly high mountain
barriers. For this reason roads and railways have perhaps been
somewhat unduly favoured by the authorities legislating far from
the rivers concerned.

However, in 1851, the Government of South Australia offered
a bonus of £4,000 to anyone who would demonstrate the practical
character of navigation on the Murray. In August 1853, Cadell's
steamer *Lady Augusta* (which had been built at Sydney) made a
successful voyage up the river to a point beyond Snow Hill. For
many years the wool crop was carried to the sea by similar small
steamers, but railways soon began to tap the rivers, and to steal
much of the traffic. This was inevitable, since the river was usually
not navigable from January to July owing to low-water conditions.
The railway to Morgan was opened in 1878, and by 1904 Victoria
had sent lines to Echuca and Swan Hill (Fig. 90).

The Darling is unfortunately very erratic in its flow, but at time
of flood it was largely used by the stations in out-back New South
Wales. Indeed, in 1870 (according to D. J. Gordon) a steamer went
from the Darling, along the course of the Paroo River, to beyond

the Queensland border, a distance of 180 miles. The spread of the water was then 60 miles wide (Fig. 66).

In the old days the trade of the lower Murray and the Darling centred at Morgan, while the upper Murray traffic radiated from Echuca. This latter traffic often included the lower Murrumbidgee, as well as the network of billabongs known as the Edwards and Wakool Rivers. With high water the river was navigable as far as Albury; but there was little traffic above Echuca, which is 666 miles from the South Australian border. On the Darling, steamers could trade as far as Walgett, which is 1,180 miles from Wentworth. A remarkably interesting account of this phase of Australian development is described in Bean's *Dreadnought of the Darling* (Sydney, 1912).

All the river-borne traffic declined greatly owing to the very dry seasons around 1902, and it is not likely to recover. The South Australian trade on the Murray fell from 58,000 tons in 1883 to 23,000 tons in 1901. Even the locking of the Murray is now directed chiefly to ensure irrigation rather than river navigation. As far as the writer can ascertain, the position is much like that obtaining in the canals of Ontario (Rideau and Trent), which are now used mainly for casual tourist traffic in the summer. Only one or two of the old river-steamers are now left of the many which plied the Murray in the closing years of the century (E. Hill).

The Spread of the Railways

The first railway in Australia was built in 1850 to cover the 15 miles between Sydney and Parramatta; and by 1859 there were 171 miles of railway in Australia. The rate of construction up to the year 1871 was very slow, being only about 80 miles per annum. By 1875 the difficult hinterland had been crossed and the cost per mile in the inland plains was much less. A very active period was from 1881 to 1891, when the rate per year jumped to 593 miles per annum, but of late years it has dropped to 174 per annum.

PROGRESS OF RAILWAY MILEAGE

Year	N.S.W.	Vic.	Q.	S.A.	W.A.	Tas.	N.T.	Total
1881	1,040	1,247	800	845	92	168	—	4,192
1901	2,926	3,238	2,904	1,736	1,984	618	145	10,123
1921	5,402	4,337	7,012	3,463	4,906	877	198	26,202
1931	6,013	4,710	6,509	3,949	4,966	786	316	27,700
1954	6,342	4,241	6,560	3,816	605	490	26	620

Taking a general survey of Australian railways, it is now possible to journey by rail from the Cloncurry mines in north-west Queensland to Wiluna in Western Australia (Fig. 128). But no less than five changes of gauge are encountered on this journey. This great hindrance to rapid traffic has evolved gradually, and there seems little likelihood of its being removed for some time. It is, however, hoped to convert the whole railway from Brisbane to Perth to the 4-foot 8½-inch gauge, first of all. In 1846 Gladstone recommended the standard 4-foot 8½-inch gauge, but Victoria in 1852 chose 5 feet 3 inches; while New South Wales adopted the standard. It

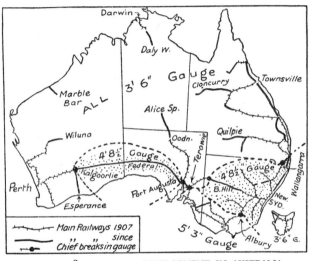

FIG. 128.—RAILWAY DEVELOPMENT IN AUSTRALIA

showing the various gauges in the six states, and the main lines before and after 1907. Areas with standard gauge are dotted

was not till 1883 that the two railways met at Albury. Queensland has always used the more economical 3-foot 6-inch gauge, and Brisbane was linked to Sydney in 1889. South Australia uses two gauges; for its main lines are largely 5 feet 3 inches, and its northern lines with lighter traffic are 3 feet 6 inches. The line from Melbourne to Adelaide, which was finished in 1887, is on the broad gauge throughout. However, the Federal Government has built a line (from Kalgoorlie to Port Augusta) to join the South Australian railways to the Western Australian railways, and for this has used the standard gauge. In Western Australia the state lines are narrow, as are those of Tasmania (Fig. 128). Reference to the map shows that the lines north of the 'standard gauge' area are mostly narrow gauge. Those to the south are broad gauge. It is proposed to build a standard gauge railway to link Birdum (near Daly Waters, Fig. 128) with Bourke, New South Wales.

The Transcontinental Railways

A glance at the railway map about 1915 shows a fair 'railway net' linking Brisbane to Melbourne and including the great wheat belt. Isolated 'nets' clustered around Perth and Adelaide. In Queensland three long lines ran straight inland from the sea at Townsville, Rockhampton and Brisbane; while similar radii branched inland from Sydney to Condobolin and Hay, and from Adelaide to Oodnadatta. In the south-west, railways ran from Perth to Laverton and from Geraldton to Meekatharra.

For many years there had been agitation to link Adelaide with Darwin by a north–south line, and Adelaide with Kalgoorlie by an east–west line. Impassioned politicians pointed to the Canadian Pacific Railway as an example of the way in which railways produced settlement. They entirely ignored the fact that the C.P.R., for almost its whole vast distance, passed through regions of *fair rainfall*; though of course the section near Lake Superior is over barren soils.

In 1908–9 a survey was carried out from Port Augusta to Kalgoorlie, and in 1912 the railway was commenced. The War of 1914–18 caused considerable delays, but the new Federal line on the 4-foot 8½-inch gauge was completed in 1917. It is 1,051 miles long, and passes through poor stock country, near the 10-inch rainfall line, nearly the whole way.

The other so-called Transcontinental Line, from Oodnadatta northward to join the Darwin railway, has much less to recommend its construction (Fig. 128). The chief argument in its favour was a promise made to South Australia by the Commonwealth that some day they would connect Adelaide and Darwin by rail. For nearly a dozen years the present writer wrote and spoke against the waste of public money on a project to build a line 500 miles long through a semi-desert apparently mainly for the benefit of about 500 people. Although the Federal authorities continued the railway from Oodnadatta to Alice Springs in 1927, they have already realized that the cost is appalling even for this short section. In 1930 for the two sections of railway in the Territory, the excess of working costs over revenue was about 180 per cent (G. Price). Some day in the future the line advocated long ago by the writer, which enters the Territory from north-western Queensland, will give Darwin a connexion by rail with the cities of the south-east. This will traverse good pastoral country over practically the whole distance (Fig. 76).

Transport by Air

When the writer was a student at the University of Sydney he occasionally attended the meetings of the Royal Society, and there listened to Lawrence Hargraves, who gave a number of papers explaining his attempts to further aviation. Hargraves' box-kite was first tried out at Stanwell Park south of Sydney, and is the basis of wing-design for early aeroplanes. Many of his models are now in the Sydney Technological Museum.

The first Australian aeroplane was built and flown near Melbourne in 1910. An early flight to test meteorological conditions was made by the writer at Point Cooke Flying School in 1915.[1] In December 1919, Ross Smith made the first flight from England to Australia in thirty days. Within a year or two extensive air services were initiated in Australia.

The first long-distance service was in use along the sparsely settled west coast of Western Australia as early as April 1922 (Fig. 127). It linked Geraldton to Broome, and was soon extended to Derby, a distance of 1,417 miles. The round journey was completed once a week, and it soon carried 20,000 letters a month. A few months later the Charleville-Cloncurry service (575 miles) started, and in 1925 it was extended to Camooweal.

In July 1925, air services were commenced between Adelaide and Cootamundra (578 miles); Hay and Melbourne (233 miles); and Mildura to Broken Hill (189 miles). By the year 1932, Wyndham was linked with Perth, and planes flew regularly from Perth *via* Adelaide and Sydney to Brisbane. Other services went from Melbourne south to Hobart and north to Charleville (Fig. 127).

The chief services today are all clearly indicated in Fig. 127. Interesting data regarding the present status of aviation are to be found in the following table (for 1936 and 1946).

	Aircrafts	Pilots	Aerodromes	Flights	Miles flown	Passengers
1936	228	950	382	129,396	5·8 million	75,000
1946	349	1,439*	399	152,130†	21·5 ,,	522,157

* Civil only. † Hours of flight.

Only 44 people were injured or killed out of the many thousand carried during 1946. Some account of the progress of aviation in New Guinea will be found on page 425.

[1] An account appears in *Australian Weather Report*, Vol. 4, No. 7.

During the last decade or two there have been a number of important changes affecting aviation in Australia. In 1939 the industry was placed under the direction of a Minister for Civil Aviation. In 1947 the International Civil Aviation Organization (ICAO) was instituted, and its convention was attended by representatives of 47 nations, including Australia. One of the results was the agreement of the Canadian and Australian Governments to operate fortnightly air services between Sydney and Vancouver. Pan-American Airways began operating a weekly service between San Francisco and Sydney in February 1947. Qantas (for the Commonwealth) and B.O.A.C. combined to give a more regular and efficient service between Australia and Britain by way of Singapore and Karachi at the close of the war. In 1947 there were eleven important operating companies within Australia, ranging from Australian National Airways (serving 22 regular routes) to Conellan Airways (four routes out of Alice Springs).

PART IV

THE DEVELOPMENT OF SECONDARY INDUSTRIES

Dwellers in a land so isolated as Australia naturally feel it advisable to build up a manufacturing industry so that they shall not be dependent on distant lands for the vital needs of the nation. Australia has had a difficult task in this respect; since as a young nation in the pioneer stage of development, her natural plan is to utilize the cheap land for the production of wool and wheat, which she can exchange for manufactured goods from the older centres of industry. The lack of convenient iron ores and the high rate of wages have also made it impossible to compete in many fundamental industries with foreign goods, except with the help of high protective duties. This has been Australia's solution of the difficulty, with the natural result that the Australian citizen pays much more for his goods than he would do under free trade.

The proportion of the population working in factories varies greatly in the different states, as may be seen from the following table. New South Wales and Victoria are much the most important from this point of view, and the proportion in these states seems to be increasing slightly at the expense of the other states.

The smaller factories are naturally the most numerous, about 82 per cent having 20 workmen or less, 15 per cent employ from 21 to 100, and only 3 per cent employ 101 workmen or more.

PERCENTAGE OF FACTORY WORKERS IN VARIOUS STATES

	1901	1928	1945-6
New South Wales	34	40	39
Victoria	34	35	33
Queensland	14	10	9
South Australia	9	8	8
Western Australia	6	5	7
Tasmania	2	2	3
Total	100	100	100

The order of importance of the factories in 1945-6 is given in the following table:

	Types of factories	Number	Workmen
1	Metals, machinery	8,816	292,477
2	Food, tobacco	5,865	105,878
3	Clothing	5,215	93,370
4	Woodwork	3,148	38,346
5	Printing	1,703	39,905
6	Furniture	1,140	13,107
7	Textiles	883	55,008

The first centre of industry was naturally Sydney, where looms were set up before 1800. In 1802, 306 yards of woollen blankets were made. Cloth mills were soon built at Botany and Penrith. In 1848 there were 272 factories (chiefly flour-mills) in New South Wales, 41 in Victoria, 99 in Tasmania and 67 in South Australia. Bonwick tells us that in June 1839, a few years after Melbourne was founded, there were 3,000 people living in 500 houses in the young city; and among these there were seventy shops, three breweries, one tannery, and two fellmongeries.

In Franklyn's *Glance at Australia* (Melbourne, 1881) we find a picture of the state of industry about the year 1880. He gives the following commodities as made in the small factories at Melbourne, and exported from the state. Agricultural implements, apparel, bags and wool-packs, boilers, boots, brushware, candles, carts, confectionery, steam engines, flour, furniture, hardware, hats, jams, jewellery, leather, malt, marble, preserved meat, paper bags, saddles, soap, wine and woollen piece goods.

The same author describes the growth of factories near Sydney 'under the fostering influences of free trade'. In addition to the items in the Melbourne list we find ship-building, chemical works and potteries. He points out that in spite of an increase of population from 1864 to 1874 by 46 per cent, the net import of the chief industrial commodities had *decreased* by nearly £3 million. This was all owing to thĕ development of local factories without the benefit of protection. In 1868 in the mother state there were 3,743 'mills and manufactories'; and these had increased to 14,057 by 1878.

As regards Queensland, Franklyn writes: 'There are no great manufactories. A woollen mill recently established at Ipswich and some large foundries in Brisbane and Maryborough are the principal industrial establishments, other than those connected with the natural products of the soil.' He mentions especially that there was a large refinery attached to the sugar mills at Gargarie (near Maryborough), where cane juice was manufactured directly into high-class refined sugar.

In South Australia Franklyn describes the usual small factories for leather, iron, coaches, wool, clothing, wine, olive oil, &c., as giving occupation to about 7,000 persons out of a total population of 249,000 in 1880.

Present-Day Industries

Turning to modern times, I quote from a valuable article by H. Burton.[1]

Although protection has made possible a greater diversity of manufacturing, the chief industries are still much the same as those which held the field when the policy was adopted (in 1901). Since 1908, however, there have been a few changes, for instance tanneries have lost rank, being replaced by rubber factories. Motor bodies are now more important than saw-milling, while the furniture industry has increased by 100 per cent.

A few large industrial plants may be referred to briefly. In 1912 the Broken Hill Proprietary Company started making steel at Newcastle. It has its own coal-mines, iron ore leases, limestone quarries, steamers, &c., and began actual production of steel in 1915. By 1921 it was employing 5,500 men on these new developments. Hoskins & Company at Lithgow have been making pig-iron and steel since 1907; though they transferred much of their interest to Port Kembla, as we shall see.

The distribution of factories in New South Wales is typical,

[1] 'Growth of Secondary Industry', *Annals Amer. Acad. Pol. Sci.*, Philadelphia, 1931.

since in this state, as in the others, a very large proportion of all the factories is collected in the capital city. In all cases the second place in a particular industry is found to be Newcastle. However, in the case of factories connected with wood, machinery and food there are a good many scattered through the other towns of the state, as is clear from the following table for the year 1935:

FACTORIES IN NEW SOUTH WALES

	Clothing	Machin-ery	Food	Printing	Furni-ture	Wood
Sydney	1,248	1,317	725	438	270	339
Newcastle	85	177	133	34	25	110
Rest of the state	175	706	507	160	18	376
Total	1,508	2,200	1,365	632	313	825

Victoria has made most progress in textiles and in the boot and shoe trade. One of the textile mills in Melbourne employs over 1,050 persons. There is also a great electrical station at Yallourn (p. 376), which is managed by the state. The Government of Tasmania controls Australia's main hydro-electric stations at Waddamanna and Tarraleah (p. 410).

Hydro-Electric Power

Tasmania, owing to her position in the wetter southern latitudes and to her mountainous topography, is in the best position as regards water power of any of the states. The Conference on Water Power (1924) places the possibilities of the Eastern Highlands of Australia somewhat as follows: Australian Alps about 400,000 horse-power, Blue Plateau 30,000, New England Plateau 350,000, and Atherton Tableland 150,000. In Tasmania, however, they believe that a total of 700,000 can ultimately be utilized.

Hydro-Electric Power in the Central Plateau of Tasmania

In the north centre of the island of Tasmania there is a plateau, formed of (Jurassic) basic lavas, at a level of about 3,500 feet. It takes the shape of an isosceles triangle pointing to the east, with sides about 70 miles long, and a base (in the west) about 50 miles long. On the whole the plateau slopes somewhat to the south-east, and hence its main drainage is into the Derwent River entering the sea at Hobart. This environment determines the site of Australia's only large hydro-electric development; and has naturally increased the size of Hobart as compared with Launceston. There are a number of shallow lakes on the plateau, but Great Lake and Lake St. Clair are the sole units which so far have been involved in power supplies (Fig. 128A).

The first use of the power was in the separation of certain zinc ores from Broken Hill and elsewhere about 1908. This scheme was

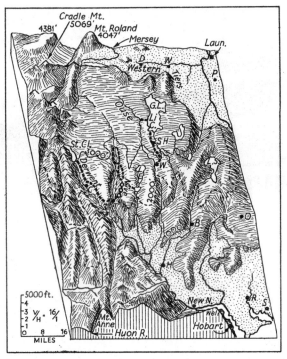

FIG. 128A.—BLOCK DIAGRAM OF THE WESTERN PLATEAU OF TASMANIA
(LOOKING NORTH)

Notice the 'five fingers' on the southern edge, where the power stations of Tarraleah (*T*) and Waddamanna (*W*) have been built. Lowlands are dotted. Shannon (*SH*) and Mount Field (*F*) are indicated

not very successful at first, and the Tasmanian Company took over the power development in 1914. The water level of the Great Lake was raised by a dam at Miena at the southern end. From this point the water is led down the Shannon River to a small power station. It then passes south by a canal to the penstock above the gorge of the adjacent River Ouse. Here a drop of about 1,000 feet brings it to the turbines in the Waddamanna power station. Here about 66,000 horse-power is developed; which is carried some 60 miles

south-east to Hobart. Another power line takes power 53 miles to
the north-east to Launceston.

From the southern portion of the plateau five 'fingers' project,
separated by deep gorges. The valley between the two eastern
fingers is occupied by the Ouse River, and here is the site of
Waddamanna power house. The valley between the two western
'fingers' contains the upper waters of the Derwent, rising in Lake
St. Clair. Here the second and third phases of the water supply
project were developed. The lake was dammed, and the water
carried in flumes some 20 miles to the deep Nive River valley to
the south-east (Fig. 128A). Here at the bottom of the gorge the
Tarraleah power station has been constructed.

What may be termed the 'middle finger' of the plateau still
remains to be exploited. It carries the upper Nive River, which is
to be dammed near Bronte, Lake Echo and the River Dee, also
to be dammed, and a series of hollows which are to be turned into
lakes and drained to the west to the gorge above Tarraleah. Here
a drop of a thousand feet will carry the water to a new power station
close to Tarraleah, but this will be known as Tungatinah. It may
be mentioned that a fourth power scheme is just being completed
below Lake St. Clair. This is the Clark Dam which will produce
a lake as large as Lake St. Clair; and its water is to be carried to
Tarraleah to supplement the St. Clair water at the same power
station.

Some notes on the country in the vicinity (made on a journey
in 1948) will be of interest. On the rather steep shores of the
estuary of the Derwent near Hobart have arisen four large centres
of factories, dependent largely on the power from the plateau.
Electrolytic zinc is manufactured close to the city of Hobart. To
the south at Electrona are large carbide works. A few miles north
of the city on the west bank of the Derwent are the chocolate
factories at Claremont; while across the river at Risdon and elsewhere are less-important users of electric power.

Good roads now traverse most of the island, including a new
scenic road across the southern edge of the plateau to the mining
towns of the west. On the road to Tarraleah we proceed north and
enter the rather narrow valley of the Derwent near New Norfolk.
Here I saw the finest example of a condensation cloud pouring
out of the valley—like a great white caterpillar—of all my travels.
Hamilton is an old settlement of about 3,000 people, noted for the
cut-stone houses built by the convicts early in the nineteenth
century. Fine forests of eucalypts are being exploited on the sides
of these valleys, but when we reached the higher levels of the
plateau the timber became smaller and scattered. In May 1948,

the Clark Dam across the Upper Derwent (*C* in Fig. 128A) was about half completed. We then followed the flume at the upper level to the east to the penstock above the gorge of the Nive at Tarraleah. Here about 100,000 horse-power is being developed. A good road leads north across the proposed Nive River catchment, past a number of hollows shown in Fig. 128A, and so to the small canal which leads the waters of the upper Ouse into the Great Lake at Liawenee (Li.). At Miena is a dam of 27 arches (each facing upstream) which has much increased the capacity of the lake. The lakes drain normally down the Shannon for about 5 miles to a small power station (14,000 h.p.); and then the water is led across the plateau in a canal to the steep drop above the Ouse River at Waddamanna. This is at present the chief supply in the island, producing about 120,000 horse-power. Most of this is carried to Hobart, but adequate supplies go to Launceston, and even to Burnie.

Future Hydro-Electric Power in the Kosciusko Region

A study of the topography and rainfall conditions in Australia shows that the necessary 'head of water' and heavy rainfall are best supplied in the vicinity of the Kosciusko Plateau. In 1949 the various governments concerned constituted the *Snowy Mountains Hydro-Electric Authority* with a view to planning very large works, whose total cost may amount to £500 million. The salient features of the plans are indicated in the map of the plateaux (north of Kosciusko) which appears as Fig. 128B. This is based on the official report of A. R. Ronalds.

In general the scheme is to collect the water into four eastern reservoirs, and then lead it by giant tunnels under the plateaux to the steep valleys on the western slopes. Here a dozen power stations are to be built to utilize these waters as they fall to the low levels of 850 feet (near Khancoban) on the Murray, or 900 feet at Tumut on the river of the same name. Two large reservoirs are also planned on the Tumut River.

In the south, only a few miles east of Kosciusko, a small reservoir is to be formed by damming Spencer Creek at an elevation of 5,760 feet. The water will be led to three small power stations (S1, S2, S3) in the gorge of the Snowy River. As it flows from the gorge it reaches the lower level of the Monaro Plateau at Jindabyne (3,000 feet), and here a large dam impounds Snowy and Eucumbene River waters. In addition, 490 miles of collecting channels (races), cut along the contours of the hills, will bring much additional water to the Jindabyne and other dams. From Jindabyne the collected waters will enter a huge tunnel (about 22 feet in diameter)

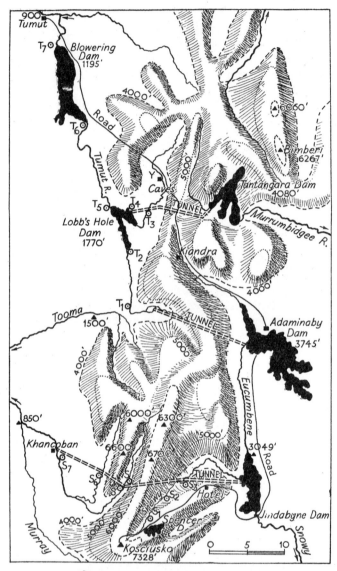

FIG. 128B.—THE PLATEAUX NORTH OF KOSCIUSKO

which are to be tunnelled (under the 'Snowy Mountains Hydro-Electric' plan) so as to produce a series of 14 power stations in the Upper Snowy River, Upper Murray and Tumut River valleys. The six dams are not yet built. The contours are approximate and form-lines indicate the areas above 4,000 feet. Cabramurra is about 5 miles to the west of Kiandra.

(*Based on the Report of A. F. Ronalds, Sydney, June 1950*)

which is 22 miles long. This will pass right under Hotel Kosciusko, and is estimated to cost £12 million. The tunnel carries the water to four power stations on the Geehi and Bogong tributaries of the Murray River.

Further north on the Eucumbene River, at the 3,745-feet level, a dam will produce a lake 15 miles long and 3 miles wide. A second tunnel will link Tantangara dam with the Adaminaby Dam. The earlier project to link Tantangara directly with Lobb's Hole Dam has been postponed. The combined waters will be harnessed at power stations T1 and T2 (above Lobb's Hole Dam) on the same river.

The third large dam blocks the headwaters of the Murrumbidgee at the 4,080-feet level; and here an 8-mile tunnel carries the water to the Lobb's Hole Dam at 1,770 feet, feeding two power stations (T3 and T4) *en route*. A drop of nearly 600 feet to Blowering Dam on the lower Tumut River enables three more power stations to utilize the descent of the water.

The total supply of power will be about 772,000 kilowatts. Moreover, the water will ultimately help to irrigate the semi-arid plains of the lower Murray and Murrumbidgee Rivers. It is expected that 565,000 acre-feet a year will reach Tumut, and 400,000 acre-feet will enter the upper Murray River. A great deal of the cost will be due to the collecting channels, while £100 million of the total is to be spent on the transmission lines to various distant factory towns. Guthega, near S3, supplied power in 1955.

Industrial Developments at Port Kembla

This brief study of the development of secondary industries may close with a description of one of the latest and most interesting examples of town evolution. Port Kembla is situated 45 miles south of Sydney on the exposed Illawarra coast (Fig. 124). A harbour containing an area of 340 acres has been constructed by building two breakwaters, each over 3,000 feet long. Here ships drawing 36 feet can be readily berthed.

There was a jetty at Port Kembla used for loading coal before 1895. But the modern town begins with the establishment of the large Electrolytic Refining and Smelting Works in 1907. This site was chosen mainly owing to the proximity of the coal in the cliffs behind the port. But it was centrally situated between the Queensland and South Australian copper-mines which supplied the crude metal. As compared with Newcastle the land was much cheaper, and the local mines were prepared to sell the coal cheaply, so as to build up a manufacturing centre in the Illawarra District. The use of much sulphuric acid led to the building of works to produce this material, and also to produce super-phosphate for fertilizer.

The sulphur used comes from Texas, and the insoluble phosphates from Nauru Island. About 50,000 tons of soluble phosphate is produced each year.

The next large development was when Hoskins and other iron-smelting firms chose Port Kembla for their new works. They transferred from their old-established works at Lithgow, which had the considerable disadvantage of being far from the coast. Since much of their ore comes from overseas (Yampi Sound being seriously considered), it is obvious that a seaport is indicated for the site of the furnaces. They bring their limestone from Marulan about 50 miles to the south.

Another smaller industry is the production of silica bricks from silica obtained at Ulladulla, 100 miles to the south. These bricks are rather fragile and are needed in large amounts by the blast furnaces, hence manufacture locally is advisable. Cement works, based on the unusually large deposits of shell at Shell-harbour near by, are also of some importance at Port Kembla. The local power house is able to obtain coal at 13s. per ton, whereas coal for similar purposes at Sydney costs 28s. Hence the Port Kembla power is in use now in most of the small towns in the Illawarra district. All the mines of the south coast send coal to Port Kembla because of the unrivalled character of the loading facilities.[1]

The factories for motor bodies, boots, confectionery, &c., in Australia are slowly increasing in size, which makes for efficiency; but Burton deplores the tariffs which keep alive a 'host of backyard factories'. 'Hand in hand with protection, money-wages have risen steadily, and this daunts new enterprise. In addition, the protection of coastal shipping by the Navigation Acts has destroyed our *natural* protection due to distance.' Freight rates from Brisbane to Perth equal those from Australia to Britain. The proportion of exports due to secondary industry is decreasing, and Burton concludes: 'Until we reduce our costs of production in some way the prospects of further expansion of manufacturing are far from bright.' A table of Exports and Imports follows on page 415.

Heavy Industry in Australia

We owe to Neville R. Wills a very complete study of the rise of heavy industry in Australia. It is entitled *Australian Steel Industry* (198 pages, Sydney, 1948); and I have made considerable use of it in the following account. As he states, the industrial revolution which has marked the last thirty years of Australian industry has been to a large extent based on the Newcastle Iron and Steel Works.

[1] 'Port Kembla and its Harbour', Crago and Lowndes, *Aus. Geog.*, 1931.

AUSTRALIAN EXPORTS IN MILLION £ (1951-2)

Articles	1951-2	1946-7	Countries importing	1951-2	1946-7
Wool	323	126·1	United Kingdom	218	89·6
Flour	33	22·5	U.S.A.	77	47·6
Meats	35	21·1	France	54	20·1
Hides	17	15·4	Belgium	25	19·1
Butter	5	12·6	Malaya	9	18·3
Lead	21	8·6	India	17	13·0
Wheat	55	6·3	New Zealand	37	12·9
Milk	8	4·3	Ceylon	11	7·1

AUSTRALIAN IMPORTS IN MILLION £ (1951-2)

Articles	1951-2	1946-7	Countries exporting	1951-2	1946-7
Machinery	126	9·1	United Kingdom	466	81·9
Motor-cars	85	15·1	U.S.A.	109	43·7
Cotton	64	—	India	48	19·2
Petrol	44	11·2	Canada	24	18·3
Drugs	29	10·5	Malaya	19	3·5
Silk	27	14·6	Ceylon	11	7·2
Paper	27	—	New Zealand	7	3·9

Mention has been made elsewhere of the blast furnace built at Mittagong in 1848. This was handicapped by the limited amount of iron ore, and by the poor quality of the local coal. The works were closed in 1877, but had rolled considerable quantities of rails before that date. Lithgow (on the western side of the coal-field) produced a good deal of iron and steel between 1876 and 1930. Around 1895-6 a great deal of copper smelting also took place at this inland centre. The site was unsuitable owing to its distance from the sea, and the works were transferred to Port Kembla about 1927. Here the largest blast furnace in the Empire (155 feet high) was built in 1928.

In 1911 Broken Hill Proprietary was known only as a producer of lead, zinc and silver; but the management were already busy with plans for establishing a large steel industry. The best coal for steel-making was found to be at Newcastle; and since 1 ton of steel needs approximately 3 tons of coal, it is wiser to erect the blast furnace on the coal-field rather than near the iron mines. In 1912 the Government agreed to the proposals of B.H.P.; and a swamp at Port Waratah, about 2 miles north of Newcastle, was

transformed during 1913 and 1914 (Fig. 128c). In April 1915 the
first steel was tapped and rolled. Some ten years later various coal-
mines in the vicinity, such as Elrington and Lambton, were purchased by the company.

As described elsewhere (Fig. 71A) the iron ore is brought from
the Middleback Ranges in Eyre's Peninsula (S. Aus.). At first
limestone was quarried near Devonport in Tasmania, but in later
years the more accessible deposits at Rapid Bay (south of Adelaide) have been used. During the last twenty years many sub-

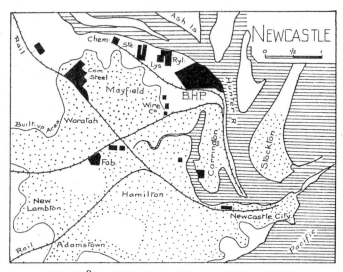

FIG. 128C.—NEWCASTLE AND ITS HEAVY INDUSTRY
showing the relation of the B.H.P. Steel Works to the harbour and to its subsidiary
industries (black). Dotted areas are built-up suburbs, &c.
(*After Neville R. Wills, 1948*)

sidiary plants have been erected in the vicinity of the main works.
Some of these are charted in Fig. 128c. For instance, chemical
works, and those producing ferro-alloys, magnesium and tungsten
steel are now in operation, while other firms such as Lysaghts are
in close connexion with the steel works. In the main plant the
three large blast furnaces are on the banks of the Hunter, with the
13 open-hearth furnaces just behind them. To the north (but close
by) are the plants producing tar and benzol; to the south-east of
the furnaces are the stores of coal. In the centre of the plant are
the coke ovens and the rolling mills; while in the west, rod and
strip steel are rolled. The slag from the blast furnaces is dumped
at the north end of the area.

In 1947 B.H.P. at Newcastle and vicinity employed 37,000 men, and controlled the chief steelworks in the British Empire. It must, however, be remembered that it only produces about 1 per cent of the world's steel, lagging far behind U.S.A. 40 per cent; Germany 20 per cent; U.S.S.R. 15 per cent and Britain 7 per cent. France, Japan and Belgium are also much larger producers; but its production is on a level with that of the next group, i.e. India and Canada.

As regards the future, Wills points out that the iron ore in Australia—almost wholly near Whyalla or Yampi (W.A.)—is likely to be exhausted in about forty years, but the company has secured concessions in New Caledonia and elsewhere. It is in a most advantageous position to supply Pacific lands, since only in Japan is there a rival centre of heavy industry; while only in Chili are there deposits of iron ore so conveniently sited as at Whyalla and Yampi. In 1946 Newcastle produced 555,565 tons of pig iron; Port Kembla 294,407, and Whyalla 146,051 tons. The peak year was 1941, when the two first named produced 772,000 and 672,000 tons respectively. In 1952 Port Kembla surpassed Newcastle in iron production.

RAPID INDUSTRIAL EXPANSION 1945-56

A remarkable change in the economy of Australia during the post-war period has been the way in which industrial activities have increased so that they are challenging the pastoral and purely agricultural industries of earlier decades. During the same period the striking increases in migrants to Australia has added largely to the population, no less than a million having been added in the last few years. Indeed this total just about equals that added to the Australian nation by the usual local birthrate.

The expansion in steel production, in the value of the wool crop, the growth of automobile manufactures and of many new industries such as electronics, plastics, etc., have all contributed greatly also. According to the valuable survey in the *Sydney Morning Herald* (June 1957) some of these expansions are given in the table on page 417A.

As regards the rural industries there has been a marked change during this period. Increases have occurred in production, but not by expanding into new areas, but by more thorough farming in lands of good rainfall which have long been alienated. Wheat acreage has indeed decreased, but owing to improvement in methods and soils the yield per acre has increased. Sheep are now about 150 millions, and it is expected that Australia will produce 6 million bales of wool per annum in the near future.

	1946–7	1956
Population	7,579,358	9,427,538
Industries values	£410 m.	£1,365 m.
Motor trade values	£12 m.	£212 m.
Oil-refined values	£0·5 m.	£7·7 m.
Plastics	£2·5 m.	£25 m.
Mineral production	£53 m.	£200 m.
Exports	£309 m.	£1,000 m.
Imports	£209 m.	£720 m.

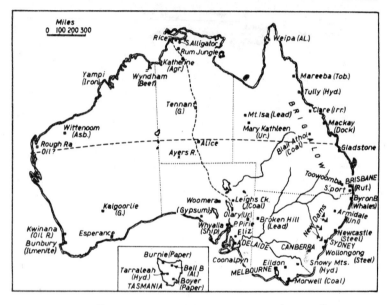

FIG. 128D.—GREAT INDUSTRIAL EXPANSION (1945–56)

Based on *Herald* map—June 1957

A quotation from the above source is worth reproducing: 'Australia's expanse of land is her richest asset, even though only a quarter of the continent round the edges gets a growing period exceeding five months each year that facilitates agriculture. The hardiness of the sheep has partly solved that problem, and has solved also the problem of manpower, so that although wool is preponderantly the nation's leading product, only 21 per cent of the population are engaged in rural occupations; and those include all types of farmers. The rest of the population work in towns (metropolitan 54 per cent and other urban 25 per cent).'

New South Wales

The site of the earliest settlement in Australia in Sydney is still the centre of the greatest industrial activity in the Commonwealth. If we include Newcastle to the north, and Wollongong to the south, then this area includes almost a quarter of the population, and one-third of the factories, and 'almost 40 per cent of the output of secondary industry—valued at £1,415 million—of the whole Commonwealth' (R. J. Wood).

New towns have been started in this area, as at Dapto and Dundas. Millions have been spent recently on new works at the harbour of Newcastle, and also at Port Kembla (Wollongong). The Warragamba Dam, about 33 miles west of Sydney, will be one of the largest built for a city's water supply. An atomic reactor is being constructed about 15 miles to the south-west of the city. Huge power stations, based upon the immense coal resources of this industrial region, are rising near Newcastle and Wollongong.

Irrigation is expanding near the northern rivers at Keepit, Glenbawn, and Burrendong. The £400 million investment of the Snowy Mountain Power Scheme is described elsewhere, but mention may be made of the new mountain town of Cabramurra, a few miles west of Kiandra (Fig. 128B), where the workers engaged on the projects along the upper Tumut River are housed. The new oil refinery at Kurnell on Botany Bay is one of the largest of its kind.

Broken Hill steel plants now produce nearly three million tons of steel ingots, a production double that of 1947 (Fig. 128A).

Victoria

In this state 33 per cent of its occupied population work in factories, compared with 20 per cent in New South Wales, but it has of course a much smaller total population. Melbourne produces 85 per cent of Victoria's factory output (C. D. Kemp). Partly as the result of its former practice of protective duties, it leads in textiles, automobiles, and electronics.

Eildon Reservoir on the Goulburn River is now Australia's largest dam, and has much increased the irrigated area to the north. The largest new developments, however, have been in the expansion of the use of brown coal at Morwell. Here one of the largest plants outside Germany has been erected to produce gas from the coal, and it is then piped 100 miles to Melbourne.

Two of the four large oil refineries in Australia are sited in this state. One is near Geelong and the other at Altona near Melbourne.

Queensland

This state, unlike most of the others, has not collected its population so largely in the capital city, but Brisbane is by far the chief centre of industry. The famous mines near Mount Isa are exhibiting greater reserves each year. In addition to lead and zinc, large copper deposits have been proved; while a new lead-zinc field has been discovered north-west of the older mines. A few miles to the south-east is Mary Kathleen, rivalling Rum Jungle as a large producer of uranium minerals. Still later were discovered the vast bauxite resources of Weipa in the north of the Peninsula. Millions of pounds are being expended to develop the ores in each of these very valuable fields. New deposits of iron ore are to be exploited at the Constance Range, about 200 miles north-west of Cloncurry. Dr. Raggatt thinks it likely that by 1961 Mount Isa may be producing more than twice the total of ore now being mined by all the mines of Broken Hill. Rutile, derived from beach sands along the coast between Brisbane and Sydney, is now being exported in values that almost equal our gold export. As regards coal the opencut at Blair Athol is said to be the largest in the world.

With the best rainfall of any of the states, Queensland has good reason to look for great agricultural expansion. Our chernozyems (black soils) are almost wholly confined to Queensland; and are at present largely occupied by a worthless brigalow scrub of close-set acacias (Fig. 128D). Many years ago I predicted that this would become a great millet belt; but it has only recently attracted the attention that it deserves. As regards sugar, recent months (1957) have shown Japan purchasing six million pounds' worth, though its former purchases have not bulked much in this commodity (Fig. 128A).

South Australia

The large deposits of coal at Leigh's Creek are being used to produce power in Port Augusta. Uranium from Radium Hill is being treated at new works at Port Pirie, and exports of uranium oxide are now stated to be worth about £1½ millions a year.

Elizabeth is a new satellite town 17 miles north of Adelaide, where large car works are being established by General Motors-Holdens.

Western Australia

The chief new developments have been at Kwinana, the town which has developed 18 miles south of Perth around the huge oil refinery. Ilmenite, a mineral source of titanium, is being mined near Bunbury. At Wittenoom (south-west of Marble Bar) are found the largest asbestos deposits in Australia, and they are now being exploited. The iron ore on Koolan Island (Yampi) is now shipped to blast furnaces at Port Kembla.

Tasmania

The hydro-electric power is being more and more utilized, and it is stated that three million horse power may ultimately be available. Large fertilizer plants and others for the production of newsprint have recently been started at Hobart. On the north coast is another large newsprint works at Burnie; while Bell Bay produces 13,000 tons of aluminium ingots a year. A new plant for the production of alloys is in production near Hobart.

Northern Territory

Uranium in notable amounts is obtained at Rum Jungle, and new plants to process the ore have been established nearby. South Alligator is another field farther east. There are large iron ore deposits on the Roper River, though they are of rather low quality. The rice-growing at Humpty Doo is progressing favourably; and an option on 500,000 acres has been taken with a view to extending this tropical industry.

Snowy Mountains Hydro-electric Scheme

Adaminaby Dam was finished in June 1957. The large artificial lake has been named Lake Eucumbene. The 14-mile Eucumbene–Tumut tunnel has also been completed, and the 283-feet-high Dam at Tumut Pond is now ready, and the power station in use.

CHAPTER XVII

SOME ISLANDS OF THE PACIFIC, WITH A BRIEF STUDY OF NEW ZEALAND

PART I

NEW GUINEA

IN the chapter on the structure of Australia we learnt that the character of the earth's crust in this part of the world changed greatly to the north and east of the continent. We pass from a region of great stability, or of gentle low warps, to a belt of some of the most profound crustal bucklings to be seen anywhere in the world. As is usual in such cases, volcanoes and frequent earthquakes are also widely distributed in this disturbed area.

As regards the region to the north, not only does it change remarkably in topography, but the climates are quite different also. Hence the resources have little resemblance to those in Australia, and the human population, always greatly affected by the environment, has different cultures and interests (Fig. 129).

New Guinea is about 1,500 miles long, and extends in an east-west direction in accord with the major crustal folds in this part of the world. The large island is divided into three provinces, of which the western is known as Dutch New Guinea. It contains 160,692 square miles, but does not come within the scope of this manual. The Territory of Papua in the south-east occupies 90,540 square miles; and the Mandate of New Guinea in the north-east contains 91,000 square miles. Both of these are controlled by Australia.

Yule, Owen Stanley, Moresby and others had mapped the coast of the eastern portion of the island (which was called indiscriminately Papua or New Guinea) before it was annexed by Britain or Germany in 1884. British Papua was a protectorate at first, but was converted into a Crown Colony in 1888, and in 1906 Papua was made a Territory of the Commonwealth of Australia.

The settlement of the northern portion of New Guinea began with a Wesleyan mission and two German trading stations in the islands to the east. In 1885 a German scientist, Dr. Finsch, explored the huge Sepik River. At the outbreak of the war an Australian naval party ascended this river for 350 miles. Rabaul

FIG. 129.—MAP OF BRITISH NEW GUINEA, SHOWING THE TERRITORY AND
THE MANDATE

Note the very shallow Torres Straits and the 'Planet' Deep. The north coasts are fringed by
volcanoes (V.V.)

(*Courtesy of Rand, McNally*)

was captured by the Australian troops, and in 1921 the mandated
territory of New Guinea was put under the control of the Commonwealth by the League of Nations.

Structure of New Guinea

Topographically the whole region consists of two parallel earth-
folds. The northern range extends eastwards from the Dutch
Territory along the north coast. It receives various names, such as
Torricelli Range, Hahl Range, &c.; and is cut across by the
estuaries of rivers like the Sepik. In the Hahl Range are peaks
about 13,000 feet high, and this fold continues eastwards, after a
considerable break, as the long mountainous island of New Britain.
It then perhaps curves to the north-west to form New Ireland.

The main range of New Guinea runs down the centre of the
larger island; and it reaches elevations of about 12,000 feet in the
Victor Emmanuel and Bismarck Ranges (Fig. 130). It continues
to the south-east as the Owen Stanley Range (13,000 feet), and
passes through various islands in the direction of distant New

Caledonia, which is probably part of the same arc of folding. The south-west portion of British New Guinea is a large area of lowland and delta watered by the huge Fly River.

David is of the opinion that the mountains of New Guinea are of the nature of horsts elevated since Cretaceous times. The central Alps seem to be built up with a core of ancient schists and slates; but some of the highest peaks are formed of crumpled Cretaceous limestones containing the foraminifera *Alveolina*. Near Mount Carstensz Rawlings discovered a precipice over 10,000 feet high, which may represent the faulted face of a horst. There seems to be a general level of the mountain tops in the east about 12,000 feet which suggests that this is a horst with the upper surface much dissected by river erosion (Fig. 130).

There seems to be a later peneplain cut in Tertiary rocks, and

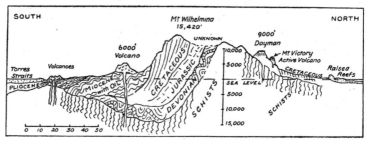

FIG. 130.—A SECTION ACROSS NEW GUINEA—SOMEWHAT SIMPLIFIED
(*After T. W. E. David*)

this has been covered with one or two thousand feet of volcanic tuffs and lavas in Pleistocene or Recent times. David sums up the major earth movements as follows: The overfolding of New Guinea has been directed, in the western half of the island from north to south; and in the eastern half from north-east to south-west. In a word, New Guinea has been overfolded towards Australia.[1]

Possibly the great arc of New Guinea may still be slowly moving to the south-west, so as to encounter the ancient fold-lines of Australia almost end-on. Slow earthfolding may be raising an 'embryonic range' between the northern outpost of Australia (which occurs in New Guinea as the block of Mabaduan granite), and the moving mass of Pre-Cambrian rock forming the Cordillera of New Guinea. David compares the wide plains of the Fly and Purari deltas with the plains of the Guadalquivir in Spain. These sediments are now being crushed against the massive shield of

[1] *Geology of the Commonwealth*, Federal Handbook, Sydney, 1914.

south-west Spain, to form an 'embryonic range' of the same type. (*Explanatory Notes*, Sydney, 1932.)

The schists are intruded by granites, diorites, and gabbros; and the gold and copper mines seem to be associated with these intrusions. The oil-belt is perhaps a continuation of the Burmese oil-belt, and is part of a vast delta-deposit containing many Miocene foraminifera. The oil strata have been exploited in the Purari region, 150 miles north-west of Port Moresby. The oil was discovered in 1911, and is associated with anticlinal arches in a bluish-grey mudstone, in which it occurs in yellowish-brown globules. It is of great interest that the Pliocene beds near Port Moresby have been strongly overfolded; whereas in Australia there is little sharp folding since Permian times. Mount Victory contains incandescent lava, and is 6,000 feet high (Fig. 130). It lies 120 miles due east of Port Moresby.

The large islands of New Ireland and New Britain seem to have much the same structure. There is a core of ancient schists and gneisses. The younger rocks seem to be mainly volcanic, or else Tertiary sediments. In New Ireland the surface rocks are largely Pleiocene or Pleistocene mudstones and sandstones like those found in Papua (Fig. 130). Many of these carry such numbers of foraminifera that they might in places be described as Pleistocene *Chalk*.

Volcanoes and Rivers

There are many volcanoes along the north coast of New Guinea, and in the numerous islands to the east. Thus there are three about 60 miles east of Aitape (Fig. 129). There are three more in the islands between the Sepik estuary and Madang. Nearly a dozen are to be found on the north coast of New Britain, including the remarkable example of Ritter Island in Dampier Strait. In 1888 this volcano exploded, lowering the island by many hundred feet. A wave 30 feet high was produced which destroyed many villages in New Britain.

In Willaumez Peninsula half-way along the north coast is one of the few geyser regions in the world (Fig. 129). It was a series of islands in 1879, but has become a peninsula since that date. The geysers appear to be situated on a fissure running east and west across the middle of the peninsula, and they erupt every few minutes. The main geyser has a crater 15 feet across and about 30 feet deep. For 10 acres around these geysers there are deposits of sinter rock on which no vegetation grows. At Rabaul, the capital of the Mandate, there are a number of active volcanoes, and there have been some serious eruptions in recent years.

The Fly River is the largest in New Guinea. Its mouth is 40 miles wide and is filled with low islands. In 1891 Sir William MacGregor ascended it for 600 miles, but found no rocks on the banks for the first 500 miles. In 1928 Karius crossed the main range from the Fly Basin to the Sepik Basin and succeeded in reaching the north coast.

The Sepik River is the second largest river, and is about 40 feet deep at its mouth. Here the river has a speed of about 3 knots, and does not build a delta. It is navigable for large steamers for 60 miles, and boats of 10 feet draught can ascend for 300 miles (Fig. 129). The Ramu River, east of the Sepik, is much smaller, but a boat drawing about 4 feet ascended it for 200 miles in 1921. In both these rivers the lower portions consist largely of swamps containing sago and nipa palms. There is much good timber and fertile land in the upper parts of these basins.

Climate of New Guinea

As usual with regions near the equator, the year may be divided into two seasons. From May to November is the South-East Trade Wind period; from December to April is that of the North-West Monsoon. The changes of the seasons last about six weeks and are marked by frequent thunderstorms. As a result of the rains and heat, the whole area is covered with thick vegetation, though for 50 miles each side of Port Moresby is the so-called Dry Belt. Here more than half the rain falls in the three months, January, February and March. The lowlands are largely swamps with meandering rivers or plains covered with coarse useless grass. At higher levels are slopes covered with pines where a more bracing climate prevails. The average temperature at sea level is about 80·2° F.; varying between 82·6° F. in December and 77·7° F. in August.

The rain regime is rather complex in Papua. Port Moresby on the south coast is protected from the Monsoons, yet this is the wettest period (Fig. 129). Samarai at the east end of Papua receives most of its rain in the Trade Wind period. Buna on the north coast has Monsoon rains; while the highlands in the interior have a fairly uniform rain regime but with a maximum in the Monsoon season.

In the mandated Territory conditions are much the same. There are only small differences of temperature through the year, and there is no cool or dry season. At Rabaul the Monsoon period is wetter than the Trade Wind period, but on the south coast of New Britain the opposite condition naturally obtains. Humidity is very high at Rabaul, the average for the year being 75·6 per cent.

At Madang conditions are worse; for the lowest monthly mean (in August) is 77 per cent; while the worst month is April, with a humidity of 83 per cent!

Natives of New Guinea

The ethnology of this corner of the Pacific is as complicated as in any part of the world. It lies on the margin of Asia, which con-

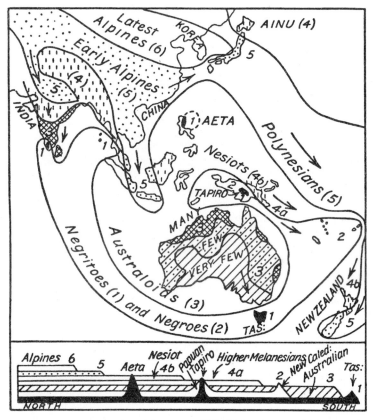

FIG. 131.—THE SIX MAJOR ZONES OF MIGRATION FROM SOUTH-EAST ASIA (MUCH GENERALIZED)

The Negritoes (1) moved out first. Then the Negroes (2), the Australoids (3), the higher Melanesians (4a), Nesiots (4b) and early Alpines (5). The section below shows the ethnological strata between central Asia and Tasmania. Note the 'inliers' of Tapiro and Aeta negritoes, and of negroes in Papua and New Caledonia. The distribution of aboriginals in Australia is indicated. (Races in Britain are akin to 4b)

tains the cradle-land of man. These high rugged islands with their thick jungles constitute ideal refuges for broken aboriginal tribes.

There seem to be relics of most of the main migrations from Asia, and these are arranged (as we should expect) so that the earliest most primitive types are 'pushed' furthest from the usual corridor of migration (Fig. 131). This latter was in general along the north coast of the great island. Hence we find many tribes of the tiny *Pygmies*, such as the Tapiro, living high up in the inland mountain regions. Below them on the southern side are the true *Negro* people with tall stature, frizzy hair and very narrow skulls. On the north coast and in the south-east are many tribes who seem to be nearer to the Nesiot (Indonesian) group. They are slighter and lighter coloured, and have broader skulls and narrower noses than the true Negroes. They constitute the so-called *Melanesians*, but nearly all of them seem to have enough Negro blood to produce frizzy hair. Last of all, on some of the smaller islands are colonies of the last migrations of broad-skulled *Alpine* folk with wavy to straight hair and of later 'Polynesian' culture.[1] (See also p. 458.)

Plantations

The cultivation of the yams, taro and coconuts needed by the natives for their food occupied only a small portion of their time, and they did not take kindly to the work of growing extra crops such as rice, coffee, cocoa, &c., in the plantations introduced by Europeans. However, by a system of indentured labour it has been found possible to develop a number of plantations of coconuts, rubber, &c. These plantations are almost all on the coast, and usually close to the various District Headquarters. In Papua there were about 11,000 such labourers in 1936.

The area of plantations in Papua has hardly changed in the last eighteen years. Today there are about 59,000 acres, of which 48,000 are in coconuts. Rubber prices fell after the war, and cotton, cocoa and coffee products find it hard to compete with similar goods grown with more dependable labour in other lands; so that many of these crops have been abandoned. The Commonwealth Navigation Act has blocked the direct trade with Britain and Germany, and this has also been a distinct handicap.

In the mandated Territory the Germans were progressing successfully with plantations and roads before the Great War; and this region has been more of a success commercially than Papua. In 1925 there were about 171,000 acres cultivated, and this has grown to 231,000 in 1936. Nearly all of this is devoted to coconuts. The number of indentured labourers is also much greater, being

[1] For a full discussion of the migrations of primitive folk in this complex region, see the writer's *Environment, Race and Migration* (1937), pp. 87–107.

37,000 in 1936. Two advantages possessed by the mandated territory are the remarkable success of the Wau Gold-field, and the
greater facilities of trade. German and British boats are allowed to
load cargoes at the ports of the territory of New Guinea.

PEOPLE AND RESOURCES OF THE TWO REGIONS IN 1954

	Papua	Mandate
White Population	6,313	11,442
Native Population	488,396	1,195,307
Copra exports	£883,000	£3,031,000
Rubber exports	£613,000	
Cocoa exports	£3,638	£246,000
Coffee exports	—	58,000
Cattle (both areas) (head)	7,522	—
Gold	£478,000	£1,409,000
Overseas vessels	131	173

Gold-fields in New Guinea

There have been many gold-mines worked in the two territories
since the first gold-rush to Port Moresby in 1877. In the islands
to the south-east a good deal of gold was won in the early days, in
the Louisiade group (1888) and in Woodlark Island (1896) (Fig.
129). In the main island the Yodda field, 50 miles east of Port
Moresby, has been worked for many years. Other mines in the
eastern part of Papua were discovered at Gira, Milne Bay and
up the Musa River. By 1916 the gold yield had amounted to
£1,436,249. Copper flourished for a time at Laloki near Port
Moresby, but the mines have been closed for some years.

The most spectacular development in New Guinea has been the
development of a very rich mining area on the backbone of the
island, largely owing to a unique flying service. The Wau Gold-
field is in the mandated territory (Fig. 132) about 180 miles NNW.
of Port Moresby. In 1922 miners found rich gold in the alluvials
of the upper Bulolo River, which is a southern tributary of the
Markham. In 1925 Salamaua became an important port, since
it was the nearest part of the coast to the new field. During
1926-7 over 3 tons of gold were sluiced in the small field on Edie
Creek.

In 1927 the first aeroplane arrived at Wau, and immediately
changed conditions tremendously. It could carry 600 lb. of cargo
and accomplish in two hours what had previously taken 250 carriers

six weeks. A year later metal Junker aeroplanes were busy conveying passengers and cargo over the precipitous gorges and thick jungle from Lae. Cattle were driven up the Buang valley, and sheep were carried to the field in aeroplanes.

In 1928 'Guinea Airways' claimed the world's record for heavy

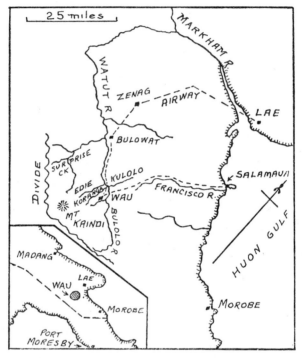

FIG. 132.—MAP OF THE WAU GOLD-FIELD, IN THE MOUNTAINS OF NEW GUINEA, REACHED BY AIR SERVICE FROM THE COAST. (SEE INSET)
(*After I. L. Idriess*)

cargoes, which included the 400-lb. cast-iron bed for a wireless station;[1] and in one month in 1931 581 tons was carried to the field, possibly more than all the other cargoes of the world in 12 months.[1] The parts of two dredges were flown in and placed in the lower valley of the Bulolo, where they recovered about £50,000 of gold per month. In June 1941 no less than 41 planes were in operation in this part of New Guinea.

[1] I. L. Idriess, *Gold Dust and Ashes*, Sydney, 1937.

PART II

SOME SMALL PACIFIC ISLANDS

Nauru

The Commonwealth administers Nauru, a coral island due north of the New Hebrides (longitude 166° E.), and 26 miles south of the equator (Fig. 133). It is oval in shape, and has an area of 5,600 acres, of which four-fifths are phosphate-bearing. Hence its importance. The structure of this island is very interesting, for the shape of the whole island irresistibly reminds one of a dented straw hat, the dent being the lagoon!

No doubt deep beneath the island is a core of rock probably of igneous origin, which originally was a small island on a subsiding sea-floor. Around this developed a fringing reef of coral, which grew upward as the rocky core sank. Gradually the core was completely covered by coral reef and coral debris. No doubt there was a central lagoon, giving rise to a ring-shaped island called an *atoll*. Later, elevation occurred and the whole islet was raised about 250 feet, so that now the atoll becomes an irregular plateau of coral rock. A raised coastal plain from 100 to 400 yards' wide surrounds the island, and some relic of the almost filled lagoon persists in the centre.

A heavy rainfall of 85 inches has carved this soft limestone into a myriad of pinnacles on which the sea birds perched. The bird guano has filled many of the hollows, and become converted into an almost insoluble phosphate rock. This is extremely valuable as fertilizer, and about four or five hundred thousand tons a year are exported. It is worth over £1 sterling per ton; and a royalty of 7½d. is paid to the natives for each ton mined. There are said to be 50 million tons on the island; and the phosphates are worked by a company which is also exploiting Ocean Island about 165 miles east of Nauru. The digging and loading is done by indentured labour, almost wholly Chinese. The population (1954) consists of 1,828 Nauruans (allied to the Micronesian peoples to the north-east), 550 Chinese, and 262 Europeans.

Norfolk Island

Norfolk Island lies about 900 miles to the east of Australia in the latitude of Brisbane, and in the same longitude as Invercargill in New Zealand. It has a somewhat oval shape (Fig. 133), being about 5 miles long and 3 miles wide. Inaccessible cliffs bound it except on the southern side, where the little settlement of Sydney

15

has grown up. The highest point is about 1,000 feet above the sea, and the interior is an undulating plateau with many picturesque grassy valleys bordered by the superb Norfolk Island pines (*Araucaria*). The average temperature is about 68° F., and there is a rainfall of 53 inches a year.

The island was discovered by Captain Cook in 1774, and was used as a convict settlement from 1788 to 1856. It is of interest that convicts from Norfolk Island helped to found New Norfolk

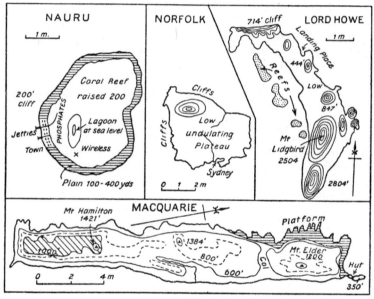

FIG. 133.—FOUR ISLAND DEPENDENCIES OF AUSTRALIA

in Tasmania in 1805. In 1856 about 200 descendants of the *Bounty* mutineers were brought to the island from Pitcairn Island far to the east. The Commonwealth Government took over the administration in 1914.

In 1954 the population was 942; and it subsists mainly on agriculture, though whaling and fish have been important interests in the past. The soil is fertile, and well suited for bananas, citrus fruits, &c. In recent years the growth of Canadian Wonder beans has been an important industry, as the island seed is in great demand. Oranges are exported to New Zealand, and there is an increase in the export of passion-fruit pulp. A considerable number of tourists visits the island from Australia and New Zealand.

Lord Howe Island

This crescent-shaped island lies 436 miles to the north-east of Sydney on the way to Norfolk Island. It is 7 miles long and about 1 mile wide, and is rapidly being eroded by the waves (Fig. 133). This is obvious from the shape of the 700-foot hill at the north, which has been cut in half by marine erosion. Numerous coral reefs fringe it on the west, and the best landing is on the north-east. The island is mainly built of basalt and allied volcanic rocks, and only about one-quarter of it is capable of cultivation. Mount Gower, 2,804 feet, is the highest point.

It was early visited by whalers, who killed off certain rare birds. The first settlement was in 1834. The early settlers cultivated maize, potatoes and onions, and the latter are exported. In 1869 there were 35 folk living on the island, and in 1954 the population was 278. It is administered as a dependency of New South Wales.

The island is covered with thick vegetation, in which are several beautiful genera of palms and tree-ferns. The top of Mount Gower is a veritable botanical museum, as several species of fern and moss are not found anywhere else in the world. There are 207 species of plants, of which 56 are endemic. The plants are akin to those found in Australia, but the shells seem to link it with New Zealand. *Porphyria*, a flightless bird, has vanished, and is only known from one skin in the Vienna Museum. The chief article of export is the seed of a dwarf palm (*Kentia* or *Howea*), of which as much as 4,000 bushels a year are sold to horticulturists all over the world.[1]

Macquarie Island

About 850 miles south-east of Tasmania, and administered by this state, lies the lonely island of Macquarie in latitude 55° S. It was discovered by Hasselborough in 1810, but has never been inhabited except by castaways, sealers and for a time by a Commonwealth Meteorological station founded by Mawson in 1910.

It resembles an elongated brick about 20 miles long and 3 miles wide. The island is placed almost directly athwart the 'Furious Fifties', which blow steadily from the west. Steep cliffs 600 to 800 feet high surround it on all sides. The upper surface of the 'brick' is an undulating plateau at a general level of 800 feet, though the southern end is all over 1,000 feet (Fig. 133). The highest point is Mount Hamilton (1,421 feet), about 5 miles from the south

[1] Stewart's *Handbook of the Pacific Isles*, published at intervals in Sydney, is the most comprehensive manual for all these little islands.

end. The island is mainly composed of igneous rocks. Gabbro is found at the north end, and 'pillow lava' also occurs.[1]

There are many small glacial tarns, and erratics and moraines are abundant. The climate resembles that of Iceland, and snow and rain occur frequently, but there is no permanent ice there in these times. The island is covered with tussock grass (*Poa foliosa*) and various bushy plants such as the 'cabbage' (*Stilbocarpa*), and is the haunt of innumerable birds. There are four species of penguins, and one of the rookeries of the Royal Penguins covers over 16 acres. Sea elephants are fairly abundant, and these and the penguins are killed and their oil extracted by visiting sealers.[2] The value of this southern station to weather forecasters in Australia and New Zealand is discussed in the writer's paper on Australian and Antarctic relations (*Problems of Polar Research*, 1928, New York).

PART III

SUMMARY OF NEW ZEALAND GEOGRAPHY

No description of the 'Australian Area' in its widest sense would be complete without some account of the neighbouring islands of New Zealand. They are in many ways complementary to Australia, since their structure and climate are very different from typical Australian conditions. They are linked to Australia by the fact that the settlers are of the same nation, but in New Zealand they are exploiting a country very much more like the homelands of Great Britain.

There are, however, several reasons why nothing but a *summary* of the geography of New Zealand can be given in this book. In the first place, while New Zealand seems to Europeans to be 'next door' to Australia, Wellington is four days away from Sydney by ordinary transport; and in point of fact is nearly as far away from Australia in accessibility as U.S.A. is from England. Secondly, New Zealand is a Dominion in every way separate from Australia in government, and inevitably moved by somewhat different interests. Thirdly, the region is remarkably diverse, and so full of interest that a complete volume is necessary to do it justice.

Structure of New Zealand

The group of three islands is about 1,000 miles long, and covers an area of about 100,000 square miles. It is thus somewhat smaller

[1] J. K. Davis, *Cruise of the Aurora*, London, 1919.
[2] D. Mawson, *Home of the Blizzard*, London, 1915.

than the British Isles, which have an area of 120,000 square miles. Reference to Fig. 9 will show that New Zealand is the summit of a crustal fold, lying between the Tonga-Kermadec Deep and the resistant shield of west Australia. Its flora and fauna differ remarkably from those of most parts of the world; but it seems likely that its last land links were to the north, with the folded 'festoon' islands of New Caledonia, New Hebrides and New Guinea, rather than with Australia.

The geological map is given in Fig. 134 at A.[1] This is much simplified, and is of the type known as a mantle-map. In these diagrams the edges of the formations are emphasized so as to give the effect of layers (or mantles) one above the other. Thus the oldest formations (1) are in the south, and constitute the core and western flanks of the high Alpine area all along the west coast of South Island. These Palaeozoic and older rocks, gneisses, &c., do not appear at the surface in North Island. Lying on the flanks of (1) is a vast series of younger beds (mainly Trias-Jura), which build up the north-east quarter of South Island. These rocks also appear in the core of the main Ruahiné Range in North Island, and again in the Paterson Range south of Auckland.

Perhaps the two northward projections of North Island may indicate a branching of the crustal folds, such as we see in the structure of the New Hebrides further north in the Pacific. Lying on the flanks of the Mesozoic rocks (2) we find Cretaceous and widespread Miocene formations in the North Island. The whole structure in general is what might result from a major earth-fold (geänticline), whose axis dips to the north. Possibly erosion has removed all the upper formations from the *high* southern end of the dipping geänticline, but they are still preserved in the lower northern portions in North Island.

The outstanding feature of New Zealand structure is the prevalence of volcanoes, recent folds, faults and earthquakes. All of these indicate very late mountain-building. Benson believes that very widespread block-faulting marked the 'Kaikoura Period' at the close of Tertiary times. These blocks were then elevated differentially, as shown in the section in Fig. 134 at A. Each block at this time consisted of a lower 'Oldermass' covered by the softer deposits of the 'Youngermass'. Subsequent erosion has cut away most of the projecting portions; but the river valleys often seem to have been carved in the softer formations, which before the faulting covered all the landscape. Many phases of uplift and subsidence have supervened. Enormous deposits, in the form of fans,

[1] *Geology of New Zealand*, James Park, Christchurch, 1910; *New Zealand Affairs*, 1929, Christchurch, for sociological data.

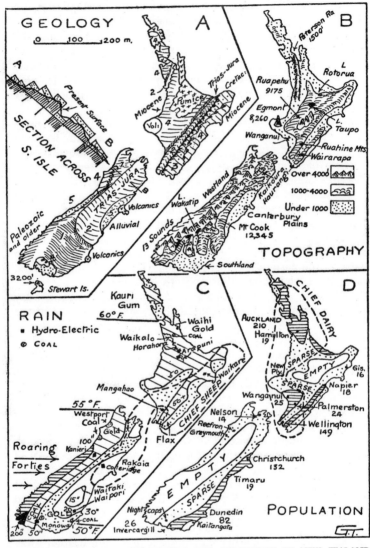

FIG. 134.—FOUR MAPS EPITOMIZING THE GEOGRAPHY OF NEW ZEALAND

A. Mantle-map to show geology and structure. Inset a section illustrating block-faulting, after Benson.
B. Topography.
C. Rain, temperature and chief hydro-electric sites. Sheep areas indicated.
D. Population. Figures show thousands in towns. Chief dairy area indicated.

have been laid down on the flanks of the mountains, and these are due in part to extensive glaciation.[1]

Volcanoes are most apparent in the North Island, but there are several extinct volcanic clusters in South Island. Thus the two prominent capes near Christchurch and Dunedin have such an origin. Egmont in North Island is a much larger example, and indeed is one of the most picturesque volcanic cones in the world. The active volcanoes lie along a plane of weakness running up the middle of North Island. They include Rua-pé-hu (9,175 feet), Ngaurohoe ('Nore-ahoy') and Tongariro. Tarawera near Lake Rotorua exploded in 1886, and completely changed the landscape in the vicinity. It produced several Hot Lakes; and geyser action is very vigorous in this area, as well as south near Lake Taupo (Fig. 134 at B). Widespread areas of sterile volcanic ash and pumice surround Rotorua.[2]

The Southern Alps culminate in Mount Cook (12,345 feet). They offer a long high barrier to the 'Roaring Forties'; so that falls of rain and snow are naturally very heavy, amounting to well over 100 inches a year. Hence this is a remarkable region for glaciers, and the Tasman Glacier is 18 miles long, and one of the largest in the Temperate Zone. Indeed, the climatic conditions are excellent for glacial erosion, and the writer has seen no region where more debris is being carried along by glaciers.

In the extreme south many of the peaks rise to a height of about 5,000 feet, which probably indicates the surface of a broad warp in an earlier geological period. Hereabouts the Haast Pass through the highlands is 1,800 feet high. In the central higher region, near Mount Cook, are many peaks over 10,000 feet; and here the Fitz-gerald Pass is 7,000 feet. Still further north the mountains are lower again, and Arthur's Pass is crossed by a main road linking Christchurch to Greymouth.

In the North Island there are two parallel ranges in the south-east, the Ruahiné (6,000 feet), and Haurangi (3,000); with the fertile Wairarapa valley between, which leads from Wellington to Napier. The former range extends under various names right to East Cape. The Paterson Range and the Coromandel Range (3,000) run each side of the Hauraki Gulf. There has been extensive sub-sidence in the centre of the North Island, which in part accounts for Lake Taupo.

The two chief rivers in North Island rise near Lake Taupo. The Waikato flows out of the lake and then bends to the north-west. It passes through the fertile Waikato Plains, and enters the

---

[1] *Geomorphology of New Zealand*, C. A. Cotton, Wellington, 1922.
[2] *Geography of New Zealand*, P. Marshall, Christchurch, n.d.

sea south of Auckland after a course of 270 miles. The Wanganui flows south into Cook Straits, and has cut a deep gorge in the lower part of its course. In the South Island the Clutha River is 154 miles long, and is the largest river. It rises in Lake Wanaka, one of the largest of the 'Cold Lakes'. In its middle course there has been much dredging for gold.

The rivers in the east, such as the Waima-kariri, issue from glacier-cut troughs in the mountains, and cross the wide gravelly Canterbury Plains by ever-varying channels. The south part of the Alps receives the most rain and snow. In the Ice Ages the enormous glaciers gouged out troughs on each side of the range. In the east such deep valleys, dammed by huge terminal moraines, explain the series of large 'Cold Lakes' in this position (Fig. 134 at B). Te Anau, Wakatip and Wanaka are the largest. On the western slopes the glacial valleys were eroded below sea level. Today these valleys are occupied by the sea, and constitute the picturesque sounds or fiords. Of these the most northerly, Milford Sound, is the best known.

Climate of New Zealand

The average isotherms are indicated at C in Fig. 134. Thus the line for 60° F. passes through Auckland, 55° F. through Wellington, and 50° F. through Invercargill. These three places have the same averages as Oporto, Bordeaux and London, which, however, are in considerably higher latitudes. Hence New Zealand is cooler than its latitude would lead one to expect. In a lengthy research of some years ago the writer came to the conclusion that much of New Zealand approaches close to the *optimum* climate as far as Western Europeans are concerned.

The rainfall is nowhere too little, though the south-west corner is too wet and cold for close settlement. In the North Island almost every portion has about 50 inches a year. The rapid change from 200 inches in the south-west corner to 15 inches further east is an excellent illustration of a rain-shadow due to the Alps (Fig. 134 at C). The rainfall usually shows a maximum in the winter, the peak occurring a little later as one progresses north. Thus May is the wettest month in Dunedin, June in Christchurch, and July in Wellington and Auckland.

Two-thirds of the indigenous plants are absolutely confined to New Zealand, a condition hardly to be paralleled for any land of equal size. No species of the universal Australian trees, the eucalypts or acacias, is native. The most abundant trees are conifers allied to Malayan types. Of these the kauri (*Agathis*) is the best known. Some of the most characteristic genera are *Coprosma*,

Olearia, Aciphylla and *Celmisia*. On the other hand a number of plants are allied to those of South America, such as the beeches and fuchsias. A very abundant shrub is Mà-nuka (*Leptospermum*), which is allied to the Australian 'tea-trees'. *Persoonia* and *Epacris* are also genera found in Australia.

The natives (Maoris) found no satisfactory edible plants, and subsisted on sweet potato, taro and yam which they brought from the northern islands.

Brief History of Settlement

New Zealand was discovered by Tasman in 1642, and was used as a rendezvous by Cook on several of his voyages from 1769 to 1776 (Fig. 8). Trade began in 1792 with a sealing expedition from Sydney. The first missionaries settled at Russell in the far north in 1814. The kauri timber near Auckland soon attracted attention, and whaling sometimes brought as many as 100 ships to these waters about 1820. A few whales are still caught, but the trade on a large scale has long since died out. A peculiar trade in mummified tattooed heads went on with the Maoris for some decades in the early days!

In 1840 the islands were annexed by Britain, and Captain Hobson was sent out to Auckland. Settlement soon took place at Wellington in 1840, at Dunedin in 1848, and at Canterbury in 1850. The two latter groups were associated with the Scottish and Anglican Churches. It is remarkable that settlement was mainly in the North Island at first, in spite of the heavy forests and the warlike Maoris. The open Canterbury Plains, in which few Maoris dwelt, were neglected, although excellent for sheep and wheat.[1]

The gold rushes in Australia in the 'fifties stimulated exports from New Zealand, such as flour from Auckland. Some wool had already been sent home from Wellington, and a good deal of the native flax *Phormium* from the same area. This fibre is from the leaves of a peculiar lily, and was collected by the Maoris. So also there was some trade in kauri gum, a fossil resin from near Auckland. Coal was first mined about this time from Whangarei, north of Auckland.

During the 'sixties gold was found in payable quantities in the Upper Clutha Valley in the far south, in Westland near Reefton, and later in North Island in the Thames and Coromandel districts. Waihi, 70 miles south-east of Auckland, has since been the chief producer, and in 1871 3 million sterling had been won in this district. (Fig. 134 at C and D).

[1] Based on an excellent paper by J. Henderson in *N.Z. Journ. Science*, Wellington, 1923.

A valuable industry developed in 1871 when wheat was first exported from the Canterbury Plains. This export reached its zenith in 1883; but the growth of railways in U.S.A. gave great advantages to American wheat, and the local export declined. The railway period began in the 'seventies, and much money was invested in various factories, especially woollen mills and iron foundries in the south. Pastoral products such as tallow and hides grew rapidly in importance, and the first frozen meat was sent away in 1882. As Henderson states, 'the fitting of refrigerating machinery to deep-sea ships has changed the whole course of economic developments in New Zealand'.

Today pastoral and dairy products are the most important, and since the North Island has a milder climate and is less rugged, it has the lead in these industries. Henderson points out that the exports are usually in a simple unprocessed condition, since labour is dear and manufacturing not advanced. Thus wool is sent away unscoured, and wheat unmilled. However, some types of secondary industry, linked closely to agriculture, have expanded of late years. Among these are the manufacture of engines, farm implements, windmills, fertilizers, &c. Mining for metals has gradually declined in importance, but coal-mining has progressed considerably. Gold to the value of 1·4 millions sterling was obtained in 1936 chiefly from Waihi and Reefton. Twenty-one dredges are working on the Clutha River and elsewhere. The coal output was worth 2 millions sterling. Very good bituminous coal occurs at Greymouth and Westport (S.I.). Brown coal comes from Kaitangata near Dunedin. Miocene coals occur at Nightcaps in the extreme south, and in the Waikato basin near Auckland (Fig. 134 at C). The Taranaki oil-field has produced 2 million gallons of oil, but is not of much commercial importance.

The agricultural lands have now all been occupied, and though very large areas of rugged country remain, they will pay best if left as forest reserves. The Pumice country in North Island is level, well-watered, and has an ideal climate. But the soil is extraordinarily deficient in plant foods, and only pine plantations seem to prosper. In New Zealand, as in Australia, we may conclude that food production can only be markedly increased by the more intensive cultivation of lands already occupied. However, much rich land used for sheep can be more profitably used for dairy produce, and no doubt secondary industries will expand in the near future.

We may readily obtain an idea of the resources of the Dominion, and of their relative importance, from the following table, which shows how the exports have varied during the last forty years. Figures indicate million pounds sterling.

EXPORTS DURING THE PERIOD 1907 TO 1947

Product	1907	1916	1926	1936	1947
Butter	1·6	2·6	8·7	15·3	28·8
Wool	7·6	12·4	11·8	13·3	31·9
Frozen meat	3·4	7·2	8·6	13·2	29·2
Cheese	0·6	3·5	5·9	5·1	11·6
Skins	0·2	0·9	0·8	3·3	—
Gold	2·0	1·2	—	1·4	1·0
Sausage-skins	0·06	0·2	0·8	0·6	1·5
Tallow	0·6	0·7	0·8	0·6	2·3
Seeds	—	—	—	—	1·6

The Pastoral Industry

With butter, wool, and frozen meat by far the most important exports, it is clear that the pastoral products are of much more importance than any cereals. Indeed, New Zealand barely grows enough wheat for its own consumption, and there is frequently some import. As regards stock, dairy cattle are grazed much more abundantly in the North Island, especially along the Waikato River and near Auckland. Wellington is the second dairy area, while Taranaki and Hawke's Bay are much less important. The distribution of the dense dairy areas is given in Fig. 134 at D, and includes most parts of the North Island except the centre and west. There are about 4·4 million cattle in New Zealand, and the Jersey is the dominant breed, but Shorthorn and Hereford are well represented. Butter factories total 469, and are scattered throughout the Dominion, except in the areas labelled 'empty' in Fig. 134 at D. The regions for grazing *beef* cattle are to be found around Wellington, Gisborne and Napier.

The distribution of sheep in the Dominion is rather different. The Merino is grown most successfully in the downs of Canterbury; and most of the New Zealand mutton and lamb is derived from crossbreds between Merino ewes and Lincoln rams. In the North Island, which is somewhat wetter than Canterbury, the Romney Marsh breed is popular. There are about 31 million sheep in New Zealand, and of these about 17 million are in the North Island and 14 million in the South Island. Romney Marsh is the most numerous of the types of sheep, and then come the Merino and Corriedale. Reference to the map, Fig. 134 at C, shows that the sheep are largely confined to the drier eastern coasts of the two larger islands.

Agriculture

Cereals, fruit, &c., are of secondary importance in the Dominion, and the chief crops are largely concerned with extra food for stock. Although barns for winter shelter are almost unknown, yet it is advisable to make provision for winter feeding in the form of turnips, mangolds, lucerne, &c. Immense areas, amounting to 17 million acres, have been sown with English grass to improve the normal grazing. Oats are largely grown, especially in the southern part of the Dominion; but most of the crops are cut green for stock.

In the Canterbury Plains is an area 150 miles long and 40 miles broad, which is the chief grain belt in New Zealand; and very high yields up to 90 and 100 bushels have been obtained from wheat and oats grown in the South Island. The average for the whole wheat area is high, amounting to 32 bushels per acre.

CROPS IN 1936 AND 1947–8

		1936	1947–8
1	Sown Grass	504,000 acres	700,000 acres
2	Turnips	431,000 ,,	400,000 ,,
3	Oats	315,000 ,,	177,000 ,,
4	Wheat	224,000 ,,	125,000 ,,

Most of these crops have expanded little during the last ten years; indeed there has been a decline in wheat and oats.

Fruit-growing is practised widely, though not much but apples is exported. Grape-fruit and passion fruit grow well near Auckland. Nelson is noted for apples (and tobacco), while apricots flourish as far south as Dunedin. Apples, peaches and pears are the most numerous fruit-trees. About 65,000 acres of *Phormium* are grown, and the fibre largely used for rope-making.

Hydro-Electric Projects [1]

The combination of high mountains and heavy rainfall favours a plentiful supply of hydro-electric power. This is distributed all over the settled parts of the islands, and is much used for machinery in the dairy industry (Fig. 134 at C). There are nine large plants in New Zealand, as in the table on page 439.

[1] *Hydro-Electric Development in New Zealand*, L. Birks, Public Works, Wellington, 1925.

The total population of the Dominion in 1937 was 1,587,000. Nearly all of these are of British descent with the exception of 68,670 Maoris. Of the latter about 45,000 are full-blood, while 6,000 are three-quarter caste, 11,000 are half-caste, and about 6,000 are quarter-caste. In the last decade the number of Maoris

ELECTRIC POWER IN 1948

Site	Town (near)	Kilo-watts*	Use
Arapuni Falls	Putaruru	157,000	General, mining
Karapiro and Horahora Falls	Cambridge	90,000	General, freezing, paper
Mangahao (1925)	Shannon	19,000	—
Waikere-moana (1929)	Gisborne	124,000	General, flour
Lake Coleridge	Christchurch	34,000	—
Waitaki (new)	Oamaru	75,000	—
Lake Monowai	Nightcaps	6,000	—
Cobb River	Nelson	12,000	—
High Bank	—	25,000	—

* One horse-power is three-quarters of a kilowatt.

is increasing, but it is inevitable that this interesting group of aboriginal peoples will merge ultimately with the more abundant European population. Their high biological position is suggested in Fig. 131; for they are relatively late migrants from Asia.

AUSTRALIAN ANTARCTICA

In August 1936 a vast territory of some 2½ million square miles passed under the control of Australia. This is Australian Antarctica, almost half of the icy continent to the south of Australia. It lies between longitudes 45° E. and 160° E. It is only about 1,600 miles away, so that a voyage from Hobart to Adelie Land is shorter than one to Cooktown in north Queensland.

Bransfield discovered the new continent to the south of Cape Horn in January 1820; but Biscoe first saw part of Australian Antarctica at Cape Ann in 1831. This is some 400 miles to the west of the present site of 'Mawson'. Armitage, in January 1903, first explored part of the Australian territory up the Taylor Glacier (in lat. 77° S.), while Scott traversed nearly 200 miles of the adjacent icy plateau later in the year. Shackleton's route towards the South Pole in 1908–9 followed the boundary (long. 160° E.)

between the Australian and British sectors. David, in 1909, discovered the South Magnetic Pole, which is well within Australian Territory near latitude 73° S. Mawson's first expedition (1911) explored much of the eastern coastlands, while in 1929–30 he surveyed the western coasts as far west as Enderby Land. The Commonwealth has maintained two stations in recent years; 'Mawson' since 1954 and 'Davis' (Vestfold Hills) since 1956.

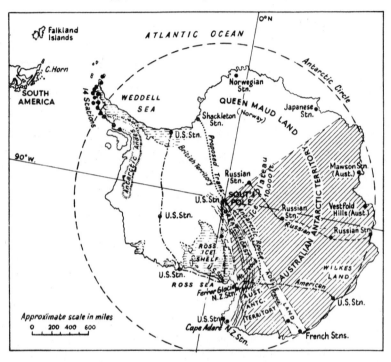

FIG. 134A.—MAP OF ANTARCTICA

Proposed stations in the International Geophysical Year manned by ten nations. Some have already been manned for several years.

The Australian sector is bounded on the north by the curved coastline, which runs close to the Antarctic Circle (lat. 66½° S.). Most of it appears to be a vast icy plateau, rising to 10,000 feet near the Pole. However, recent soundings show that much of this elevation may consist of ice, for the crust under the ice-cap is perhaps 5,000 feet *below* sea level in Marie Byrd Land (long. 150° W.).

Apart from whaling in adjacent oceans the area offers few

economic resources; but has the hundreds of investigators in the Geophysical Year show, many of the problems in magnetism, cosmic rays, radio work, aurora, world meteorology, zoological distributions, glaciology, etc., can only be answered in the Antarctic.

Two new stations have been manned in the Australian sector. One is for weather and aurora observations, and is 60 miles west of Mawson near a large emperor-penguin colony. It has been named 'Taylor' after the first Commonwealth officer to explore Australia. The second is at 'Wilkes', which was handed over to Australian care in 1959 by the retiring American scientists.

CHAPTER XVIII

CONDITIONS AFFECTING TROPICAL SETTLEMENT IN AUSTRALIA

IN 1918 the writer published a lengthy study of the conditions affecting Tropical Settlement in Australia in the *Queensland Geographical Journal*. It was reprinted in the American *Geographical Review* for August 1919. It will be of interest to see how the problem looked twenty years ago, and then to summarize what we have learnt, and what progress has been made, since 1918.

The American editor (in 1919) wrote the following introduction to the paper:

To the politician who makes a flying visit to tropical Australia in the most favorable time of the year there appears to be 'no reason why a thriving white population should not fill the tropical areas'. The government official, usually engaged in promoting some branch of industry, has his accounts buried beneath a mass of advertising literature. It is useless to consult the squatter living wholly out-of-doors, and following the most healthful occupation in the world; his opinion is valuable only as regards the conditions of pastoral life. In view of these difficulties it might not be amiss to study the facts comparatively and in a scientific spirit. What is tropical Australia? Will it support a large white population? What are the experiences of whites in similar climates elsewhere?

Tropical Australia is divided politically among the three divisions of Queensland, the Northern Territory and West Australia, and constitutes 38·6 per cent of the area of the Commonwealth. The areas of the tropical lands and the percentages of population in the tropics in 1915 and 1935 are given in the following table. In 1935 the total tropical population was 193,000, and it occupied an area of over 1 million square miles. Of these thousands about 96 per cent lived in tropical Queensland. Indeed a tremendous

AREAS AND POPULATIONS IN TROPICAL LANDS

State	Area	In tropics	%	Population, 1915	Tropics	%	1935	Tropics	%
Queensland	670,500	359,000	54	677,000	160,000	24	972,000	185,000	19
N. Territory	523,600	426,000	81	4,500	4,200	90	5,138	4,870	95
West Australia	975,900	364,000	37	323,000	5,000	1·5	448,000	3,324	0·7

majority live right along the 'Sugar Coast'; and a moment's inspection of the distributions shows that simple control by temperature is by no means the main part of the problem.

Salient Features of Tropical Environment

Many of the details have been fully discussed in earlier parts of the book; but it will be convenient to summarize the salient features in one group of maps. The topography of the tropical lands is simple (Fig. 135 at A). The highest land in the west and centre is along the tropics, and only exceeds 2,000 feet in the Hammersley Plateau and in the Macdonnells. The effect of the Geo-syncline is obvious in the map; and the gap between the Murray Basin and the Gulf of Carpentaria may be called the 'Kynuna Gate'. In the east the Atherton Tableland is obvious, but not much of the rest exceeds 1,000 feet in elevation.

The average temperatures are also shown in the same map. Wyndham has an average of 85° F. and is one of the hottest places in the world (p. 53). All the north coast is over 80° F., and here (on the coast) is where all the population of any density lives; so that their environment is as hot as most tropical settlements. The upland character of the interior ameliorates the temperature a little, but unfortunately this region is so dry that no close settlement is possible. However, the constant south-east Trade Winds improve conditions on the east coast.

The total rainfall has been fully discussed earlier (p. 62). The uniformity of a rainfall is a very vital factor, as I showed before 1917. In Fig. 135 at B I adopt as a criterion for uniformity a rain regime where *each month has one inch* or more of rain. Places are classified according to the number of months with this condition, and the figures are plotted on Fig. 135 at B. The small area in the south-east is the only portion to have *eight* months with an inch of rain in each month. This is cross-ruled, and is the sole tropical area with a fairly *uniform* rainfall.

The question of comfort is a very important one in the tropics. This is stressed in Fig. 135 at C, where the humidity in the hottest month (January) is charted. It is seen that almost all the towns in the tropics, of which the chief are Broome, Wyndham, Darwin, Thursday Island, Cairns, Townsville and Mackay, have a relative humidity over 70 per cent. This, coupled with the high temperature (all near 80° F. as shown in Fig. 135), means very uncomfortable muggy conditions for dwellers on the coasts. Conditions in the interior of Queensland and the Territory are not so bad in this respect, for here the humidity is only about 50 per cent.

In the last map in the series (Fig. 135 at D) I showed in 1917 the

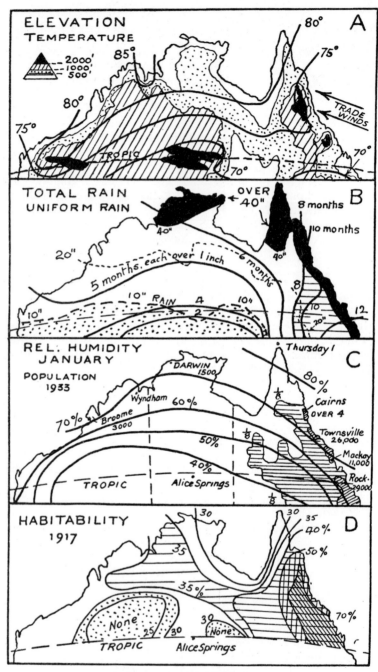

FIG. 135.—SALIENT FEATURES IN TROPICAL AUSTRALIA

All (except 1933 population) from the paper of 1917

way in which the population must spread. I classified the districts
according to certain advantageous controls, which may be studied
in the original paper (Brisbane, 1918), and showed that the south-
east corner near Rockhampton had 70 per cent of these advantages,
and that they fell off as we reached the desert lands in the west. It
will be seen from the data plotted in Fig. 135 at C that population
is spreading very much as I forecasted. It clusters along the east
coast, where there are patches with over four people per square
mile. It falls off very rapidly, so that the *one per square mile* line is
not shown hereabouts in the official map. The next isopleth
charted is the low one of *one person per 8 square miles*, which is
indicated by the fraction *one-eighth* in the map. It can readily be
seen that if the population on the *coast* of east Queensland were
removed there would be very little left in tropical Australia, in spite
of the attempts for more than a century to colonize the tropics.

Some Political and Social Aspects

The writer believes that the white man can settle in any part of
the world provided that sufficient precautions are taken to counteract the natural disabilities, and provided that the advantages
(economic or otherwise) are enough to attract him to the place. In
the northern coast-lands of Australia average folk can live satisfactorily only if they take unusual care with their health, diet,
housing, methods of exercise, hours of work, &c. Since it is beyond
cavil that the character of the climate is the main reason why the
settler must take all these extra precautions, it is clear that the
average immigrant will prefer to find a job in the non-tropical parts
of the continent, until the latter is so far saturated with population
that the pressure to go elsewhere is much greater than at present.
In other words, the comfort factor and the economic factor have
kept people out of northern Australia. In 1954 there were 16,452
Europeans, 325 Chinese, 1,955 half-castes and 13,744 full-blood
aborigines in the Territory.

POPULATION IN THE NORTHERN TERRITORY (EXCLUDING ABORIGINES)
(estimated only, in early years)

	1879	1890	1900	1910	1921	1933	1940	1947
Total	3,400	4,900	4,800	3,301	4,000	4,818	8,977	10,868
European	400	1,159	1,000	—	2,500	3,306	—	9,116

[1] *Northern Territory*, Grenfell Price, Adelaide, 1930.
Population in 1957 was 19,170, as well as about 16,000 full-blood
aborigines.

It is true that the population is increasing along the 'Sugar Coast', but this is because it is an unusually well-endowed portion of Australia's tropics. No student of climatology would use the settlement in the *uniform-rain* region of east Queensland as a conclusive argument in favour of close settlement of the 1,600 miles of coast-lands which extend from Cooktown to Geraldton.

A politician who starts off with the naïve belief that there can be no part of his native land too dry or too hot for settlement, and who furthermore is convinced of the necessity for a White Australia, is bound to disapprove of the teachings of climatology and anthropology. He will waste enormous sums on attempts to develop the desert and the tropics, while withholding aid needed for the intensive settlement of lands in the south. He will stoutly maintain that Australian arid lands differ from other folks' deserts, and that the Australian tropical lands are higher or cooler or more fertile that those of other countries. He will justify his policy of exclusion by appeals for racial purity, though history teaches us that Athens, Rome, Paris and London grew up where two distinct races, perhaps as diverse as those of Britain and China, met and mingled in earlier centuries.

For twenty years the present writer endeavoured to inform the Australian public in regard to these important aspects of settlement. He stoutly maintained that it was useless to try and fill up the arid and more northern tropic lands as long as there was better land not fully utilized in the south and east. The argument holds good today. Excellent work has been done by the Government by supporting schools of research in medicine, agriculture, &c., in these difficult areas. Unfortunately this support is rarely persistent. For instance, the closing of the Townsville School of Tropical Medicine seems very short-sighted. But the geographer realizes that the environment does not change, and all the applied science in the world cannot turn a sow's ear into a silk purse!

There is one new factor which I discussed many years ago, and may refer to here; the question of *'central cooling'*. It would perhaps have seemed impossible to folk in Britain in A.D. 1600 that a prosperous civilization of 10 millions should develop in a land where artificial *heating* of the whole house is necessary for around six months of the year. (In Toronto my house is heated every month except June, July, August and September.) Perhaps in the near future we shall find all the prosperous homes in the tropics with central cooling. There is a well-known type of cooling plant, based like most such on the cooling due to the expansion of gases, in which a small source of heat from gas or oil, &c., supplies all the energy required to expand the gas and produce the refrigeration. It should be possible to cool a bedroom down to 60° F. without undue cost with some such plant. Personal experience in many tropic lands has shown me that it is the hot sticky restless nights which sap the energy and health of white folk in the tropics. It will perhaps be a long while before the *poor* settler can afford central cooling; but like cars and radio, such apparatus will become relatively cheap when the demand is world-wide.

My research on tropical problems, beginning in 1906, may be described as one long period of continuous disillusionment. First one found that there were no luxurious forests; there never are, where a period of six months' absolute drought obtains. Next I found that the soils in the coast-lands, where alone the rainfall is abundant, are as a whole unusually poor. Many of the rivers in their lower reaches are occupied by the sea in their dry season, though heavy floods sweep down in the summer. The Tropic of Capricorn is, unfortunately, a rational climatic boundary, for the tropical coast-lands are as hot as any tropics in the same latitude, except perhaps the Sahara. There is no region in the same latitudes with such paucity of elevated land, even the Sahara having wide plateaux, whereas Australia has only the small Atherton Tableland. The so-called Barkly Tableland is barely 1,000 feet above sea level.[1]

Health in the Tropics

It is gratifying that the vital statistics of tropical Australia show it to rank very favourably among such regions. As I have pointed out, the data are few in number, and as regards the agricultural regions of the tropics the population considered is only about 120,000. Personally I fear the value of these figures depends entirely on the character of this small percentage of people. Are they typical of Australia, or do they contain larger proportions of men in the prime of life, and fewer invalids, old folk and children than in the cooler parts of Australia? It is difficult to get exact figures. In 1921 the masculinity of tropical Queensland was about 114 (i.e. per 100 women), while that of all Australia was 101. The percentage of women over 50 was 11·6 in tropical Queensland as contrasted with 15·5 in the whole continent. Women of the chief child-bearing age (20 to 30) were 35·4 per cent in the tropics and 29·5 in the rest. Naturally the births per thousand are high in the tropics since the proportion of mothers is high. The infant mortality is better than in the rest of Australia. I discuss later the higher death rates for men and women.

[1] Much of the data in this chapter is expanded from the section on Tropical Settlement in my book *Environment, Race and Migration*, published by the University of Toronto Press in 1937.

Optimists often quote the data collected at the Medical Congress on Tropical Settlement in Brisbane in 1920. But if the official report in the *Medical Journal* (Sydney, September 18th, 1920) be consulted, it will be found that of the sixteen doctors whose opinions are quoted at length eight pointed out grave disadvantages which were directly due to the climate. For instance, Dr. T. A. Nisbet, a physician with thirty-one years' experience in north Queensland, stated: 'The death rate of north Queensland was one of the lowest in the world; but the ever-present desire of the inhabitants to get away from the north during the autumn of their lives kept the death rate low.' Dr. Macleod stated that the climate was a nasty one, and that it was the hardest thing in the world to get men from cold climates to adopt the customs which the climate dictated. Dr. Priestley gave it as his opinion that the women had a very hard time in the tropics, for they had to stay at home while the men could get out. The kitchens were truly awful. The climate was uncomfortable, and if a man could earn the same wages in a favourable climate he would not stay in the tropics. Dr. Paton of Broome said that the women and children suffered. For the first two years the children were the happiest and healthiest they could see. But from the age of three up to seven they shot up rapidly and became anaemic, and unless they went for a change of air they grew up weedy. Dr. Paton spoke of the tragedy that hung over a woman's life when isolated in the tropics, in that they could not get domestic labour. Dr. Mabel Murray Prior suggested that the reason why the infantile mortality was lower than in the south was because there were no slums in the north, and many women went south before their babies were born. These quotations will at least show that responsible physicians see many reasons why white settlement in the tropics is likely to be a very slow and difficult process.

It will be of interest to study the conclusions of Sir Raphael Cilento, a Government medical official, who takes what seems to the writer to be an unduly optimistic view of the problem. He has written a lengthy pamphlet, 'The White Man in the Tropics', Melbourne, 1925, which is full of valuable data on the medical side, though the climatology leaves something to be desired. His slogan is 'that the most outstanding fact in the world's history is disease and its distribution'. He believes that all the arguments put forward by Ellsworth Huntington and others can be explained in terms of tropical disease, which he expects to be abolished some time in the future. Dr. Cilento realizes the distinction between the *dry* tropics (between 12 and 23 degrees of latitude) and the *wet* tropics near the Equator; but it is a pity that he seems to be unaware of the numerous publications of the present writer dealing with climatic control in the Australian tropics. For instance, he has not grasped the important fact that *comfort* and *crops* are in a sense antagonistic in the *dry* tropics, which is the type we find in three-quarters of tropic Australia. He complains that travellers judge the tropics by a few muggy days which they spend in a *coastal* town, 'which cannot be taken as a criterion of life in a tropical climate'. Unfortunately it is only near these same coastal towns that the rainfall is enough to ensure crops. It is regrettable that the lack of comfort is due to the same relatively high humidity. Inland the comfort is greater, but so also is the lack of rainfall.

It is absurd of Dr. Cilento to say that tropical Australia is cooler than other continental areas in the Southern Hemisphere. Most of South Africa is above 2,000 feet, while only about 2 per cent of tropical Australia is above this elevation. The tropics in South America are almost wholly below 80° F. in January, while those of Australia are all over 80° F. in this month.

The physiological data given by Cilento are worthy of attention. He states that a black skin absorbs heat more readily and loses it more readily than a white skin; hence the Negro's body is raised more readily to the sweating-point, and so to the relief experienced at that stage. He sweats much more evenly and easily, which is a distinct advantage. The normal fairly tight clothes of cool lands are an absurdity in the tropics, and one can agree with every word written by Cilento on this topic.

The sallowness of tropical settlers is due in his opinion to a thickening of the skin, and has no relation to anaemia. Sundstroem found a definite deficiency of the normal phosphorus contents of the blood as a result of living in the tropics; and a definite alkalosis of the blood which produced the easy fatigue and depression of the tropics. This latter condition tended to be neutralized by hard physical work. Cilento thinks that neurasthenia is due to lazy habits and lack of interesting congenial work. It was found that among Townsville patients, a charwoman was least affected by neurasthenia, while a sedentary girl stenographer was worst affected. Sundstroem makes the interesting observation that the hair of Australians is gradually becoming darker.

Cilento goes on to describe the fair folk who are descended from the Dutch garrison of Kisar near Timor. These have bred for five or six generations, and are now about 300 in number. He believes there is nothing in their history to show that a tropical climate *per se* has tended to produce degeneration or to limit fertility. Similar data come from Saba, a long-continued Dutch settlement in the West Indies.

The death rates for Queensland and for Australia are given in the following table for varying ages. They indicate to my mind that the much hotter conditions in the northern state have affected the rate adversely, except in the earliest years.

DEATH RATE PER THOUSAND—1920-2

(top line gives ages)

	0–4	5–9	10–14	15–19	20–24	25–29	30–34
Men: Q.	20·7	1·96	1·58	2·90	3·54	4·37	4·58
Aus.	21·6	2·02	1·59	2·30	3·10	3·70	4·16
Women: Q.	16·1	1·89	1·43	1·99	2·81	3·61	4·11
Aus.	17·1	1·82	1·27	1·90	2·75	3·59	4·06

	35–39	40–44	45–49	50–54	55–59	60–64	65–69
Men: Q.	5·95	7·86	10·60	14·23	20·34	30·36	44·93
Aus.	5·48	6·89	9·91	12·90	19·04	28·71	43·74
Women: Q.	5·80	6·03	6·76	9·11	13·60	19·71	30·81
Aus.	5·00	5·51	6·87	9·27	12·92	19·05	31·76

Breinl shows that in the hottest part of the year in north Queensland the efficiency of wharf labourers is reduced by 11 per cent, which is surely no advertisement for living in the tropics. Cilento believes that a special 'tropical Australian' is developing. He is tall and rangy with somewhat sharp features and long arms and legs. He is not lacking in muscular strength, while his endurance is equal in his own circumstances to that of the temperate dweller in his. The north Queenslander moves slowly, and conserves his muscular heat-producing energy in every possible way. One can pick him out in the streets by the fact that he walks more deliberately. The hair colour is darkening, and there is a pallor of the skin which has been referred to previously.

Cilento nowhere answers Huntington's statement that the age-constitution of tropical settlers is different from that in cooler lands. The present writer believes (as mentioned a little later on) that there is a somewhat larger proportion of young mothers in the north, and a smaller proportion of old people. This obviously leads to misleading ideas as to birth rates and death rates when we compare groups in the north and south of Australia.

That there is a real difference between the populations of the tropical and temperate lands is suggested by the following table.

POPULATION OF AUSTRALIA (1921) ARRANGED IN AGE GROUPS, AS PERCENTAGES

Age	0–4	5–9	10–14	15–19	20–24	25–29	30–34
Australia	9·1	9·1	9·7	8·5	8·4	8·6	8·2
Queensland	12·0	11·5	10·0	8·7	8·7	8·7	8·4

Age	35–39	40–44	45–49	50–54	55–59	60–64	65–69	70–74
Australia	7·1	6·0	5·1	4·6	4·0	3·1	1·9	1·2
Queensland	7·0	5·7	4·8	4·4	3·0	2·8	1·7	1·1

The table shows a greater proportion of young people (up to 34) in the relatively tropical state of Queensland as compared with Australia as a whole. This suggests that the older folk tend to leave the tropical lands, and that there is there a slightly larger proportion of child-bearing mothers. The figures would be more striking, one imagines, if we could isolate the hotter northern part of Queensland from the non-tropical southern part.

Dr. Cilento's manual includes valuable data as to the special types of water-supply, houses, sewage disposal, clothing, diet and exercise. He is strongly of the opinion that the working hours should be changed. Business should occupy the hours from 6 a.m. to 2 p.m., and from that hour the worker should be absolutely free.

It would be interesting to learn how the protagonists of rapid tropical settlement can explain the common experience of dwellers in the warm *temperate* lands. Every person in Sydney knows the effect of the muggy days which are usual even in that favoured city during the *single* month of February. No one has denied my statement put forward many years ago that the muggy conditions (as measured by the wet-bulb thermometer) are much the same for five months in Brisbane, for eight months in Townsville, and for pretty nearly the whole twelve months in Thursday Island. Constant breezes may ameliorate these conditions, but they do not remove them altogether. In the following table the comfort of the various months is arbitrarily classified in four divisions according to wet-bulb data. It is easy to contrast New York and Darwin; and the results do not in the least support Cilento's inference that New York has worse temperature conditions than much of Tropical Australia (*loc. cit.*, p. 61).

NUMBER OF MONTHS OF DISCOMFORT (see Fig. 26)

(based on average monthly wet-bulb data)

Very comfortable 45° to 55° wet bulb		Sometimes uncomfortable 55° to 65° wet bulb		Often uncomfortable 65° to 75° wet bulb		Almost continuously uncomfortable over 75° wet bulb	
Wellington, N.Z.	8	Wellington, N.Z.	4 (under 60°)	Batavia	10	Batavia	2
Coolgardie	7	Coolgardie	5 (3 under 60°)				
Hobart *	6	Hobart	3 (under 60°)	Thursday Is.	6	Thursday Is.	6
Melbourne	6	Melbourne	6 (under 60°)	Darwin	6	Darwin	6
San Francisco	6	San Francisco	6 (under 60°)	Madras	6	Madras	6
Alice Springs	5	Alice Springs	6	Alice Springs	1		
Sydney	5	Sydney	7			Sierra Leone	12
Perth	5	Perth	7 (3 under 60°)				
London (U.K.) *	5	London	3 (under 60°)				
Cairo	4	Cairo	3	Cairo	5		
New York *	4	New York	3				
Brisbane	3	Brisbane	4	Brisbane	5		
		Calcutta	3 (over 60°)	Calcutta	3	Calcutta	6
		Townsville	3 (over 60°)	Townsville	6	Townsville	3

* These places have a few months in winter which are slightly *below* the optimum for comfort.

Tropical Areas outside Australia

Yet if we get no conclusive proof here, there are ways of studying the effects of the tropics, which speak with no uncertain voice. Thus we may see what the mortality tables show us for the United States of America. There is of course no actual tropical area in the States, but the accompanying table shows how the mortality rates (based on Huntington) increase as the temperature increases. I have used the actual July temperatures in the comparison, which does not pretend to be more than indicative of a well-known general relation.

TEMPERATURE AND DEATH RATE IN U.S.A.

Death rate	130	118	100	96	92
July temperature	82° F.	79° F.	75° F.	72° F.	68° F.

We see that the hot wet coasts of the Gulf of Mexico with a high summer temperature of 82° F. have the highest death rate; while the cooler states in the north are distinctly better off. The death rates are based on the returns of three of the largest insurance companies in the States, and Huntington affirms that the individuals concerned are taken from the more prosperous classes of the community, so that Negroes and 'poor whites' are largely excluded. This seems to answer the objections of certain critics, who would put the high death rate in the south down to hookworm or other diseases of the poor or careless settler.

It must be remembered that there is an *optimum* temperature for human health, which Huntington has investigated under varying conditions. He shows that in France the optimum (lowest death rate) seems to occur with a temperature of 65° F., and that the health falls off fairly rapidly as temperatures increase to 80 degrees. But of course conditions of too great cold are not favourable either; though the effect of temperature on the *lower* side of 65° F. is not so marked as on the warmer side. Readers who are interested in the graphic analysis of health data by means of Climographs, &c.,

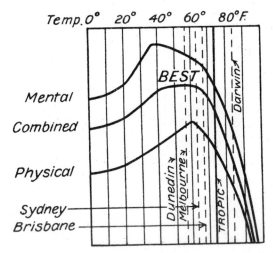

FIG. 136.—THE TEMPERATURE CONTROL OF MENTAL AND PHYSICAL ENERGY
Note the poor position of tropical places in Australia. (*Based on Huntington*)

should read the chapter on Climatic Optima of animals and man in Huntington's book *Economic and Social Geography*, New York, 1933.

Another suggestive graph by the same distinguished geographer (Fig. 136) shows that the best mental and physical work is done at temperatures between 30° and 70° F., and that there is a startling deterioration in the amount of work done as the temperature rises above 70° F. The average temperature along the Tropic of Capricorn in Australia is 72° F., so that here we have the clearest evidence of a fundamental disability due to living in the tropics.

The Australian tropics are remarkably free from the worst tropical diseases. Only malaria and hookworm are at all important, and we may anticipate their eradication in the future. Some of my readers will have in mind the history of the Panama Canal. They will know that malaria and yellow fever no longer have the mastery of that tropical region. But it is not generally known how arduous is the struggle to maintain healthy conditions; nor has Panama much hope to give us as to close settlement by true white *settlers*. Mr. J. B. Bishop, who was Secretary of the Isthmian Canal Commission, writes in his book *The Panama Gateway*:

Health statistics of the Canal Zone are misleading when used in comparison with like data of communities in the Temperate Zone. In the first place the American colony is a selected white community, there are no aged or infirm persons to swell the sick and death rates. In the second place the health of the American colony is cared for as that of no other community on earth has ever been. The visitor does not see those who have been obliged to return to the United States because they could not withstand the climate, and there have been a great many of these.

There were 7,000 cases in the American hospitals (out of 40,000 employees) during the year 1911–12; and Bishop adds that every clerk in his office had suffered from malaria, though all of them occupied screened quarters.

Agriculture in the Tropics

The distribution of agriculture in the tropics has been considered in some detail in Chapter XI. But we shall do well to study the possibilities of *future* crop-growing in this two-fifths of the continent. A very timely discussion of this problem by one of the few men who have had a long experience has recently appeared. Mr. Wynne Williams also stands out as one who believes that unpalatable truths must be discussed if Australia is to advance.

Williams has made a careful survey of the agriculture north of Brisbane and has come to some definite conclusions which we must examine.[1] He points out that near Brisbane itself, with a rainfall of 46 inches, there are usually periods when an extra amount of water must be given to crops during the drier winter season. He has concentrated his attention on this extra amount of water necessary in winter. It obviously depends on the winter rainfall, and also on the reliability of the rain. He has adopted a criterion as follows: *the number of months in twenty years when the rainfall was negligible* (i.e. under 10-hundredths of an inch). For Brisbane the percentage is 0·8, or two dry months in 240 months. In the Dawson Valley (at Theodore) this figure becomes 10 per cent. In Williams's opinion this marks the extreme limit of economic agriculture of a continuous nature.

No area within the tropics has a lower percentage than 10 except

[1] 'The Settlement of the Australian Tropics', *Econ. Rec.*, Melbourne, 1935. N.B.—Peanuts (ground-nuts) are grown successfully near Katherine.

just near Mackay, Prosperpine and the Sugar Coast near Cairns. At Ayr, and all places where the figure is greater than 10, it is absolutely necessary to use artificial supplies of water to keep the sugar and similar crops alive. One can show the main features of this relation in a table.

Place	Total Rain	Winter* Rain	% Dry months	Agriculture
Brisbane	46	14	0·8	Irrigation sometimes needed
Gladstone	42	10	8	Little agriculture. Cattle
Upper Burnett	35	8	8	Crops failed, three years in ten
Dawson Valley	28	10	9·5	Precarious agriculture
Rockhampton and north	40	9	10	Only *limited* permanent pasture in the small holdings. Cattle
Mackay	69	12	6	Successful dairying. Sugar.
Ayr	42	7	22	Sugar grown with irrigation
Townsville	50	6	21	No agriculture
Millaa-Millaa	97	26	1·5	Best sugar
Mareeba	37	2	24	Agriculture fails (except tobacco?)
Burketown	28	1	46	Hopeless, in Williams's opinion
Borraloola	27	1	41	do.
Darwin	62	3	32	do.
Derby	27	2	45	do.

* Winter rain, i.e. falling within the months May–October.

While the present writer sees no reason to doubt the general truth of the conclusions drawn by Williams, he wishes to point out once more that there are crops, which have hardly been tried by English settlers in the drier tropics of Australia, which are grown successfully in other parts of the world with a lower standard of living and with cheap labour. The essential features are indicated in Fig. 137, where the conditions of the tropical hinterland are compared with the interior of Nigeria. It would be well worth while, as I stated many years ago, to send young agriculturalists to this African environment to find out what are the differences between, say, Daly Waters and Kuka, near Lake Chad. The following table shows that in their climatic essentials they cannot be far apart.

In this region in northern Nigeria are many fairly large towns such as Kuka, Kano and Sokoto. The country is mostly level, and not at a very high elevation. I have no data as to the character of the soils, but a vast area in Australia is not unlike northern Nigeria in its rain régime, as may be seen from Fig. 137. However, Dr. H.

DALY WATERS AND ITS HOMOCLIME: KUKA, NIGERIA

	Köppen grade	Average temp.	Hottest month	Coldest month	Total rainfall	Wettest month	Driest month
Daly Waters	BShw	80·4° F.	86·9	68·6	27 in.	6·7	0
Kuka	BShwg	82·6° F.	92·3	70·7	32 in.	11·3	0

Trumble suggests that the rains may fall more steadily and over longer periods in Nigeria, thus reducing the evaporation as compared with Northern Territory.

The lower map in Fig. 137 is based on one given by L. S. Suggate in *Africa* (London, 1929). In these wetter areas of the

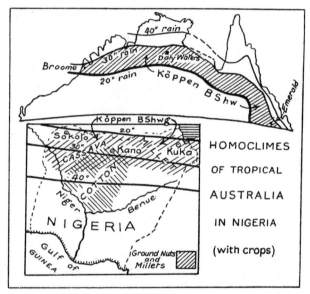

FIG. 137.—SUGGESTED NEW CROPS WHICH MAY BE GROWN IN THE FUTURE IN THE TROPICAL HINTERLAND

Sudan the ground-nuts (*Arachis hypogaea*) are planted during the early summer rains, and the crop is reaped four or five months later.[1] It seems to the writer that the character of the dry season is not so vital for short-season crops of this kind as for sugar, tobacco,

[1] About 1,000 acres in the Territory is used for growing ground-nuts. Mining has been of so little importance in recent years that it seems unlikely that it will ever lead to the prosperity of the north and north-west. Mount Isa is perhaps an exception.

&c. It is stated that a great increase may be expected in the harvest of nuts from the densely peopled region around Kano and Sokoto. (*Vide Production and Trade*, by E. G. R. Taylor.) However, Prescott is much less hopeful (Fig. 24).

The question of rain reliability is of course a very vital one in these inland areas. In Australia the reliability varies from 20 to 35 per cent along the Broome-Emerald belt. Judging from Biel's map of the rain reliability for the whole world (see p. 426 in my book *Environment, Race and Migration*), the Sokoto area exhibits much the same degree of rain variability.

This problem offers a good illustration of the value of comparative geography, and of its limitations. I do not expect any agriculture to develop in this area in the near future, nor in the distant future until there is a very great change in the character and profits of Australian agriculture. But I do feel that climatically there is something to be said for the Broome-Emerald Hinterland. Whether our technological advances, our standards of living, our political control, our labour unions, &c., will permit any use to be made of this hypothetical agricultural area is something that I do not here feel called upon to discuss.

Labour Supply in Tropical Queensland

Grenfell Price in his recent book *White Settlers in the Tropics* (New York, 1939) gives some interesting data as to the migratory and foreign-born people in the Queensland sugar fields. He states that in 1930 (at the peak period of the year) there were 28,737 men engaged, of whom 7,684 were cane farmers, and 6,823 field workers in regular employment; while 8,142 cane-cutters and 6,088 mill workers were *seasonal* employees. Some of these cane-cutters came from the southern states, and as soon as the crop was harvested they returned to the south, to engage in such work as apple-picking in Tasmania or to live at home on the dole. (Price, p. 72.)

Price also gives an interesting account of the growth of the Italian population in the far north. In the northern sugar district (perhaps the most important of all) the percentage of foreign employees was 23·4, and of naturalized employees 20 per cent. The Census of 1933 gives 5,336 males and 2,112 females born in Italy (now in the sugar districts), most of whom are in the far north near Mourilyan and Innisfail (Fig. 92). The living standards of the Italians were lower than those of the Australians; but in spite of preference agreements, which have favoured the British cane-cutter, farms are gradually being transferred from British to non-British owners. The Italian works harder and for longer hours than the British-Australian, and northern employers informed

Price that it was untrue that Italian cane-cutting gangs were inferior to the British.

The most tragic example of failure in the tropics is the collapse of Vestey's Meat Works at Darwin. The Commonwealth took over the Territory in 1911; and a year or two later they entered into an agreement with Vestey's to extend the railway south to the Katherine River. This was to span the belt of coarse grass across which it is very difficult to drive cattle. Grenfell Price goes on to say that these efforts at expansion, combined with lavish increases in the number and salaries of officials, together with ruinous arbitration awards, involved Australia in an enormous expenditure which was quite unwarranted by the results achieved (Fig. 76).

Between 1910 and 1929 railway mileage rose from 622 to 1,219; cattle from 513,000 to 835,000, cattle exports from 37,000 to 55,000 beasts. But both railways showed enormous losses, agriculture made no real headway, and the population only rose from 3,301 to 3,982.

Vestey's bought properties amounting to 30,000 square miles and grazing 200,000 cattle. They spent on the meat-works nearly a million pounds. Yet this promising industry was ruined, in the opinion of many competent judges, by the suicidal policy of the trade unions. The latter were controlled in Darwin by extremists, who insisted upon the employment of gangs of so great a size that all the members could not work at one time. Lumpers secured wages of £101 per head in a period of seventeen days. The men struck for all sorts of trivial causes. (See map, p. 226.)

Towards the end of 1918 the economic struggle culminated in a minor rebellion, in which the Administrator was roughly handled, and the mob took control.

Hopelessly dependent upon Industrial Arbitration and the Government Railways and wharves, Vestey's found their position impossible, and they closed their works in 1919. Their employees of 48 mixed races lost their living, and for the most part left the Territory. The railway traffic was decimated, the cattle men sought the inland gateways, and the northern portal at Darwin fell back into its former state.[1]

One of the most hopeful signs of a healthy change in the way in which the authorities are viewing the future of Australia is the publication of a number of official memoirs defining her varied disabilities. One may cite the memoirs of Prescott and MacTaggart, and the valuable report of the Payne Commission. The circulars of the conservative Bank of New Wales also deserve mention in this connexion. One of the latter, 'Australia's Empty Spaces'

[1] Grenfell Price, *Problems of Northern Territory*, Adelaide, 1930.

CHAPTER XIX

THE AUSTRALIAN POPULATION

IN this last chapter we have to consider how the environments now fairly fully considered have affected the people who live in Australia. There are many aspects of this problem, some of which we may only examine briefly, since they belong more to the field of sociology and anthropology than to geography. Among these problems may be mentioned the following topics: the aboriginal peoples of Australia and their merging into the dominant 'white' race; the 'foreign element' among the Australians; the varying rate of growth of the total population and its effect on the future population; the actual distribution as shown by the 1933 census; the remarkable urbanization illustrated by this young nation; a discussion of the various attempts to forecast the probable future population of the continent. The bearing of this lengthy study on the contrasted theories of the two schools of geographical thought, which we may label Possibilism and Determinism, is a subject of much interest to all geographers. Finally a problem of considerable, if indirect importance, is the attitude of Australians to geographical research in general.

The Australian Aborigines

In a preceding map (Fig. 131) the distribution of the aborigines is indicated. As a result of the clash of the two cultures the primitive type has crumbled away wherever there are large numbers of white settlers. Today the 60,000 full-bloods are almost all found along the north-west littoral, and furthest away from the 'Fertile Crescent' of 'Economic Australia' (Fig. 1). It is interesting to note that the proportion of half-castes illustrates the same principle. They are most numerous where the dark race has diminished most.

About 35,000 of these aborigines are described as nomadic. They are living more or less like their forefathers, but are subsidized with blankets and food at times by the Government. Another 9,000 are in regular employment, while 10,000 are living in organized camps. The 'blackfellows' have long been found of great help as rough 'hands' about the sheep and cattle stations, especially in the far north. Until lately there was no place for the women ('gins'); with the result that the economic status of the blackfellow was

(August, 1936), is a remarkably good study by one of my form
students, utilizing scientific findings as a basis for wise econom
and financial treatment.

Very valuable work is being carried out in the field by th
Council for Scientific and Industrial Research. Half a doze
parties, each containing research workers in several scientific fields
have been making surveys in typical areas in Australia's tropica
and semi-arid lands. The final reports were not yet available to the
public when the author was in Australia in 1948.

DISTRIBUTION OF WHITES AND ABORIGINES, 1944

State	Area	Whites	Half-castes	Full-bloods	Proportion H./F.
Tasmania	26,215	245,623	375	— —	—
Victoria	87,884	1,990,192	925	29	32 to 1
New S. Wales	309,433	2,886,576	10,022	594	17 to 1
S. Australia	380,070	619,496	2,208	2,868	1 to 1
Queensland	670,500	1,061,325	5,546	7,979	1 to 1·5
W. Australia	975,920	481,630	4,882	22,210	1 to 4
N. Territory	523,620	10,423	822	13,331	1 to 17

N.B.   A table for 1954 appears on page 13.

girl, when trained, has been found to be as useful as many of the Negro women in U.S.A. They are capable of becoming of vital assistance in the settlement of tropical Australia, where it is almost impossible for white women to obtain female help for any sort of domestic service. When both men and women find that their services are of considerable value in Australia their status will greatly improve, and their 'will to live' may perhaps become strong enough to insure the survival of this interesting race. (For 1954 population, see p. 13.)

The Tasmanian aborigines were probably hybrids between negritoes and Australian aboriginals. Only a few hundred of their descendants, all mixed with the white race, now survive in islands in the Bass Straits. It is reported that several tribes akin to the Tasmanians still survive in the jungles near Cairns (Q).

The aboriginal Australoids migrated into Australia by way of the East Indian islands (Fig. 131). There are kinsmen still to be found all the way back to Asia; such as the Sakai of Perak and Toala of Celebes. In southern India thousands of Veddahs (in Ceylon) and millions of Pre-Dravidians belong to the same race. There is some evidence suggesting that they arrived in Australia during the Würm Ice Age about 40,000 years ago; but the Talgai skull indicates predecessors in Australia perhaps one million years ago.

The physical features of the blackfellow may be described as negroid, with the very vital difference that the hair is wavy and never woolly. The writer has measured Australoids all over the continent, and has been struck with the wide range of features. The hair does not alter in its wave, yet the writer has described many aborigines in the arid part of Western Australia where the hair is tawny.[1] The shape of the nose is very variable, and is often

[1] *Proc. Pan-Pacific Congress,* Tokyo, 1926, pp. 2386–9.

almost leptorrhine (narrow) in the Broome district (W.A.). So also the lips are at times well-shaped and not particularly negroid. Yet a living aboriginal from Tamworth (N.S.W.) is described by Burkitt (in 1922) as possessing fourteen Neanderthal features. The aboriginal is therefore of special interest since he seems to be rather near the original 'plastic' type from which perhaps modern man evolved. This problem, however, is fully discussed in Chapters VI and VII of the writer's recent book, *Environment, Race and Migration*, Oxford, 1937.

It is very difficult to find aborigines who still retain quite unaltered their primitive culture. But there are a few tribes in this condition, especially in the rarely visited islands off the north coast. The writer has travelled very widely in Australia and has never seen absolutely primitive aborigines. The conflict between the two cultures has always interested him, and the character of this conflict in northern New South Wales is described (in perhaps the first scientific study of the hybrids) in a paper by F. Jardine and the writer.[1] In this study numerous photographs of half-castes and quarter-castes are given. It is easy to understand that since there is no difference in the hair of 'black' and 'white', the quarter-caste differs hardly at all in appearance from a strongly tanned European.

Characteristics of the Early Settlers

In an earlier chapter a summary is given of the spread of settlement in Australia. We may now consider in a little more detail the make-up of the population. The first arrivals consisted of 770 convicts and 250 free men. It is customary to explain the convicts as largely criminals of a rather harmless pattern. G. V. Portus in his *Australia* (1933) states that they were

for the most part men and women of abnormal mentality, broken by punishment, enfeebled by starvation and debauched by their former lives. There were as yet no Scottish martyrs, no Irish rebels suffering for conscience' sake, no Dorchester labourers audacious enough to ask ten shillings a week in wages, no noble Chartists.

Yet as early as 1828 it is likely that the free population equalled the convicts in numbers; and by 1841 there were nearly four times as many free men as convicts.

Portus points out that urbanization, the most striking feature of Australia's population, was rampant in 1833. This in spite of the fact that the 'assisted immigrants' were expected to develop the rural districts rather than settle in the one metropolis of the new country. Perhaps the most permanent effect of the gold rushes was

[1] 'Kamilaroi and White', Roy. Soc. N.S. Wales, Sydney, 1924.

upon the outlook of the people. Up till 1850 the squatters were acquiring as much power in Australia as the landlords had in Britain. But the inrush of thousands of enterprising 'diggers' produced a party powerful enough to oppose the 'squattocracy'. As Portus puts it, 'Gold challenged wool'. It stimulated trade unionism, and a belief that every man should be his own boss. In effect it created an atmosphere in which democracy flourished.

One other important aftermath of the 'alluvial gold' period of the 'fifties was the rise of anti-Asiatic feelings. There were 42,000 Chinese on the Victorian fields in 1859, and though most of these departed when the easily won alluvial gold was exhausted, yet Labour exploited racial feeling among those outside its ranks who were in no danger of competition from Chinese cheap labour. This sentiment spread rapidly, and blossomed again at the end of the century in the White Australian policy (Portus).

There is so much emphasis on 'race' in various discussions of world problems that it is a pity that so few educated persons realize what the word 'race' implies. It does not mean unity through a common language, or common religion, or even a common culture. It means a group linked together by common descent, i.e. by a *biological* kinship. I have rarely read any article outside of anthropological journals where this fundamental definition seems to be understood.

There is nothing necessarily common between nationality and race. For instance, there is no British Race, no French Race, no German Race and no Italian Race, though the corresponding national groups are fairly clearly defined. If we are concerned with the *biological* aspects of population which is developing in Australia, then a knowledge of the *country of birth* of the people is of no direct value in a racial discussion. However, since we have a fair idea of the racial composition of the folk in the various islands of Britain and in France, Germany, &c., such knowledge enables us to make a guess at the racial make-up of the Australians. Europeans are usually divided into three races:—Nordic, Mediterranean and Alpine.

The people of the British Isles consist of the descendants of the primitive British population (not much affected by the Roman occupation for 400 years); and of the numerous Nordic tribes who arrived during the period A.D. 450–1100. Thus the region east of a line from Aberdeen to Southampton contains a dominant group of Nordics. To the west of this line the folks become more and more Mediterranean in race. The short dark people of Cornwall, South Wales, Argyle and west Ireland consist of an almost pure Mediterranean stock. The outstanding fact in Britain is the absence of any important Alpine component. There are a few small districts where such broad-head folk are common, but dominantly we may say that England and Scotland are about half Nordic and half Mediterranean; while Ireland and Wales are dominantly Mediterranean.

In his book on *Non-Britishers in Australia* Lyng has discussed this problem in a commendably objective spirit. He gives a table which shows that folk of English birth are proportionally somewhat more abundant in Tasmania and South Australia. The Scotch are relatively numerous in Victoria, and the Irish in the three eastern states. I do not, however, agree with his estimate that the English are predominantly Nordic. Beddoes' map[1] shows that most of the densely populated areas are inhabited by brunette (i.e. Mediterranean) folk, the pure blondes being chiefly in York, Lincoln, Suffolk and the vicinity. It seems to me that we cannot make any deductions from English and Scottish origins, except that the folk concerned are just as likely to be Mediterranean as Nordic. About 23 per cent of the immigrants specified were Irish, and we can assume that they were mainly Mediterranean. But they spread themselves throughout all the states except South Australia in much the same way.

As regards the relation of race and temperament, I do not trust the current opinions that a Nordic is more venturesome, an Alpine more persistent, and a Mediterranean more emotional. It may be so, but the best studies such as those by Ellesworth Huntington (*Character of Races*) show that eminence in science, art and philosophy is found equally among Nordic and Alpine peoples. Surely the differences are so slight, and the records of the three races so full of vicissitudes, that we must assume that there is not much to choose among any of them. The writer's belief, based on a study of the whole course of human migration, is that the Alpine race (which is peculiarly lacking among Britishers) is on the whole the best fitted to survive! [2]

People of Foreign Birth in Australia [3]

The last two censuses give the following as the birthplaces of the Australian population, of whom 99 per cent are of British origin.

[1] See Ripley's *Races of Europe*, London, 1900, p. 318.
[2] See the last chapter in the writer's *Environment and Nation*, Oxford, 1936.
[3] The writer has used Jens Lyng's interesting book *Non-Britishers in Australia* (Melbourne, n.d.) in this section.

	1933	1947		1933	1947
1. Australia	5,716,787	6,835,171	9. China	8,855	6,404
2. England	486,039	381,592	10. Greece	8,293	12,291
3. Scotland	132,290	102,998	11. India	6,768	8,160
4. Ireland	78,548	44,813	12. S. Africa	6,178	5,866
5. New Zealand	45,913	43,610	13. United States	6,054	6,232
6. Italy	26,693	33,632	14. Canada	3,920	4,009
7. Germany	16,829	14,567	15. Other Europeans	43,139	49,849
8. Wales	14,486	11,864	16. Other Asiatics	9,192	9,532

The most numerous foreign nationals in Australia in June 1954 were: Italians 90,000; Polish 49,000; German 31,000; Russian 22,000; Jugo-Slav 18,000; Greek 18,000; Dutch 17,000. There were also 15,000 from India and 10,000 from China.

Germans.—There are very few districts in Australia where non-Britishers are numerous enough to be noticeable. But one such area is in South Australia about 20 miles east of Adelaide (see inset, Fig. 138). Here, just east of Angaston, two sub-divisions were named North Rhine and South Rhine. On the road thither were many small towns with such names as Hahndorf, Lobethal and Blumberg. At Lobethal one of the first woollen mills was started by German settlers in the 'seventies. Near Tanunda, Seppelt, a German vigneron, founded perhaps the largest winery in Australia.

The origin of these German settlements was somewhat as follows. The religious troubles in Germany in 1830–45 led to a pastor from Klemzig leading many of his parishioners to found a settlement of the same name near Adelaide in 1838. Some of these Germans were found to be the most expert shearers in the young wool industry of the state. By 1869 the number of Germans had grown to 8,863, which represented 11·5 per cent of the state's population. The German district extended from Hahndorf to Waterloo, a distance of about 80 miles, and included much of the southern portion of the Flinders Range.

As Lyng writes:

It is to be regretted, if on no other ground than for historical reasons, that during the Great War German names to the number of seventy were removed from the map and replaced by names associated with the war. It is generally believed that no settlers were more valuable than these early Germans; and it seems rather foolish to remove names, which in essence represented opposition to German oppression, by other names with very much the same significance.

In Victoria many of the towns of the Wimmera, such as Horsham and Murtoa, were founded by Germans; and from here they spread into the Mallee country when it was opened later. In New South Wales there were small communities near Grafton in the north-east and Albury in the south-east. Queensland has always had a strong element of Germans in the vicinity of Brisbane and Too-woomba, so that by 1881 there were 12,000 in this state. As regards religion, Lyng tells us that in 1914 the various Lutheran churches maintained about fifty-six ministers in South Australia, sixteen in Victoria, and nine in Queensland.

Italians.—The early Italian immigrants seem to have become

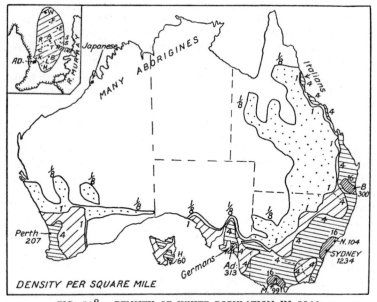

FIG. 138.—DENSITY OF WHITE POPULATION IN 1933
The seven largest towns and their populations (in thousands) are shown. Inset are the early German settlements north-east of Adelaide

merged with the populations of the large towns. One interesting community settled near Woodburn on the Richmond River (N.S.W.) in 1881. They were the forlorn remnants of a colony planted in New Ireland, and later played a worthy part in develop-ing the North Coast district. In 1891 Italians were encouraged to enter Queensland, when the Kanaka labour was gradually abolished in the cane-fields. When U.S.A. restricted immigration many Italians flocked to Australia, and naturally settled in the northern cane-fields near their countrymen (Fig. 138).

Labour troubles developed in 1925, since by this time there were nearly as many Italians as British in the northern sugar area. Thus, near the Herbert River there were thirteen British cane-cutters and 575 Italians, and in the Cairns district 301 were British and 395 aliens (mostly Italians). However, the employees in the mills were mostly British. The Commissioner who investigated the trouble stated that the Italians showed a great capacity for team-work and co-operation, and so gradually ousted the British. Yet assimilation is proceeding apace, since in 1921 nearly half the Italian farmers had British wives.

Greeks.—These people have never been popular in Australia, primarily because they cluster in the cities and rarely become farmers of primary producers. They are most numerous in Sydney, where two Greek newspapers are published. Many of the fish and fruit shops and the cheap lodging houses in Sydney and Melbourne are in their hands.

Jews.—There is a similar tendency for the Jews to congregate in the cities, where a number of the most valuable citizens have been Jews. In 1921 over 87 per cent lived in the six capital cities; and indeed no less than 40 per cent of the Australian Jews are found in Sydney.

Chinese.—Immigration from China began soon after convict labour was abolished. Nearly 3,000 coolies left Amoy for Australia in 1851–2, but they deserted their employers to flock to the gold diggings. As stated earlier, in 1859 there were about 40,000 in the Victorian gold-fields. Restriction Acts were passed by Victoria in 1855, by New South Wales in 1861 and by Queensland in 1876. The Chinese have no great desire to settle permanently in Australia; and in 1921 there were only 237 women as compared with 14,820 men. When they have made enough money they invariably return to China. About one-third are market-gardeners, and one-tenth are furniture-makers, another tenth are store-keepers, while domestic service and laundrymen account for about another tenth.

Japanese.—The 2,000 Japanese in Australia consist mainly of two groups. In the cities are a number of merchants and temporary visitors, perhaps mainly associated with the wool industry. In the tropics is a special class of Japanese who kept the pearling industry alive until the recent war.

In the 'nineties the Queensland Government introduced Japanese fishermen to develop the pearling grounds of the Torres Straits. By 1908 practically all the 165 divers were Japanese. In Western Australia Britishers declined to enter the hazardous and uncomfortable trade of pearl-diving, and here also it has long been in Japanese hands. Small towns like Broome and Thursday Island largely depend on the pearling industry; and if it were abandoned these centres of tropical settlement would almost certainly decay and perhaps disappear. When the writer visited Broome (in 1923), of the 3,000 inhabitants about 1,200 were Japanese (Fig. 138). Of these 900 were indentured labourers connected with pearling, and about 1,500 were Koepangers from Timor. The Japanese are a hard-working, peaceable population; but they offer clear, if un-welcome, evidence that in at least one field the Asiatic can readily surpass the European worker. (For changes since the war see p. 230.)

The Distribution of Population

The previous discussion on the spread of settlement will prepare the reader for the distribution of the population at the present day. The important growth in population is taking place in the 'Fertile Crescent' (Fig. 1), south or east of the line through Shark's Bay, Eucla, Broken Hill and Cloncurry. A very simple correlation with environment is indicated here. There is no important settlement in any region with less than 10 inches of rain (excluding one or two mining towns); and in tropical lands there is no important settlement where there is less than eight months in the year with a rainfall over 1 inch per month (see Fig. B in Frontispiece). I deduced these criteria twenty-five years ago, and only in central Queensland (Fig. 138) is a very scattered population gradually pushing towards the cattle lands of Northern Territory.

The density map (Fig. 138) shows that the population is gradu-ally spreading from Kalgoorlie along the East–West Railway. The better rainfall of the Flinders Range accounts for the northward bulge of the 4-isopleth in South Australia. In New South Wales the effect of the rugged highlands in the south-east is clear. Indeed in this state a large area, amounting to about 23,000 square miles, of the well-watered littoral is nearly empty, and this in spite of the fact that the rainfall and temperature controls are excellent. In Fig. 139 eight of these rugged and sterile regions are charted, and in them the population is still negligible. These districts for the most part correspond to the elevated areas of the state; but the regions around Armidale, Katoomba and Cooma have fairly close settlement around them. This is because they are capable of some pastoral occupation or are attractive to tourists. Their relation to the 25-inch isohyet is stressed in the map (Fig. 139).

The density map (Fig. 138) shows that there are five particularly attractive areas in Australia. These are the 'Western Slopes' behind Sydney, the greater part of Victoria, the south-east corner of Queensland, the southern Flinders Range in South Australia, and the south-west corner of Swanland. Tasmania and Northern Territory have no such large areas of good agricultural land.

In an address to the Geographical Society of New South Wales I discussed at considerable length the potentialities of the six states and the Northern Territory. The original paper appeared in the first number of the *Australian Geographer* (Sydney, 1928), and the conclusions are of considerable importance. I state there that the agricultural and industrial populations must always greatly out-number the pastoral population. Since the coal and hydro-electric power in Australia occur in agricultural lands, it is obvious that the main value of the state lands depends essentially on the rainfall.

FIG. 139.—THE LEAST-ATTRACTIVE PORTIONS OF THE WETTER FARMING BELT OF NEW SOUTH WALES ARE INDICATED IN THIS MAP. THEY REPRESENT AREAS OF LEAST-FAVOURABLE RELIEF AND SOILS

(*From 'Economic Geography'*)

The following table is based on measurements of lands suitable for Close Settlement (*a*) in temperate lands, (*b*) in tropical lands, (*c*) good pastoral lands, (*d*) fair to poor pastoral lands, (*e*) useless desert lands. The figures given represent *thousands of square miles* and are naturally only approximate.

Three states (Queensland, New South Wales and Western Australia) have about equal amounts of fair temperate farming land. Queensland, however, has in addition her fertile tropical lands along the east coast. Hence this state is likely to take the lead, especially as her pastoral lands are much greater than those of

POTENTIAL VALUE OF THE VARIOUS STATES (THOUSAND SQUARE MILES)

State	Order	Close settlement		Pastoral		Desert	Total
		Temperate	Tropical	Good	Fair to poor		
Queensland	1	134	100	367	69	—	670
New S. Wales	2	188	—	77	45	—	310
W. Australia	3	150	—	140	240	446	976
Victoria	4	68	—	10	10	—	88
S. Australia	5	60	—	50	160	110	380
Tasmania	6	16	—	5	5	—	26
N. Territory	7	—	—	130	260	130	520
Total	—	616	100	779	789	686	2,970
Percentage	—	21	3	26	27	23	100

New South Wales. In the distant future the coal of Sydney may balance the tropical agriculture of Queensland. The 686,000 square miles of arid lands in Western Australia hardly enter into the question. The Collie coal-field, however, is a valuable asset.

In the second rank come Victoria and South Australia. In agriculture they are about equal. South Australia has more pastoral lands (mostly of a poor type), but Victoria has really abundant coal at Morwell. Her rainfall is more uniform, and therefore she will probably always surpass South Australia. The arid 270,000 square miles in the latter state are unimportant. Tasmania is too small to enter into competition with the other states. Much of her south-west area is so bleak that there is hardly a settler there. Even so, her restricted agricultural land is good, and her 26,000 square miles are of much more use to the Commonwealth than the 520,000 square miles of the Northern Territory.

A useful method of considering environmental control is illustrated in Fig. 140. Here the graph uses as ordinates average rainfall and temperature. Upon these ordinates are plotted the population densities in the various districts in Australia. Thus the one-eighth isopleth in Fig. 140 occurs in various environments, such as 62° and 10 inches near Morgan (S.A.); or 80° and 40 inches near Croydon (Q.). The 4-isopleth in Fig. 140 in the same way is found with 60° and 25 inches near Mount Gambier (S.A.); and 70° and 35 inches near Gayndah (Q.). If these densities ($\frac{1}{8}$, 1, 4, 16) are plotted on the graph, and isopleths drawn through them, we obtain the *isopract* diagram given in Fig. 140. These isopract diagrams can be used to compare the 'saturation' of various countries; as for instance Algeria with South Australia. It will be found that Algeria has far greater densities under similar conditions of temperature and rainfall.

Of course the graph is necessarily generalized, since the controls exercised by political forces (e.g. in the capitals) or by the coal

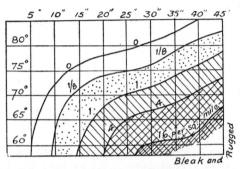

FIG. 140.—GENERALIZED ISOPRACT GRAPH TO SHOW THE EFFECT OF
TEMPERATURE AND RAINFALL UPON POPULATION IN AUSTRALIA
The small areas of cool rainy highlands in the south-east are not included

of Newcastle and Morwell are ignored. But these non-climatic controls are relatively unimportant compared with rainfall and temperature, which are of paramount significance in all parts of the continent. The graph suggests that a temperature of about 63° and a rainfall around 40 inches are the optimum conditions for close settlement in the Australian continent. A few *bleak* districts in the south-east of low population density have been ignored.

Rate of Growth of Population

It is natural for Australians to desire to keep to themselves the land which they have developed. But the density of population is remarkably low; only about two per square mile, whereas Europe has a density of about 100 per square mile. Some few decades ago politicians talked about the 'infinite potentialities of our empty spaces'. Nowadays it is realized that this is a poor policy, since it suggests to rival nations a marked 'dog-in-the-manger' attitude. In point of fact we have learnt that the 'manger', if large, is not a very full one; though it is still attractive enough to arouse the cupidity of certain nations. Be that as it may, the growth of the population is a very vital problem in this connexion; and it is not generally realized that the rate is almost the highest in the world.

During the present century the annual rate of increase has averaged 1·66 per cent. Unfortunately the depression since 1929 has lowered this rate to 0·76. There is always a close relation between prosperity and the growth of population. Fenner has drawn up some very interesting curves dealing with the population of South Australia which he calls 'Prosperity Curves'. They are illustrated on pages 210 and 211 of his valuable book *South Australia* (Melbourne, 1931). The variations of migration, into or out of the state, are linked up with the periods of prosperity or depression. From 1836 to 1884 was on the whole a period of prosperity and immigration. Then followed twenty years of depression and emigration from 1885 to 1905. From 1906 to 1928 were good years, except for the effects of the War. The last ten years have on the whole shown small immigration and an absence of prosperity. Fenner adds on his graphs the chief factors which have added to or taken from the prosperity of the state. Similar graphs could be drawn for the other states.

The birth-rate in Australia is dropping rapidly, as in most other civilized countries. Thus from 1909 to 1913 the birth-rate in Australia was 18·8 per thousand, almost the highest on record. For Russia it was 15·8, Japan 13·1, Germany 12·8, England 10·7. But for the period 1931 to 1936 these figures had dropped to 10·2 for Australia, to 5·3 for Germany, and 3·0 for England. The Russian rate has actually increased to 17·4, while the Japanese rate is stationary.

Another feature common to almost all civilized populations is the decline in the percentage of children. This, as regards Australia, is exhibited only too clearly in the following table.

	Percentage under 15 years	15 to 64	65 or older
1871	42	56	2
1921	32	64	4
1933	28	66	6
1947	25	67	8

The Urbanization Factor

One of the outstanding features of Australia is the concentration of the population in the cities. This is shown in the following table, in which figures represent thousands.

Thus in 1947 51 per cent of the population live in the six capital cities; while if we separate the actual rural population from the town population, we find that no less than 69 per cent of the

URBAN AND RURAL POPULATIONS, 1933 (THOUSANDS)

State	Total	Capital	Towns	Rural	Percentage in capital	Percentage in all towns
New S. Wales	2,601	1,234	565	795	48	69
Victoria	1,820	992	198	629	54	62
S. Australia	581	313	51	215	54	62
Queensland	948	300	199	444	32	53
W. Australia	439	207	45	183	47	57
Tasmania	228	60	57	109	27	51
N. Territory	5	—	2	3	—	32
Australia 1933	6,630	3,107	1,124	2,381	47	64
,, 1947	7,581	3,845	1,364	2,352	51	69
,, 1954	8,986	4,845	2,280	1,888	54	77

Australian population are town-dwellers. This is a truly remarkable feature in a relatively new country like Australia. It seems, at first glance, that one-third of the population live on farms and stations and are the true primary producers, and that they support over two-thirds of the population who live in towns.

To some extent this is true, and it is only possible because land is relatively cheap in Australia, and mechanization has enabled the farmer to produce far more on his farm to-day than in earlier years, even though his human helpers are fewer today.

A useful discussion by E. T. McPhee appears in *Peopling of Australia* (Melbourne, 1928). He points out that in England in 1851 urban and rural populations were about equal, but that by 1911 the percentages were 78 and 22. In Germany in 1910 the percentages were 60 and 40. In the United States in 1920 they were 53 and 47; while in Australia in 1933 the figures are 64 and 36. I have not the latest figures, but it seems likely that today Australia is as much urbanized as Germany, and more so than the United States with its vast industrial populations.

It is clear, however, that all the high standard nations of the world are moving in the same direction. The determining factor is the economic one, as McPhee insists, and turns on the question of *remunerative employment*. If we class together the industrial transport and commercial trade (and ignore one or two groups such as the professional and domestic) then the change in the composition of the bread-winners in Australia is as follows. (In the southern continent bread-winners constitute 43 per cent, and dependants 57 per cent of the total population.)

PER CENT OF TOTAL POPULATION

	1871	1881	1891	1901	1911	1921
Primary	18·2	15·5	13·2	14·2	13·6	11·2
Industrial	15·9	17·5	21·4	20·5	22·9	23·9

The food requirements per head have not changed, but they need far less attention nowadays. This sets free much labour for other less vital needs, and in part accounts for the rise of factories in Australian towns. McPhee points out that the tendency to cluster into cities does not necessarily imply a change for the worse, and indeed he suggests it is really evidence of social progress. There is of course inevitably much opposition from the rural population to this centralization of power and wealth, but this aspect cannot be discussed in this book. I think McPhee is correct in his outlook as long as Australians are in the enviable condition of having a large *unsaturated* continent at their disposal, with by no means the largest population which it will support (at present standards) living therein.

Some further discussion may be given to the problem of 'Migration to the Capital' as it is exhibited in New South Wales. The increase in the population of a region is made up of two parts, the *natural increase*, represented by children born to the settlers, and the *immigrants* who may decide to settle in the region. When we consider the increase in the various divisions of New South Wales (see Fig. 93) during the twenty-two years from 1911 to 1933, we find that the large arid Western Division had fewer settlers in 1933 than in 1911, for the population dropped from 59,165 to 51,994. This is because the emigration out of the division was greater than the natural increase.

In other cases, however, every division has gained in population in the twenty-two years; but in only three out of fourteen divisions was the immigration greater than the emigration. Since this latter balance shows which are the more attractive divisions, I have charted the migration data (from the *New South Wales Year-Book*) with the result shown in Fig. 141. The three most attractive regions were the *Metropolis*, which received 371,502 immigrants in the twenty-two years; the *Hunter* Division, which received 22,000 immigrants; and the *Riverina*, which increased in this fashion by 7,800 migrants.

It is certain that the chief attraction has been the remunerative employment in the factories of Sydney and Newcastle. Probably the Murrumbidgee Irrigation accounts in part for the gain in the Riverina. In the rest of the state the Northern and Southern Table-lands have lost nearly as many migrants as the Western Division, though the natural increases have given slightly greater population figures in 1933 as compared with 1922. The South Coast and the

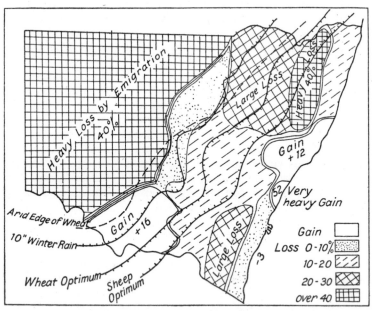

FIG. 141.—CHANGES IN THE POPULATION OF NEW SOUTH WALES (1911–33) DUE TO MIGRATION—BUT EXCLUDING NATURAL INCREASE

Four very important isopleths concerning wheat and sheep are also charted. It is clear that the sheep optimum is in wetter country than the wheat optimum

wetter edge of 'the sheep without wheat' country have not lost much through migration.

In Fig. 141 I have also plotted the two chief optima in New South Wales; those for sheep and wheat. It is clear that country carrying dense sheep needs a wetter climate than does the best wheat country, which is perhaps contrary to the generally accepted opinion. The southern part of the state is clearly the more attractive in both these occupations if we can accept the migration data in Fig. 141 as a measure of relative prosperity.

The Optimum Population for Australia

There have been many suggestions as to the future population of Australia. The politician of a few decades ago had a simple technique based on his admiration for American progress. Since Australia and the United States have the same area, in his opinion Australia must be able to support 120 millions of white settlers, when she had been developed as long as U.S.A. Sometimes this kind of investigator went a little more deeply into the problem, and fitted most of the countries of Europe into the map of Australia. Since the southern continent is three-quarters of the area of Europe, simple division will tell us that Australia should support about 380 million people! Not many estimates are as naïve as these today.

A second method is to copy certain biological experiments with the humble fruit-fly. This creature under certain conditions (which need not concern us) breeds rapidly to an optimum, and then its birth-rate falls off remarkably. Thus we obtain a curve of population-increase which resembles a much elongated S. Some scientists believe that the population curve of the United States can be 'fitted' to this curve, and that thus they can ascertain when the population will cease to increase in U.S.A. This may occur with a population of some 200 millions about the year 2,000. There is something to be said for this method.

In 1922 the writer published a lengthy paper entitled 'Future White Settlement' (*Geographical Review*, New York), which tried to take into account standards of living as well as the remarkable diversity of environments in the world.[1] It is clear that Europe offers the only example where white settlers have produced a fairly stable population which has 'saturated' a continent of considerable complexity. Briefly the writer took the European distribution of population as his criterion. He divided the world into 74 economic regions, and deduced the population which each would support (using criteria of temperature, rain, coal and location) under European conditions. By a graphic method of analysis he then drew isopleths of habitability over the world, as shown in Fig. 142.

This map shows approximately how the various new lands compare with Europe as regards future population. It assumes that the coal supplies will increase the respective populations as coal has done in Europe, and that the standards of living will be like those of Europe. Hence if higher standards are required, fewer people can be supported. Under these hypothetical conditions the future Australian Population comes out about 60 millions. If the standard of living in Australia is twice as costly as in Europe, then the future population of Australia will rest at 30 millions. This agrees rather closely with other quite independent estimates,

[1] This article is reproduced almost in full in the writer's book *Environment, Race and Migration*, Oxford, 1937.

such as that made by H. Barkley in *Peopling of Australia*. His
deduction was 29·6 millions. (The present writer cannot agree with
certain details in Barkley's estimate, such as that Northern Territory can support more than four times the population of Victoria;
but the article is well worth attention.)

More detailed suggestions as to the possibilities are charted in
the Frontispiece, which is surrounded by six small maps in which
some of the chief environmental controls are given. It is the consideration of such maps as this which makes the writer a confirmed
determinist and a believer in environmental control.

In an early attempt (in 1916) to forecast population I divided
tropical Australia into six regions, ranging from Desert to Farmlands. It seemed probable to me that the deserts would never support any noteworthy population. The 'Sparselands' of Arizona,
and similar regions with European settlers, have few inhabitants.
However, we must remember that in the northern fringe of the
Sahara populations are not altogether negligible, ranging upward
from *two* to the square mile.[1] Yet with Australian standards of
living I think it will be long before the Sparselands support even
one per square mile. The following table compares in an approximate fashion the density of population in Algeria and south-east
Australia. (See also p. 125.)

Rainfall inches per annum:	4	10	16	40
Density in Algeria per square mile	2?	25	45?	120
Density in S.E. Australia per square mile	0	0	1 or 2	over 8

This is an eloquent commentary on the ability of the poverty-
stricken Arab to live where an Australian could not.

In the good pasture lands of Australia I suggest that the population may rise to three per square mile on the wetter margin. This is
about the density of similar lands in western United States. The
belt labelled 6 (in the Frontispiece) has no agriculture in the north
at present. In the south it resembles parts of Texas and Oklahoma
with densities around six. The better agricultural lands of Australia
should have little difficulty, later on, in supporting eighteen per
square mile, which is the lowest density in the warm agricultural
lands of the United States. I have suggested that great industrial
populations may develop near the chief coal-fields, which are

[1] 'Sea to Sahara', Griffith Taylor, *Geog. Review*, New York, 1939.

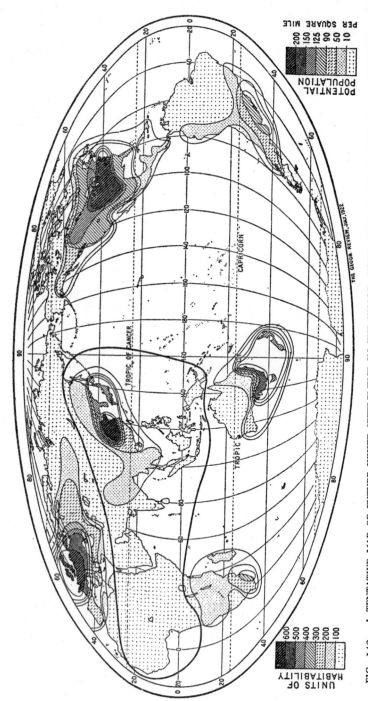

FIG. 142.—A TENTATIVE MAP OF FUTURE WHITE SETTLEMENT IN THE WORLD, USING THE DENSITY OF EUROPE AS A STANDARD
N.B.—Recent surveys improve prospects in Siberia. ('*Geographical Review*' 1922)

shown in black. I have not attempted to give densities for these areas.

In this book the writer is concerned primarily with the expansion of the present population by natural increase or by immigration. It is unnecessary to state that Australia has her unemployment problems like all other young countries. We shall do well to remember that unemployment was rife in England in Plantagenet times, but the population has vastly increased since that date. However, the influx of immigrants into Australia in the future is certain to be a slower process than when large areas of first-class land were available.

The cost of settling a farmer must be borne in mind (see p. 277). Regarding settlement by peoples of lower standards of living, one can only state that there is nothing in the Australian climate to deter Asiatic or southern European immigrants. It is largely a matter of standards of living. The Chinaman works a farm of 4 acres, the European one of 40 acres, the prairie farmer of Canada needs 400 acres under present conditions of development. Later the prairie farm may be conceivably subdivided as population grows in that district.

The classification of the lands of Australia made by the writer twenty years ago [1] is now generally accepted by Australians. It was as follows, and may be compared with the slightly revised estimate given in the table on page 468.

About 42 per cent of Australia is *Arid*, of which
> 20 per cent of the whole is almost *useless* for stock,
> 22 per cent is *fair pastoral* country, except in drought years.

About 34 per cent is *good pastoral* country.

About 21 per cent is *fair temperate farming land* suitable for close settlement; of which
> 13 per cent receives over 20 inches per annum,
> 8 per cent receives less than 20 inches per annum.

About 3 per cent of *Tropical* Queensland has a uniform rainfall through most of the year, and has crop possibilities.

The future millions of Australia are going to find their dwelling-places and occupations in the lands already known by 1865. The 'Empty Lands' of Australia are a burden to the Commonwealth rather than an asset, and their vast potentialities exist only in the mind of the ignorant booster. Yet the 7 millions of Australia possess in the south and east of the continent one of the best areas in the world for white settlement. In this quarter of Australia the

[1] *Australia, Physiographic and Economic*, Oxford, 1919 (p. 261).

writer expects that some 20 millions will dwell when the land is developed to the same extent as the United States.

If we adopt the lower standards of Central Europe and elsewhere, and assume that the coal is adequately used for manufactures, then there seems no good reason why this figure should not be doubled or trebled. As stated earlier in the discussion, it is far easier to determine the *relative* order of the values of the settlement zones of Australia, than it is to assign *absolute* figures to the population that may in the distant future inhabit these zones. The figures on the isopleths given in the central map of the Frontispiece are merely tentative; but the writer believes that the continent will 'fill up' pretty closely along the lines suggested by these figures.

What Australia teaches the Geographer

In the early days of our science national progress was discussed in terms of Providence, priests, potentates and politicians, and environment was hardly considered. Yet whether the writer studies Europe, where man has reached some degree of equilibrium in settlement, or the newer land of the United States, or finally Australia and Canada, he is still fixed in his belief that Nature has largely decided the future of a country before man occupies it. In Europe the present *population-pattern* bears no marked relation to the actions or desires of the aforesaid potentates and politicians. Nor do biological and cultural factors like race, religion and language exercise any dominant influence. Yet what we may term the three servants of Nature, King Frost, King Drought and King Coal, to a very large degree have determined how man has developed the European Scene. The relation is just as clear in Australia and Canada; and although environmental control is not a popular concept in the United States, it is as potent there also.

Protagonists of the Possibilist Theory [1] instance the carrying of

---

[1] According to the 'Possibilist School', man himself decides which of various possible methods of exploiting Nature he shall pursue. This theory, especially in relation to Canada, is discussed on page 355 of the writer's recent book *Environment, Race and Migration* (see also p. 459 therein). A somewhat extreme example, drawn from conditions in the Antarctic, may be used to illustrate this divergence of views. The Determinist states the general law that environment in that continent precludes settlement. The ardent Possibilist, eager to show how man dominates his environment, would dwell at length on the undoubted achievements and comforts of Little America. To the Determinist it is the *quite temporary and unusual* character of the settlement there which is significant. He does not accept it as relevant in the discussion, and many 'anti-environmental' examples will be found to be of a similar character. I expanded these ideas in *Geography in the 20th Century*, London, 1951.

fertilizer to the Canadian Prairies, or the remarkable development of somewhat sterile northern Denmark as examples of *human* control, which have determined the utilization of the regions concerned. I do not for a moment deny that man plays a very important part, but he does not take fertilizer to the 'barren grounds'; nor would the Danes have developed their less attractive regions if they had been free to choose among the good lands of the world. They have merely pushed ahead in Nature's 'plan' for their terrain. Even when their example is followed in other similar parts of the world it will only indicate that man has advanced one more stage in his *adjustment to the limits* laid down by Nature. Man is not a free agent.

The writer, then, is a determinist. He believes that the best economic programme for a country to follow has in large part been decided by Nature, and it is the geographer's duty to interpret this programme. Man is able to accelerate, slow or stop the progress of a country's development. But he should not, if he is wise, depart from the directions as indicated by the natural environment. He is like the traffic-controller in a large city, who alters the *rate* but not the *direction* of progress; and perhaps the phrase 'Stop-and-Go Determinism' expresses succinctly the writer's geographical philosophy.

Geography in Australian Universities

At the Council Meeting of the section of Geography in the British Association for the Advancement of Science in 1931, the writer moved that a committee investigate the position of geography in the Dominion universities. The Report showed that of forty-four universities only eight had departments of Geography, and of these only two were adequately developed.[1] The Committee commented on the remarkable contrast presented by the retarded development of geography in the Dominions as contrasted with that of Great Britain and the United States.

In my Presidential Address to the same section in 1938 I dwelt at length on this topic, and I think it will be of interest to quote from this address. I pointed out that when Augustine reached Britain about A.D. 600 with a mission to educate the barbarians, he first found it necessary to establish grammar schools to teach the classical grammar. Not until the students knew Latin could they begin to study mathematics, logic, music, and the rudimentary science of the day. Undoubtedly we are a conservative people, and many of the authorities in the Dominions seem to think that what

[1] See also the discussion on the 'Value of Geography to the Community', C. Fenner, *Roy. Geog. Soc.*, Adelaide, 1938.

was good enough for St. Augustine ought to be good enough for us. This is one of the main reasons why so many of our schools still give the lion's share of their time to the acquisition of an inadequate knowledge of the Latin language. The newer *modern* subjects are inevitably crowded out.

Would that the classical protagonist realized the real value of the Greek education as taught by Aristotle, and would encourage its adaptation to modern times! Plato and Aristotle in 350 B.C. did not occupy the invaluable time of their students by wearisome repetition of the vocabularies of the Egyptians, from whom the Greeks derived much of their culture; or of folk-tales written in some foreign language two thousand years before their date. *They trained youth to deal intelligently with existing conditions.*

We must train *our* young folk to deal intelligently (i.e. scientifically) with existing conditions. It will be of interest to draw from my own experience in this connexion in Cambridge, Australia, Canada and Chicago. At the University of Cambridge today there is a new and imposing building four stories high replete with laboratories, and entirely devoted to Geography. Here are 200 students who, I believe, give almost all their time to geography in a three years' course. At Chicago, one of the three leading universities in the United States, Geography as regards staff and students is on an equal footing with classics. There are a number of universities in the States with four full professors in Geography; and throughout most of U.S.A. the legend that culture is impossible without classics is nearly dead.

In Canada and Australia the picture is very different. Precisely where the satisfactory development of young nations depends on a wise knowledge of the environment, there was until lately a complete neglect of study of the environment at universities. In Canada only at Toronto is there an independent and complete Department of Geography.[1] But lecturers in the subject have recently been appointed at two other universities in Ontario. In Australia there is a well-established and complete department at Sydney, but no adequate courses extending over three years are given at any of the other universities. This seems inexplicable to the present writer.

In Australia we see 7 million Anglo-Saxons living in a warm, arid continent with an environment resembling North Africa, and quite unlike any portion of the British Isles. Bordering the Commonwealth on the north are 350 million Indians, nearly 400 million

---

[1] There has been a gratifying change since 1940. By 1950 the following universities had professors in geography: Vancouver, London (Ont.), Hamilton, Toronto, McGill, Montreal, and Quebec.

Chinese, and 70 million Japanese. The empire of Japan once reached to the borders of Australasia. Yet it is safe to say that the students in the better schools, as I knew them in Sydney and Melbourne, learned little or nothing of these environments and of their effect on the inhabitants; or about the huge over-populated areas to the north menacing the Australian Commonwealth; or indeed much that was really geographic about Australia itself! Conditions of matriculation meant that they spent one-fifth of their time in schools studying classical languages; though only a few per cent would ever use such knowledge at the university or in later life. This state of affairs must be altered.

The aim of civilization, as I see it, is not to prepare for a better world *beyond* this earth, but to prepare a better world *on* this earth. Our immediate objective should be a world at peace. This can only be attained by studying world problems, especially those involving other nations and regions. This is the special province of the modern geographer, especially if he gives considerable attention to the new department of *Cultural* Geography. What should be the training of the educated man today? If we omit for the moment the specialized knowledge he needs for his profession, then we might do worse than adopt Aristotle's idea, 'To learn to deal in the best way possible with existing conditions'. Three subjects would seem to be vital in such a scheme of education. First *Biology*, which deals with the evolution of man as an animal; secondly *History*, which deals largely with the growth of his ideals and institutions; and thirdly *Geography*, which deals with his present ever-varying environment. A knowledge of Evolution in the broadest sense should be the aim of education. Modern Geography is precisely the best discipline to teach man that he is conditioned by his environment; that he himself is changing, however slightly, and is part of the mechanism of evolution; and that he can only understand his own place in the scheme of things if he has a real knowledge of the relation of man to his environment.

Postscript

It is gratifying to note that by 1953 there was a complete change in the geographical field. Eight Australian Universities possessed Professors or Senior Lecturers in Geography; and Melbourne, Adelaide, and Perth each had over 100 students.

By 1960 there were Senior Professors of Geography at the following Universities: Sydney, Canberra, Hobart, Adelaide, Brisbane Melbourne and Armidale.

INDEX

Scientific Terms in Italics